ORGANIC CHEMISTRY

ORGANIC CHEMISTRY

SECOND EDITION

Reynold C. Fuson
PROFESSOR OF ORGANIC CHEMISTRY
UNIVERSITY OF ILLINOIS

H. R. Snyder
PROFESSOR OF CHEMISTRY
UNIVERSITY OF ILLINOIS

JOHN WILEY & SONS, INC., NEW YORK
CHAPMAN & HALL, LIMITED, LONDON

Library of Congress Catalog Card Number: 54-5655

PRINTED IN THE UNITED STATES OF AMERICA

Preface

Teachers who are acquainted with the first edition of this textbook will find that, in spite of many changes, the present edition adheres closely to the original plan of presentation. In particular, the accelerated introduction to the subject has been retained. The early chapters acquaint the student with the structure and behavior of the principal types of organic molecules, including aromatic and heterocyclic as well as aliphatic and alicyclic compounds.

In these chapters, which make up about a third of the book, the student quickly becomes acquainted with the terminology of the subject and is given a comprehensive view of its content and importance. Thus oriented and made "literate" in the field, he is prepared for a mature and well-rounded treatment in the subsequent sections of the course.

This arrangement of subject matter has proved to have certain practical advantages not originally foreseen. For example, it makes the book equally suitable for a two-semester course or one divided into three quarters. In either case the first term may serve the needs of students who want only a brief terminal course as well as those who wish to lay a foundation for further study. It may be pointed out also that the later sections of the book have been used extensively by graduate students in connection with survey courses and in preparation for examinations for advanced degrees. Probably the chief advantage gained by this plan is due to the repetition which is involved. In this book the amount of repetition is, for obvious reasons, considerably less than that employed in the classroom. Such details of presentation are left to the teacher.

In the present edition increased attention is given to explaining why molecules behave as they do, i.e., why the functional groups are the primary seats of reaction in molecules and why a given group is vulnerable to attack by certain types of reagents. To this end theoretical considerations have been given much more extensive treatment than in the previous edition. The reaction patterns are emphasized throughout the book, specific reactions being grouped according to type rather than according to the formal classification of the raw materials or the nature of the end products. The functional groups thus become the center of attention rather than the homologous series.

A principal consequence of this change in emphasis is the virtual disappearance of sections on methods of preparation, the reactions in question being located by cross references. The new treatment not only eliminates much duplication but also avoids the introduction of reactions out of context. The space thus saved has made possible the inclusion of new material on the theoretical aspects of the subject and more extensive treatment of various topics, such as the reactions of halogen compounds and polymerization.

Reynold C. Fuson
H. R. Snyder

Urbana, Illinois
January, 1954

Contents

CHAPTER 1

Introduction

In the early development of the science of chemistry, attention was devoted largely to the acids, bases, and salts, substances which are soluble in water and whose reactions are generally rapid. From the study of these and other compounds the laws governing the combination of the elements were gradually elucidated. However, during this period a very large group of compounds, those present in or obtained from living organisms, was set apart. It was believed that the formation of these so-called *organic* substances could be brought about only in the living plant or animal, and that organic materials could not be treated according to the concepts employed with *inorganic* compounds.

The first of these beliefs had to be abandoned when it was found that organic compounds could be synthesized apart from any complex life process. Thus the major distinction between inorganic and organic chemistry became meaningless. Further investigations of organic compounds showed that these materials are governed by the same fundamental laws which apply to inorganic substances, and that the real distinction between the two types is that most organic materials contain both carbon and hydrogen whereas most inorganic substances do not. The separation of the two fields has been maintained for practical reasons. As a matter of fact the exact boundary line between the two fields is not clearly defined. Many chemists define organic chemistry as the science of compounds containing carbon. However, this definition is not entirely satisfactory since such compounds as the metal carbonates, traditionally regarded as inorganic, are included among organic compounds.

The picture called to the mind of the well-informed man by the words organic chemistry is not one focused on a vast array of carbon compounds, however. Rather it is a practical, everyday picture of the innumerable articles which he manufactures, buys, sells, and uses. The mere mention of synthetic fabrics, the treatment of leathers, the manufacture of dyes, soaps, and new detergents, the production of better gasolines, oils, and automobile tires, more enduring paints, new medicines, or cosmetics, brings to mind the extensive fields in the development of which organic chemistry has played an important role. It is no longer news that organic chemistry is an inseparable part of the industries and arts of present-day life.

The task of the organic chemist in this connection is to produce what is needed by processing the materials that are at hand. In fact, in many instances he has gone further and provided materials of previously unknown types, which have created new markets. The three main sources of raw material are coal, petroleum, and vegetable products. The ingenuity of the organic chemist is such as to enable him to supply all our needs from any one of these sources alone if the need should arise.

CHAPTER 2

The Structure of Molecules

The property of carbon which distinguishes it most conspicuously is its tendency to form non-ionizing links, both with other carbon atoms and with atoms of different elements. In other words, the type of union most frequently encountered in the carbon compounds is the covalent bond, whereas the polar or electrovalent bond may be considered typical of the inorganic compounds. The differences between these two kinds of valence may be seen by examination of examples.

The formation of sodium chloride from the elements illustrates the simplest mode of formation of an electrovalent bond. The sodium atom has one electron (Group I of the periodic table) in its valence shell. Beneath this valence electron lies a complete shell of eight electrons. The chlorine atom has an outer shell of seven electrons (Group VII of the periodic table). When these two atoms react, the electron simply passes from the sodium atom to the chlorine atom so that both resulting particles have outer shells of eight electrons. The sodium atom, by losing the negatively charged electron, becomes the positive sodium ion. The chlorine atom, by gaining the electron, becomes the negative chloride ion. There is actually no bond between the two ions. They attract each other, by virtue of their opposite charges, but an individual sodium ion will be attracted by any negative ion which happens to be near it, and not solely by the particular chloride ion to which it originally yielded its electron. The following equation represents the formation of sodium chloride from the elements.

$$\mathrm{Na}\cdot + \cdot\underset{\cdot\cdot}{\overset{\cdot\cdot}{\mathrm{Cl}}}\!: \longrightarrow \mathrm{Na}^{+} + :\underset{\cdot\cdot}{\overset{\cdot\cdot}{\mathrm{Cl}}}\!:^{-}$$

In carbon tetrachloride the atoms are held together by bonds of a different type, the nature of which may be indicated by imagining that the compound is formed by the interaction of a carbon atom with four chlorine atoms. The carbon atom (Group IV of the periodic table) has four electrons in its valence shell. The valence bond is made up of a pair of electrons, one from the carbon atom and one from the chlorine atom, held jointly by the two atoms. In combination with four chlorine atoms the carbon atom has a shell of eight electrons.

$$\cdot\dot{\underset{\cdot}{C}}\cdot + 4{:}\ddot{\underset{\cdot\cdot}{Cl}}\cdot \longrightarrow \begin{array}{c} :\ddot{Cl}: \\ :\ddot{\underset{\cdot\cdot}{Cl}}:\ddot{\underset{\cdot\cdot}{C}}:\ddot{\underset{\cdot\cdot}{Cl}}: \\ :\underset{\cdot\cdot}{Cl}: \end{array}$$

As indicated in the formula there is no actual transfer of electrons here, but rather a sharing in such a way that each atom is able to complete its octet. The result is a *fixed* bond between the carbon atom and the chlorine atom.

A comparison of the properties of sodium chloride and carbon tetrachloride illustrates the differences between ionic compounds and covalent compounds. For instance, sodium chloride is high-melting and nonvolatile. It is soluble in water. Its reactions, being the reactions of the sodium ion and the chloride ion, are extremely rapid. Carbon tetrachloride, on the other hand, is a volatile liquid. It is insoluble in water. Most of its reactions are extremely slow in comparison with those of sodium chloride. Thus, sodium chloride reacts instantly with silver nitrate to give a precipitate of silver chloride, but under ordinary conditions carbon tetrachloride does not react at all with silver nitrate. This shows that each chlorine atom is firmly attached to the carbon atom and that no chloride ions are present.

It is not to be concluded from the foregoing discussion that inorganic compounds contain only ionic or electrovalent bonds, or that all links in all organic compounds are covalent bonds. Actually, many inorganic compounds contain covalent bonds, and many organic substances have one or more electrovalent linkages.

A third type of valence, known as the *coordinate covalence*, also occurs in both organic and inorganic materials. It consists of a shared pair of electrons, both of which are contributed by one of the atoms. It is present in the molecule of nitric acid. In the formula below, the electrons originally belonging to the nitrogen and hydrogen atoms are indicated by dots, and those of the oxygen atoms are represented by crosses.

$$\begin{array}{c} \overset{\times\times}{O}\!\overset{\times}{_\times} \\ \times\!\cdot\!\times \\ H\overset{\times}{\cdot}\underset{\times\times}{\overset{\times\times}{O}}\overset{\times}{\cdot}N \\ \cdot\cdot \\ {}^\times_\times\underset{\times\times}{O}{}^\times_\times \end{array} \quad \text{or} \quad H{-}O{-}N\begin{array}{l}\nearrow O \\ \searrow O\end{array}$$

Nitric acid

It will be noted that in this formula the nitrogen atom has a complete octet. One of the oxygen atoms in nitric acid has achieved this state by sharing the *pair* furnished by the nitrogen atom. Formulas of this kind are usually abbreviated as shown, an arrow indicating the coordinate covalent link. The arrow points from the *donor* to the *acceptor* of the electron pair. The coordinate covalent link is sometimes called the semipolar bond. The origin of this term becomes clear from a consideration of the nitrogen-oxygen coordination bond in nitric acid. Since it still has all its original six electrons plus an interest in the pair which holds it to the nitrogen atom, the oxygen atom must have a negative charge. The nitrogen atom, on the other hand, since it has given up a share of the pair to the oxygen atom without gaining any interest in the latter's electrons, must bear a positive charge.

The carbon atom forms covalent links not only with chlorine but also with a great variety of elements, including the other halogens, hydrogen, oxygen, nitrogen, sulfur, phosphorus, and occasionally other elements. Most striking of all is the formation of stable covalent bonds with other carbon atoms. Thus, organic compounds may contain carbon atoms in *chains* of two, three, four, or more. In fact, there is no known limit to the number of carbon atoms that may be united in this way. When this remarkable fact is considered, together with the various elements mentioned that may be united with the carbon atoms in these chains, it becomes evident that the number of possible organic compounds is extremely large. In addition, as a consequence of the fixed nature of a covalent bond, it is often possible to obtain many different compounds from the same group of atoms by varying the *arrangement* of the atoms within the molecule. Such compounds are said to be *isomers;* the phenomenon, known as *isomerism,* is very common among organic compounds.

Because of the formation of carbon chains and the existence of isomers, there is no mathematical limit to the number of possible carbon compounds. The successful treatment of organic chemistry must, therefore, depend upon the classification of the compounds into broad groups of related substances. A very satisfactory classification is based on *structure.* By structure is meant the manner of attachment of the various atoms that make up a particular compound. For example, carbon atoms can be joined by one, two, or three bonds, giving rise to three different species of compounds. Carbon forms stable single, double, and triple bonds with nitrogen also. Moreover, it may be joined to sulfur, the halogens, and many other elements.

As a result of the remarkable and varied capacity of carbon for combining with itself and with other elements, many different types of organic compounds are possible. Except for the paraffins and cycloparaffins each type or class is characterized by a particular group known as its *functional group*. A few of the principal functional groups and the classes of compounds to which they give rise are shown in Table I.

TABLE I

SOME SIMPLE FUNCTIONAL GROUPS

Class of Compound	Functional Group	
	Formula	Name
Alcohols	–OH	Hydroxyl group
Acids	$-\overset{\displaystyle /\!\!/ O}{C}-OH$	Carboxyl group
Aldehydes and ketones	$>C=O$	Carbonyl group
Amines	$-NH_2$	Amino group
Mercaptans	–SH	Sulfhydryl group
Nitro compounds	$-NO_2$	Nitro group
Sulfonic acids	$-SO_3H$	Sulfonic acid or sulfo group

The chemical behavior of an organic compound is determined by the number and distribution of its electrons. Electron-deficient molecules generally react with molecules that have a high concentration of electrons in such a way as to reduce the deficiency. The points of high and low electron density in molecules are associated with the functional groups. The *hydroxyl group*, which is present in alcohols and organic acids, illustrates the electron-rich type of group. In it the oxygen atom is joined to carbon and to hydrogen, the bonds being made up of shared electron pairs, each of the bonded atoms furnishing one electron.

$$-\overset{|}{\underset{|}{C}}:\overset{\cdot\cdot}{\underset{\cdot\cdot}{O}}:H \qquad\qquad -\overset{|}{\underset{|}{C}}:\overset{\displaystyle H}{\overset{\cdot\cdot}{\underset{\cdot\cdot}{\underset{\displaystyle H}{N}}}}:$$

The hydroxyl group The amino group

Since an oxygen atom possesses six valence electrons and in a hydroxyl group supplies only two for bonding purposes, it retains four that are *unshared*. Because the oxygen atom of a hydroxyl group thus has more electrons than are needed for bonding, it is vulnerable to attack by molecules that are electron-deficient. In a similar way the nitrogen atom of an *amino group* contributes three of its five valence electrons to bond formation, retaining one unshared pair.

Molecules in which atoms are joined by double or triple bonds (p. 19), on the other hand, generally behave as though they were electron-deficient. Aldehydes and ketones fall in this category, being characterized by the *carbonyl group*. Although this group is ordinarily represented by the structure $-\underset{|}{C}::\overset{\cdot\cdot}{\underset{\cdot\cdot}{O}}$, its reactions correspond more closely to those to be expected for the structure $-\underset{|}{C}:\overset{\cdot\cdot}{\underset{\cdot\cdot}{O}}:$ in which the carbonyl carbon atom has only six electrons. The failure of this and similar functional groups to behave as would be expected on the basis of the conventional formulas will be discussed later (pp. 38, 78).

Of the dozens of classes of organic compounds, the basic type is that composed of *hydrocarbons*, compounds containing only hydrogen and carbon. The simplest hydrocarbons have only single bonds and therefore have no points of markedly high or low electron density. For this reason they are resistant to attack by most chemical reagents and are said to be *saturated*. Hydrocarbons having double or triple bonds are *unsaturated* and are much more reactive. Since the hydrocarbons constitute the foundations upon which all other types of organic compounds are constructed, it is desirable to consider them first.

CHAPTER 3

Saturated Hydrocarbons

Methane

The hydrocarbons can be grouped into various classes on the basis of their chemical reactions. Those called *saturated* hydrocarbons have been so named because of their relative inertness. The name *paraffin* (too little affinity) carries the same connotation.

The simplest of the paraffin hydrocarbons is methane, CH_4. It is the chief constituent of natural gas, and as such occurs in large quantities. It has been called *marsh gas* because of its formation during the anaerobic fermentation of vegetable matter beneath the stagnant water of swamps. Methane usually occurs along with coal, and, because it forms an explosive mixture ("fire damp") with air, its presence constitutes one of the hazards of mining.

Since carbon has a valence of 4, it is obvious that each of the hydrogen atoms in the methane molecule must be attached directly to the carbon atom. The bonds are covalent, and so the formula may be written as follows.

```
  H
  ..
H:C:H
  ..
  H
```

Electronic formula of methane

In practice, formulas of this type are used only when it is necessary to call particular attention to the electrons of the bonds. For convenience the links are usually represented by lines. Each line in the formula below is, then, to be considered as an abbreviation indicating a pair of electrons shared between the two atoms which it joins.

```
  H
  |
H-C-H
  |
  H
```

Structural formula of methane

This structural formula fails to represent correctly the distribution in space of the atoms in the methane molecule. It is known that the four pairs of electrons about a carbon atom arrange themselves so that each pair is at the greatest possible distance from each of the other pairs. The result is that the four valences are directed in such a way that the four attached groups bear the same spatial relation to each other as do the four points of a regular tetrahedron. An accurate representation of the methane molecule must, then, involve a three-dimensional drawing.

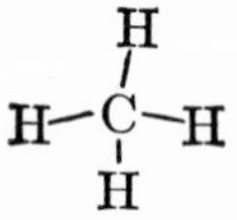

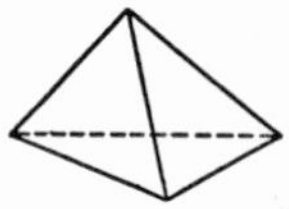

```
    H
    /
H—C—H
    |
    H
```

Because of this distribution of valences, carbon is often referred to as a *tetrahedral* atom. It will become apparent later that the spatial relationship of the groups about a carbon atom may have a profound influence on the properties of a compound. However, because they are difficult to draw, the three-dimensional formulas are used only when they are necessary.

Although the paraffins are the least reactive of the hydrocarbons, they do nevertheless undergo a variety of transformations under the influence of appropriate reagents. Thus, whereas methane resists the action of mild oxidizing agents such as aqueous solutions of potassium permanganate, it is readily oxidized when heated sufficiently with oxygen. This, of course, is the reaction which takes place when natural gas is burned.

$$CH_4 + 2O_2 \longrightarrow CO_2 + 2H_2O$$

Reactions of methane necessarily involve breaking a carbon-hydrogen bond and generally require drastic treatment. A typical example is *chlorination*, a process involving replacement of a hydrogen atom by a chlorine atom. The production of methyl chloride is illustrative.

$$CH_4 + Cl_2 \longrightarrow HCl + \underset{\text{Methyl chloride}}{CH_3Cl}$$

The reaction is brought about by high temperatures or ultraviolet light, agencies that are known to dissociate the chlorine molecule into chlorine atoms.

$$:\ddot{\underset{..}{Cl}}:\ddot{\underset{..}{Cl}}: + \text{Energy} \longrightarrow 2:\ddot{\underset{..}{Cl}}\cdot$$

The chlorine atoms so generated are extremely reactive since they possess valence shells having only seven electrons. As would be expected, they react with methane in such a way as to gain the electron necessary to reestablish the stable shell of eight. A hydrogen atom is captured along with the electron, leaving a free *methyl radical.*

$$\begin{matrix}\text{H}\\ \text{H}:\underset{\cdot\cdot}{\ddot{\text{C}}}:\text{H}\\ \text{H}\end{matrix} + :\underset{\cdot\cdot}{\ddot{\text{Cl}}}\cdot \longrightarrow \underset{\substack{\text{Methyl}\\ \text{radical}}}{\begin{matrix}\text{H}\\ \text{H}:\underset{\cdot\cdot}{\ddot{\text{C}}}\cdot\\ \text{H}\end{matrix}} + \text{H}:\underset{\cdot\cdot}{\ddot{\text{Cl}}}:$$

Like a chlorine atom, the methyl radical needs an electron to complete its octet. It can gain the needed electron, along with a chlorine atom, by attacking a chlorine molecule.

$$\begin{matrix}\text{H}\\ \text{H}:\underset{\cdot\cdot}{\ddot{\text{C}}}\cdot\\ \text{H}\end{matrix} + :\underset{\cdot\cdot}{\ddot{\text{Cl}}}:\underset{\cdot\cdot}{\ddot{\text{Cl}}}: \longrightarrow \begin{matrix}\text{H}\\ \text{H}:\underset{\cdot\cdot}{\ddot{\text{C}}}:\underset{\cdot\cdot}{\ddot{\text{Cl}}}:\\ \text{H}\end{matrix} + :\underset{\cdot\cdot}{\ddot{\text{Cl}}}\cdot$$

The products of this reaction are methyl chloride and a chlorine atom, which attacks a second molecule of methane. The chlorine atom required for the first step in chlorination is thus regenerated in the second. Theoretically, then, one such chlorine atom, in the presence of molecular chlorine, is sufficient to bring about the chlorination of an infinite number of methane molecules. Such self-sustaining reactions, known as *chain reactions*, are commonly encountered in photochemical processes, i.e., processes brought about by light.

The chlorination of methane can be continued until all the hydrogen atoms have been replaced by chlorine, the additional products being methylene chloride, chloroform, and carbon tetrachloride.

$$CH_3Cl + Cl_2 \xrightarrow[\text{light}]{\text{heat}} HCl + \underset{\text{Methylene chloride}}{CH_2Cl_2}$$

$$CH_2Cl_2 + Cl_2 \xrightarrow[\text{light}]{\text{heat}} HCl + \underset{\text{Chloroform}}{CHCl_3}$$

$$CHCl_3 + Cl_2 \xrightarrow[\text{light}]{\text{heat}} HCl + \underset{\substack{\text{Carbon}\\ \text{tetrachloride}}}{CCl_4}$$

The reaction is of the type known as a *substitution.* By substitution is meant the direct replacement of hydrogen by other atoms. A similar substitution occurs when bromine is used.

$$CH_4 + Br_2 \xrightarrow[\text{light}]{\text{heat}} HBr + \underset{\text{Methyl bromide}}{CH_3Br}$$

$$CH_3Br + Br_2 \xrightarrow[\text{light}]{\text{heat}} HBr + \underset{\text{Methylene bromide}}{CH_2Br_2}$$

$$CH_2Br_2 + Br_2 \xrightarrow[\text{light}]{\text{heat}} HBr + \underset{\text{Bromoform}}{CHBr_3}$$

$$CHBr_3 + Br_2 \xrightarrow[\text{light}]{\text{heat}} HBr + \underset{\text{Carbon tetrabromide}}{CBr_4}$$

Iodine, the least reactive of the halogens, does not react with methane. However, the iodine derivatives of methane, methyl iodide, methylene iodide, iodoform, and carbon tetraiodide, can be obtained by other methods. Fluorine is so extremely reactive that direct fluorination is a successful reaction only under special conditions.

Like nearly all organic compounds, methane decomposes under the influence of extreme heat. The products are carbon and hydrogen.

$$CH_4 \longrightarrow C + 2H_2$$

This reaction is used in the preparation of lampblack from natural gas. A simple way of effecting it is to burn methane with a limited quantity of air. The heat of the flame causes the decomposition of the methane which is in excess of the oxygen present. Thermal decomposition of organic compounds is usually referred to as *pyrolysis*. When a hydrocarbon is concerned, the reaction is sometimes called *cracking*.

The Higher Paraffins

Methane is the simplest member of a series of hydrocarbons of very similar chemical characteristics. The next higher member is ethane (C_2H_6), and following ethane are propane (C_3H_8) and butane (C_4H_{10}). These compounds may be represented by the general formula C_nH_{2n+2}, in which n is the number of carbon atoms. The formulas and boiling points of a number of them are given in Table II. It will be seen that the formula of any member can be obtained by adding CH_2 to that of the preceding member. Such a series of compounds is known as a *homologous series.* A homologous series may be defined as a group of structurally similar compounds, each member of which differs from the preceding member by CH_2. The concept of homology is one of the fundamentals of organic chemistry.

TABLE II

STRAIGHT-CHAIN SATURATED HYDROCARBONS

Name	Boiling Point	Formula	Structural Formula
Methane	−161°	CH_4	CH_4
Ethane	−88	C_2H_6	CH_3CH_3
Propane	−45	C_3H_8	$CH_3CH_2CH_3$
Butane	0	C_4H_{10}	$CH_3CH_2CH_2CH_3$
Pentane	36	C_5H_{12}	$CH_3CH_2CH_2CH_2CH_3$
Hexane	69	C_6H_{14}	$CH_3CH_2CH_2CH_2CH_2CH_3$
Heptane	98	C_7H_{16}	$CH_3CH_2CH_2CH_2CH_2CH_2CH_3$
Octane	125	C_8H_{18}	$CH_3CH_2CH_2CH_2CH_2CH_2CH_2CH_3$
Nonane	151	C_9H_{20}	$CH_3CH_2CH_2CH_2CH_2CH_2CH_2CH_2CH_3$
Decane	174	$C_{10}H_{22}$	$CH_3CH_2CH_2CH_2CH_2CH_2CH_2CH_2CH_2CH_3$

Only one carbon skeleton can be written for each of the hydrocarbons up to and including propane. However, in the formula C_4H_{10}, the carbons may be arranged either in a *straight chain*, $-\overset{|}{\underset{|}{C}}-\overset{|}{\underset{|}{C}}-\overset{|}{\underset{|}{C}}-\overset{|}{\underset{|}{C}}-$, or in a *branched chain*, $-\overset{|}{\underset{|}{C}}-\overset{|}{\underset{\underset{|}{-C-}}{C}}-\overset{|}{\underset{|}{C}}-$. Actually two different butanes, called normal butane (*n*-butane) and isobutane, are known.

$$\underset{n\text{-Butane}}{CH_3CH_2CH_2CH_3} \qquad \underset{\text{Isobutane}}{CH_3\underset{\underset{CH_3}{|}}{C}HCH_3}$$

These compounds have entirely different physical properties. For instance, the boiling point of isobutane (−10°) differs by 10 degrees from that of *n*-butane (0°). It will be seen later that there are also differences in their chemical properties.

Butane and isobutane are *isomers* of each other. *Isomerism* may be defined as the existence of two or more compounds of the same molecular formula but of different structures.

In a similar manner it is possible to write three structures for the formula C_5H_{12}, and, in fact, three isomeric pentanes are known. They are *n*-pentane, isopentane, and neopentane.

$$\underset{n\text{-Pentane}}{CH_3CH_2CH_2CH_2CH_3} \qquad \underset{\text{Isopentane}}{CH_3\underset{\underset{CH_3}{|}}{C}HCH_2CH_3} \qquad \underset{\text{Neopentane}}{CH_3-\overset{\overset{CH_3}{|}}{\underset{\underset{CH_3}{|}}{C}}-CH_3}$$

The number of possible isomers increases rapidly as the number of carbon atoms in the hydrocarbon molecule is increased. Thus, there are five hexanes, nine heptanes, eighteen octanes, and thirty-five nonanes. The method used above for naming the isomeric butanes and pentanes would become extremely cumbersome if an attempt were made to extend it to larger molecules. For this reason a simple system of naming such organic compounds was devised by a group of chemists meeting in Geneva in 1894. The following fundamental principles of the *Geneva system of nomenclature* form the basis of the modern system.

1. A compound is named as a derivative of the hydrocarbon corresponding to the longest carbon chain present in the molecule. The name of this hydrocarbon serves as the stem of the name of the compound.
2. The type of the compound, that is, the homologous series to which it belongs, is indicated by a suffix. For the paraffins this suffix is *ane*.
3. Groups attached to the carbon chain are indicated by suitable prefixes. In order to specify the location of these groups the carbon chain is numbered in such a way that the numbers used in the name are the smallest possible.

The use of these rules is illustrated by the names of the five hexanes. The CH_3 group is known as the methyl group.

$CH_3CH_2CH_2CH_2CH_2CH_3$

Hexane

$$\begin{array}{l} CH_3\underset{|}{C}HCH_2CH_2CH_3 \\ \quad\;\; CH_3 \end{array}$$

2-Methylpentane

$$\begin{array}{l} CH_3CH_2\underset{|}{C}HCH_2CH_3 \\ \qquad\quad\; CH_3 \end{array}$$

3-Methylpentane

$$\begin{array}{c} CH_3 \\ | \\ CH_3CCH_2CH_3 \\ | \\ CH_3 \end{array}$$

2,2-Dimethylbutane

$$\begin{array}{l} CH_3CH—CHCH_3 \\ \quad\;\; | \qquad | \\ \quad\; CH_3 \;\; CH_3 \end{array}$$

2,3-Dimethylbutane

The paraffin hydrocarbons resemble methane in their chemical properties. They resist the action of chemical oxidizing agents such as aqueous potassium permanganate. They react with chlorine and bromine at high temperatures or in the presence of strong ultraviolet radiation. The reaction, like that of methane, is one of substitution.

The introduction of a single chlorine atom into the propane molecule gives rise to two isomers, isopropyl chloride and *n*-propyl chloride.

$$CH_3CH_2CH_3 + Cl_2 \xrightarrow[\text{light}]{\text{heat}} \underset{\underset{\text{Isopropyl chloride}}{Cl}}{CH_3CHCH_3} \quad \text{or} \quad \underset{n\text{-Propyl chloride}}{CH_3CH_2CH_2Cl} + HCl$$

With the higher hydrocarbons, the number of monochloro derivatives increases rapidly. The production of isomers which are not easily separated, together with further chlorination of part of the monochloro derivatives, limits the usefulness of this reaction. However, the chlorination of a mixture of the pentanes is operated as a commercial process for preparing materials used as solvents (p. 67).

The paraffins undergo nitration, but only at elevated temperatures; the reaction is accompanied by cleavage of the carbon chains. For instance, propane can be converted to a mixture of nitromethane, nitroethane, 1-nitropropane, and 2-nitropropane.

$$CH_3CH_2CH_3 \xrightarrow[HONO_2]{420^\circ} \begin{cases} CH_3NO_2 & \text{Nitromethane} \\ CH_3CH_2NO_2 & \text{Nitroethane} \\ CH_3CH_2CH_2NO_2 & \text{1-Nitropropane} \\ \underset{NO_2}{CH_3CHCH_3} & \text{2-Nitropropane} \end{cases}$$

Thermal decomposition, or cracking, converts the paraffins into hydrocarbons of lower molecular weight. Thus, when *n*-octane is heated to the temperature of 600° the reaction product consists of a mixture of *saturated* and *unsaturated* hydrocarbons having from one to eight carbon atoms. The decomposition involves the breaking of the carbon chain at random points. Cleavage at the end of the chain produces methane and the unsaturated hydrocarbon heptene.

$$\underset{n\text{-Octane}}{C_8H_{18}} \xrightarrow{600^\circ} CH_4 + \underset{\text{Heptene}}{C_7H_{14}}$$

Cleavage at the second carbon of the chain may produce either ethane and hexene, or ethylene and hexane.

$$C_8H_{18} \xrightarrow{600^\circ} \underset{\text{Ethane}}{CH_3CH_3} + \underset{\text{Hexene}}{C_6H_{12}}$$

$$\text{or} \quad \underset{\text{Ethylene}}{C_2H_4} + \underset{\text{Hexane}}{C_6H_{14}}$$

The decomposition appears to take place in all the possible ways, so that a variety of products is formed. Cracking is of extreme importance in the production of gasoline. It will be considered in greater detail in connection with petroleum (p. 31).

Certain catalysts are capable of *isomerizing* paraffin hydrocarbons. For instance, in contact with aluminum chloride, *n*-butane changes to an equilibrium mixture of *n*-butane and isobutane.

$$\underset{n\text{-Butane}}{CH_3CH_2CH_2CH_3} \xrightleftharpoons{AlCl_3} \underset{\text{Isobutane}}{\underset{\displaystyle CH_3}{CH_3\overset{}{C}HCH_3}}$$

The Cycloparaffins

The cycloparaffins correspond to the formula C_nH_{2n}, yet have many of the properties of the paraffins. Their structures are characterized by the presence of carbon *rings*. The formulas and boiling points of some of the simpler cycloparaffins are given in Table III.

TABLE III

CYCLOPARAFFINS

Name	Structural Formula	Boiling Point
Cyclopropane	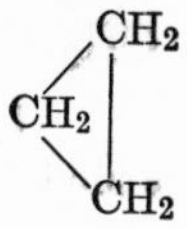 CH_2 ring of three CH_2 groups	−34.4°
Cyclobutane	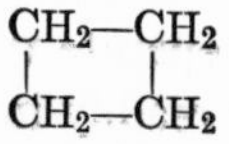 $CH_2—CH_2$ / $CH_2—CH_2$ (ring of four CH_2 groups)	13
Cyclopentane	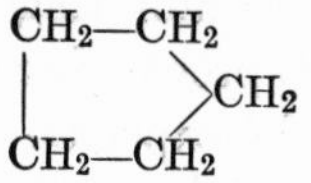 $CH_2—CH_2$, CH_2, $CH_2—CH_2$ (ring of five CH_2 groups)	49.5
Cyclohexane	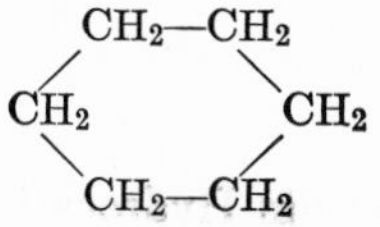 $CH_2—CH_2$, CH_2, CH_2, $CH_2—CH_2$ (ring of six CH_2 groups)	81.4

Cyclopropane is much more reactive than the open-chain paraffins. It absorbs bromine at room temperature and in the absence of light to give the open-chain dibromide, as shown by the following equation.

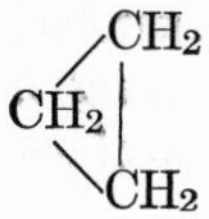

$$(CH_2)_3 \text{ (cyclopropane)} + Br_2 \longrightarrow \underset{\text{1,3-Dibromopropane}}{BrCH_2CH_2CH_2Br}$$

Cyclobutane is much less reactive toward bromine than is cyclopropane, and cyclopentane and cyclohexane cannot be distinguished from their straight-chain analogs by means of this reagent. The abnormal reactivity of cyclopropane and cyclobutane can be ascribed to the distortion of the carbon valences in the small rings. In cyclopropane the angle between any two valences in the ring is 60°, whereas the normal angle between carbon valences is 109° 28′. The compression of the valence angles in the small ring results in a *strain* within the molecule. In cyclobutane the angles are less highly compressed so that less strain and consequently less tendency toward ring opening exist. The angle of the regular pentagon is 108°, or almost identical with the tetrahedral angle. It follows, then, that cyclopentane should be practically free from strain and that its chemical behavior should approximate very closely that of *n*-pentane.

Cyclohexane is free from strain; because all six carbon atoms do not lie in the same plane, the normal valence angle need not be distorted. Two such models of cyclohexane can be constructed. They are called the *boat* and *chair* forms.

```
                                                   CH2
                                                  /  /
CH2              CH2          CH2—CH2 /
 \ \             /           /     CH2—CH2
  \  CH2—CH2 /              /  /
   \ CH2—CH2              CH2

      Boat form                  Chair form
```

Cyclohexane models

Since it has not been possible to separate two isomeric cyclohexanes, it is believed that the two forms are readily interconvertible.

Compounds containing cycloparaffin rings with more than thirty carbon atoms in the ring have been prepared and none of them exhibits any appreciable strain. This is to be expected from a study of models, for all such rings of six or more members can exist in non-planar, nearly strainless forms (p. 362).

The Relation of the Paraffin Hydrocarbons to Other Classes of Compounds

It has been mentioned that the various types of organic compounds are classified according to the *functional groups* (p. 6) which they contain. Most of the simple types may be regarded as *derivatives* of the paraffin hydrocarbons, the derivative differing from the parent hydrocarbon in having a functional group in place of one or more hydrogen atoms. For example, methyl chloride (CH_3Cl) differs from methane (CH_4) in having a chlorine atom in place of one hydrogen atom. The corresponding derivative of ethane is ethyl chloride (CH_3CH_2Cl). Two such derivatives may be obtained from propane; they are *n*-propyl chloride (1-chloropropane, $CH_3CH_2CH_2Cl$) and isopropyl chloride (2-chloropropane, $CH_3\underset{\underset{Cl}{|}}{C}HCH_3$). These substances are the first members of the homologous series of *alkyl chlorides*. The functional group of the series is the chlorine atom; it is attached to an *alkyl radical*, the radical obtained from a paraffin hydrocarbon by the removal of one hydrogen atom. The alkyl chlorides thus have the general formula $C_nH_{2n+1}Cl$. This formula is sometimes abbreviated as RCl ($R- = C_nH_{2n+1}-$).

The alcohols form a similar series in which the functional group is the hydroxyl group. The first members are methyl alcohol (CH_3OH), ethyl alcohol (CH_3CH_2OH), and the isomeric propyl alcohols, *n*-propyl alcohol ($CH_3CH_2CH_2OH$) and isopropyl alcohol ($CH_3\underset{\underset{OH}{|}}{C}HCH_3$). They conform to the general formula $C_nH_{2n+1}OH$ (ROH).

In most cases, a single functional group gives rise to only one homologous series. An interesting exception occurs in compounds containing the carbonyl group ($>C{=}O$). The simple carbonyl compounds may be regarded as derived from paraffins by replacement of two hydrogen atoms with a doubly bound oxygen atom. If the carbon atom carrying this oxygen atom is located at the end of a carbon chain the substance is an *aldehyde*. Examples are $H\overset{\nearrow O}{C}\text{–}H$ (formaldehyde), $CH_3\overset{\nearrow O}{C}\text{–}H$ (acetaldehyde), and $CH_3CH_2\overset{\nearrow O}{C}\text{–}H$ (propionaldehyde). When the carbonyl group is connected to two carbon atoms, that is, when it is located at some point other than an end of the carbon chain, the substance is a *ketone*. The simplest ketone is $CH_3\overset{\nearrow O}{C}\text{–}CH_3$ (acetone). The aldehydes and ketones are considered to constitute separate homologous series because their reactions differ in some important respects. For example, the aldehydes mentioned above are very easily oxidized to the corresponding acids ($H\overset{\nearrow O}{C}\text{–}OH$, formic acid; $CH_3\overset{\nearrow O}{C}\text{–}OH$, acetic acid; and $CH_3CH_2\overset{\nearrow O}{C}\text{–}OH$, propionic acid), but ketones are unaffected by mild oxidizing agents.

In the following chapters the properties conferred upon compounds by the various functional groups are considered in some detail. The classes most closely related structurally to the paraffins are those consisting of unsaturated hydrocarbons.

PROBLEMS

1. Define and illustrate the following terms: isomers, homologs, substitution, chlorination, cracking, strainless rings.
2. Write structural formulas of the following compounds: 2,3,4-trimethylpentane, 2,2,3-trimethylbutane, 3-ethylpentane, 2,2,3,3-tetramethylbutane, cycloheptane, methylcyclohexane, 1,3-dimethylcyclopentane.
3. Compare the reactivity toward bromine of propane and cyclopropane; of *n*-hexane and cyclohexane. Write the formulas of all the monochloro derivatives of *n*-hexane; of cyclohexane; of methylcyclohexane.
4. Write the electronic formulas and abbreviated electronic formulas of the following compounds: ethane, ethyl chloride, ethyl alcohol, acetaldehyde, acetic acid, nitroethane.
5. With the aid of suitable electronic formulas indicate the function of light in promoting the chlorination of a paraffin. Why is the process referred to as a *chain reaction?*

SUGGESTED READINGS

N. Levy and J. D. Rose, "The Aliphatic Nitro Compounds," *Quart. Revs.*, *1*, 358 (1947).

C. E. Frank, "Hydrocarbon Autoxidation," *Chem. Revs.*, *46*, 155 (1950).

A. L. Henne, "The Preparation of Aliphatic Fluorine Compounds," *Org. Reactions*, *2*, 49.

CHAPTER 4

Unsaturated Hydrocarbons

The Olefins

The simplest unsaturated hydrocarbons are those of the general formula C_nH_{2n}. They are called olefins or, since ethylene is the first member of the series, ethylenic hydrocarbons. Ethylene has the formula C_2H_4. It can be shown that each of the carbon atoms is connected to two hydrogen atoms, thus accounting for eight of the twelve valence electrons (four belonging originally to each carbon atom, and one to each hydrogen atom). The remaining four electrons are shared between the two carbon atoms. The carbon atoms are thus connected by *two* valence bonds, and the structural formula $CH_2{=}CH_2$ may be written. The presence of the *double bond* is characteristic of the olefins; it is the functional group of the series.

The names of the simple olefins are derived from those of the corresponding paraffins by changing the ending *ane* to *ylene*. The higher members are named according to the Geneva system, which uses the ending *ene*. In applying this system to compounds other than the paraffins, two modifications of the principles set forth on p. 13 are employed. These are as follows.

1. The substance is named as a derivative of the hydrocarbon corresponding to the longest chain *carrying the functional group*.
2. The location of the functional group is specified by numbering the carbon chain and incorporating into the name the number of the carbon atom to which the functional group is attached.

The use of these principles is illustrated in Table IV. For the lower members the common names are given in parentheses. It will be noted that only one number is used to locate the double bond. This is the *lower* of the two numbers corresponding to the carbon atoms connected by the double linkage.

TABLE IV

OLEFINS OR ETHYLENIC HYDROCARBONS

Name	Formula	Boiling Point
Ethene (ethylene)	$CH_2{=}CH_2$	−103.9°
Propene (propylene)	$CH_3CH{=}CH_2$	−47
1-Butene (butylenes)	$CH_3CH_2CH{=}CH_2$	−5
2-Butene (butylenes)	$CH_3CH{=}CHCH_3$	2
Methylpropene (isobutylene)	$CH_3C(CH_3){=}CH_2$	−6
1-Pentene	$CH_3CH_2CH_2CH{=}CH_2$	40
2-Pentene	$CH_3CH_2CH{=}CHCH_3$	36.4
2-Methyl-2-butene	$CH_3CH{=}C(CH_3)CH_3$	38.4
3-Methyl-1-butene	$CH_3CH(CH_3)CH{=}CH_2$	25
2-Methyl-1-butene	$CH_2{=}C(CH_3)CH_2CH_3$	31

The characteristic chemical property of the olefins is their tendency to revert to saturated compounds. Thus, they combine with hydrogen in the presence of catalysts to give paraffins. Reactions of this type, involving the combination of two molecules to form a single product, are known as *addition* reactions.

$$\underset{\text{Propylene}}{CH_3CH{=}CH_2} + H_2 \xrightarrow{\text{Pt}} \underset{\text{Propane}}{CH_3CH_2CH_3}$$

Olefins also undergo addition of chlorine and bromine at moderate temperatures and in the absence of catalysts. The products are again saturated compounds. Ethylene combines rapidly with bromine to give ethylene bromide.

$$CH_2{=}CH_2 + Br_2 \longrightarrow \underset{\text{Ethylene bromide}}{\underset{Br\quad Br}{CH_2CH_2}}$$

The addition of bromine to an ethylene is believed to proceed in steps and can be represented schematically by dissociation of the bromine molecule into a positive and a negative ion, followed by the successive attachment of the two ions to the olefin. If a line is used to represent a pair of electrons and if unshared pairs are neglected, the three steps are as follows.

$$Br{-}Br \longrightarrow Br^+ + Br^-$$

$$CH_2{=}CH_2 + Br^+ \longrightarrow BrCH_2{-}CH_2^+$$

$$BrCH_2{-}CH_2^+ + Br^- \longrightarrow BrCH_2{-}CH_2Br$$

Because this reaction causes the red color of bromine to disappear, it serves as a laboratory test for unsaturation.

Halogen acids react similarly, although less rapidly unless a catalyst is used. Ethyl chloride may be made by combining ethylene with hydrogen chloride in the presence of a catalyst such as antimony or bismuth trichloride.

$$CH_2{=}CH_2 + HCl \xrightarrow{SbCl_3} \underset{\text{Ethyl chloride}}{CH_3CH_2Cl}$$

When an unsymmetrical reagent such as a hydrogen halide combines with an unsymmetrical olefin, two products might be expected. Propylene and hydrogen chloride, for example, might give either *n*-propyl chloride or isopropyl chloride, or both.

$$CH_3CH{=}CH_2 + HCl \nearrow \left(\underset{n\text{-Propyl chloride}}{CH_3CH_2CH_2Cl}\right)$$

$$CH_3CH{=}CH_2 + HCl \searrow \underset{\text{Isopropyl chloride}}{CH_3\underset{\underset{Cl}{|}}{C}HCH_3}$$

Actually, only isopropyl chloride is obtained. In such cases it is generally true that the positive part of the reagent combines with the olefinic carbon atom that holds the larger number of hydrogen atoms. This principle was first formulated by Markownikoff and is known as Markownikoff's rule.

As in the addition of bromine, the reaction is believed to proceed by initial attack by the positive ion, in this case H^+, followed by attachment of the halide ion. At the moment of attack of the hydrogen ion the propylene molecule behaves as though it had structure *a*, and the positive hydrogen ion attaches itself to the terminal carbon atom.

$$\underset{a}{CH_3\overset{+}{C}H{-}\overset{-}{C}H_2} \qquad \underset{b}{CH_3\overset{-}{C}H{-}\overset{+}{C}H_2}$$

Structures of propylene

The alternative structure (*b*) would attract the positive ion to the central carbon atom. The actual steps are represented as follows.

$$CH_3\overset{+}{C}H{-}CH_2^- + H^+ \longrightarrow CH_3\overset{+}{C}H{-}CH_3$$

$$CH_3\overset{+}{C}HCH_3 + Cl^- \longrightarrow CH_3\underset{\underset{Cl}{|}}{C}HCH_3$$

A positive ion such as $CH_3\overset{+}{C}HCH_3$ in which the positive charge resides on a carbon atom is known as a *carbonium ion.*

Olefins combine with sulfuric acid to form alkylsulfuric acids. The reaction is useful because the alkylsulfuric acids can be hydrolyzed to alcohols and sulfuric acid. By this method ethylene is converted to ethyl alcohol.

$$CH_2{=}CH_2 + HOSO_2OH \rightleftharpoons \underset{\text{Ethylsulfuric acid}}{CH_3CH_2OSO_2OH}$$

$$CH_3CH_2OSO_2OH + H_2O \rightleftharpoons \underset{\text{Ethyl alcohol}}{CH_3CH_2OH} + HOSO_2OH$$

The addition of sulfuric acid is believed to proceed in steps, the ions H^+ and OSO_2OH^- being attached in succession.

$$CH_2{=}CH_2 + H^+ \rightleftharpoons CH_3\overset{+}{C}H_2$$

$$CH_3\overset{+}{C}H_2 + OSO_2OH^- \rightleftharpoons CH_3CH_2OSO_2OH$$

However, in the presence of water the second step may be a reaction of the carbonium ion ($CH_3\overset{+}{C}H_2$) with water to form ethyl alcohol directly without intermediate production of ethylsulfuric acid.

$$CH_3\overset{+}{C}H_2 + H\ddot{\underset{\cdot\cdot}{O}}H \longrightarrow [CH_3CH_2\underset{\cdot\cdot}{O}H_2]^+ \rightleftharpoons CH_3CH_2OH + H^+$$

The electron deficit of the carbonium ion is made up by coordination of the deficient carbon atom with the oxygen atom of the water molecule. The resulting ion loses a proton, forming the alcohol.

If propylene is employed the product is isopropyl alcohol.

The addition of halogen acids generally follows Markownikoff's rule, the halogen atom going to the carbon atom holding the fewer hydrogen atoms. It has been found, however, that the addition of *hydrogen bromide* takes place in the reverse sense if peroxides are present. This is known as the "peroxide effect" and has been observed with such compounds as allyl bromide, vinyl bromide, propylene, and isobutylene; the double bond in every case involves a terminal carbon atom.

$$CH_3CHBrCH_3 \xleftarrow[\substack{\text{peroxides}\\ \text{absent}}]{HBr} CH_3CH{=}CH_2 \xrightarrow[\substack{\text{peroxides}\\ \text{present}}]{HBr} CH_3CH_2CH_2Br$$

The peroxide causes the addition to be initiated by the electron-seeking bromine atom ($:\ddot{\underset{\cdot\cdot}{Br}}\cdot$), which attacks the terminal carbon of structure *a* above.

Hypochlorous acid combines with olefins to produce compounds known as *chlorohydrins.* Ethylene yields ethylene chlorohydrin.

$$CH_2{=}CH_2 + HOCl \longrightarrow \underset{\substack{|\quad\;|\\ OH\;\;Cl}}{CH_2CH_2}$$

Ethylene chlorohydrin

When hypochlorous acid reacts with unsymmetrical olefins the chlorine atom combines with the carbon atom that has the more hydrogen atoms. This further illustrates Markownikoff's rule. An example is the formation of propylene chlorohydrin from propylene.

$$CH_3CH{=}CH_2 + HOCl \longrightarrow CH_3\underset{\substack{|\quad\;|\\ CH\;\;Cl}}{CH{-}CH_2}$$

Propylene chlorohydrin

Olefins also unite with branched-chain paraffins to give saturated hydrocarbons. For example, isobutane combines with propylene to form a heptane. The reaction is of value in the preparation of high-grade gasoline (p. 34).

Olefins may also be caused to combine with themselves, yielding unsaturated hydrocarbons of higher molecular weight. For example, 2,4,4-trimethyl-1-pentene and 2,4,4-trimethyl-2-pentene, known as "diisobutylenes," are obtained by treatment of isobutylene with sulfuric acid.

$$CH_3\overset{\substack{CH_3\\ |}}{\underset{\substack{\|\\ CH_2}}{C}} + CH_3\overset{\substack{CH_3\\ |}}{C}{=}CH_2 \xrightarrow{H_2SO_4}$$

$$CH_3\overset{\substack{CH_3\\ |}}{\underset{\substack{|\\ CH_3}}{C}}{-}CH_2\overset{\substack{CH_3\\ |}}{C}{=}CH_2 \quad \text{and} \quad CH_3\overset{\substack{CH_3\\ |}}{\underset{\substack{|\\ CH_3}}{C}}{-}CH{=}\overset{\substack{CH_3\\ |}}{C}{-}CH_3$$

2,4,4-Trimethyl-1-pentene and 2,4,4-Trimethyl-2-pentene

The ethylenic double bond is readily attacked by oxidizing agents, and this property is the basis of the Baeyer test for unsaturation. Potassium permanganate is used as the oxidizing agent because its reduction can be followed easily by the color change and, if the test is carried out in alkaline solution, by the formation of a precipitate of manganese dioxide.

$$3CH_2{=}CH_2 + 2KMnO_4 + 4H_2O \longrightarrow 3\underset{\substack{|\quad\;\;|\\ OH\;\;OH}}{CH_2CH_2} + 2MnO_2 + 2KOH$$

Ethylene glycol

The reaction is not often useful for preparative purposes, since many of the glycols which might be made in this way are susceptible of oxidation by the permanganate.

The oxidation of ethylene by atmospheric oxygen can be controlled so that ethylene oxide is produced. The reaction is carried out in the presence of a silver catalyst and at moderately high temperatures.

$$2CH_2{=}CH_2 + O_2 \xrightarrow[200\text{–}400°]{Ag} 2\underset{\text{Ethylene oxide}}{CH_2CH_2 \atop \diagdown O \diagup}$$

Ozone converts ethylenic hydrocarbons into ozonides, which are easily decomposed with cleavage of the carbon chain. For example, ethylene yields an ozonide which, upon hydrolysis in the presence of a reducing agent, is converted to formaldehyde.

$$CH_2{=}CH_2 + O_3 \longrightarrow {CH_2\text{–}O\text{–}CH_2 \atop \diagdown O\text{–}O \diagup}$$

$${CH_2\text{–}O\text{–}CH_2 \atop \diagdown O\text{–}O \diagup} + 2[H] \longrightarrow \underset{\text{Formaldehyde}}{2H\text{–}\overset{\text{O}}{\overset{\|}{C}}\text{–}H} + H_2O$$

This reaction is often used in the determination of structures of unsaturated substances. For example, of the three butylenes, one (*A*) on ozonization and reduction yields formaldehyde and propionaldehyde; the second (*B*) is converted to acetaldehyde; and the third (*C*) yields acetone and formaldehyde. It follows, then, that *A* is 1-butene, *B* is 2-butene, and *C* is isobutylene.

$$\underset{\text{1-Butene }(A)}{CH_3CH_2CH{=}CH_2} \xrightarrow{O_3} {CH_3CH_2CH\text{–}O\text{–}CH_2 \atop \diagdown O\text{–}O \diagup} \xrightarrow{2[H]} \underset{\text{Propional-dehyde}}{CH_3CH_2\overset{\text{O}}{\overset{\|}{C}}\text{–}H} + \underset{\text{Formal-dehyde}}{H\overset{\text{O}}{\overset{\|}{C}}\text{–}H}$$

$$\underset{\text{2-Butene }(B)}{CH_3CH{=}CHCH_3} \xrightarrow{O_3} {CH_3CH\text{–}O\text{–}CHCH_3 \atop \diagdown O\text{–}O \diagup} \xrightarrow{2[H]} \underset{\text{Acetaldehyde}}{2CH_3\overset{\text{O}}{\overset{\|}{C}}\text{–}H}$$

$$\underset{\text{Isobutylene }(C)}{CH_3\overset{CH_3}{\overset{|}{C}}{=}CH_2} \xrightarrow{O_3} {CH_3\overset{CH_3}{\overset{|}{C}}\text{–}O\text{–}CH_2 \atop \diagdown O\text{–}O \diagup} \xrightarrow{2[H]} \underset{\text{Acetone}}{CH_3\overset{CH_3}{\overset{|}{C}}{=}O} + \underset{\text{Formaldehyde}}{H\overset{\text{O}}{\overset{\|}{C}}\text{–}H}$$

The Acetylenes

Acetylene is the first member of a series of more highly unsaturated hydrocarbons; its formula is C_2H_2 and, since it can be shown that each of the two carbon atoms carries one hydrogen atom, the structure must be $HC{\equiv}CH$. The series takes its name from the first member, and any compound containing the *triple bond* is said to be an acetylene. The systematic names of these hydrocarbons employ the ending *yne;* the simpler members, however, are usually named as substituted acetylenes. Examples of both systems of naming are given in Table V.

TABLE V

ACETYLENES

Name	Formula	Boiling Point
Acetylene (ethyne)	$HC{\equiv}CH$	−88°
Methylacetylene (propyne)	$CH_3C{\equiv}CH$	−24
Ethylacetylene (1-butyne)	$CH_3CH_2C{\equiv}CH$	18.5
Dimethylacetylene (2-butyne)	$CH_3C{\equiv}CCH_3$	29
n-Propylacetylene (1-pentyne)	$CH_3CH_2CH_2C{\equiv}CH$	40

Acetylene is an important industrial raw material. It is obtained by heating coke with lime and decomposing the resulting calcium carbide with water. Carbon monoxide is formed along with calcium carbide.

$$CaO + 3C \xrightarrow{\text{heat}} \underset{\text{Calcium carbide}}{CaC_2} + \underset{\text{Carbon monoxide}}{CO}$$

$$CaC_2 + H_2O \longrightarrow CaO + CH{\equiv}CH$$

Acetylene is also obtained by cracking petroleum at high temperatures.

Acetylene and its homologs, like the olefins, are chacterized by a marked tendency to combine with other reagents in such a way as to form saturated compounds. Their reactions usually differ from those of the olefins in that two moles of the adding reagent are required for saturation. The intermediate olefinic compound can often be obtained by limiting the amount of the reagent. Thus, either ethylene or ethane can be produced by hydrogenation of acetylene.

$$CH{\equiv}CH \xrightarrow[H_2]{\text{catalyst}} CH_2{=}CH_2 \xrightarrow[H_2]{\text{catalyst}} CH_3CH_3$$

In a similar manner one or two molecules of halogen may combine with an acetylene. Thus, acetylene may be converted to the dibromide which in turn absorbs a molecule of bromine to yield the tetrabromide.

$$CH{\equiv}CH \xrightarrow{Br_2} \underset{\substack{|\quad\ |\\ Br\ \ Br}}{CH{=}CH} \xrightarrow{Br_2} \overset{\substack{Br\ \ Br\\ |\quad\ |}}{\underset{\substack{|\quad\ |\\ Br\ \ Br}}{CH{-}CH}}$$

1,2-Dibromoethene (acetylene dibromide) — 1,1,2,2-Tetrabromoethane (acetylene tetrabromide)

One of the important commercial uses of acetylene involves its reaction with water in the presence of sulfuric acid and mercury salts. Only one molecule of water is added. The addition product to be expected, vinyl alcohol, is instable and rearranges to form acetaldehyde.

$$CH{\equiv}CH + HOH \xrightarrow[H_2SO_4]{Hg^{++}} [CH_2{=}CHOH] \longrightarrow CH_3C\overset{\nearrow O}{-}H$$

Vinyl alcohol — Acetaldehyde

Nearly all simple compounds containing a hydroxyl group on a carbon atom which also carries an ethylenic double bond undergo the same rearrangement; $-\underset{|}{C}{=}\underset{|}{C}{-}OH \longrightarrow -\underset{|}{CH}{-}\underset{|}{C}{=}O$. Much of the acetaldehyde produced by hydration of acetylene is converted to acetic acid (p. 96). Acetylene thus serves as a raw material in the commercial preparation of acetic acid.

It is to be noted that none of the homologs of acetylene can yield aldehydes by hydration. Since the addition of water proceeds according to Markownikoff's rule, all higher acetylenes are converted to ketones by this reaction. Acetone is formed by hydration of methylacetylene.

$$CH_3C{\equiv}CH + HOH \xrightarrow[H_2SO_4]{Hg^{++}} \left[CH_3\overset{\substack{OH\\ |}}{C}{=}CH_2\right] \longrightarrow CH_3\overset{\substack{O\\ \|}}{C}{-}CH_3$$

Acetone

The reaction of one molecule of halogen acid with acetylene produces a vinyl halide. Vinyl chloride is prepared in this way.

$$CH{\equiv}CH + HCl \longrightarrow CH_2{=}CHCl$$

Vinyl chloride

The commercial use of vinyl chloride depends on the fact that many molecules of the substance can be caused to combine with each other to give a very large molecule which is a valuable plastic. Such a reaction is known as a *polymerization*, and the large molecule is said to be a *polymer* of the smaller one.

$$(n + 2)CH_2{=}CHCl \xrightarrow{\text{peroxides}} XCH_2\underset{\substack{|\\ Cl}}{CH}\left(CH_2\underset{\substack{|\\ Cl}}{CH}\right)_n CH_2\underset{\substack{|\\ Cl}}{CH}Y$$

Vinyl chloride — Polyvinyl chloride

The exact nature of the groups X and Y which must occupy the end positions in the polymer is not known; they may be fragments of the catalyst molecule.

The function of a peroxidic catalyst in the polymerization appears to be to supply a free radical which adds to a molecule of vinyl chloride. The product of the addition is a free radical which adds to another molecule of vinyl chloride, and similar succeeding steps lead to the formation of very large molecules. The steps can be represented as shown.

$$H_2O_2 \longrightarrow 2HO\cdot$$

$$HO\cdot + CH_2{=}CHCl \longrightarrow HOCH_2\underset{\displaystyle Cl}{\underset{|}{C}}H\cdot$$

$$\xrightarrow{CH_2=CHCl} HOCH_2\underset{\displaystyle Cl}{\underset{|}{C}}HCH_2\underset{\displaystyle Cl}{\underset{|}{C}}H\cdot$$

$$\xrightarrow{CH_2=CHCl} HOCH_2\underset{\displaystyle Cl}{C}HCH_2\underset{\displaystyle Cl}{C}HCH_2\underset{\displaystyle Cl}{C}H\cdot \quad \text{etc.}$$

On this basis, a fragment of the catalyst is expected on at least one end of the polymer molecule.

It is possible, of course, to effect the addition of two molecules of halogen acid to acetylene. Thus, if excess hydrogen chloride is present, the product is ethylidene chloride rather than vinyl chloride.

$$CH{\equiv}CH + HCl \longrightarrow \underset{\text{Vinyl chloride}}{CH_2{=}CHCl} \xrightarrow{HCl} \underset{\text{Ethylidene chloride}}{CH_3CHCl_2}$$

By a similar reaction either vinyl acetate or ethylidene acetate may be obtained from acetylene and acetic acid.

$$CH{\equiv}CH + CH_3\overset{\overset{\displaystyle O}{/\!/}}{C}{-}OH$$

$$\longrightarrow \underset{\text{Vinyl acetate}}{CH_2{=}CH{-}O\overset{\overset{\displaystyle O}{/\!/}}{C}{-}CH_3} \xrightarrow{CH_3CO_2H} \underset{\text{Ethylidene acetate}}{CH_3CH(O\overset{\overset{\displaystyle O}{/\!/}}{C}CH_3)_2}$$

Vinyl acetate, like vinyl chloride, polymerizes readily; the product is known as polyvinyl acetate.

$$(n + 2)CH_2{=}\underset{\displaystyle OCOCH_3}{\underset{|}{C}}H$$

$$\longrightarrow XCH_2\underset{\displaystyle OCOCH_3}{\underset{|}{C}}H{-}\left(CH_2\underset{\displaystyle OCOCH_3}{\underset{|}{C}}H{-}\right)_n{-}CH_2\underset{\displaystyle OCOCH_3}{\underset{|}{C}}HY$$

If vinyl acetate and vinyl chloride are mixed before polymerization, the polymer formed contains both units in the chain. Polymers of this type are known as *copolymers*. In this case the copolymer has properties which make it superior, for certain uses, to the polymer of either component. In general, the vinyl polymers are clear, transparent solids. They soften on heating, and so can be pressed into any desired shape in a hot mold; or the molten polymer can be drawn into filaments suitable for yarns. The textile Vinyon is made in this way from a vinyl chloride-vinyl acetate copolymer.

The uses of ethylidene diacetate in the chemical industry are discussed in Chapter 9.

The Diolefins

Many hydrocarbons with more than one point of unsaturation are known. Among the most important are those that contain two olefinic linkages; these are called diolefins or simply dienes. 1,3-Butadiene and isoprene are interesting examples.

$$CH_2{=}CHCH{=}CH_2 \qquad\qquad \begin{array}{l} CH_2{=}\overset{}{C}{-}CH{=}CH_2 \\ \qquad\;\; | \\ \qquad\; CH_3 \end{array}$$

1,3-Butadiene **Isoprene**

Each of these hydrocarbons has a system of *conjugated double bonds*, that is, a system of alternating double and single bonds. In such systems each double bond is strongly influenced by the other. A striking illustration is the reaction between bromine and isoprene.

$$\begin{array}{l} \overset{1}{C}H_2{=}\overset{2}{C}{-}\overset{3}{C}H{=}\overset{4}{C}H_2 \\ \qquad\;\; | \\ \qquad\; CH_3 \end{array} + Br_2 \longrightarrow \begin{array}{l} Br\overset{1}{C}H_2\overset{2}{C}{=}\overset{3}{C}H\overset{4}{C}H_2Br \\ \qquad\quad\;\; | \\ \qquad\quad\; CH_3 \end{array}$$

1,4-Dibromo-2-methyl-2-butene

This is an example of the process known as 1,4-addition. It is often true that addition takes place at the ends of a conjugated system. Apparently the double bonds partially neutralize each other when they are in this position, and the property of unsaturation develops only at points, such as the ends of the system, where the conjugation is interrupted. An explanation is to be found in the theory of resonance (compare p. 341).

Isoprene is obtained when rubber is heated in the absence of air. In the presence of sodium the isoprene changes to a material closely resembling natural rubber. Since analysis of rubber shows it to have the formula $(C_5H_8)_n$, it is apparent that rubber is a polymer of isoprene.

$$(C_5H_8)_n \underset{\text{polymerization}}{\overset{\text{depolymerization}}{\rightleftharpoons}} n\,CH_2{=}\underset{\underset{CH_3}{|}}{C}{-}CH{=}CH_2$$

Isoprene

Evidence indicates that the isoprene units in rubber are combined by a process similar to 1,4-addition, and that the polymeric molecule contains about 10,000 isoprene units.

$$XCH_2\underset{\underset{CH_3}{|}}{C}{=}CHCH_2\left(CH_2\underset{\underset{CH_3}{|}}{C}{=}CHCH_2\right)_n CH_2\underset{\underset{CH_3}{|}}{C}{=}CHCH_2Y$$

Rubber

Chemists have been successful in the synthesis of rubberlike materials. The best-known synthetic rubbers are those made from 1,3-butadiene. The diene can be obtained by dehydrogenation of *n*-butane, which is available in large quantities from petroleum.

$$\underset{n\text{-Butane}}{CH_3CH_2CH_2CH_3} \xrightarrow{\text{oxide catalysts}} H_2 + \underset{\text{1-Butene}}{CH_3CH_2CH{=}CH_2}$$

$$\xrightarrow{\text{oxide catalysts}} H_2 + \underset{\text{1,3-Butadiene}}{CH_2{=}CHCH{=}CH_2}$$

$$(n+2)CH_2{=}CHCH{=}CH_2 \xrightarrow{\text{polymerization}}$$

$$\underset{\text{Polybutadiene}}{XCH_2CH{=}CHCH_2(CH_2CH{=}CHCH_2)_nCH_2CH{=}CHCH_2Y}$$

The best types of synthetic rubber are *copolymers;* that is, another substance capable of polymerization is added to the butadiene and the resulting polymer contains both units in the chain (p. 382).

Neoprene is a synthetic rubber manufactured from acetylene. The first operation is the *dimerization* of acetylene, in the presence of cuprous salts, to vinylacetylene.

$$CH{\equiv}CH + CH{\equiv}CH \xrightarrow{Cu^+} \underset{\text{Vinylacetylene}}{HC{\equiv}CCH{=}CH_2}$$

Vinylacetylene combines with hydrogen chloride but, although the expected 1,4-addition occurs, the product rearranges in the presence of copper salts to give chloroprene.

$$HC{\equiv}CCH{=}CH_2 + HCl$$

$$\longrightarrow CH_2{=}C{=}CH{-}CH_2Cl \xrightarrow{Cu^+} CH_2{=}\underset{\underset{Cl}{|}}{C}{-}CH{=}CH_2$$

Chloroprene

If the reaction is carried out in the presence of copper salts chloroprene is obtained directly. Chloroprene differs from isoprene in having a chlorine atom in place of the methyl group, and like isoprene it polymerizes readily. The polymer is known as Neoprene.

$$\mathrm{XCH_2\underset{\underset{Cl}{|}}{C}{=}CHCH_2}\left(\mathrm{CH_2\underset{\underset{Cl}{|}}{C}{=}CHCH_2}\right)_n\mathrm{CH_2\underset{\underset{Cl}{|}}{C}{=}CHCH_2Y}$$

Neoprene

Neoprene has many of the physical properties of rubber. Unlike rubber, it retains its tensile strength and elasticity when it is in contact with organic liquids. Consequently it finds uses in gasoline and oil lines, for which rubber is not suited.

PROBLEMS

1. Write equations for the reaction of 1-butene with: hydrogen (platinum catalyst); bromine (at room temperature and in the absence of strong light); sulfuric acid, followed by hydrolysis; hydrogen chloride; ozone, followed by treatment with zinc and water; aqueous alkaline potassium permanganate; hypochlorous acid.
2. Define and illustrate the following terms: functional group; addition reaction; conjugated system; 1,4-addition; polymerization; copolymer.
3. Write the formulas of *n*-butane, cyclobutane, 1-butene, 1-butyne, 1,3-butadiene. Compare their reactions with bromine, with respect to type of reaction, conditions required, and number of products obtained.
4. What are the commercial sources of ethylene? acetylene? 1,3-butadiene?
5. By means of a formula, show the probable structure of rubber. Give equations for the preparation of Neoprene from acetylene; of a rubber made from petroleum.
6. Give equations for a synthesis of 1-butyne from ethylene, acetylene, and any required inorganic reagents.
7. Indicate the probable steps in the peroxide-catalyzed polymerization of vinyl acetate.

SUGGESTED READING

"$6.5 Million Rubber Research and Development Program," *Chem. Eng. News*, *30*, 3170 (1952).

CHAPTER 5

Petroleum

The principal constituents of petroleum are saturated hydrocarbons. Both paraffins and cycloparaffins may be present; cycloparaffins occurring in petroleum are often called naphthenes. Crude oils are usually classified as paraffinic, naphthenic, or aromatic (p. 36), depending on which type of hydrocarbon is present in greatest amount. In addition to hydrocarbons, crude petroleum contains smaller amounts of organic nitrogen and sulfur compounds.

Because it contains many related hydrocarbons, petroleum is difficult to separate into its individual components. By controlled distillation it can be separated into fractions of decreasing volatility. These fractions, each of which contains a large number of hydrocarbons, are used as fuels and lubricants. An idea of the composition of the common petroleum products may be gained from Table VI.

TABLE VI

FRACTIONAL DISTILLATION OF PETROLEUM

Boiling Point	Composition	Name
Gaseous	CH_4–C_4H_{10}	Natural gas
20–100°	C_5H_{12}–C_7H_{16}	Naphtha, ligroin, petroleum ether
70–200	C_6H_{14}–$C_{12}H_{26}$	Gasoline
200–275	$C_{12}H_{26}$–$C_{15}H_{32}$	Kerosene
Above 275	$C_{15}H_{32}$–$C_{18}H_{38}$	Gas oil (cracking stock)
	$C_{16}H_{34}$–$C_{20}H_{42}$	Lubricating oil, mineral oil
	$C_{18}H_{38}$–$C_{22}H_{46}$	Grease stocks
	$C_{20}H_{42}$–$C_{24}H_{50}$	Paraffin wax
Residue		Asphalt tar, petroleum coke

The fractional distillation of an average crude oil yields a relatively small gasoline fraction, with larger amounts of kerosene and gas oil. Consequently chemists have long sought methods of converting these higher-boiling materials into gasoline. This is now accomplished in the cracking process, by which the large paraffins are decomposed at high temperatures, usually in the presence of suitable catalysts, to give a mixture of smaller paraffins and olefins (p. 11). The operation is carried out in cracking stills which permit the escape of the newly formed volatile hydrocarbons from the cracking zone. A portion of the cracking distillate is too volatile for use as gasoline, since cleavage near the end of the carbon chains produces hydrocarbons of low molecular weight (p. 14). Nevertheless, the process is of tremendous economic value, since it enables refiners to convert as much as 80 per cent of the crude oil into gasoline whereas only about 20 per cent could be obtained by fractional distillation.

The cracking process not only has increased the quantity of gasoline available but also has improved its quality. Gasoline made in this way has less tendency to cause knocking in a high-compression engine than the straight-run gasoline obtained by direct distillation of petroleum. The unsaturated hydrocarbons in the cracked gasoline are responsible for the improved anti-knock property.

$$C_{18}H_{38} \xrightarrow{\text{heat}} C_9H_{20} + C_9H_{18}$$
$$C_{10}H_{22} + C_8H_{16}, \text{ etc.}$$

The anti-knock value of a gasoline is usually expressed in terms of the octane number. This term came to be used in the early studies of knocking because, of a great variety of *pure* hydrocarbons tested, "isooctane" (2,2,4-trimethylpentane) was found to have the least tendency to knock. *n*-Heptane was found to have the poorest characteristics, so far as knocking is concerned.

```
    CH3  CH3
     |    |
CH3CCH2CHCH3        CH3CH2CH2CH2CH2CH2CH3
     |
    CH3
"Isoöctane"                n-Heptane
```

These two hydrocarbons were selected as reference points for the evaluation of gasolines. A fuel of 80 octane rating is one which has the same tendency to knock as a mixture of 80 parts of isoöctane and 20 parts of *n*-heptane. It should be emphasized that the octane number does not refer to the composition of a gasoline, but only to its knocking characteristics.

The improvements in the anti-knock qualities of gasoline have had far-reaching effects on the design of internal-combustion engines. An engine of given size can be made to operate more efficiently by increasing its compression ratio. However, when the compression ratio is increased it becomes necessary to employ a fuel of higher octane rating to avoid knocking. Consequently, as the octane value of commercial gasoline is increased, automobile engines become smaller, more powerful, and more efficient. These factors are of even greater importance in connection with airplane engines, since an improved fuel not only results in a more powerful machine but also extends the cruising range without increasing the fuel load.

As indicated above (p. 14), the cracking process converts a part of the heavier paraffins into gaseous hydrocarbons. Both saturated and unsaturated hydrocarbons are produced. These are methane, ethane, ethylene, propane, propylene, *n*-butane, 1-butene, 2-butene, isobutane, and isobutylene, together with pentanes and pentenes. Since the unsaturated hydrocarbons are reactive they are of value as raw materials, and large quantities of ethylene, propylene, butenes, and isobutylene are utilized by the chemical industry.

Methods of recombining the small hydrocarbon molecules have been discovered. These processes yield hydrocarbons of the gasoline range, and the products have very high octane ratings. The method first employed consists in treating isobutylene with sulfuric acid to produce isoöctenes. Hydrogenation of the latter converts it to isoöctane (p. 32).

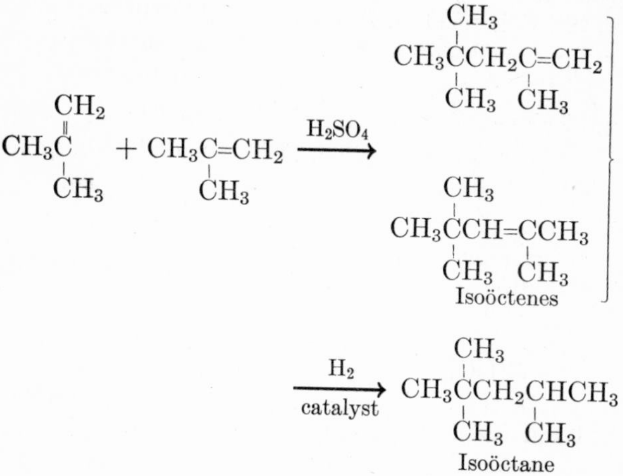

$$\begin{array}{c} CH_2 \\ \| \\ CH_3C \\ | \\ CH_3 \end{array} + \begin{array}{c} CH_3C{=}CH_2 \\ | \\ CH_3 \end{array} \xrightarrow{H_2SO_4} \left.\begin{array}{c} \begin{array}{c} CH_3 \\ | \\ CH_3CCH_2C{=}CH_2 \\ |\quad\quad | \\ CH_3 \quad CH_3 \end{array} \\ \\ \begin{array}{c} CH_3 \\ | \\ CH_3CCH{=}CCH_3 \\ |\quad\quad | \\ CH_3 \quad CH_3 \end{array} \\ \text{Isoöctenes} \end{array}\right\}$$

$$\xrightarrow[\text{catalyst}]{H_2} \begin{array}{c} CH_3 \\ | \\ CH_3CCH_2CHCH_3 \\ |\quad\quad | \\ CH_3 \quad CH_3 \\ \text{Isoöctane} \end{array}$$

If a mixture of isobutylene and the butenes (1-butene and 2-butene) is employed, the isobutylene reacts preferentially with the butenes. The product is a mixture of octenes which can be hydrogenated to a mixture of octanes.

$$\text{Isobutylene} + \text{Butenes} \xrightarrow{H_2SO_4} \text{Octenes} \xrightarrow[\text{catalyst}]{H_2} \text{Octanes}$$

It has been found that branched-chain paraffins combine with olefins under the influence of acid catalysts (p. 23). The reaction between isobutane and the butylenes produces octanes directly.

$$\text{Isobutane} + \text{Butenes} \xrightarrow{H_2SO_4} \text{Octanes}$$

The paraffins produced in condensations of this type are not those which would be expected if the reaction were a simple addition of the isoparaffin to the olefin. For example, isobutane condenses with propylene to yield chiefly 2,3-dimethylpentane rather than 2,2-dimethylpentane. The isobutane molecule appears to undergo cleavage to a methyl and an isopropyl radical and these become attached to the propylene molecule.

$$\underset{\displaystyle\quad CH_3}{CH_3\overset{}{C}HCH_3} \longrightarrow \underset{\displaystyle\quad CH_3}{CH_3CH-} + CH_3-$$

$$CH_3CH{=}CH_2 + CH_3- + \underset{\displaystyle\quad CH_3}{CH_3CH-} \longrightarrow \underset{\text{2,3-Dimethylpentane}}{CH_3\overset{CH_3}{C}H-\overset{CH_3}{C}HCH_2CH_3}$$

The condensation of isobutane with the butenes appears to take a similar course. This reaction is accompanied by the formation of lower and higher paraffins (pentanes to decanes) which are also suitable for gasoline.

In commerical practice, the fraction containing all the four-carbon hydrocarbons (*n*-butane, isobutane, 1-butene, 2-butene, and isobutylene) is treated with sulfuric acid. All the components except *n*-butane are converted into gasoline hydrocarbons; the *n*-butane is easily separated from the gasoline produced. Part of it is isomerized to isobutane and part is dehydrogenated to butenes.

$$CH_3CH_2CH_2CH_3 \xrightarrow{AlCl_3} CH_3\overset{CH_3}{C}HCH_3$$

$$CH_3CH_2CH_2CH_3 \xrightarrow[\text{heat}]{\text{oxide catalysts}} \text{Butenes} + H_2$$

These are added to the next charge, so that conversion to gasoline is substantially complete. The product contains highly branched saturated and unsaturated hydrocarbons. It has an octane rating of about 100 and thus makes an excellent aviation fuel.

The refining of higher-boiling fractions of petroleum to produce lubricating oils involves processes designed to remove objectionable constituents. Among them are treatment with sulfuric or other acid to remove gum-forming materials, chilling to cause crystallization of paraffin wax which is then separated by filtration, and extraction with solvents to remove non-lubricating constituents.

Crude oil which contains a high percentage of naphthenes (cycloparaffins) affords a source of aromatic hydrocarbons. Benzene may be prepared from cyclohexane and toluene from methylcyclohexane. More striking is the conversion of straight-chain paraffins to aromatics. Toluene is obtained in good yields by dehydrogenation and cyclization of *n*-heptane. Aromatic hydrocarbons will be discussed in the following chapter.

SUGGESTED READINGS

A. V. Grosse, "Catalytic Chemistry of Hydrocarbons," *Record Chem. Progr. Kresge-Hooker Sci. Lib.*, *13*, 55 (1952).

F. D. Rossini, "Hydrocarbons in Petroleum," *Chem. Eng. News*, *25*, 230 (1947).

CHAPTER 6

Aromatic Hydrocarbons

A number of hydrocarbons have been isolated from coal tar, the black viscous material which distils when coke is prepared by heating coal at 1100–1300°. These are sometimes called the coal tar hydrocarbons, but they are more generally referred to as the aromatic hydrocarbons. The simplest member of this family is benzene, C_6H_6.

Comparison of the formula of benzene with that of a paraffin of six carbon atoms indicates that the hydrocarbon is highly unsaturated. Yet it is almost devoid of the properties which distinguish the olefins and acetylenes. For example, it does not respond to the Baeyer test (p. 23), and when it is treated with a halogen in the absence of light or a catalyst no reaction occurs. If a catalyst such as an iron or aluminum halide is present, a reaction does occur, but it is one of substitution rather than of addition. Thus, so far as the type of reaction with halogens is concerned, benzene resembles the paraffins rather than the olefins. On the other hand, the halogenation of benzene differs from that of a hexane in requiring a different catalyst and in producing a single product rather than a mixture of isomers. For example, an excellent yield of bromobenzene is obtained by treating benzene with bromine in the presence of iron. Presumably the iron is converted to ferric bromide, which is the catalyst.

$$\underset{\text{Benzene}}{C_6H_6} + Br_2 \xrightarrow{FeBr_3} \underset{\text{Bromobenzene}}{C_6H_5Br} + HBr$$

The fact that a single bromobenzene is formed, although it might be expected that the bromine could become attached to any one of the six carbon atoms, suggests that benzene is a cyclic compound in which all the carbon atoms are equivalent. That a ring is present is proved by the catalytic hydrogenation of benzene. Under conditions similar to those employed in hydrogenating olefins or acetylenes, benzene is unaffected, but at higher temperatures and pressures it is converted to cyclohexane.

```
                         CH2
                        /   \
               Ni    CH2     CH2
C6H6 + 3H2  ---->     |       |
                     CH2     CH2
                        \   /
                         CH2
Benzene              Cyclohexane
```

$$C_6H_6 + 3H_2 \xrightarrow{Ni} \text{Cyclohexane}$$

This indicates that the formula of benzene differs from that of cyclohexane by the presence of three double bonds. Such a formula was proposed by Kekule in 1865.

```
        H
        C
      /   \\
   HC       CH
   ||       |
   HC       CH
      \   //
        C
        H
     Benzene
```

Although benzene reacts under certain conditions as though it contained double linkages, it is not to be compared to the olefins. It will be recalled that in the conjugated dienes the double bonds tend to neutralize each other except at the ends of the system, and consequently tend to undergo 1,4 addition. Benzene may be regarded as having a *completely* conjugated system, so that the mutual neutralization of the double bonds is at a maximum. Another approach to this problem is offered by the theory of resonance (p. 38).

A number of homologs of benzene are found along with it in the light fraction from the distillation of coal tar. Among them are toluene and the xylenes. The xylenes, or dimethylbenzenes, illustrate a type of isomerism which is very common in the aromatic series. The two methyl groups may be placed in three different positions with respect to each other; these isomers differ in *orientation*.

```
     CH3              CH3               CH3              CH3
      C                C                 C                C
    /   \\           /   \\            /   \\           /   \\
  HC     CH        HC     CCH3       HC     CH        HC     CH
  ||     |         ||     |          ||     |         ||     |
  HC     CH        HC     CH         HC     CCH3      HC     CH
    \   //           \   //            \   //           \   //
      C                C                 C                C
      H                H                 H               CH3
   Toluene        ortho-Xylene      meta-Xylene      para-Xylene
```

For convenience in writing formulas the benzene nucleus is ordinarily represented by a hexagon with alternate double and single bonds. In naming aromatic substances the prefixes *ortho*, *meta*, and *para* are abbreviated, only the first letters being used. These abbreviations are illustrated in the formulas below.

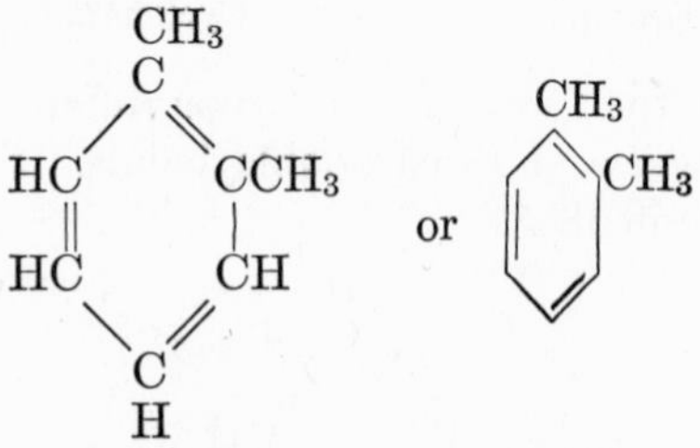

```
        CH3
         C
       /   \\
    HC       CCH3                  CH3
    ||        |           or     (hexagon) CH3
    HC       CH
       \\   //
         C
         H
   ortho-Xylene                  o-Xylene
```

One of the early objections to Kekule's formula for benzene was based on the argument that it indicates the existence of two forms of *ortho*-xylene, depending on the position of the double bonds.

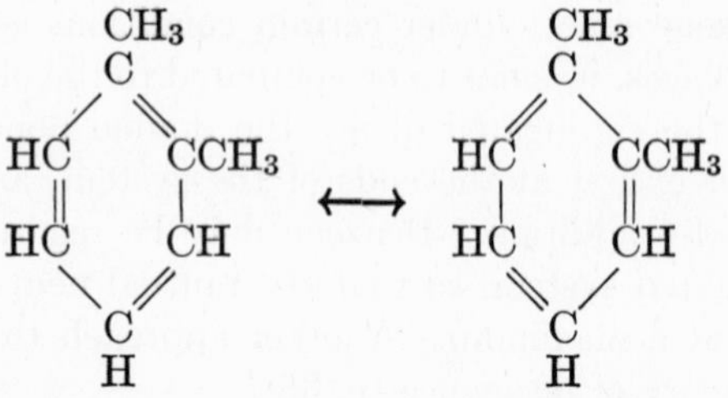

```
        CH3                      CH3
         C                        C
       /   \\                   //   \
    HC       CCH3            HC       CCH3
    ||        |       <-->    |        ||
    HC       CH              HC       CH
       \   //                   \\   /
         C                        C
         H                        H
```

It has been found, by examination of the products of ozonization (p. 24), that *ortho*-xylene reacts as though both forms were present.

It will be noticed that the two structures differ only in the positions of the electrons. A similar observation has been made with respect to many unsaturated compounds. Such compounds are said to possess *resonance*. Resonance is a property of compounds the structures of which can be written in two or more equivalent or nearly equivalent electronic arrangements. However, substances that possess this property are not to be thought of as mixtures of different compounds but rather as a single compound related to the electronic structures that can be written for it. The fact is that our method of writing structural formulas is not adequate and has to be supplemented. In benzene, for example, the six bonds of the ring are identical, being somewhere between a true single bond and a true double bond. Since we have no symbol for such a bond, the practice has been established of describing resonating compounds by writing the various electronic structures and connecting them with double-headed arrows as shown for *o*-xylene.

The concept that the bonds forming an aromatic ring are intermediate in nature between single and double bonds accords well with the fact that such rings do not ordinarily respond to tests for unsaturation but do, nevertheless, behave like unsaturated compounds when confronted with powerful reagents.

The aromatic hydrocarbons react with the halogens, with nitric acid, and with sulfuric acid to give products of substitution. The reactions can be made to give good yields of mono-substituted products by limiting the amounts of the reagents.

Chlorination $C_6H_6 + Cl_2 \xrightarrow{FeCl_3} C_6H_5Cl + HCl$

Chlorobenzene

As in the reaction of halogens with olefins (p. 20), it is assumed that the first step is the attack of the benzene ring by a positive entity. Then, however, the resulting fragment expels a proton in order to restore the resonance-stabilized aromatic ring. Thus chlorination involves attack of the ring by the positive chlorine ion.

$C_6H_6 + Cl^+ \longrightarrow [C_6H_6Cl]^+ \xrightarrow{-H^+} C_6H_5Cl$

Similar mechanisms can be written for nitration and sulfonation, the postulated attacking species being NO_2^+ and SO_3H^+, respectively.

Nitration $C_6H_6 + HON{=}O(\rightarrow O) \xrightarrow{H_2SO_4} C_6H_5N{=}O(\rightarrow O) + H_2O$

Nitrobenzene

Sulfonation $C_6H_6 + HOSO_2OH \xrightarrow{SO_3} C_6H_5SO_2OH + H_2O$

Benzenesulfonic acid

These reactions occur at moderate temperatures when the catalysts indicated are present.

By using appropriate amounts of reagents disubstituted products can be obtained. With two molecules of chlorine, benzene yields a mixture of *o*- and *p*-dichlorobenzenes. The same products are obtained from chlorobenzene and one molecule of chlorine.

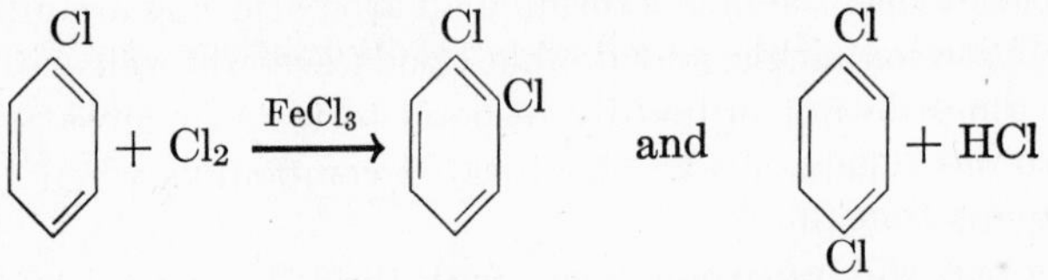

$$C_6H_5Cl + Cl_2 \xrightarrow{FeCl_3} o\text{-}C_6H_4Cl_2 \text{ and } p\text{-}C_6H_4Cl_2 + HCl$$

o-Dichlorobenzene *p*-Dichlorobenzene

In other substitutions chlorobenzene likewise yields both *ortho* and *para* isomers.

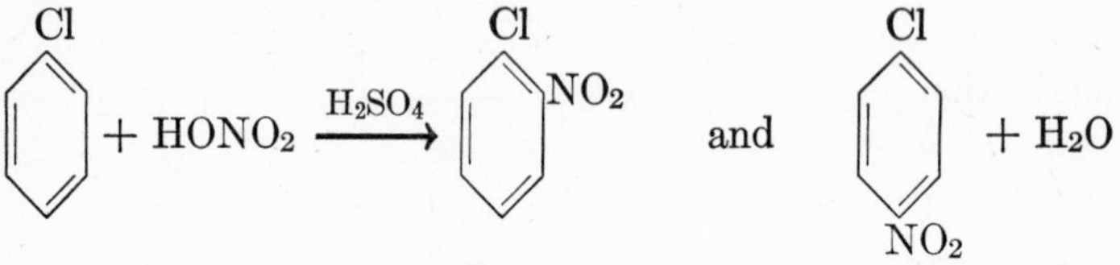

$$C_6H_5Cl + HONO_2 \xrightarrow{H_2SO_4} o\text{-}ClC_6H_4NO_2 \text{ and } p\text{-}ClC_6H_4NO_2 + H_2O$$

o-Chloronitrobenzene *p*-Chloronitrobenzene

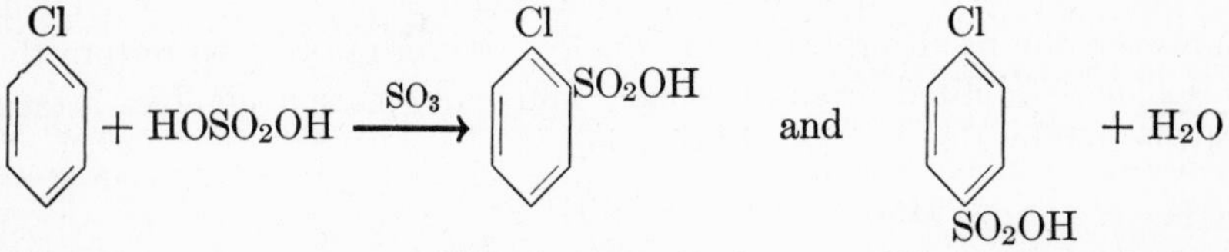

$$C_6H_5Cl + HOSO_2OH \xrightarrow{SO_3} o\text{-}ClC_6H_4SO_2OH \text{ and } p\text{-}ClC_6H_4SO_2OH + H_2O$$

o-Chlorobenzenesulfonic acid *p*-Chlorobenzenesulfonic acid

On the other hand, substitutions carried out on nitrobenzene yield the *meta* isomer.

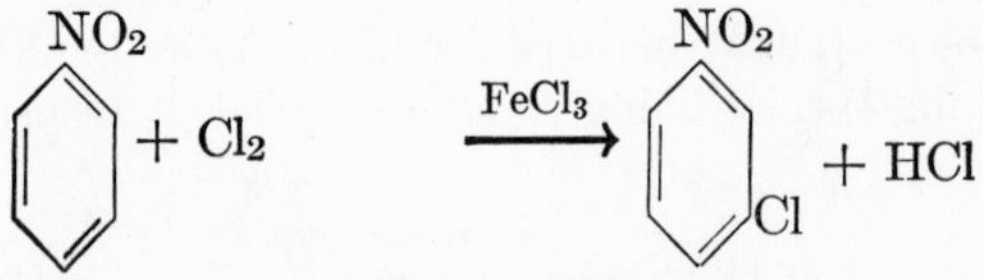

$$C_6H_5NO_2 + Cl_2 \xrightarrow{FeCl_3} m\text{-}ClC_6H_4NO_2 + HCl$$

m-Chloronitrobenzene

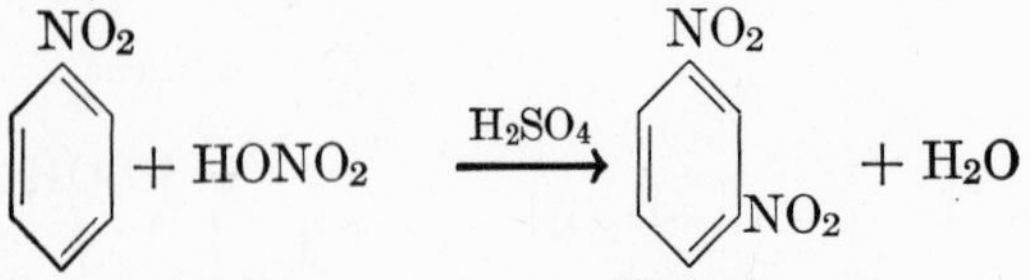

$$C_6H_5NO_2 + HONO_2 \xrightarrow{H_2SO_4} m\text{-}C_6H_4(NO_2)_2 + H_2O$$

m-Dinitrobenzene

$$C_6H_5NO_2 + HOSO_2OH \xrightarrow{SO_3} m\text{-}O_2NC_6H_4SO_2OH$$

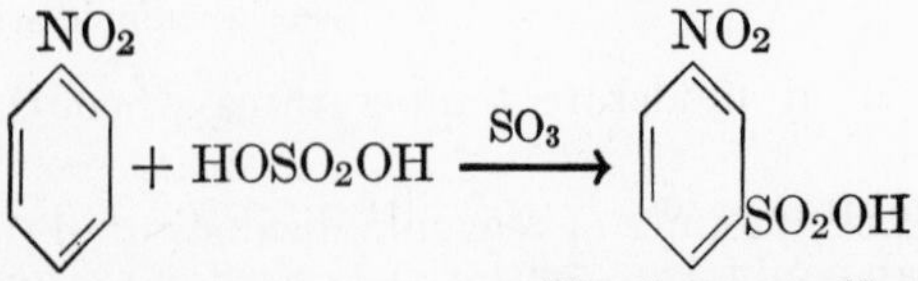

m-Nitrobenzenesulfonic acid

These examples illustrate a general truth: the position taken by the second substituent entering a benzene ring is determined by the nature of the substituent already present.

The Influence of Substituents on the Benzene Ring. As has been indicated the ordinary substitution reactions in the aromatic series are ascribed to the attack of the ring by a positive entity (Cl^+, NO_2^+, etc.), i.e., a reagent that is electron-seeking or *electrophilic*. It follows that such reactions will proceed most easily with aromatic nuclei having readily available electrons. The availability of electrons, i.e., the electron density of a given ring, depends to a greater or less degree on the substituents that it holds. Thus toluene has a higher electron density then benzene; i.e., the methyl group contributes electrons to the ring. The nuclei of the xylenes have a still higher electron density, as would be predicted. Other substituents that cede electrons to the ring are hydroxyl and amino. Thus, in hydroxybenzene and aminobenzene, generally called phenol and aniline, respectively, the nuclei have high electron density.

On the other hand, the nitro group not only does not cede electrons to the ring but actually withdraws them. Hence the electron density of the nitrobenzene ring is lower than that of benzene.

The transfer of electrons to and from the aromatic nucleus is primarily a resonance phenomenon, as will be apparent from the following resonance structures of aniline.

```
    ..                ..
  H-N-H             H-N-H             H-N-H
    |                 |                 ||
    C                 C                 C
   / \\             // \               / \..
HC     CH        HC     CH         HC     CH
||     |    <->   |     ||    <->  ||     |
HC     CH        HC     CH         HC     CH
  \   //           \\   /            \   //
    CH               CH                CH
    a                b                 c

                  H-N-H             H-N-H
                    ||                ||
                    C                 C
                 ../ \               / \
               HC     CH          HC     CH
         <->    |     ||    <->   ||     ||
               HC     CH          HC     CH
                 \\   /             \   /
                   CH                 CH
                                      ..
                   d                  e
```

The first two structures (*a* and *b*) will be recognized as those proposed by Kekule. Although equivalent they are not identical, since the carbon atoms joined by double bonds in *a* are linked by single bonds in *b*, and vice versa. In the other three the unshared pair of electrons of the nitrogen atom has migrated to the ring. The geometry of the molecule permits the entering electron pair to take up an *ortho* position (*c* or *d*) or the *para* position (*e*). At these positions, therefore, the availability of electrons is greatest, which explains the fact that substitution by electrophilic agents occurs at these points in preference to a *meta* position.

The behavior of the aniline molecule is explained by reference to all five structures of which it is said to be a *resonance hybrid*. At the instant of reaction, however, it behaves as though it actually possessed one of the contributing structures. Salt formation, for example, is the behavior to be expected of structure *a* or *b*. In yielding *p*-bromoaniline by bromination, on the other hand, aniline acts as though it had structure *e*. The *ortho*, *para*-directing power of alkyl groups (p. 43), the hydroxyl group (p. 168), and other substituents of this category are explained in a similar way.

Nitrobenzene is a resonance hybrid of several structures, chief of which are the following.

```
 - ..  +  ..          - ..  +  ..            - ..  +  .. -
 :O–N=O               :O–N=O:                :O–N–O:
  ..  |  ..            ..  |  ..              ..  ‖  ..
      C                    C                      C
    /   \\               //   \                  /   \+
 HC       CH          HC       CH             HC       CH
 ‖        ‖     ⟷     |        ‖      ⟷       ‖        |
 HC       CH          HC       CH             HC       CH
    \   //               \\   /                  \   //
      CH                   CH                     CH
      a                    b                      c

                      - ..  +  .. -          - ..  +  .. -
                      :O–N–O:                :O–N–O:
                       ..  ‖  ..              ..  ‖  ..
                           C                      C
                         /   \                  /   \
                      +HC      CH             HC       CH
               ⟷      |        ‖      ⟷       ‖        ‖
                      HC       CH             HC       CH
                         \\   /                  \   /
                           CH                     CH
                                                  +
                           d                      e
```

In structures *c*, *d*, and *e* an electron pair has been transferred *from the ring*, decreasing the electron content of the ring. As a consequence of this decrease, nitrobenzene undergoes ordinary substitution reactions less readily than benzene. The geometry of the molecule causes the deficit to be localized at a position *ortho* or *para* to the substituent. As a result these positions have such a low electron density as to be practically immune to the attack of an electron-seeking agent. The *meta* positions, however, have suffered electron depletion only indirectly and to a relatively minor degree. They are, therefore, more vulnerable to electrophilic attack than the *ortho* and *para* positions, which accounts for the fact that nitrobenzene undergoes *meta* substitution preferentially.

By reference to structures similar to those written for aniline and nitrobenzene, it is possible to account for the effect of various other substituents on the benzene ring by the theory of resonance. The methyl group, however, presents a special problem. It is *ortho*, *para*-directing yet has no unshared pair of electrons for donation to the nucleus. Its behavior is about what would be expected of the negative ion that would be formed by removal of a proton. This ion presents a close analogy to aniline, as the following structures show. The behavior of toluene in-

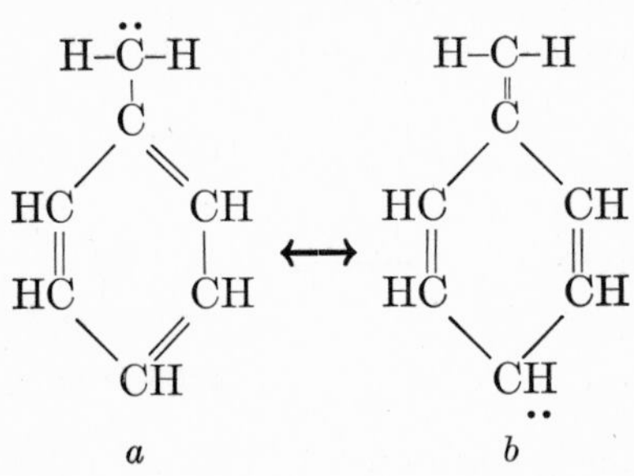

```
        ..
      H-C-H                H-C-H
        |                    ||
        C                    C
      /   \\               /   \
   HC       CH          HC       CH
   ||       |     <-->  ||       ||
   HC       CH          HC       CH
      \   //               \   /
        CH                   CH
                             ..
        a                    b
```

dicates that migration of electrons to the ring (as in *b*) does occur even though there seems to be no justification for assuming detachment of a proton. Moreover, the magnitude of the effect depends on the number of hydrogen atoms attached to the lateral carbon atom; it is greater in toluene, which has three such hydrogen atoms, then in ethylbenzene, which has only two. This peculiar type of resonance, called *hyperconjugation*, is observed with many classes of compounds to be discussed later (p. 77).

The Relative Electron-Releasing Power of Substituents. Experiment has shown that, on the basis of the relative effects on the vulnerability of the benzene ring to attack by electrophilic agents, substituents can be arranged in the following order.

$$NH_2 > HO > CH_3 > X \text{ (halogens)} > C{=}O > NO_2$$

Other substituents, to be mentioned later, take their places in this series at points that can be predicted with a fair degree of accuracy. The halogen atoms require special mention. They occupy an intermediate position between the substituents that cede electrons to the ring (*ortho*, *para*-directing) and those that withdraw electrons (*meta*-directing). Actually the halogens are *ortho*, *para*-directing, as though contributing electrons to the ring. On the other hand, they stabilize the benzene ring to electrophilic attack, as though withdrawing electrons from the ring.

A rule that is very useful in predicting the directive influence of a group attached to the benzene ring has been formulated by Hammick and Illingworth. The rule states that if, in the compound ⟨benzene ring⟩XY, Y is to the right of X in the periodic table or above X, if X and Y are in the same group, then –XY is *meta*-directing. In all other cases, including that in which –XY is a single atom, –XY is *ortho, para*-directing. There are few exceptions to this rule.

Polysubstitution. When a third group is introduced into the ring the directive influences of both the first two must be considered. Sometimes the directive influences reinforce each other, as in *m*-dinitrobenzene. Introduction of a third nitro group gives only the symmetrical trinitrobenzene, since each nitro group directs the entering group to the 5 position.

$$C_6H_4(NO_2)_2\ (1,3) + HONO_2 \xrightarrow{H_2SO_4} C_6H_3(NO_2)_3\ (1,3,5) + H_2O$$

1,3,5-Trinitrobenzene

A similar situation is encountered in the nitration of toluene. The first products are, of course, *o*- and *p*-nitrotoluene.

$$C_6H_5CH_3 + HONO_2 \xrightarrow{H_2SO_4} o\text{-}CH_3C_6H_4NO_2 \text{ and } p\text{-}CH_3C_6H_4NO_2 + H_2O$$

o-Nitrotoluene *p*-Nitrotoluene

In *o*-nitrotoluene both the methyl group and the nitro group will direct a third group to the 4 and 6 positions. In the *para* isomer the 2 and 6 positions are activated. If a second nitro group is introduced by nitration of the mixture of *o*- and *p*-nitrotoluenes two isomeric dinitrotoluenes may be produced.

$CH_3C_6H_3(NO_2)_2$ (1-CH_3, 2,4-NO_2) $CH_3C_6H_3(NO_2)_2$ (1-CH_3, 2,6-NO_2)

2,4-Dinitrotoluene 2,6-Dinitrotoluene

In the first of these isomers further substitution will take place in the 6 position, and in the second isomer in the 4 position. Further nitration of the mixture therefore gives a single product, 2,4,6-trinitrotoluene (TNT).

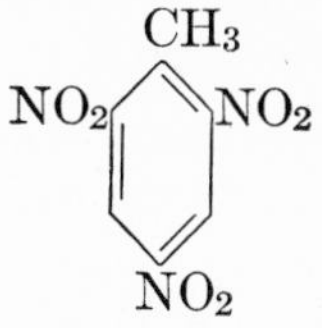

CH_3
NO_2 NO_2
NO_2
2,4,6-Trinitrotoluene

When the directive influences oppose each other a variety of further substitution products may be formed. In *m*-chloronitrobenzene, for example, the entering group will be directed to the 5 position by the nitro-group and to the 2, 4, and 6 positions by the chlorine atom.

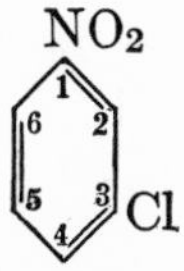

NO_2
1 6 2 5 3 4 Cl

Friedel-Crafts Reaction. A type of reaction somewhat different from the substitutions discussed above is the Friedel-Crafts reaction. It takes place when aluminum chloride is added to a mixture of an aromatic hydrocarbon and an alkyl halide. For example, ethyl chloride and benzene yield ethylbenzene.

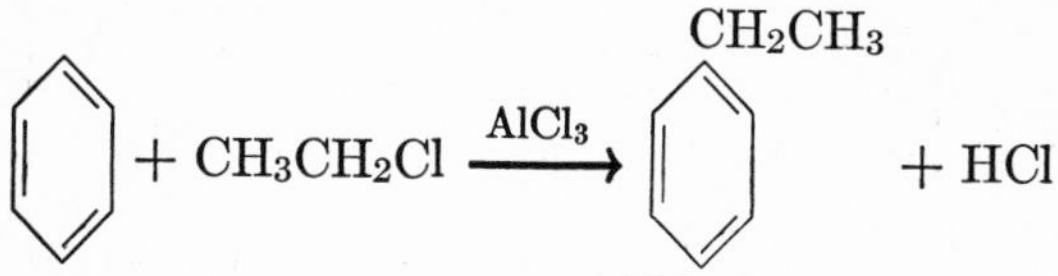

$$C_6H_6 + CH_3CH_2Cl \xrightarrow{AlCl_3} C_6H_5CH_2CH_3 + HCl$$

Ethylbenzene

In the manufacture of styrene, ethylene is used in place of the halide.

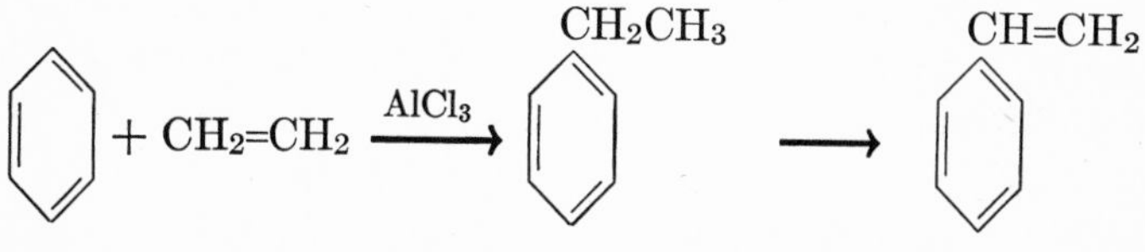

$$C_6H_6 + CH_2{=}CH_2 \xrightarrow{AlCl_3} C_6H_5CH_2CH_3 \longrightarrow C_6H_5CH{=}CH_2$$

Certain substances, like toluene, ethylbenzene, and the xylenes, can be considered mixed hydrocarbons, since they contain both aromatic and paraffinic portions. The properties of such compounds are of interest in affording comparisons of aromatic and paraffinic hydrocarbons.

For instance, when toluene is subjected to vigorous oxidation, it is the methyl group rather than the benzene ring that is affected. The product is benzoic acid, the simplest aromatic acid.

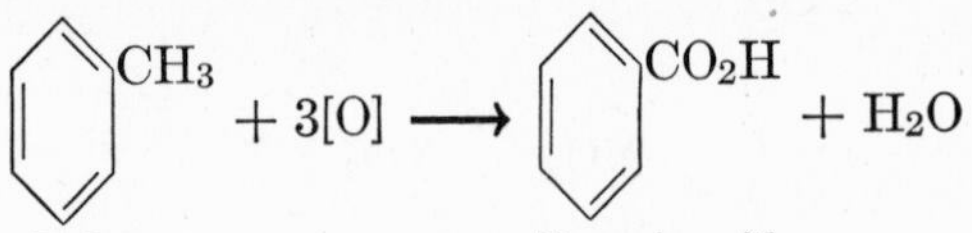

$$C_6H_5CH_3 + 3[O] \longrightarrow C_6H_5CO_2H + H_2O$$

Toluene — Benzoic acid

If a longer paraffin radical is present all its carbon atoms except the one attached to the ring are removed.

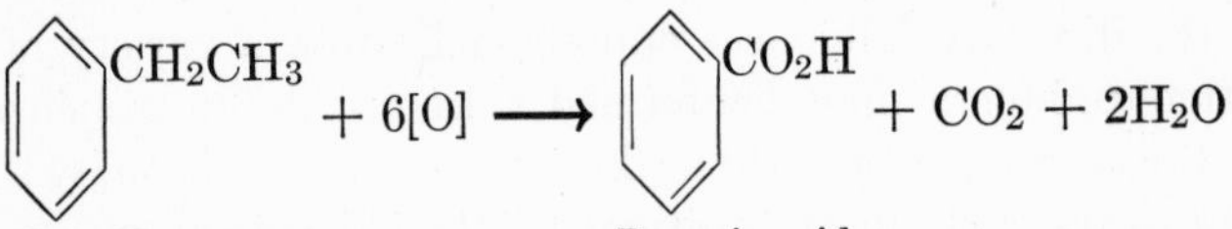

$$C_6H_5CH_2CH_3 + 6[O] \longrightarrow C_6H_5CO_2H + CO_2 + 2H_2O$$

Ethylbenzene — Benzoic acid

In a similar way propylbenzene and isopropylbenzene, also called cumene, likewise yield benzoic acid,

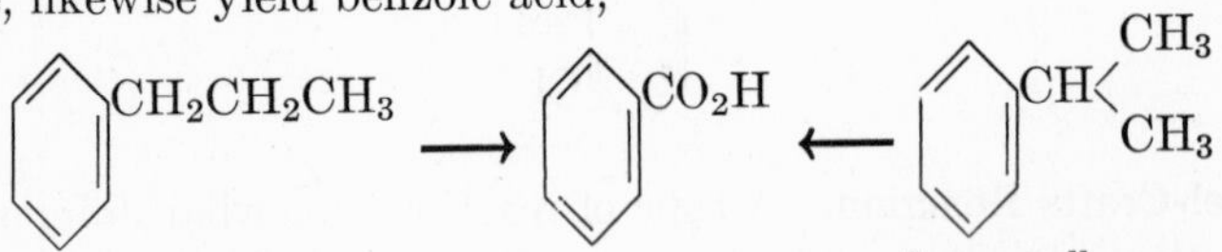

$$C_6H_5CH_2CH_2CH_3 \longrightarrow C_6H_5CO_2H \longleftarrow C_6H_5CH(CH_3)_2$$

Propylbenzene — Isopropylbenzene (Cumene)

Substituents that are joined to the aromatic nucleus by a carbon-to-carbon bond are known as *side chains*. The methyl group in toluene, the ethyl group in ethylbenzene, the propyl group in propylbenzene, the isopropyl group in cumene, and the carboxyl group in benzoic acid are examples. Side-chain oxidation does not affect nitro or sulfo groups or halogen atoms. An example is the oxidation of *p*-nitrotoluene to *p*-nitrobenzoic acid by treatment with a mixture of potassium dichromate and sulfuric acid.

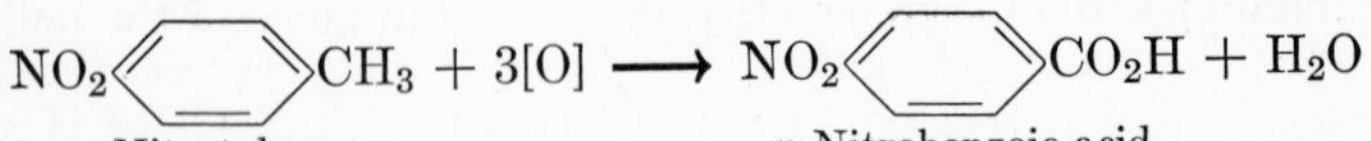

$$NO_2C_6H_4CH_3 + 3[O] \longrightarrow NO_2C_6H_4CO_2H + H_2O$$

p-Nitrotoluene — *p*-Nitrobenzoic acid

Similarly *o*-chlorotoluene is converted to *o*-chlorobenzoic acid by the action of potassium permanganate.

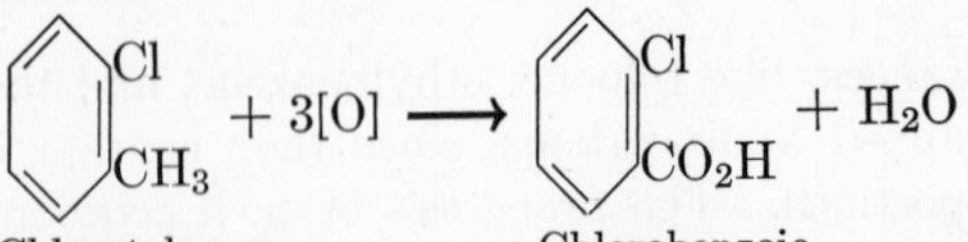

$$ClC_6H_4CH_3 + 3[O] \longrightarrow ClC_6H_4CO_2H + H_2O$$

o-Chlorotoluene — *o*-Chlorobenzoic acid

The halogenation of toluene affords an illustration of the specificity of catalysts. If toluene is chlorinated in the presence of strong light, substitution in the side chain occurs. Either one, two, or three hydrogens can be replaced by regulating the amount of chlorine used.

$$C_6H_5CH_3 + Cl_2 \xrightarrow{\text{ultraviolet light}} C_6H_5CH_2Cl + HCl$$

Benzyl chloride

$$C_6H_5CH_2Cl + Cl_2 \xrightarrow{\text{ultraviolet light}} C_6H_5CHCl_2 + HCl$$

Benzal chloride

$$C_6H_5CHCl_2 + Cl_2 \xrightarrow{\text{ultraviolet light}} C_6H_5CCl_3 + HCl$$

Benzotrichloride

If chlorination is carried out in the presence of ferric chloride, substitution in the aromatic nucleus occurs, yielding a mixture of *o*- and *p*-chlorotoluenes.

$$C_6H_5CH_3 + Cl_2 \xrightarrow{FeCl_3} o\text{-}ClC_6H_4CH_3 \text{ and } p\text{-}ClC_6H_4CH_3 + HCl$$

o-Chlorotoluene *p*-Chlorotoluene

Catalysts such as ferric chloride, which promote chlorination in the aromatic nucleus, are known as *carriers*.

Oxidation and chlorination without a carrier are examples of reactions that involve alkyl side chains. Halogenation with a carrier, nitration, sulfonation, and the Friedel-Crafts reaction, on the other hand, are reactions typical of aromatic nuclei.

Condensed Aromatic Nuclei. A second type of aromatic hydrocarbon found in coal tar is that containing more than one benzene ring. Examples are naphthalene ($C_{10}H_8$), anthracene ($C_{14}H_{10}$), and phenanthrene ($C_{14}H_{10}$).

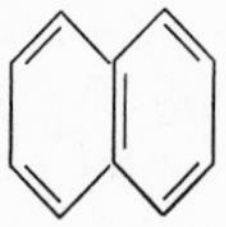

Naphthalene 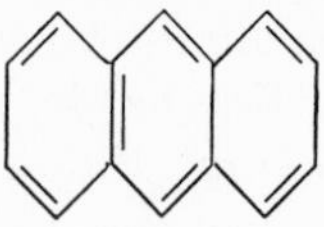 Anthracene 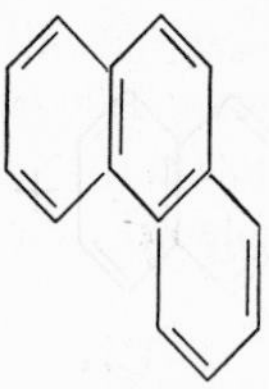 Phenanthrene

From the commercial standpoint the most important of these is naphthalene. It is the most abundant of the hydrocarbons isolated from coal tar and has found many uses in the preparation of dyes, medicinals, and other substances.

Examination of the formula of naphthalene reveals that there are two possible monosubstitution products. The positions designated by α in the formula below are equivalent, as are also those designated by β.

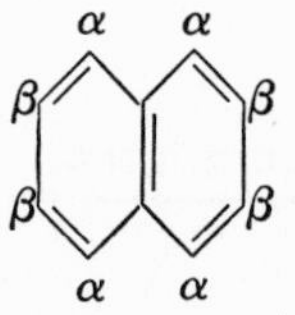

α α
β β
β β
α α

Generally, naphthalene yields the α-derivative in substitutions. For example, bromination gives α-bromonaphthalene, and nitration yields α-nitronaphthalene.

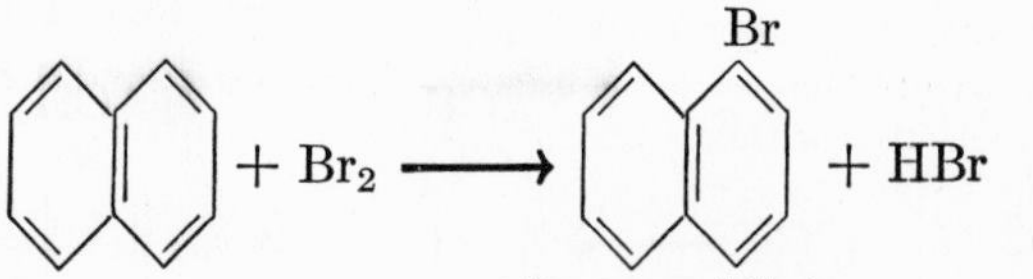

$$C_{10}H_8 + Br_2 \longrightarrow C_{10}H_7Br + HBr$$

α-Bromonaphthalene

$$C_{10}H_8 + HONO_2 \xrightarrow{H_2SO_4} C_{10}H_7NO_2 + H_2O$$

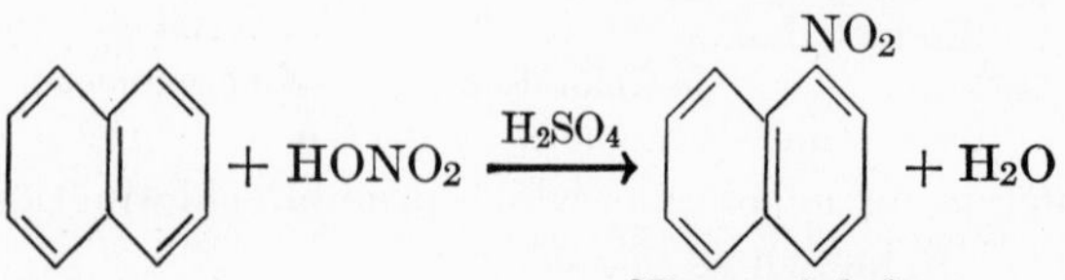

α-Nitronaphthalene

Sulfonation, on the other hand, may produce either the *alpha* or *beta* derivative, depending on the temperature of the reaction mixture. At low temperatures (80°) α-naphthalenesulfonic acid is produced. If this product is heated to about 160° in the presence of sulfuric acid it rearranges to the *beta* isomer. Consequently sulfonation at 160° produces β-naphthalenesulfonic acid.

$$C_{10}H_8 + HOSO_2OH \xrightarrow{80^\circ} C_{10}H_7SO_2OH + H_2O$$

α-Naphthalenesulfonic acid

H_2SO_4 ↓ 160°

$$C_{10}H_8 + HOSO_2OH \xrightarrow{160^\circ} C_{10}H_7SO_2OH + H_2O$$

β-Naphthalenesulfonic acid

PROBLEMS

1. With respect to the type of reaction and the conditions required, compare the reactions of cyclohexane, cyclohexene, and benzene with bromine.
2. By application of the Hammick-Illingworth rule, predict the directive influence of the trichloromethyl group in benzotrichloride.
3. Give equations for useful methods of synthesis of the following: *p*-dibromobenzene, *m*-nitrobromobenzene, *p*-nitrobromobenzene, *p*-nitrobenzotrichloride, α-chloronaphthalene.
4. What is the maximum number of monosubstitution products that can be obtained by the action of bromine in the presence of iron on *o*-xylene? *m*-xylene? *p*-xylene?
5. By means of appropriate electronic formulas show the significance of the following terms: resonance; electrophilic reagent; electrophilic substitution; hyperconjugation; electron-withdrawing substituent.

SUGGESTED READINGS

A. A. Ashdown, "Earliest History of the Friedel-Crafts Reaction," *Ind. Eng. Chem.*, *19*, 1063 (1927).

R. C. Ferreira, "Hyperconjugation: An Elementary Approach," *J. Chem. Educ.*, *29*, 554 (1952).

A. Gero, "The Concept of Resonance Energy in Elementary Organic Chemistry," *J. Chem. Educ.*, *29*, 82 (1952).

V. A. Crawford, "Hyperconjugation," *Quart. Revs.*, *3*, 226 (1949).

R. J. Gillespie and D. J. Millen, "Aromatic Nitration," *Quart. Revs.*, *2*, 277 (1948).

G. M. Badger, "The Aromatic Bond," *Quart. Revs.*, *5*, 147 (1951).

L. N. Ferguson, "Orientation of Substitution in the Benzene Nucleus," *Chem. Revs.*, *50*, 47 (1952).

C. M. Suter and A. W. Weston, "Direct Sulfonation of Aromatic Hydrocarbons and Their Halogen Derivatives," *Org. Reactions*, *3*, 141, 1946.

CHAPTER 7

Alcohols

Those compounds which contain a hydroxyl group attached to an aliphatic or alicyclic hydrocarbon residue are known as alcohols. The simple alcohols thus have the formula $C_nH_{2n+1}OH$. Their functional group is the hydroxyl group. Their chemical properties are those of the hydroxyl group and those of the paraffin group C_nH_{2n+1}. It will be seen that the properties of the hydrocarbon residue are modified by the presence of the hydroxyl group. The following are some of the simpler alcohols; in the systematic names the suffix *ol* indicates the hydroxyl group.

TABLE VII

STRAIGHT-CHAIN PRIMARY ALCOHOLS

Name	Structural Formula	Boiling Point
Methyl alcohol (methanol)	CH_3OH	65°
Ethyl alcohol (ethanol)	CH_3CH_2OH	78
n-Propyl alcohol (1-propanol)	$CH_3CH_2CH_2OH$	97
n-Butyl alcohol (1-butanol)	$CH_3CH_2CH_2CH_2OH$	117
n-Amyl alcohol (1-pentanol)	$CH_3CH_2CH_2CH_2CH_2OH$	137
n-Hexyl alcohol (1-hexanol)	$CH_3CH_2CH_2CH_2CH_2CH_2OH$	157

It is interesting to note that these compounds have boiling points much higher than those of the corresponding paraffins. Compounds having hydroxyl groups usually are less volatile than other substances of similar molecular weight. Indeed, water (b.p. 100°) boils much higher than the hydrides of other elements near oxygen in the periodic table (NH_3, b.p. −78°; H_2S, b.p. −62°; HCl, b.p. −84°). It has been found that the abnormal boiling point of water is due to the association of water molecules. This association involves the formation of a coordination bond between the hydrogen atom of one molecule of water and the oxygen atom of another. In the process the hydrogen atom acquires a shell of four electrons.

$$\begin{array}{c} :\ddot{\underset{\cdot\cdot}{O}}:H:\ddot{\underset{\cdot\cdot}{O}}:H \\ \;\;H\qquad\;\; H \end{array} \quad \text{or} \quad \begin{array}{c} O\text{–}H\leftarrow O\text{–}H \\ |\qquad\quad\;\; | \\ H\qquad\quad\; H \end{array}$$

Association of water

The boiling points of the alcohols indicate that a similar association occurs even though one of the hydrogen atoms of water has been replaced by an alkyl group.

$$\begin{array}{c} :\ddot{\underset{\cdot\cdot}{O}}:H:\ddot{\underset{\cdot\cdot}{O}}:H \\ \;R\qquad\; R \end{array} \quad \text{or} \quad \begin{array}{c} O\text{–}H\leftarrow O\text{–}H \\ | \qquad\quad | \\ R \qquad\quad R \end{array}$$

Association of alcohols

The coordination bond formed between a hydrogen atom and a donor atom, such as exists in water and the alcohols, is often called the "hydrogen bond"; a better although less generally used term is "hydrogen bridge."

Isomerism and Classification of Alcohols

In the examples given in Table VII the hydroxyl group is situated at the end of the carbon chain. These alcohols, represented by the formula RCH_2OH, are *primary* alcohols. The isomeric propyl alcohol has the formula $\underset{\displaystyle OH}{CH_3\underset{|}{C}HCH_3}$ and is known as isopropyl alcohol (2-propanol). Alcohols such as this, represented by R_2CHOH, are *secondary* alcohols. There are four butyl alcohols, including two that are primary, one that

TABLE VIII

THE ISOMERIC BUTYL ALCOHOLS

Name	Class	Formula	Boiling Point	Solubility in Water at 20°, g. per 100 g. H_2O
n-Butyl alcohol (1-butanol)	Primary	$CH_3CH_2CH_2CH_2OH$	118°	7.9
Isobutyl alcohol (2-methyl-1-propanol)	Primary	$CH_3\underset{\underset{\displaystyle CH_3}{\vert}}{C}HCH_2OH$	108	9.5
sec-Butyl alcohol (2-butanol)	Secondary	$CH_3CH_2\underset{\underset{\displaystyle OH}{\vert}}{C}HCH_3$	100	12.5
t-Butyl alcohol (2-methyl-2-propanol)	Tertiary	$CH_3\overset{\overset{\displaystyle CH_3}{\vert}}{\underset{\underset{\displaystyle CH_3}{\vert}}{C}}OH$	83	∞

is secondary, and one, represented by the formula R_3COH, that is *tertiary*. Their formulas and names are given in Table VIII. The boiling points and solubilities in water of these alcohols provide an excellent example of the wide variations that may exist in the properties of isomeric substances. There are eight amyl alcohols. Three are derived from *n*-pentane, four from isopentane, and one from neopentane (see p. 12). Their names, formulas, and classes are given in Table IX. A system of naming alcohols as carbinols is illustrated in this table. In this system methyl alcohol (CH_3OH) is given the name *carbinol*, and higher alcohols are named as substituted carbinols; e.g., ethyl alcohol is methylcarbinol, isopropyl alcohol is dimethylcarbinol, and *t*-butyl alcohol is trimethylcarbinol.

TABLE IX

THE AMYL ALCOHOLS

Name		Class	Formula
Geneva system	Carbinol system		
1-Pentanol	*n*-Butylcarbinol	Primary	$CH_3CH_2CH_2CH_2CH_2OH$
2-Pentanol	Methyl-*n*-propyl-carbinol	Secondary	$CH_3CH_2CH_2CHCH_3$ | OH
3-Pentanol	Diethylcarbinol	Secondary	$CH_3CH_2CHCH_2CH_3$ | OH
3-Methyl-1-butanol	Isobutylcarbinol	Primary	$CH_3CHCH_2CH_2OH$ | CH_3
3-Methyl-2-butanol	Methylisopropyl-carbinol	Secondary	$CH_3CH{-}CHCH_3$ | | CH_3 OH
2-Methyl-2-butanol	Dimethylethyl-carbinol	Tertiary	OH | $CH_3CCH_2CH_3$ | CH_3
2-Methyl-1-butanol	*sec*-Butylcarbinol	Primary	$CH_3CH_2CHCH_2OH$ | CH_3
2,2-Dimethyl-1-propanol	*t*-Butylcarbinol	Primary	CH_3 | $CH_3C{-}CH_2OH$ | CH_3

Preparation of Alcohols. A number of general methods of preparing alcohols from other organic compounds, such as aldehydes, ketones, and esters, are discussed in later chapters. In this section are given some of the commercial methods of preparing the lower alcohols.

Methyl alcohol. Most of the methyl alcohol produced today is prepared from carbon monoxide and hydrogen. The raw materials are coke and water. Water gas is first prepared, then mixed with hydrogen and passed over a zinc chromite catalyst at a pressure of about 3000 lb per square inch and at a temperature of 450°.

$$C + H_2O \longrightarrow CO + H_2 \text{ (water gas)}$$

$$CO + 2H_2 \xrightarrow[450°,\ 3000\ \text{lb./sq. in.}]{\text{zinc chromite}} \underset{\text{Methanol}}{CH_3OH}$$

The methyl alcohol produced in this way is of very high purity (99.9%).

Methyl alcohol has been called wood alcohol because it is a by-product of the wood charcoal industry. Water, acetone, and acetic acid are formed along with methyl alcohol, so that it is difficult to obtain the alcohol in a pure state from this source. The method is of little importance at the present time.

Ethyl alcohol is prepared from sugar by fermentation. When pure alcohol for industrial purposes is desired the raw material is molasses. In the preparation of alcoholic beverages from grains, the starch of the grain must first be converted to sugar. This is accomplished by treating the grain with malt. Malt is prepared by heating sprouted barley to a temperature sufficiently high to kill the barley but not to destroy a substance, known as diastase, which catalyzes the transformation of starch into sugar. Diastase is an example of a group of substances known as enzymes, compounds synthesized by living organisms for the purpose of catalyzing certain organic reactions. The transformation of sugar into alcohol is brought about by the enzyme zymase which is present in yeast.

$$\text{Starch} \xrightarrow[\text{(malt)}]{\text{diastase}} \text{Sugar} \xrightarrow[\text{(yeast)}]{\text{zymase}} CH_3CH_2OH + CO_2$$

The fermentation is carried out in water solution and yields a dilute solution (14 to 18 per cent) of ethyl alcohol, along with small amounts of amyl alcohols. By fractional distillation the constant-boiling mixture of 95.5 per cent alcohol and 4.5 per cent water is obtained. This is the ordinary ethyl alcohol of commerce. If anhydrous ("absolute") alcohol is desired the water is removed chemically or by redistillation in the presence of benzene. The latter method depends on the fact that benzene, water, and alcohol form a constant-boiling mixture of boiling point 65°. Benzene and alcohol form another constant-boiling mixture of boiling point 68°. Thus, if benzene is added to ordinary alcohol and the mixture is fractionated, the first fraction, consisting of benzene, water, and alcohol, is collected at 65°. If benzene is present in excess, this will be followed by a fraction at 68°, consisting of benzene and alcohol. The last fraction, distilling at 78.3°, is anhydrous ethyl alcohol.

The conversion of ethylene (from cracking stills) to ethanol already has been mentioned (p. 22). The ethylene is dissolved in concentrated sulfuric acid, yielding ethylsulfuric acid. Water is then added to hydrolyze the ethylsulfuric acid to ethyl alcohol and sulfuric acid.

$$CH_2{=}CH_2 + HOSO_2OH \rightleftharpoons \underset{\text{Ethylsulfuric acid}}{CH_3CH_2OSO_2OH}$$

$$CH_3CH_2OSO_2OH + H_2O \rightleftharpoons CH_3CH_2OH + HOSO_2OH$$

Isopropyl alcohol is prepared from propylene by the same method (p. 22). It is to be noted that ethylene is the only olefin that leads to a primary alcohol (Markownikoff's rule, p. 21).

$$CH_3CH{=}CH_2 + HOSO_2OH \rightleftharpoons \underset{\text{Isopropylsulfuric acid}}{\underset{\displaystyle OSO_2OH}{CH_3\overset{}{C}HCH_3}}$$

$$\underset{\displaystyle OSO_2OH}{CH_3CHCH_3} + H_2O \rightleftharpoons \underset{\displaystyle OH}{CH_3CHCH_3} + HOSO_2OH$$

n-Propyl alcohol and *isobutyl alcohol* are obtained by the condensation under high pressure of carbon monoxide with hydrogen in the presence of zinc chromite and an alkali. The products with the alkaline catalyst are methanol, ethanol, *n*-propyl alcohol, isobutyl alcohol, and higher branched-chain alcohols. These are separated by fractional distillation.

sec-Butyl alcohol and *t-butyl alcohol* are obtained from olefins. Both 1-butene and 2-butene yield *sec*-butyl alcohol; isobutylene yields *t*-butyl alcohol.

$$\left.\begin{array}{l} CH_3CH_2CH{=}CH_2 \\ CH_3CH{=}CHCH_3 \end{array}\right\} \xrightarrow{H_2SO_4} \underset{\displaystyle OSO_2OH}{CH_3CH_2CHCH_3} \xrightarrow{H_2O} \underset{\text{sec-Butyl alcohol}}{\underset{\displaystyle OH}{CH_3CH_2CHCH_3}}$$

$$\overset{\displaystyle CH_3}{CH_3C{=}CH_2} \xrightarrow{H_2SO_4} \underset{\displaystyle OSO_2OH}{\overset{\displaystyle CH_3}{CH_3CCH_3}} \xrightarrow{H_2O} \underset{\text{t-Butyl alcohol}}{\underset{\displaystyle OH}{\overset{\displaystyle CH_3}{CH_3CCH_3}}}$$

n-Butyl alcohol is prepared by the fermentation of starch or sugar in the presence of the bacterium *Clostridium acetobutylicum.* The process is usually known as the Weizmann fermentation, after the discoverer. The sugar may be obtained either as molasses or from corn. The products are *n*-butyl alcohol (60 per cent), acetone (30 per cent), and ethyl alcohol (10 per cent). These are separated by fractional distillation.

Another commercial synthesis of *n*-butyl alcohol employs acetaldehyde as the raw material (p. 231). Since acetaldehyde is obtained from acetylene this amounts to the synthesis of *n*-butyl alcohol from coke or petroleum (p. 25).

Reactions of the Alcohols

1. Replacement of the Hydroxyl Group. Alcohols suffer replacement of the hydroxyl group when treated with certain reagents, notably the hydrogen and phosphorus halides. When an alcohol and a halogen acid are brought together the hydroxyl group of the alcohol is replaced by a halogen atom, an alkyl halide and water being formed. This method is employed extensively in the preparation of alkyl halides. In the synthesis of bromides, sulfuric acid ordinarily serves as the catalyst and aqueous hydrobromic acid as the reagent. If dry hydrogen bromide is used at a temperature of about 100° no catalyst is necessary. These methods are illustrated by the preparation of *n*-butyl bromide and cyclohexyl bromide, respectively.

$$\underset{n\text{-Butyl alcohol}}{CH_3CH_2CH_2CH_2OH} + HBr \xrightarrow{H_2SO_4} \underset{n\text{-Butyl bromide}}{CH_3CH_2CH_2CH_2Br} + H_2O$$

$$\underset{\text{Cyclohexanol}}{\text{cyclo-}(CH_2)_5CHOH} + HBr\ (\text{gas}) \xrightarrow{100^\circ} \underset{\text{Cyclohexyl bromide}}{\text{cyclo-}(CH_2)_5CHBr} + H_2O$$

In the preparation of alkyl chlorides from alcohols and concentrated hydrochloric acid, anhydrous zinc chloride is an excellent catalyst. A solution of the chloride in concentrated hydrochloric acid, known as the Lucas reagent, is used in the laboratory for classifying the lower alcohols. The test takes advantage of the fact that under these conditions tertiary alcohols react rapidly with halogen acids, secondary alcohols much less rapidly, and primary alcohols very slowly. Reaction is indicated by the appearance of cloudiness in the solution; the solution becomes cloudy because the alkyl chloride is insoluble. The use of the test can be made clear by considering its application to the butyl alcohols.

$$\underset{t\text{-Butyl alcohol}}{(CH_3)_3C\text{–}OH} + HCl\ (ZnCl_2) \xrightarrow[\text{one minute}]{20^\circ} \underset{t\text{-Butyl chloride}}{(CH_3)_3C\text{–}Cl} + H_2O$$

$$CH_3CH_2\underset{\displaystyle OH}{\underset{|}{C}}HCH_3 + HCl\ (ZnCl_2) \xrightarrow[\text{ten minutes}]{20°} CH_3CH_2\underset{\displaystyle Cl}{\underset{|}{C}}HCH_3 + H_2O$$

sec-Butyl alcohol — *sec*-Butyl chloride

$$CH_3CH_2CH_2CH_2OH + HCl\ (ZnCl_2)$$

n-Butyl alcohol

$$\xrightarrow[\text{several hours}]{20°} CH_3CH_2CH_2CH_2Cl + H_2O$$

n-Butyl chloride

$$\begin{matrix} CH_3 \\ CH_3 \end{matrix}\!\!>\!CHCH_2OH + HCl\ (ZnCl_2) \xrightarrow[\text{several hours}]{20°} \begin{matrix} CH_3 \\ CH_3 \end{matrix}\!\!>\!CHCH_2Cl + H_2O$$

Isobutyl alcohol — Isobutyl chloride

When this reaction is adapted to the preparation of primary chlorides it can be made to proceed more rapidly by raising the temperature.

Halides of phosphorus react with alcohols to give alkyl halides. Alkyl iodides can be prepared from alcohols and hydriodic acid but are generally made by treating an alcohol with red phosphorus and iodine. The latter reagents combine to form phosphorus triiodide, which then converts the alcohol to the corresponding alkyl iodide. The synthesis of ethyl iodide from ethyl alcohol is an example.

$$3CH_3CH_2OH + P + 3I \longrightarrow 3CH_3CH_2I + H_3PO_3$$

2. Replacement of the Hydrogen Atom. Certain reagents react with alcohols to replace only the hydrogen atom. For example, metals such as sodium, potassium, and magnesium produce hydrogen and a metal *alkoxide.* Thus sodium and ethyl alcohol yield hydrogen and sodium ethoxide.

$$2CH_3CH_2OH + 2Na \longrightarrow 2CH_3CH_2ONa + H_2$$

Sodium ethoxide

In a similar way methanol and magnesium give hydrogen and magnesium methoxide

$$2CH_3OH + Mg \longrightarrow (CH_3O)_2Mg + H_2$$

Magnesium methoxide

The hydrogen atom is replaced also by oxygen acids, the products being water and *esters.* The process is called esterification. When organic acids are employed a small amount of mineral acid is added as a catalyst. Methyl alcohol reacts with sulfuric acid to yield either methylsulfuric acid or methyl sulfate, depending on the conditions.

$$CH_3OH + HOSO_2OH \rightleftharpoons H_2O + \underset{\text{Methylsulfuric acid}}{CH_3OSO_2OH}$$

$$2CH_3OSO_2OH \xrightarrow{\text{heat}} \underset{\text{Methyl sulfate}}{CH_3OSO_2OCH_3} + HOSO_2OH$$

Ethyl alcohol and nitric acid form ethyl nitrate.

$$CH_3CH_2OH + HONO_2 \rightleftharpoons H_2O + \underset{\text{Ethyl nitrate}}{CH_3CH_2ONO_2}$$

When acetic acid is esterified with *n*-butyl alcohol the product is *n*-butyl acetate.

$$CH_3CH_2CH_2CH_2OH + \underset{\text{Acetic acid}}{CH_3\overset{\overset{O}{\|}}{C}{-}OH}$$

$$\overset{H^+}{\rightleftharpoons} H_2O + \underset{n\text{-Butyl acetate}}{CH_3\overset{\overset{O}{\|}}{C}{-}OCH_2CH_2CH_2CH_3}$$

3. Removal of the Elements of Water. The loss of the elements of water from an alcohol may be brought about by reagents such as sulfuric acid, the product being an olefin. In this reaction it is generally assumed that the first step is the removal of the hydroxyl group with the bonding electron pair. The carbonium ion so produced then stabilizes itself by expelling a proton. An example is the conversion of 2-pentanol to 2-pentene.

$$CH_3CH_2CH_2\underset{\underset{OH}{|}}{C}HCH_3 \xrightarrow{H_2SO_4} CH_3CH_2CH_2\overset{+}{C}HCH_3$$

$$CH_3CH_2CH_2\overset{+}{C}HCH_3 \longrightarrow CH_3CH_2CH{=}CHCH_3 + H^+$$

It is to be noted that the temperature employed in the above preparation is lower than that required for ethylene. In general, primary alcohols are most stable and tertiary alcohols are least stable to dehydrating agents; secondary alcohols are of intermediate stability.

If a carbonium ion is generated in the presence of an alcohol, an *ether* may be produced. The second step of the reaction is analogous to that involved in the formation of alcohols by the interaction of a carbonium ion and water (p. 22). The synthesis of ethyl ether is illustrative.

$$CH_3CH_2OH \xrightarrow{H_2SO_4} CH_3CH_2^+$$

$$CH_3CH_2^+ + CH_3CH_2OH \longrightarrow \underset{\text{Ethyl ether}}{CH_3CH_2OCH_2CH_3} + H^+$$

The electron shortage of the carbonium ion is relieved by coordination of the deficient carbon atom with one of the unshared electron pairs of the hydroxyl group, the resulting ion being stabilized by the loss of a proton.

$$CH_3CH_2OH + CH_3CH_2^+ \longrightarrow [CH_3CH_2\text{–}\overset{\overset{\displaystyle H}{|}}{O}\text{–}CH_2CH_3]^+ \longrightarrow CH_3CH_2OCH_2CH_3 + H^+$$

Other acids, such as potassium acid sulfate, phosphoric acid, or benzenesulfonic acid, can be used in place of sulfuric acid in the preparation of olefins from alcohols. Olefins may also be obtained by passing the vapor of an alcohol over a hot catalyst. Ethylene can be made from ethyl alcohol by this scheme.

$$CH_3CH_2OH \xrightarrow[350°]{Al_2O_3} CH_2{=}CH_2 + H_2O$$

4. Dehydrogenation. Alcohols containing the group $\text{–}\overset{\overset{\displaystyle H}{|}}{\underset{|}{C}}\text{–OH}$ may lose hydrogen when heated in the presence of certain metals or when treated with oxidizing agents. If a primary alcohol is employed, the product is an aldehyde. Methanol, for example, is converted to formaldehyde on a commercial scale by passing it through a silver gauze at a temperature in the neighborhood of 600°.

$$CH_3OH \xrightarrow[600°]{Ag} \underset{\text{Formaldehyde}}{H\text{–}\overset{\nearrow O}{C}\text{–}H} + H_2$$

The desired temperature is maintained by admitting air to burn a part of the hydrogen.

One method of manufacture of acetaldehyde consists in passing ethyl alcohol over copper at 300°.

$$CH_3CH_2OH \xrightarrow[300°]{Cu} \underset{\text{Acetaldehyde}}{CH_3\overset{\nearrow O}{C}\text{–}H} + H_2$$

In a similar way propyl, *n*-butyl, and isobutyl alcohols may be converted to propionaldehyde, *n*-butyraldehyde, and isobutyraldehyde, respectively.

$$CH_3CH_2CH_2OH \longrightarrow CH_3CH_2C(=O){-}H + H_2$$

Propionaldehyde

$$CH_3CH_2CH_2CH_2OH \longrightarrow CH_3CH_2CH_2C(=O){-}H + H_2$$

n-Butyraldehyde

$$CH_3CH(CH_3)CH_2OH \longrightarrow CH_3CH(CH_3)C(=O){-}H + H_2$$

Isobutyraldehyde

Secondary alcohols yield ketones, the conversion of isopropyl alcohol to acetone being the most important example.

$$(CH_3)_2CHOH \longrightarrow (CH_3)_2C{=}O + H_2$$

Isopropyl alcohol → Acetone

Similarly 2-butanol and cyclohexanol yield methyl ethyl ketone and cyclohexanone, respectively.

$$CH_3CH(OH)CH_2CH_3 \longrightarrow CH_3C(=O)CH_2CH_3 + H_2$$

2-Butanol → Methyl ethyl ketone

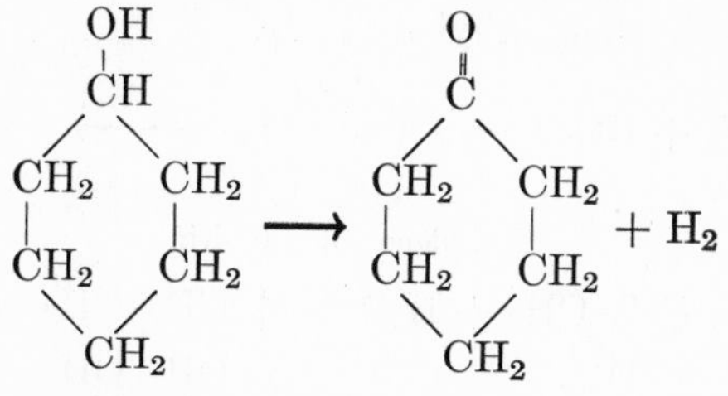

$$\underset{\text{(ring: }CH(OH)\text{, }5\ CH_2)}{C_6H_{11}OH} \longrightarrow \underset{\text{(ring: }C{=}O\text{, }5\ CH_2)}{C_6H_{10}O} + H_2$$

5. Oxidation. In the laboratory a mixture of potassium dichromate and sulfuric acid is the usual oxidizing agent. The use of this reagent is illustrated by the conversion (49 per cent yield) of propyl alcohol to propionaldehyde.

$$CH_3CH_2CH_2OH + (O) \longrightarrow CH_3CH_2C(=O){-}H + H_2O$$

The method is successful only for the more volatile aldehydes, which are immediately volatilized and thus are not allowed to remain in contact with the oxidizing agent. Otherwise they would be oxidized to acids.

The oxidation of saturated primary alcohols to the corresponding acids may be accomplished in a variety of ways. The "quick vinegar" process for acetic acid is an air oxidation of ethyl alcohol under the influence of "mother of vinegar."

$$CH_3CH_2OH + (2O) \longrightarrow CH_3CO_2H + H_2O$$

This method is useful only for obtaining dilute acetic acid. The best way to make pure acetic acid is to oxidize acetaldehyde catalytically (p. 311).

Oxidation of methanol is not a useful procedure for producing formic acid, since, having an aldehyde group, this acid is easily oxidized to carbon dioxide and water.

$$H\!-\!\overset{\overset{O}{\|}}{C}\!-\!OH + (O) \longrightarrow CO_2 + H_2O$$

Higher fatty acids can be made by oxidation of the corresponding primary alcohols with the dichromate-sulfuric acid mixture, nitric acid, and a variety of other oxidizing agents. However, these acids are more conveniently obtained in other ways such as the oxidation of the corresponding aldehydes (p. 77).

Polyfunctional Alcohols

Alcohols containing two hydroxyl groups are known as glycols. The most important of this group of compounds is the simplest member, ethylene glycol. It is prepared commercially from ethylene by way of ethylene chlorohydrin and ethylene oxide.

$$CH_2{=}CH_2 + HOCl \longrightarrow \underset{\text{Ethylene chlorohydrin}}{\underset{OH\quad Cl}{CH_2{-}CH_2}} \xrightarrow{-HCl} \underset{\diagdown O \diagup}{CH_2{-}CH_2}$$

$$\underset{\diagdown O \diagup}{CH_2{-}CH_2} + H_2O \longrightarrow \underset{\text{Ethylene glycol}}{\underset{OH\quad OH}{CH_2{-}CH_2}}$$

Ethylene glycol is a viscous liquid boiling at 197°. It has a sweet taste; indeed, the name glycol (γλυκύς, sweet; *ol*, alcohol) derives from this fact. Most compounds containing several hydroxyl groups are extremely soluble in water; ethylene glycol and water are miscible in all proportions. Because of its high boiling point, its low solvent action on rubber and lacquers, and its solubility in water, ethylene glycol is widely used as an antifreeze for automobile radiators. It has also come to prominence as the cooling liquid for airplane engines. One of its advantages over water in this connection is that it permits a higher operating temperature, which increases the efficiency of the engine.

Ethylene glycol has the chemical properties to be expected of an alcohol with two primary hydroxyl groups. The most common derivatives are its esters and ethers (p. 72). Esters are formed with both inorganic and organic acids. An example of the former type is the dinitrate.

$$\begin{array}{l} CH_2OH \\ | \\ CH_2OH \end{array} + 2HONO_2 \xrightarrow{H_2SO_4} \begin{array}{l} CH_2ONO_2 \\ | \\ CH_2ONO_2 \end{array} + 2H_2O$$

Ethylene glycol dinitrate

Ethylene glycol dinitrate bears a close structural relationship to nitroglycerine and like it is a powerful explosive. It is used extensively as an ingredient of dynamite (p. 62).

Esters of organic acids may be obtained by the methods used with simple alcohols. For example, acetic acid and the glycol form the diacetate.

$$\begin{array}{l} CH_2OH \\ | \\ CH_2OH \end{array} + 2CH_3C{\overset{\displaystyle O}{\diagup\!\!\diagup}}\!\!-OH \xrightleftharpoons{H_2SO_4} \begin{array}{l} CH_2OC(=O)-CH_3 \\ | \\ CH_2OC(=O)-CH_3 \end{array} + 2H_2O$$

Ethylene glycol diacetate

The glycols obtained from the higher olefins, such as propylene glycol, $CH_3CH(OH)-CH_2(OH)$, and the butylene glycols, $CH_3CH_2CH(OH)-CH_2(OH)$ and $CH_3CH(OH)-CH(OH)CH_3$, have not attained the industrial importance that attaches to ethylene glycol. Glycols such as trimethylene glycol, $HOCH_2CH_2CH_2OH$, and tetramethyleneglycol, $HOCH_2CH_2CH_2CH_2$-OH, are prepared by other methods.

Glycerol, or glycerine, is a trihydroxy alcohol of the formula $CH_2(OH)CH(OH)-CH_2(OH)$. It boils at 290° and is more viscous than ethylene glycol. It is also completely miscible with water. Glycerol is obtained as a by-product of soap manufacture.

$$\text{Fat} + \text{Alkali} \longrightarrow \text{Soap} + \begin{array}{l} CH_2OH \\ | \\ CHOH \\ | \\ CH_2OH \end{array}$$

Glycerol

Because it takes up water from the air, glycerol finds many uses as a moistening agent. Its use in tobaccos depends on this property. Large quantities of glycerol are used by the rayon industry (p. 212). It is one of the raw materials for the preparation of resins for use in varnishes and enamels (p. 147).

Glyceryl trinitrate, or nitroglycerine, is made by the treatment of glycerol with nitric acid in the presence of sulfuric acid.

$$\begin{array}{l} CH_2OH \\ | \\ CHOH \\ | \\ CH_2OH \end{array} + 3HONO_2 \xrightarrow{H_2SO_4} \begin{array}{l} CH_2ONO_2 \\ | \\ CHONO_2 \\ | \\ CH_2ONO_2 \end{array} + 3H_2O$$

Nitroglycerine

Nitroglycerine is one of the most powerful high explosives. It is a colorless liquid which freezes just above 0°. In the liquid state it is very sensitive to shock and so is dangerous to handle. It is generally used as dynamite, which consists of a porous material such as clay or sawdust impregnated with nitroglycerine and cast into sticks. In this form it is much less sensitive to shock and can be transported with little risk. When dynamite is subjected to temperatures below 0°, the nitroglycerine crystallizes and the dynamite becomes so stable that it does not respond to the detonation caps. Low-freezing dynamites are made with mixtures of nitroglycerine and ethylene glycol dinitrate (m.p. −20°). Ethylene glycol dinitrate is itself a more powerful explosive than nitroglycerine, and so the efficiency of the dynamite is not lessened by such addition.

Mercaptans (Thio Alcohols)

From the close relationship of oxygen and sulfur in the periodic table it might be expected that substances analogous to alcohols, but containing sulfur instead of oxygen, could be prepared. Such compounds are well known. The simplest is methyl mercaptan, CH_3SH. The names and boiling points of a few members of this series are given in Table X. The systematic names of these compounds are derived in the same manner as those of the alcohols, the name ending being *thiol.*

TABLE X

MERCAPTANS

Name	Formula	Boiling Point
Methyl mercaptan (methanethiol)	CH_3SH	6°
Ethyl mercaptan (ethanethiol)	CH_3CH_2SH	37
n-Propyl mercaptan (1-propanethiol)	$CH_3CH_2CH_2SH$	68
Isopropyl mercaptan (2-propanethiol)	$CH_3\underset{\overset{\mid}{SH}}{CH}CH_3$	60
n-Butyl mercaptan (1-butanethiol)	$CH_3CH_2CH_2CH_2SH$	98

It will be noted that the mercaptans have lower boiling points than the corresponding alcohols, although their molecular weights are greater. This indicates that they do not associate as do the alcohols (p. 51).

A comparison of the chemical properties of mercaptans and alcohols reveals more contrasts than similarities. For example, the mercaptans are weak acids, whereas alcohols are neutral. Benzyl mercaptan reacts with sodium hydroxide to give the corresponding salt, sodium benzyl mercaptide.

$$C_6H_5CH_2SH + NaOH \longrightarrow C_6H_5CH_2SNa + H_2O$$

Benzyl mercaptan — Sodium benzyl mercaptide

The acidity of the mercaptans is in harmony with the view that they are the alkyl derivatives of hydrogen sulfide, which is an acid. The alcohols may be considered as the alkyl derivatives of water.

The behavior of mercaptans toward oxidizing agents is altogether different from that of the alcohols. A mild oxidizing agent removes the hydrogen atom of the functional group, giving rise to a disulfide. The oxidation may be brought about by iodine, hydrogen peroxide, hypoiodite solutions, or even the oxygen of the air. Iodine, for example, converts methyl mercaptan to dimethyl disulfide.

$$2CH_3SH + I_2 \longrightarrow CH_3SSCH_3 + 2HI$$

Dimethyl disulfide

This reaction is quantitative and can be used for the analytical determination of mercaptans. The mercaptan can be regenerated by reduction of the disulfide.

Strong oxidizing agents convert mercaptans to sulfonic acids. Methyl mercaptan, for example, yields methanesulfonic acid.

$$CH_3SH + 3[O] \longrightarrow CH_3SO_2OH$$

Methanesulfonic acid

This reaction is sometimes used for the preparation of aliphatic sulfonic acids.

Alkyl Halides

Alkyl halides are available in large numbers and great variety, being produced chiefly by halogenation of paraffins (p. 13), by the action of hydrogen halides or phosphorus halides on alcohols (p. 55), and by the addition of hydrogen halides to olefins (p. 21). Alkyl halides are classified as primary, secondary, or tertiary, depending on whether they are related, respectively, to primary, secondary, or tertiary alcohols (p. 51).

Methyl chloride serves as a refrigerant and as a solvent. The chief use of alkyl halides, however, is in synthesis.

Formation of Grignard Reagents. One of the most interesting and valuable reactions of alkyl halides is with magnesium metal. In the presence of anhydrous ether, alkyl halides react with magnesium to form ether solutions of organomagnesium halides. Such a solution is known as a *Grignard reagent,* after the discoverer, the French chemist Victor Grignard. An example is the formation of methylmagnesium iodide from methyl iodide.

$$\mathrm{CH_3I + Mg \longrightarrow \underset{\text{Methylmagnesium iodide}}{CH_3MgI}}$$

The ethyl Grignard reagent most commonly employed is ethylmagnesium bromide.

$$\mathrm{CH_3CH_2Br + Mg \longrightarrow CH_3CH_2MgBr}$$

Alkyl chlorides react in a similar way, as is illustrated by the preparation of *t*-butylmagnesium chloride

$$\mathrm{CH_3\overset{\displaystyle CH_3}{\underset{\displaystyle CH_3}{\overset{|}{\underset{|}{C}}}}Cl + Mg \xrightarrow{\text{ether}} \underset{t\text{-Butylmagnesium chloride}}{CH_3\overset{\displaystyle CH_3}{\underset{\displaystyle CH_3}{\overset{|}{\underset{|}{C}}}}MgCl}}$$

The use of the Grignard reagent in synthesis will be mentioned frequently in subsequent chapters.

The Wurtz Synthesis of Paraffins. Another metal that can be made to react with alkyl halides in a useful way is sodium. By its use an alkyl halide can be converted to a paraffin of twice the number of carbon atoms. For example, a convenient method of preparing *n*-octane involves a Wurtz reaction with *n*-butyl bromide.

$$\mathrm{2CH_3CH_2CH_2CH_2Br + 2Na \longrightarrow \underset{\textit{n}\text{-Octane}}{CH_3CH_2CH_2CH_2CH_2CH_2CH_2CH_3} + 2NaBr}$$

Reaction with Sodium Lead Alloy. Organolead compounds are obtained from alkyl halides by treatment with sodium-lead alloy. The most important example is tetraethyllead, made on a large scale from ethyl chloride.

$$\mathrm{4CH_3CH_2Cl + Pb + 4Na \longrightarrow Pb(CH_2CH_3)_4 + 4NaCl}$$

Mercaptan Formation. When the hydrosulfide ion (SH^-) is used in place of the hydroxyl ion to displace the halogen atom of an alkyl halide, a mercaptan is produced. Thus *n*-butyl mercaptan is formed from *n*-butyl bromide and sodium hydrosulfide.

$$CH_3CH_2CH_2CH_2Br + NaSH \longrightarrow NaBr + \underset{n\text{-Butyl mercaptan}}{CH_3CH_2CH_2CH_2SH}$$

The Williamson Synthesis of Ethers. Another type of displacement reaction is the Williamson ether synthesis. It involves the reaction of primary alkyl halides with metal alkoxides, i.e., displacement of a halide by an alkoxide ion. An example is the formation of ethyl isopropyl ether

$$CH_3CH_2Br + \begin{matrix}CH_3\\ \\ CH_3\end{matrix}\!\!>\!CHONa \longrightarrow \underset{\text{Ethyl isopropyl ether}}{\begin{matrix}CH_3\\ \\ CH_3\end{matrix}\!\!>\!CHOCH_2CH_3} + NaBr$$

This synthesis may yield either symmetrical or unsymmetrical ethers whereas the synthesis of ethers from alcohols and sulfuric acid (p. 57) is useful only for symmetrical ethers. When a mixed or unsymmetrical ether (ROR′) is desired, the starting materials are usually the two alcohols ROH and R′OH. One of them is converted to the alkoxide by treatment with metallic sodium, and the other is transformed to a halide. Interaction of these two reagents yields the unsymmetrical ether. The preparation of *n*-butyl methyl ether from methyl alcohol and *n*-butyl alcohol serves as an example.

$$2CH_3OH + 2Na \longrightarrow 2CH_3ONa + H_2$$

$$CH_3CH_2CH_2CH_2OH + HBr \xrightarrow{H_2SO_4} CH_3CH_2CH_2CH_2Br + H_2O$$

$$CH_3ONa + CH_3CH_2CH_2CH_2Br \longrightarrow \underset{n\text{-Butyl methyl ether}}{CH_3OCH_2CH_2CH_2CH_3} + NaBr$$

Chlorohydrins, which possess both the functions involved in the Williamson synthesis, may undergo ring closure to yield cyclic ethers. Ethylene chlorohydrin, in the presence of alkalies, loses hydrogen chloride and forms ethylene oxide

$$\underset{|\quad\;\;|}{CH_2{-}CH_2}\atop{Cl\quad OH} \longrightarrow \underset{\diagdown\;\diagup}{CH_2{-}CH_2}\atop{O} + HCl$$

A side reaction, involving two molecules of ethylene chlorohydrin, gives a cyclic diether known as dioxane.

$$\begin{matrix} \text{Cl} & & \text{HO} \\ \text{CH}_2 & & \text{CH}_2 \\ | & + & | \\ \text{CH}_2 & & \text{CH}_2 \\ \text{OH} & & \text{Cl} \end{matrix} + 2NaOH \longrightarrow \underset{\text{Dioxane}}{\begin{matrix} & \text{O} & \\ \text{CH}_2 & & \text{CH}_2 \\ | & & | \\ \text{CH}_2 & & \text{CH}_2 \\ & \text{O} & \end{matrix}} + 2NaCl + 2H_2O$$

Dioxane is also obtained from the glycol by the ordinary sulfuric acid process for making ethers.

In the Williamson ether synthesis the alkyl halide serves to introduce an alkyl group, i.e., as an alkylating agent. Additional examples of the use of alkyl halides as alkylating agents will be given later (p. 247).

When a mercaptide is employed in place of the alkoxide, the product is a sulfide or thio ether. An example is the formation of benzyl methyl sulfide from sodium benzyl mercaptide and methyl iodide.

$$\underset{\text{Sodium benzyl mercaptide}}{C_6H_5CH_2SNa} + CH_3I \longrightarrow \underset{\text{Benzyl methyl sulfide}}{C_6H_5CH_2SCH_3} + NaI$$

A modification employed in the preparation of symmetrical sulfides consists in treating an alkyl halide with sodium sulfide. Sodium sulfide acts upon *n*-butyl bromide to give di-*n*-butyl sulfide.

$$2CH_3CH_2CH_2CH_2Br + Na_2S \longrightarrow \underset{\text{Di-}n\text{-butyl sulfide}}{(CH_3CH_2CH_2CH_2)_2S} + 2NaBr$$

The best-known sulfide is β,β'-dichlorodiethyl sulfide, or mustard gas. It is prepared from ethylene and sulfur chloride.

$$2CH_2{=}CH_2 + S_2Cl_2 \longrightarrow \underset{\text{Mustard gas}}{ClCH_2CH_2SCH_2CH_2Cl} + S$$

Another method employs ethylene oxide and hydrogen sulfide. The primary product is thiodiglycol, which is converted to mustard gas by hydrochloric acid.

$$2\overset{\text{O}}{CH_2{-}CH_2} + H_2S \longrightarrow \underset{\text{Thiodiglycol}}{HOCH_2CH_2SCH_2CH_2OH}$$

$$HOCH_2CH_2SCH_2CH_2OH + 2HCl \longrightarrow ClCH_2CH_2SCH_2CH_2Cl + 2H_2O$$

Mustard gas is a powerful vesicant; it penetrates the skin without causing any immediate pain, but within a short time deep blisters, which heal very slowly, form on the exposed area. The name mustard gas is misleading. The substance is a liquid boiling at 215°. Because of its high boiling point is evaporates very slowly, and a sector which has been subjected to a mustard-gas attack remains hazardous for many days.

Formation of Paraffins. Metals such as sodium and zinc react with alkyl halides in the presence of water, alcohol, or dilute acids to produce the parent hydrocarbons.

$$RX + H_2 \longrightarrow RH + HX$$

The reaction, which may be classed as a reduction, can be accomplished also with such reducing agents as stannous chloride and sodium arsenite. Hydrogen iodide may effect this change in certain cases at higher temperatures. Since this reagent converts alcohols to alkyl iodides, it may also serve to transform them to hydrocarbons. Thus benzyl alcohol yields toluene when treated with an excess of hydriodic acid at 140°.

$$\underset{\text{Benzyl alcohol}}{C_6H_5CH_2OH} + 2HI \xrightarrow{140^\circ} \underset{\text{Toluene}}{C_6H_5CH_3} + H_2O + I_2$$

Hydrolysis. When treated with aqueous alkali, an alkyl halide undergoes hydrolysis, yielding an alcohol. An example is the formation of allyl alcohol from allyl chloride, produced commercially by the *chlorination* of propylene at 300°.

$$\underset{\text{Allyl chloride}}{CH_2{=}CHCH_2Cl} + H_2O \longrightarrow \underset{\text{Allyl alcohol}}{CH_2{=}CHCH_2OH} + HCl$$

The hydrolysis involves reversing the reaction by which alkyl halides are usually prepared, and in consequence it is of value only if the halide is prepared from a raw material other than an alcohol. An important example is the commercial preparation of ethylene glycol (p. 60). The reaction is also utilized commercially in the preparation of a mixture of amyl alcohols by chlorinating pentanes and hydrolyzing the resulting amyl chlorides (p. 240).

$$\underset{\text{Mixed pentanes}}{C_5H_{12} + Cl_2} \longrightarrow HCl + \underset{\text{Mixed amyl chlorides}}{C_5H_{11}Cl}$$

$$2C_5H_{11}Cl + Ca(OH)_2 \longrightarrow \underset{\text{Mixed amyl alcohols}}{2C_5H_{11}OH} + CaCl_2$$

By a similar method, benzyl alcohol can be obtained from toluene.

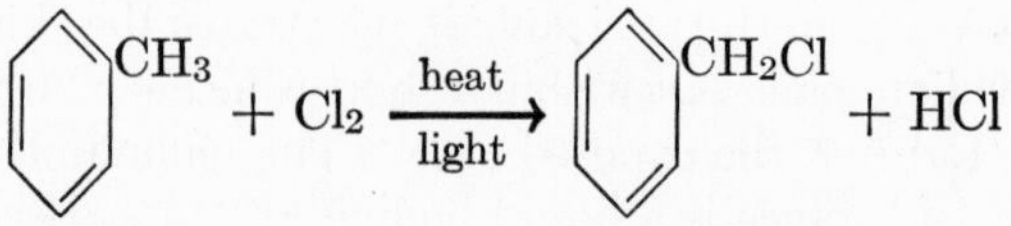

$$C_6H_5CH_3 + Cl_2 \xrightarrow[\text{light}]{\text{heat}} C_6H_5CH_2Cl + HCl$$

Toluene — Benzyl chloride

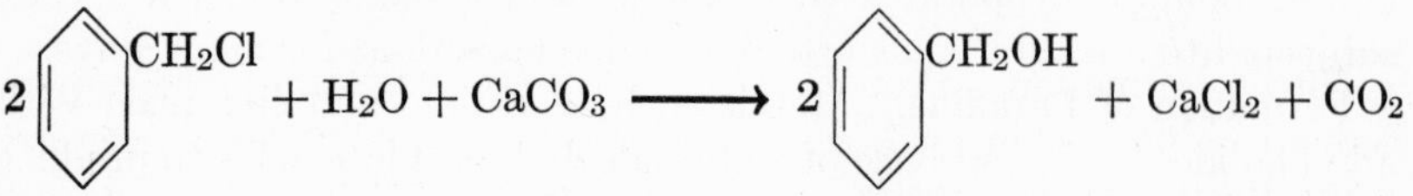

$$2\,C_6H_5CH_2Cl + H_2O + CaCO_3 \longrightarrow 2\,C_6H_5CH_2OH + CaCl_2 + CO_2$$

Benzyl alcohol

The hydrolysis of an alkyl halide may be represented by the general equation

$$RX + OH^- \longrightarrow ROH + X^-$$

It illustrates a very large group of reactions in which one substituent is replaced by another. Such reactions are known as *displacement reactions* (p. 234).

The hydrolysis of 1,1-dihalides provides a convenient method for the preparation of aromatic aldehydes. For example, benzaldehyde is obtained from toluene by the following reactions.

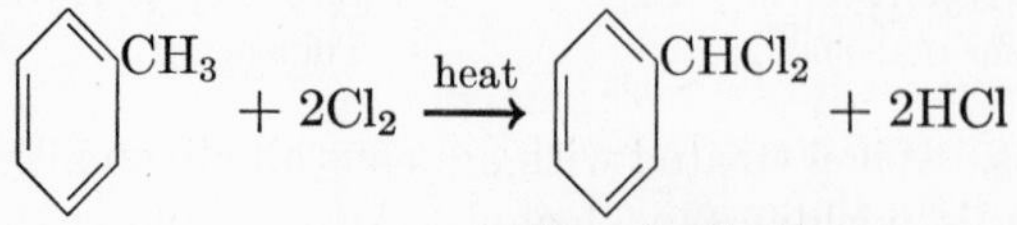

$$C_6H_5CH_3 + 2Cl_2 \xrightarrow{\text{heat}} C_6H_5CHCl_2 + 2HCl$$

Benzal chloride

$$C_6H_5CHCl_2 + H_2O \longrightarrow C_6H_5C(=O)H + 2HCl$$

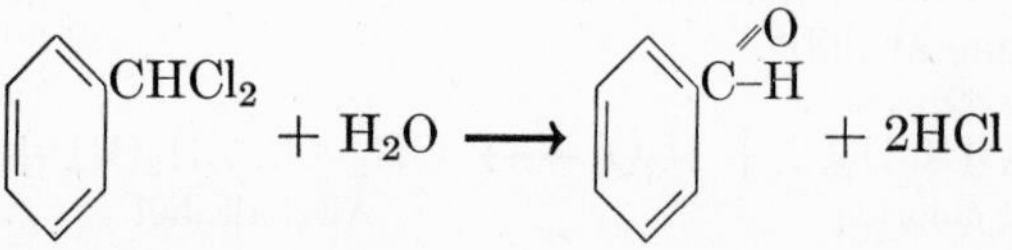

The second step is carried out in the presence of an alkali or carbonate which neutralizes the hydrochloric acid.

Aromatic acids may be made in a similar way from benzotrichloride (p. 47) and its nuclear substitution products. The synthesis of benzoic acid from toluene is illustrative.

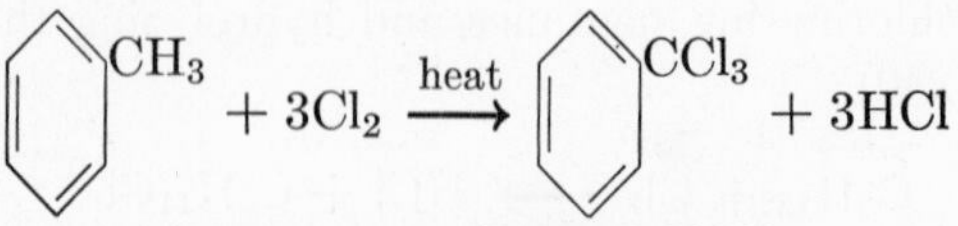

$$C_6H_5CH_3 + 3Cl_2 \xrightarrow{\text{heat}} C_6H_5CCl_3 + 3HCl$$

Benzotrichloride

$$2\,C_6H_5CCl_3 + 4Ca(OH)_2 \longrightarrow (C_6H_5C(=O)O)_2Ca + 3CaCl_2 + 4H_2O$$

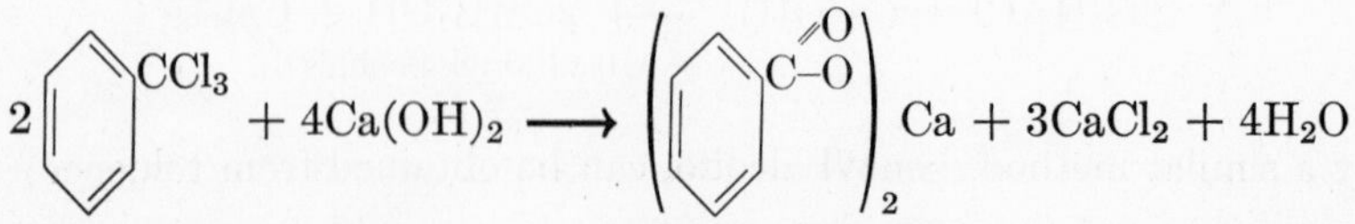

Calcium benzoate

$$\left(C_6H_5C{\overset{O}{\diagup\!\!\diagup}}\!\!-O\right)_2Ca + 2HCl \longrightarrow 2\,C_6H_5COOH + CaCl_2$$

Benzoic acid

Nitrile Formation. Primary alkyl halides react metathetically with sodium or potassium cyanide. The organic cyanides so produced are generally known as *nitriles.* In this type of displacement reaction a halogen atom is displaced by a cyano group. Examples are propionitrile and isovaleronitrile, formed by the action of sodium cyanide on ethyl bromide and isobutyl bromide, respectively.

$$CH_3CH_2Br + NaCN \longrightarrow \underset{\text{Propionitrile}}{CH_3CH_2CN} + NaBr$$

$$\begin{matrix}CH_3\\ CH_3\end{matrix}\!\!>\!CHCH_2Br + NaCN \longrightarrow \underset{\text{Isovaleronitrile}}{\begin{matrix}CH_3\\ CH_3\end{matrix}\!\!>\!CHCH_2CN} + NaBr$$

The value of nitriles depends chiefly on the fact that they can be hydrolyzed to acids (p. 120). If the alkyl halide is made from an alcohol (p. 55), the process constitutes a synthesis of an acid having one more carbon atom than the original alcohol.

Formation of Amines. Since ammonia and amines, like the hydroxyl, alkoxyl, and cyanide ions, possess an unshared pair of electrons, it is not surprising that they too are capable of attacking alkyl halides. When ammonia is used the addition product is an alkylated ammonium halide which, in the presence of ammonia, yields a primary amine and an ammonium halide. The primary amine can react with the alkyl halide in a similar way to yield a secondary amine. The secondary amine in turn may give a tertiary amine. The following equations illustrate the course of the reaction.

$$RX + NH_3 \longrightarrow [RNH_3]^+X^- \xrightarrow{NH_3} \underset{\text{Primary amine}}{RNH_2} + NH_4{}^+X^-$$

$$RX + RNH_2 \longrightarrow [R_2NH_2]^+X^- \xrightarrow{NH_3} \underset{\text{Secondary amine}}{R_2NH} + NH_4{}^+X^-$$

$$RX + R_2NH \longrightarrow [R_3NH]^+X^- \xrightarrow{NH_3} \underset{\text{Tertiary amine}}{R_3N} + NH_4{}^+X^-$$

A fourth product is formed from the tertiary amine and the alkyl halide. It is known as a quaternary ammonium salt and may be regarded as an ammonium halide in which all four hydrogen atoms of the ammonium ion have been replaced by organic radicals

$$RX + R_3N \longrightarrow [R_4N]^+X^-$$

Quaternary ammonium salt

This method of preparing amines, known as the Hofmann method, suffers from the disadvantage that the product is a mixture the separation of which may be difficult. The boiling points of the ethylamines are far enough apart to permit separation by fractional distillation, and the method is used commercially to prepare all three amines from ethyl chloride and ammonia.

The Hofmann reaction is generally useful as a laboratory method only with primary alkyl halides. However, by employing drastic conditions it can be used with aryl halides. One of the commercial methods for the preparation of aniline utilizes the reaction that occurs when chlorobenzene and ammonia are heated to about 200° under pressure. Under the conditions required, the reaction is reversible.

$$C_6H_5Cl + 2NH_3 \xrightleftharpoons{200°} C_6H_5NH_2 + NH_4Cl$$

Aniline

However, by addition of cuprous oxide it can be made irreversible. The cuprous oxide not only destroys the ammonium chloride but also seems to catalyze the reaction; other substances that would liberate ammonia from ammonium chloride are not as effective as cuprous oxide. The cuprous oxide is regained by treatment of the cuprous chloride with alkali.

$$2C_6H_5Cl + 2NH_3 + Cu_2O \xrightarrow{200°} 2C_6H_5NH_2 + 2CuCl + H_2O$$

Dehydrohalogenation. Molten alkalies or alcoholic or concentrated aqueous solutions of alkalies may serve to remove the elements of a halogen acid from an alkyl halide, i.e., bring about *dehydrohalogenation.* The product is an olefin, as is illustrated by the formation of isobutylene from *t*-butyl chloride.

$$CH_3\overset{\displaystyle CH_3}{\underset{\displaystyle CH_3}{\overset{|}{\underset{|}{C}}}}Cl + NaOH \longrightarrow CH_3\underset{\displaystyle CH_3}{\underset{|}{C}}{=}CH_2 + NaCl + H_2O$$

The Ethers

Ethers are usually prepared by the action of sulfuric acid on alcohols (p. 57) or by the Williamson method (p. 65), the latter being employed when mixed ethers (ROR′) are sought. The names and boiling points of a few ethers are given in Table XI.

TABLE XI

TABLE OF ETHERS

Name	Formula	Boiling Point	Class
Methyl ether	CH_3OCH_3	−24°	Aliphatic
Methyl ethyl ether	$CH_3OCH_2CH_3$	10	Mixed, aliphatic
Ethyl ether	$C_2H_5OC_2H_5$	35	Aliphatic
n-Butyl ether	$C_4H_9OC_4H_9$	142	Aliphatic
Anisole (methyl phenyl ether)	$CH_3OC_6H_5$	155	Mixed
Phenyl ether	$C_6H_5OC_6H_5$	259	Aromatic
Phenyl *p*-tolyl ether	$C_6H_5OC_6H_4CH_3$	278	Mixed, aromatic

The most common of these is ethyl ether, ordinarily known simply as ether. It is the most widely used general anesthetic. It is an excellent solvent for many organic compounds and is employed in industry and in the laboratory in this connection.

The ordinary ethers are inert toward most reagents. They can be cleaved by halogen acids. For example, ethyl ether is converted to ethyl bromide by the action of excess concentrated hydrobromic acid.

$$CH_3CH_2OCH_2CH_3 + HBr \longrightarrow CH_3CH_2OH + CH_3CH_2Br$$

$$CH_3CH_2OH + HBr \longrightarrow CH_3CH_2Br + H_2O$$

Ethylene oxide is a cyclic ether of unusual interest. It is prepared by the action of alkali on ethylene chlorohydrin (p. 65) or by the controlled oxidation of ethylene (p. 24). It is much more reactive than the simple open-chain ethers. For example, although ethyl ether is so inert toward Grignard reagents that it is employed as the solvent in their preparation, ethylene oxide reacts readily with these compounds. β-

Phenylethyl alcohol, a constituent of attar of roses, is made by this method.

$$C_6H_5MgCl + CH_2CH_2(O) \longrightarrow C_6H_5CH_2CH_2OMgCl$$

Phenylmagnesium chloride

$$C_6H_5CH_2CH_2OMgCl + HCl \longrightarrow C_6H_5CH_2CH_2OH + MgCl_2$$

β-Phenylethyl alcohol

This reaction is often employed in synthetic work as a process for lengthening carbon chains. By converting the alcohol to the bromide and repeating the synthesis it is possible to build up carbon chains of any desired length; $RBr \longrightarrow RCH_2CH_2OH \longrightarrow RCH_2CH_2Br \longrightarrow RCH_2CH_2CH_2CH_2OH$, etc.

Ethylene oxide reacts with alcohols to give monoethers of ethylene glycol.

$$CH_3CH_2OH + CH_2CH_2(O) \longrightarrow CH_3CH_2OCH_2CH_2OH$$

Monoethyl ether of ethylene glycol

The product from ethyl alcohol is sold under the name cellosolve for use as a solvent. Other similar solvents are methylcellosolve, $CH_3OCH_2CH_2OH$, and butylcellosolve, $CH_3CH_2CH_2CH_2OCH_2CH_2OH$, obtained from the oxide and methyl and *n*-butyl alcohols, respectively.

When ethylene oxide is allowed to react with ethylene glycol the product is diethylene glycol.

$$HOCH_2CH_2OH + CH_2CH_2(O) \longrightarrow HOCH_2CH_2OCH_2CH_2OH$$

Diethylene glycol

By employing cellosolve in this reaction carbitol is obtained.

$$CH_3CH_2OCH_2CH_2OH + CH_2CH_2(O) \longrightarrow CH_3CH_2OCH_2CH_2OCH_2CH_2OH$$

Cellosolve — Carbitol

Methylcarbitol and butylcarbitol are produced from the corresponding cellosolves.

Ethylene oxide may be regarded as the monomolecular ether of ethylene glycol.

The thio ethers show as little resemblance to ethers, so far as chemical properties are concerned, as do the mercaptans to the alcohols. The outstanding difference between ethers and thio ethers is their behavior toward oxidizing agents. Ethers are generally unreactive, whereas thio ethers are easily oxidized, taking up one or two atoms of oxygen. Mild oxidizing agents convert them to sulfoxides, which can be further oxidized to sulfones.

$$\text{R–S–R} + \underset{H_2O_2}{[O]} \longrightarrow \begin{matrix} R \\ \quad \rangle SO \\ R \end{matrix}$$

A sulfoxide

$$\downarrow [O]HNO_3$$

$$\text{R–S–R} + \underset{HNO_3}{2[O]} \longrightarrow \begin{matrix} R \\ \quad \rangle SO_2 \\ R \end{matrix}$$

A sulfone

PROBLEMS

1. Write equations for the transformation of *n*-amyl alcohol into: (*a*) *n*-amyl bromide, (*b*) *n*-amyl ether, (*c*) ethyl *n*-amyl ether, (*d*) 1-pentene, (*e*) 2-pentanol, (*f*) *n*-valeraldehyde ($CH_3CH_2CH_2CH_2CHO$), (*g*) *n*-valeric acid, (*h*) *n*-pentane, (*i*) *n*-amyl mercaptan, (*j*) *n*-amyl acetate, (*k*) *n*-amylcarbitol, (*l*) *n*-amyl disulfide, (*m*) *n*-amyl sulfide, (*n*) 1-pentanesulfonic acid.

2. Write the formulas of the following alcohols, and indicate their classes and names: (*a*) *n*-amylcarbinol, (*b*) isoamylcarbinol, (*c*) methylisobutylcarbinol, (*d*) neopentylcarbinol, (*e*) methyldiethylcarbinol, (*f*) benzylcarbinol.

3. By means of equations, show how the following compounds can be prepared on an industrial scale from petroleum refinery products: (*a*) isopropyl alcohol, (*b*) acetic acid, (*c*) ethylene glycol, (*d*) acetone, (*e*) acetaldehyde.

4. What is meant by the term carbonium ion? Suggest a mechanism involving a carbonium ion for the reaction of isopropyl alcohol with hydrobromic acid.

SUGGESTED READINGS

D. H. Killeffer, "Butanol and Acetone from Corn," *Ind. Eng. Chem.*, *19*, 46 (1927).
E. C. Weaver, "Glycerol," *J. Chem. Educ.*, *29*, 524 (1952).

CHAPTER 8

Aldehydes and Ketones

The Aldehydes

Those compounds containing the group $-\overset{O}{\overset{\|}{C}}-H$ are known as aldehydes. The name originated from the consideration that the compounds are obtained from primary alcohols by dehydrogenation (*al*cohol *dehyd*rogenatum). The common aldehydes are named with reference to the acids which they yield on oxidation. The systematic nomenclature employs the ending *al*. Examples are given in Table XII.

TABLE XII
ALDEHYDES

Name	Formula	Boiling Point	Name of the Corresponding Acid
Formaldehyde (methanal)	$H\overset{O}{\overset{\|}{C}}-H$	$-21°$	Formic
Acetaldehyde (ethanal)	$CH_3\overset{O}{\overset{\|}{C}}-H$	20.2	Acetic
Propionaldehyde (prcpanal)	$CH_3CH_2\overset{O}{\overset{\|}{C}}-H$	48.8	Propionic
n-Butyraldehyde (butanal)	$CH_3CH_2CH_2\overset{O}{\overset{\|}{C}}-H$	75.7	Butyric
Benzaldehyde	$C_6H_5\overset{O}{\overset{\|}{C}}-H$	179.5	Benzoic
p-Tolualdehyde	$CH_3-C_6H_4-\overset{O}{\overset{\|}{C}}-H$	204	*p*-Toluic
α-Naphthaldehyde	$C_{10}H_7-\overset{O}{\overset{\|}{C}}-H$	291.6	*α*-Naphthoic

Formaldehyde is a colorless gas of very irritating odor. It is a strong poison, and has been used as a disinfectant and as a fumigant. It is usually sold as a 40 per cent aqueous solution under the name formalin. The stability of this solution indicates that it may contain the hydrate of formaldehyde (p. 301).

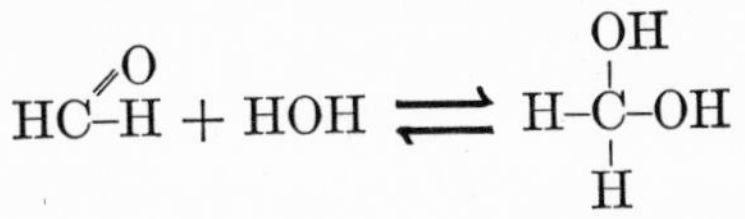

$$HC\overset{\displaystyle /\!\!/O}{}{-}H + HOH \rightleftharpoons H{-}\underset{\displaystyle H}{\overset{\displaystyle OH}{\underset{|}{\overset{|}{C}}}}{-}OH$$

Formaldehyde is also transported and sold as the solid polymer, paraformaldehyde, which can be obtained by evaporation of formalin. The polymerization involves self-addition of many molecules of formaldehyde.

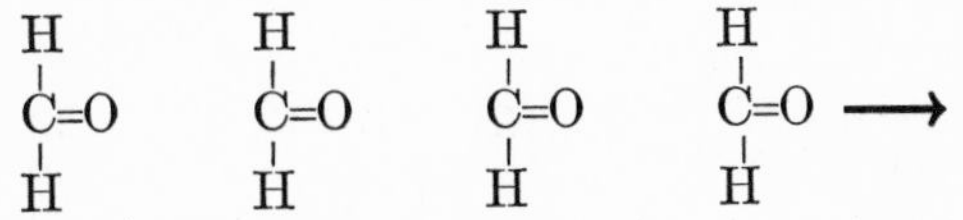

$$\underset{\displaystyle H}{\overset{\displaystyle H}{\underset{|}{\overset{|}{C}}}}{=}O \quad \underset{\displaystyle H}{\overset{\displaystyle H}{\underset{|}{\overset{|}{C}}}}{=}O \quad \underset{\displaystyle H}{\overset{\displaystyle H}{\underset{|}{\overset{|}{C}}}}{=}O \quad \underset{\displaystyle H}{\overset{\displaystyle H}{\underset{|}{\overset{|}{C}}}}{=}O \longrightarrow$$

$$-CH_2OCH_2OCH_2OCH_2O- \quad \text{or} \quad (CH_2O)_x$$

Paraformaldehyde

Paraformaldehyde undergoes depolymerization when it is heated, forming gaseous formaldehyde. When the latter is desired in the laboratory it is usually obtained in this way. The use of "formaldehyde candles" in fumigation is another application of this process. The candle is paraformaldehyde, which is depolymerized over a miniature alcohol stove. The most important use of formaldehyde is in the manufacture of plastics (pp. 171, 395). Aldehydes, being very reactive compounds, serve as raw materials in the production of many other substances.

The Ketones

The ketones, as was noted earlier (p. 17), contain a carbonyl group attached to two organic residues, $R{-}\overset{/\!\!/O}{C}{-}R$. Acetone, the simplest member of the series, has been known for nearly three centuries. It derives its name from the fact that it can be obtained from acetic acid. The other simple ketones are usually named with reference to the radicals attached to the carbonyl group. In the systematic nomenclature the ending *one* is employed. The use of both systems is shown in Table XIII.

Ketones may be obtained from secondary alcohols by either oxidation or catalytic dehydrogenation (p. 59). In industry the latter process

TABLE XIII

SIMPLE KETONES

Name	Formula	Boiling Point
Acetone (propanone)	$CH_3C(=O)-CH_3$	56.1°
Methyl ethyl ketone (butanone)	$CH_3CH_2C(=O)-CH_3$	79.6
Diethyl ketone (3-pentanone)	$CH_3CH_2C(=O)-CH_2CH_3$	101.7
Methyl *n*-propyl ketone (2-pentanone)	$CH_3C(=O)-CH_2CH_2CH_3$	101.7
Isopropyl methyl ketone (methylbutanone)	$CH_3C(=O)CH(CH_3)-CH_3$	93
Cyclohexanone	ring: CH_2–CH_2–CH_2–$C{=}O$–CH_2–CH_2	156.7
Acetophenone (methyl phenyl ketone)	$CH_3C(=O)-C_6H_5$	202.3
Benzophenone (diphenyl ketone)	$C_6H_5-C(=O)-C_6H_5$	306.0

is used. Acetone, for example, is prepared from isopropyl alcohol (p. 54). Since isopropyl alcohol is synthesized from propylene, acetone may be regarded as a petroleum product. This is not the only commercial source of acetone. As mentioned earlier (p. 54), it is obtained along with *n*-butyl alcohol in the Weizmann fermentation.

Methyl ethyl ketone is prepared by the dehydrogenation of *sec*-butyl alcohol (p. 59).

Acetone is produced in large quantities for use as a solvent in nitrocellulose processing and as a raw material in the preparation of drugs, such as iodoform (p. 90) and sulfonal (p. 83), and synthetic plastics (p. 154). Similar uses of methyl ethyl ketone have been found.

The degree of reactivity of a carbonyl group depends on the nature of the radicals to which it is attached. If these radicals are large, access to the functional group is blocked and reactions are sluggish. In general, the more bulky the radicals the lower is the rate of reaction. In formaldehyde, in which the carbonyl group is joined to two hydrogen atoms, the steric factor is at a minimum and the reactivity of the carbonyl group at a maximum.

Other aldehydes are less reactive, the reactivity falling off as the size of the radical increases. Ketones, having two hydrocarbon radicals, are still less reactive. It should be pointed out that the hyperconjugation effect, where it is operative, tends to neutralize the electron deficit of the carbonyl carbon atom, thus reducing the reactivity of the functional group. This effect is at a maximum in acetone.

Reactions of Aldehydes and Ketones

As has been noted (p. 7), the carbonyl group is a resonance hybrid of the structure having a double bond between the carbon and oxygen atoms (*a*) and that (*b*) in which they are joined by a single bond. Alde-

$$\underset{a}{>C{=}\ddot{\underset{\cdot\cdot}{O}}} \qquad\qquad \underset{b}{>\overset{+}{C}{-}\ddot{\underset{\cdot\cdot}{O}}{:}^{-}}$$

hydes and ketones behave for the most part as though the functional group possessed structure *b*, in which the carbonyl carbon atom is electronically deficient. Most of their reactions are of such nature as to make up this deficit.

Reagents that attack the carbonyl group, then, are those that possess an unshared electron pair. Examples are water, alcohols, ammonia and amines, and the cyanide ion. Certain "carbonyl" reagents which do not fall in this category nevertheless *behave as though they are sources of such agents*. The Grignard reagent, for example, acts as a source of carbanions (R^-) (p. 277).

Oxidation. Perhaps the outstanding property of aldehydes is the ease with which they are oxidized to acids. Such mild oxidizing agents as alkaline solutions containing silver or copper salts suffice to bring about the reaction. If a silver salt is to be used it is first dissolved in an excess of ammonium hydroxide. The resulting solution, known as Tollens' reagent, deposits metallic silver when an aldehyde is added. If the reaction is carried out in scrupulously clean glassware the silver forms a mirror on the walls of the vessel. This reaction is widely used as a laboratory test for aldehydes; it is known as the Tollens test or as the silver mirror test. The following equation represents the reaction for formaldehyde.

$$\underset{\text{Formaldehyde}}{H\overset{\displaystyle O}{\overset{/\!\!/}{C}}{-}H} + 2AgOH \longrightarrow \underset{\text{Formic acid}}{H\overset{\displaystyle O}{\overset{/\!\!/}{C}}{-}OH} + 2Ag + H_2O$$

Aromatic aldehydes also give a positive silver mirror test as illustrated by the behavior of benzaldehyde

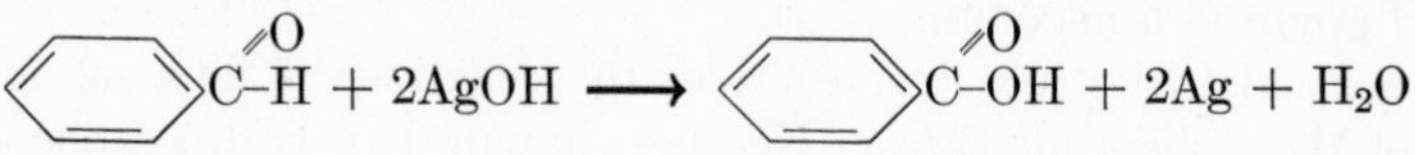

$$C_6H_5\overset{\displaystyle O}{\overset{\|}{C}}\text{-}H + 2AgOH \longrightarrow C_6H_5\overset{\displaystyle O}{\overset{\|}{C}}\text{-}OH + 2Ag + H_2O$$

The Fehling test and the Benedict test differ from that of Tollens in that a copper salt is employed. Alkaline solutions containing a cupric salt and salts of certain organic acids are stable, although cupric hydroxide is insoluble in water. Fehling's solution contains potassium sodium tartrate (p. 150), and Benedict's solution contains sodium citrate (p. 150). When an aldehyde is added the copper is reduced and separates as cuprous oxide. For convenience in writing equations the reagents may be considered as containing cupric oxide. The behavior of propionaldehyde is illustrative.

$$\underset{\text{Propion-aldehyde}}{CH_3CH_2\overset{\displaystyle O}{\overset{\|}{C}}H} + 2CuO \longrightarrow \underset{\text{Propionic acid}}{CH_3CH_2\overset{\displaystyle O}{\overset{\|}{C}}OH} + Cu_2O$$

A carbonyl group attached to an aromatic ring forms part of a resonating system similar to that indicated for nitrobenzene.

For benzaldehyde, for example, may be written not only the Kekule structures of type *a* but also other contributing structures such as *b*

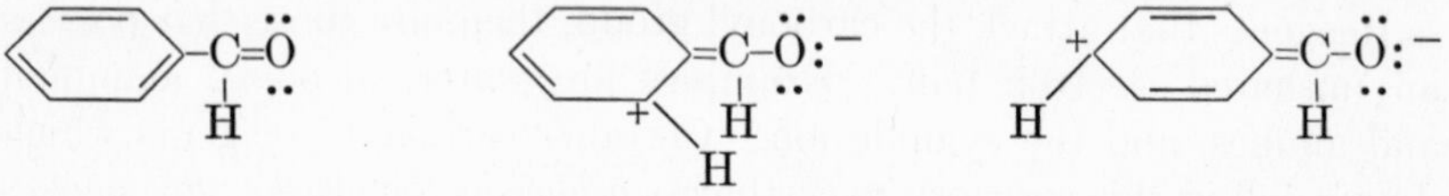

$$\underset{a}{C_6H_5\text{-}\underset{H}{\underset{|}{C}}{=}\ddot{\underset{..}{O}}} \qquad \underset{b}{{}^{+}(H)C_6H_5{=}\underset{H}{\underset{|}{C}}\text{-}\ddot{\underset{..}{O}}{:}^{-}} \qquad \underset{c}{H\text{-}{}^{+}C_6H_4{=}\underset{H}{\underset{|}{C}}\text{-}\ddot{\underset{..}{O}}{:}^{-}}$$

and *c*. As a consequence of resonance stabilization, the reactivity of the carbonyl group is lower than in aliphatic ketones. This difference between aliphatic and aromatic aldehydes is revealed in their behavior with the Fehling and Benedict solutions. These reagents are not strong enough to oxidize aromatic aldehydes, and thus they serve to distinguish compounds of the two classes.

Ketones, as would be expected from their structure, are much more difficult to oxidize, being resistant to Tollens' reagent as well as to most of the other ordinary oxidizing agents.

Reduction. The dehydrogenation of primary and secondary alcohols to aldehydes and ketones, respectively, is a reversible process. By treating an aldehyde or ketone with hydrogen in the presence of a catalyst such as platinum or nickel the parent alcohol can be obtained in good yields. Thus *n*-butyraldehyde, normally made from *n*-butyl alcohol by dehydrogenation, can be converted to it by hydrogenation.

$$\underset{n\text{-Butyraldehyde}}{CH_3CH_2CH_2C(=O)\text{–}H} + H_2 \xrightarrow{Pt} \underset{n\text{-Butyl alcohol}}{CH_3CH_2CH_2CH_2OH}$$

In a similar way hydrogen combines with acetone to yield isopropyl alcohol.

$$CH_3C(=O)\text{–}CH_3 + H_2 \xrightarrow{Ni} CH_3CH(OH)CH_3$$

Chemical reducing agents, such as iron and acetic acid, also may be used to transform carbonyl compounds to the corresponding alcohols.

Hydration. The attack of nucleus-seeking reagents is illustrated by the behavior of formaldehyde in water, where it exists as the hydrate. The hydration process probably involves sharing of an electron pair of the water molecule with the deficient carbonyl carbon atom with the formation of a transition complex such as *a*, which is stabilized by the migration of a proton to give the hydrate (*b*).

$$H_2\overset{+}{C}\text{–}\ddot{O}:^- + :\ddot{O}H_2 \rightleftharpoons \underset{a}{H_2C(\text{–}\ddot{O}:^-)(\text{–}\overset{+}{O}H_2)} \rightleftharpoons \underset{b}{H_2C(\ddot{O}H)_2}$$

Hydration is a reversible reaction, and only with the most reactive aldehydes is it possible to isolate hydrates.

Reaction with Ammonia. In a very similar way aldehydes such as acetaldehyde form addition compounds with ammonia, known as aldehyde-ammonias.

$$CH_3\text{–}\overset{+}{C}H\text{–}\ddot{O}:^- + :NH_3 \rightleftharpoons CH_3\text{–}CH(\overset{+}{N}H_3)\text{–}\ddot{O}:^- \rightleftharpoons \underset{\text{Aldehyde-ammonia}}{CH_3\text{–}CH(NH_2)\text{–}OH}$$

This type of reaction is reversible, making it possible to recover the original aldehyde by treating the aldehyde-ammonia with dilute acids, which remove the ammonia and thus cause reversal of the reaction. In only a few of the most active aldehydes is the equilibrium favorable to the formation of aldehyde-ammonias. The aldehyde-ammonia from formaldehyde, however, reacts further to yield a very complex molecule. The product is called hexamethylenetetramine, since it is derived from six molecules of formaldehyde and four of ammonia.

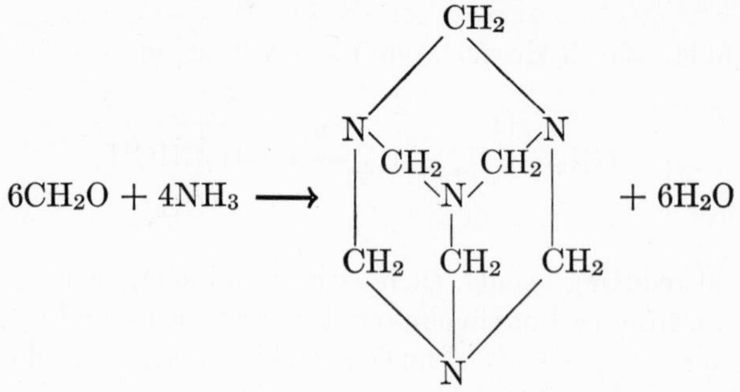

$$6CH_2O + 4NH_3 \longrightarrow (CH_2)_6N_4 + 6H_2O$$

Hexamethylenetetramine

Hexamethylenetetramine, under the name urotropine, is used in medicine as a urinary disinfectant. It is also employed as a catalyst in the vulcanization of rubber. Treatment with 96 per cent nitric acid at 0° converts hexamethylenetetramine into trimethylenetrinitroamine, which is known as RDX and is a high explosive resembling tetryl (p. 418).

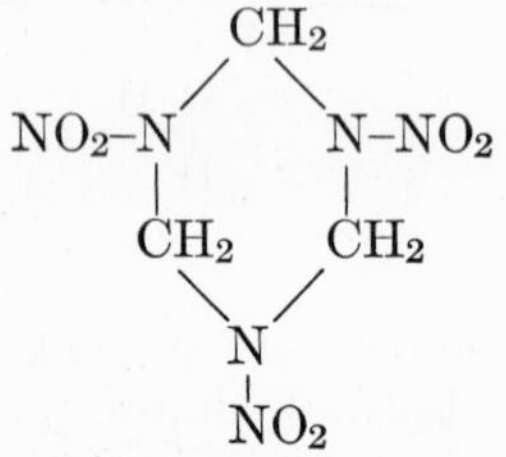

$$(CH_2N{-}NO_2)_3$$

RDX

Aromatic aldehydes and ammonia react in a manner which differs from that with aliphatic aldehydes (p. 305).

Condensation with Hydroxylamine and Derivatives of Hydrazine. Certain derivatives of ammonia form unstable addition products with aldehydes. These addition products lose the elements of water to form compounds containing a double bond between carbon and nitrogen. The general scheme for reactions of this type is as follows.

$$RC(=O)H + H_2NA \rightleftharpoons \left[R{-}CH(OH){-}NH{-}A \right] \rightleftharpoons RCH{=}NA + H_2O$$

The reaction of aldehydes with hydroxylamine leads to the formation of *oximes*. Benzaldoxime is synthesized in this way.

$$C_6H_5\text{-}\overset{\displaystyle O}{\overset{\|}{C}}\text{-}H + \underset{\text{Hydroxylamine}}{H_2NOH} \longrightarrow \left[C_6H_5\text{-}\underset{\displaystyle H}{\underset{|}{\overset{\displaystyle OH}{\overset{|}{C}}}}\text{-}NHOH\right] \longrightarrow \underset{\text{Benzaldoxime}}{C_6H_5\text{-}CH{=}NOH} + H_2O$$

If phenylhydrazine is employed the product is a phenylhydrazone. Propionaldehyde forms a typical phenylhydrazone.

$$CH_3CH_2\overset{\displaystyle O}{\overset{\|}{C}}\text{-}H + \underset{\text{Phenylhydrazine}}{H_2NNHC_6H_5} \longrightarrow \left[CH_3CH_2\underset{\displaystyle H}{\underset{|}{\overset{\displaystyle OH}{\overset{|}{C}}}}\text{-}NHNHC_6H_5\right]$$

$$\longrightarrow \underset{\text{Propionaldehyde phenylhydrazone}}{CH_3CH_2CH{=}N\text{-}NHC_6H_5} + H_2O$$

With semicarbazide, semicarbazones are obtained. This reaction has been carried out with formaldehyde, for example.

$$H\text{-}\overset{\displaystyle O}{\overset{\|}{C}}\text{-}H + \underset{\text{Semicarbazide}}{H_2NNH\overset{\displaystyle O}{\overset{\|}{C}}\text{-}NH_2} \longrightarrow \left[H\text{-}\underset{\displaystyle H}{\underset{|}{\overset{\displaystyle OH}{\overset{|}{C}}}}\text{-}NHNH\overset{\displaystyle O}{\overset{\|}{C}}\text{-}NH_2\right]$$

$$\longrightarrow \underset{\text{Formaldehyde semicarbazone}}{H\text{-}\underset{\displaystyle H}{\underset{|}{C}}{=}NNH\overset{\displaystyle O}{\overset{\|}{C}}\text{-}NH_2} + H_2O$$

The oximes, phenylhydrazones, and semicarbazones are of value in the identification of carbonyl compounds because they are usually easily purified solids of definite melting points. Phenylhydrazine is particularly useful as a reagent for sugars (p. 201).

Ketones react with hydroxylamine, phenylhydrazine, and semicarbazide in the same manner as do the aldehydes. Using acetone, diethyl ketone, and acetophenone as examples we may represent the type reactions as follows.

$$\underset{\text{Acetone}}{(CH_3)_2C{=}O} + H_2NOH \longrightarrow \underset{\text{Acetone oxime}}{(CH_3)_2C{=}NOH} + H_2O$$

$$\begin{matrix} CH_3CH_2 \\ CH_3CH_2 \end{matrix}\!\!>\!C{=}O + H_2NNHC({=}O){-}NH_2 \longrightarrow \begin{matrix} CH_3CH_2 \\ CH_3CH_2 \end{matrix}\!\!>\!C{=}NNHC({=}O){-}NH_2 + H_2O$$

Diethyl ketone — Semicarbazone of diethyl ketone

$$C_6H_5{-}C(CH_3){=}O + H_2NNH{-}C_6H_5 \longrightarrow C_6H_5{-}C(CH_3){=}NNH{-}C_6H_5 + H_2O$$

Phenylhydrazone of acetophenone

Reaction with Alcohols. A *hemiacetal* is formed when an aldehyde and an alcohol are brought together. Hemiacetals are ordinarily unstable and decompose to the aldehyde and alcohol during attempted isolation. Formaldehyde and ethyl alcohol are believed to react in this manner.

$$H{-}C({=}O){-}H + CH_3CH_2OH \rightleftharpoons H{-}C(OH)(H){-}OCH_2CH_3$$

Hemiacetal from formaldehyde and ethyl alcohol

In the presence of a trace of mineral acid the hemiacetal reacts with another molecule of alcohol, by elimination of a molecule of water, forming an *acetal.* The acetals are stable under ordinary conditions. In the presence of acid and water they revert to aldehydes and alcohols. This is illustrated by the reversible formation of the diethyl acetal of formaldehyde.

$$H{-}C(OH)(H){-}OCH_2CH_3 + CH_3CH_2OH \overset{HCl}{\rightleftharpoons} H{-}C(OCH_2CH_3)(H){-}OCH_2CH_3 + H_2O$$

Formaldehyde diethyl acetal

Hemiacetals of ordinary ketones are rarely encountered, and special methods are required to convert ketones to the corresponding *ketals* (p. 304).

Formation of Mercaptoles. Alcohols do not form addition products even with methyl ketones. Mercaptans, however, react readily.

Aliphatic ketones react with mercaptans to give mercaptoles. Certain of these are intermediates in the preparation of drugs. Sulfonal is obtained from acetone as follows.

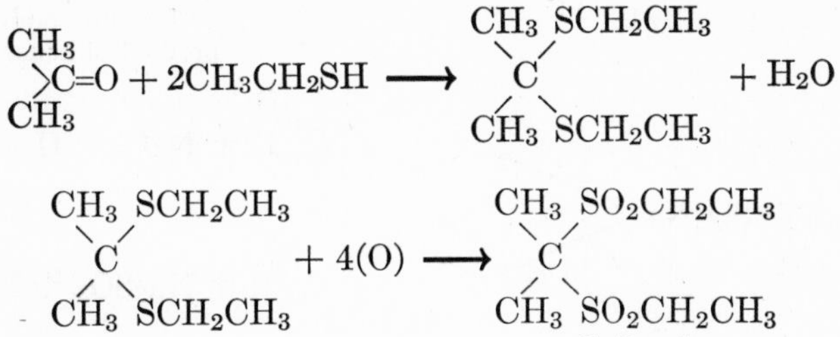

$$(CH_3)_2C{=}O + 2CH_3CH_2SH \longrightarrow (CH_3)_2C(SCH_2CH_3)_2 + H_2O$$

$$(CH_3)_2C(SCH_2CH_3)_2 + 4(O) \longrightarrow (CH_3)_2C(SO_2CH_2CH_3)_2$$

Sulfonal

By the same reactions Trional is prepared from methyl ethyl ketone and Tetronal from diethyl ketone.

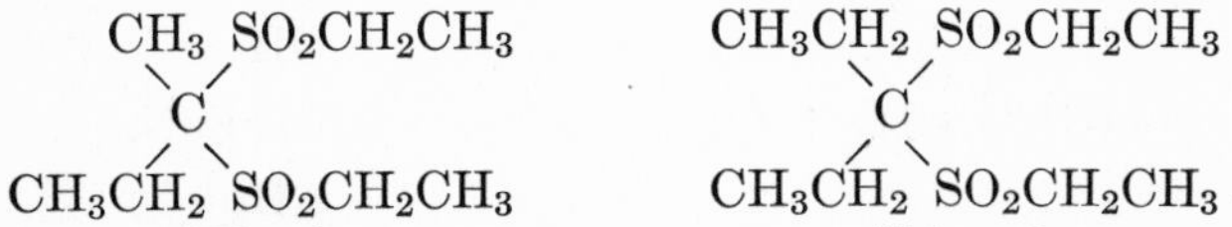

$$(CH_3)(CH_3CH_2)C(SO_2CH_2CH_3)_2$$

Trional

$$(CH_3CH_2)_2C(SO_2CH_2CH_3)_2$$

Tetronal

The Addition of Sodium Bisulfite. Sodium bisulfite addition products of aldehydes are obtained when the aldehyde, sometimes in alcohol solution, is added to aqueous sodium bisulfite. The addition to *n*-butyraldehyde is an example.

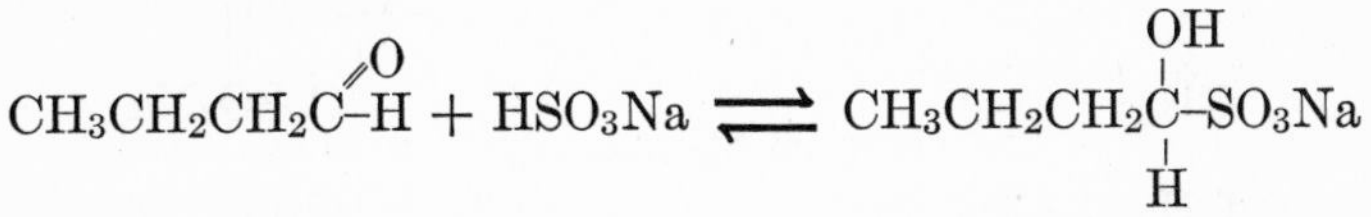

$$CH_3CH_2CH_2C(=O){-}H + HSO_3Na \rightleftharpoons CH_3CH_2CH_2C(OH)(H){-}SO_3Na$$

n-Butyraldehyde — Bisulfite addition product of *n*-butyraldehyde

Since the addition products are salts, their solubilities are greatly different from those of the aldehydes. Because of this they are sometimes very useful in purifying aldehydes. For instance, if benzaldehyde (b.p. 179.5°) were prepared in the laboratory by the dehydrogenation of benzyl alcohol (b.p. 205°) the crude product would probably contain some of the unchanged alcohol. Purification could be effected by treating the material with sodium bisulfite solution and adding alcohol to precipitate the addition product. The latter, being a salt, is insoluble in ether and can be washed free of benzyl alcohol with this solvent. Treatment of the purified addition product with either acid or base regenerates benzaldehyde.

$$C_6H_5C(=O)H + HSO_3Na \rightleftharpoons C_6H_5C(OH)(H)SO_3Na$$

Benzaldehyde — Bisulfite addition product of benzaldehyde

$$C_6H_5C(OH)(H)SO_3Na \xrightarrow{HCl} C_6H_5C(=O)H + NaCl + H_2O + SO_2$$

$$C_6H_5C(OH)(H)SO_3Na \xrightarrow{Na_2CO_3} C_6H_5C(=O)H + Na_2SO_3 + NaHCO_3$$

Aliphatic ketones containing the grouping $-C(=O)-CH_3$ are sufficiently reactive to undergo addition of sodium bisulfite. Acetone readily forms a bisulfite addition compound when treated with sodium bisulfite.

$$CH_3C(=O)-CH_3 + HSO_3Na \longrightarrow CH_3C(OH)(CH_3)-SO_3Na$$

Bisulfite addition product of acetone

Cyclic ketones have about the same reactivity as methyl ketones. Cyclopentanone may be converted to a bisulfite addition compound.

```
   CH2                          CH2   OH
  /   \                        /   \ /
CH2    C=O                   CH2    C-SO3Na
 |     |     + HSO3Na  ──→    |     |
CH2────CH2                   CH2────CH2
Cyclopentanone               Bisulfite addition
                             product of cyclopentanone
```

Formation of Cyanohydrins. Cyanohydrins, compounds containing both a cyano group and a hydroxyl group, are obtained from aldehydes and hydrocyanic acid. That from acetaldehyde may be taken as an example.

$$CH_3C(=O)-H + HCN \longrightarrow CH_3C(OH)(H)-CN$$

Acetaldehyde — Acetaldehyde cyanohydrin

Cyanohydrins are formed by a number of the more reactive ketones, acetone being the most important example.

$$CH_3C(=O)CH_3 + HCN \longrightarrow CH_3C(OH)(CH_3)CN$$

Acetone cyanohydrin

Cyanohydrins are used in the synthesis of substituted acids (pp. 149, 311). Because hydrocyanic acid is a poisonous gas the cyanohydrins are usually made indirectly by treating a bisulfite addition product with sodium or potassium cyanide. Sodium cyanide and the bisulfite addition compound of benzaldehyde react according to the following scheme.

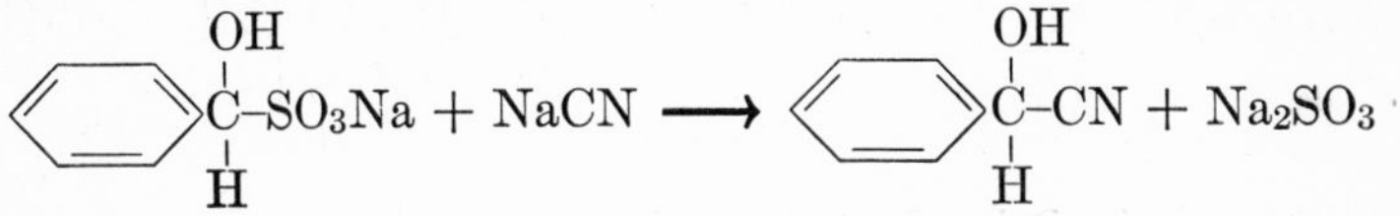

$$C_6H_5CH(OH)SO_3Na + NaCN \longrightarrow C_6H_5CH(OH)CN + Na_2SO_3$$

Benzaldehyde cyanohydrin

Addition of the Grignard Reagent. The Grignard reagent adds to carbonyl compounds to form derivatives of alcohols. With formaldehyde a primary alcohol is obtained. *n*-Butyl alcohol can be made in this way from *n*-propyl bromide.

$$H\text{–}C(=O)\text{–}H + CH_3CH_2CH_2MgBr \longrightarrow CH_3CH_2CH_2CH_2OMgBr$$

n-Propylmagnesium bromide

$$CH_3CH_2CH_2CH_2OMgBr + HCl \longrightarrow CH_3CH_2CH_2CH_2OH + MgBrCl$$

n-Butyl alcohol

It will be noted that the primary alcohol produced contains one more carbon atom than the Grignard reagent. The process thus enables one to convert an alcohol to the corresponding primary alcohol of one additional carbon atom; $ROH \longrightarrow RBr \longrightarrow RMgBr \longrightarrow RCH_2OH$ (p. 283).

All other aldehydes yield derivatives of secondary alcohols upon treatment with a Grignard reagent. Methylphenylcarbinol may be obtained either from acetaldehyde and phenylmagnesium bromide or from benzaldehyde and methylmagnesium bromide.

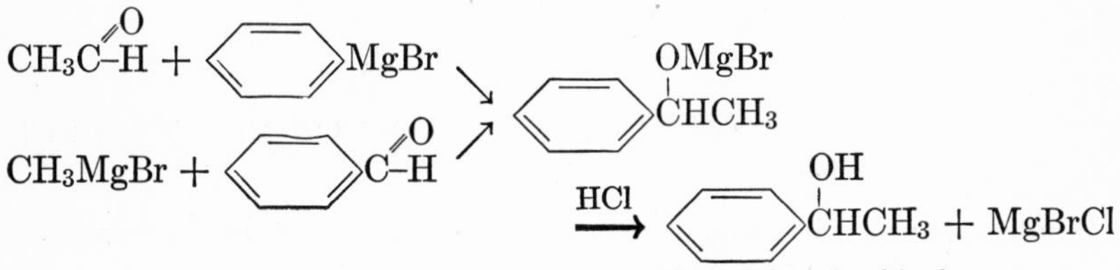

$$CH_3C(=O)H + C_6H_5MgBr \searrow$$

$$CH_3MgBr + C_6H_5C(=O)H \nearrow \quad C_6H_5CH(OMgBr)CH_3$$

$$\xrightarrow{HCl} C_6H_5CH(OH)CH_3 + MgBrCl$$

Methylphenylcarbinol

Addition of the Grignard reagent to the carbonyl group of a ketone leads to the formation of a tertiary alcohol derivative. This is a general method for the preparation of tertiary alcohols. The synthesis of triethylcarbinol from diethyl ketone and ethylmagnesium bromide is an example.

$$CH_3CH_2\overset{\overset{\displaystyle O}{\|}}{C}CH_2CH_3 + CH_3CH_2MgBr \longrightarrow CH_3CH_2\overset{\overset{\displaystyle OMgBr}{|}}{\underset{\underset{\displaystyle CH_2CH_3}{|}}{C}}-CH_2CH_3$$

$$CH_3CH_2\overset{\overset{\displaystyle OMgBr}{|}}{\underset{\underset{\displaystyle CH_2CH_3}{|}}{C}}-CH_2CH_3 + HCl \longrightarrow \underset{\text{Triethylcarbinol}}{(CH_3CH_2)_3COH} + MgBrCl$$

When this synthesis is adapted for the preparation of tertiary alcohols of the type $R-\overset{\overset{\displaystyle OH}{|}}{\underset{\underset{\displaystyle R'}{|}}{C}}-R''$, in which the groups attached to the carbinol carbon atom are different, three variations are possible. Any one of the R groups may be furnished by the Grignard reagent, the other two being derived from the ketone. The three possibilities are illustrated in the preparation of 2-phenyl-2-butanol.

$$\underset{\text{Acetophenone}}{C_6H_5-\overset{\displaystyle O}{\overset{\|}{C}}-CH_3} + CH_3CH_2MgBr \searrow$$

$$\underset{\text{Propiophenone}}{C_6H_5-\overset{\displaystyle O}{\overset{\|}{C}}-CH_2CH_3} + CH_3MgBr \longrightarrow C_6H_5-\overset{\overset{\displaystyle OMgBr}{|}}{\underset{\underset{\displaystyle CH_3}{|}}{C}}-CH_2CH_3$$

$$\underset{\text{Methyl ethyl ketone}}{CH_3\overset{\displaystyle O}{\overset{\|}{C}}-CH_2CH_3} + C_6H_5MgBr \nearrow$$

$$C_6H_5-\overset{\overset{\displaystyle OMgBr}{|}}{\underset{\underset{\displaystyle CH_3}{|}}{C}}-CH_2CH_3 + HCl \longrightarrow \underset{\text{2-Phenyl-2-butanol}}{C_6H_5-\overset{\overset{\displaystyle OH}{|}}{\underset{\underset{\displaystyle CH_3}{|}}{C}}-CH_2CH_3} + MgBrCl$$

The choice of the pair of reagents to be used is usually made on the basis of their availability. Since propiophenone is the most expensive reagent in the above scheme, either the first or third pair would be selected.

Reactions in the Presence of Alkali. Aldehydes may be classified into two groups according to their behavior in the presence of alkali. The basis of the separation lies in the reactivity of the hydrogen atoms attached to the carbon adjacent to the carbonyl group. This carbon atom is usually called the α-carbon. The use of the Greek letters in this sense is illustrated with *n*-butyraldehyde.

$$\underset{\gamma}{CH_3}\underset{\beta}{CH_2}\underset{\alpha}{CH_2}\overset{\diagup\!\!\diagup O}{C}\!-\!H$$

n-Butyraldehyde

The α-carbon atom is the one to which the functional group is attached. When the functional group is a carbonyl group the hydrogen atoms on the α-carbon atom are very reactive. This activation does not extend to the hydrogen atoms on the β- and γ-carbon atoms; these appear to have very little more reactivity than the hydrogen atoms in *n*-butane.

The Aldol Condensation. Aldehydes which have a hydrogen atom on the α-carbon atom undergo self-addition in the presence of alkali. Thus, acetaldehyde gives aldol.

$$CH_3\overset{\diagup\!\!\diagup O}{C}\!-\!H + CH_3\overset{\diagup\!\!\diagup O}{C}\!-\!H \xrightleftharpoons{NaOH} CH_3\underset{\displaystyle H}{\overset{\displaystyle OH}{C}}\!-\!CH_2\overset{\diagup\!\!\diagup O}{C}\!-\!H$$

Aldol

The reaction closely resembles the other additions of the aldehydes. A hydrogen atom of the second molecule attaches to the oxygen atom, and the remainder to the carbon atom of the carbonyl group of the first molecule.

Aldol contains a hydroxyl group and an active hydrogen atom on adjacent carbon atoms. These can be removed easily, either by heating or by treatment with a dehydrating agent, to give crotonaldehyde.

$$CH_3\overset{\displaystyle OH}{CH}\!-\!CH_2\overset{\diagup\!\!\diagup O}{C}\!-\!H \xrightarrow{heat} CH_3CH{=}CH\overset{\diagup\!\!\diagup O}{C}\!-\!H + H_2O$$

Crotonaldehyde

If crotonaldehyde is desired, aldol is prepared under mild conditions and then dehydrated. If a mixture of acetaldehyde and sodium hydroxide solution is heated, the crotonaldehyde reacts with acetaldehyde.

$$CH_3CH{=}CHC(=O){-}H + CH_3C(=O){-}H \xrightarrow[\text{heat}]{\text{NaOH}} CH_3CH{=}CHCH{=}CHC(=O){-}H + H_2O$$

The process can be repeated indefinitely, so that a mixture of colored products of high molecular weight will result; these are the *aldehyde resins*.

Since the aldol condensation involves the hydrogen atom of the α-carbon atom, the homologs of acetaldehyde give branched-chain aldols. Propionaldehyde yields 2-methyl-3-hydroxypentanal.

$$CH_3CH_2C(=O){-}H + CH_3CH_2C(=O){-}H \xrightleftharpoons{\text{NaOH}} CH_3CH_2CH(OH)CH(CH_3)C(=O){-}H$$

2-Methyl-3-hydroxypentanal

$$CH_3CH_2CH(OH)CH(CH_3)C(=O){-}H \xrightarrow{\text{heat}} CH_3CH_2CH{=}C(CH_3)C(=O){-}H + H_2O$$

2-Methyl-2-pentenal

A remarkable feature of the aldol condensation is that it is reversible.

The simple ketones also undergo condensations of the aldol type in the presence of alkali. Diacetone alcohol is obtained from acetone.

$$(CH_3)_2C{=}O + CH_3C(=O){-}CH_3 \xrightleftharpoons{\text{Ba(OH)}_2} (CH_3)_2C(OH){-}CH_2C(=O){-}CH_3$$

Diacetone alcohol

The equilibrium point is far to the left, so that a special method must be used to obtain a good yield of diacetone alcohol. The reaction is run in an extractor, so arranged that the ketone is boiled under reflux and the condensed acetone comes in contact with barium hydroxide as it returns to the boiler. The catalyst causes a small portion of the acetone to change to diacetone alcohol. The liquid which reaches the boiler thus contains a small amount of the addition product, and since no alkali is present in the boiler the diacetone alcohol accumulating there does not revert to acetone. The ketone, diacetone alcohol, contains a β-hydroxyl group and an α-hydrogen atom. Under mild conditions these are eliminated as water, yielding mesityl oxide.

$$CH_3C(OH)(CH_3){-}CH_2C(=O){-}CH_3 \xrightarrow{I_2} CH_3C(CH_3){=}CHC(=O){-}CH_3 + H_2O$$

Mesityl oxide

The dehydration can be accomplished by heating diacetone alcohol with iodine or a trace of acid.

Mesityl oxide is also formed from acetone in the presence of strong acid; it reacts with another molecule of acetone to produce phorone.

$$\begin{matrix} CH_3 \\ \quad \rangle C{=}O \\ CH_3 \end{matrix} + CH_3COCH_3 \xrightarrow{HCl} CH_3\overset{\overset{OH}{|}}{\underset{\underset{CH_3}{|}}{C}}{-}CH_2\overset{\nearrow O}{C}{-}CH_3$$

$$\xrightarrow{HCl} H_2O + CH_3\underset{\underset{CH_3}{|}}{C}{=}CH\overset{\nearrow O}{C}{-}CH_3 \xrightarrow[HCl]{CH_3COCH_3} CH_3\underset{\underset{CH_3}{|}}{C}{=}CH\overset{\overset{O}{\|}}{C}CH_2\overset{\overset{OH}{|}}{\underset{\underset{CH_3}{|}}{C}}{-}CH_3$$

$$\xrightarrow{HCl} \underset{\text{Phorone}}{CH_3\underset{\underset{CH_3}{|}}{C}{=}CH\overset{\overset{O}{\|}}{C}CH{=}\underset{\underset{CH_3}{|}}{C}CH_3} + H_2O$$

The Cannizzaro Reaction. Aldehydes which have no hydrogen atom on the α-carbon atom obviously cannot give the aldol condensation. They do react in the presence of alkali, however. In such cases an oxidation-reduction reaction occurs. Benzaldehyde, for example, is converted to benzyl alcohol and sodium benzoate.

$$C_6H_5\overset{\nearrow O}{C}{-}H + C_6H_5\overset{\nearrow O}{C}{-}H \xrightarrow{NaOH} \underset{\text{Benzyl alcohol}}{C_6H_5CH_2OH} + \underset{\text{Sodium benzoate}}{C_6H_5\overset{\nearrow O}{C}{-}ONa}$$

The net result of the Cannizzaro reaction is that one molecule of the aldehyde is reduced to the primary alcohol and the other is oxidized to the acid (produced as the sodium salt). This reaction is characteristic of aromatic aldehydes since these cannot have a hydrogen atom on the α-carbon atom. Certain aliphatic aldehydes also give the same reaction, notably formaldehyde, $H{-}\overset{\nearrow O}{C}{-}H$.

$$H\overset{\nearrow O}{C}{-}H + H\overset{\nearrow O}{C}{-}H \xrightarrow{NaOH} \underset{\text{Methyl alcohol}}{CH_3OH} + \underset{\text{Sodium formate}}{H\overset{\nearrow O}{C}{-}ONa}$$

The Haloform Reaction. One of the characteristic properties of the α-hydrogen atoms in ketones and aldehydes is the ease of replacement by halogen. Even the salts of hypohalous acids bring about halogenation of aldehydes and ketones which have such hydrogen atoms. The reaction is of particular interest in connection with acetaldehyde and methyl ketones because, in the presence of alkalies, cleavage of the carbon-carbon bond occurs. The products from acetaldehyde and sodium hypochlorite are chloroform and sodium formate.

$$CH_3\overset{\displaystyle /\!\!/O}{C}\text{–}H + 3NaOCl \longrightarrow \underset{\text{Chloroform}}{CHCl_3} + \underset{\text{Sodium formate}}{H\overset{\displaystyle /\!\!/O}{C}\text{–}ONa} + 2NaOH$$

Bromoform and iodoform are obtained by employing sodium hypobromite and sodium hypoiodite, respectively. When the reaction is used as a test, sodium hypoiodite is employed because the yellow crystals of iodoform can be recognized easily.

The higher aldehydes contain no more than two α-hydrogen atoms and so cannot yield haloforms upon treatment with hypohalites. Since formaldehyde contains no α-carbon atom, acetaldehyde is the only aldehyde which gives the haloform reaction.

Among the ketones only those having the group $\text{–}\overset{\displaystyle /\!\!/O}{C}\text{–}CH_3$ can give haloforms. Thus acetone, methyl ethyl ketone, acetophenone, and other methyl ketones give a positive iodoform test.

$$CH_3\overset{\displaystyle /\!\!/O}{C}\text{–}CH_3 + 3NaOI \longrightarrow \underset{\text{Sodium acetate}}{CH_3\overset{\displaystyle /\!\!/O}{C}\text{–}ONa} + \underset{\text{Iodoform}}{CHI_3} + 2NaOH$$

As oxidizing agents the hypohalites are capable of attacking primary and secondary alcohols. When ethyl alcohol is treated with sodium hypoiodite it is converted to acetaldehyde and the latter then yields iodoform. Since acetaldehyde is the only aldehyde which gives a positive iodoform test, ethyl alcohol is the only primary alcohol which responds to the test.

$$CH_3CH_2OH + NaOI \longrightarrow CH_3\overset{\displaystyle /\!\!/O}{C}\text{–}H + H_2O + NaI$$

$$CH_3\overset{\displaystyle /\!\!/O}{C}\text{–}H + 3NaOI \longrightarrow CHI_3 + H\overset{\displaystyle /\!\!/O}{C}\text{–}ONa + 2NaOH$$

Of the secondary alcohols only those which are methylcarbinols, i.e., which contain the group $\text{–}\underset{\displaystyle OH}{\underset{|}{C}}HCH_3$, can be oxidized to methyl ketones.

Hence only these can give a positive iodoform test. An example is 2-pentanol.

$$CH_3CH_2CH_2\underset{\underset{OH}{|}}{C}HCH_3 + NaOI \longrightarrow CH_3CH_2CH_2C(=O)\text{–}CH_3 + H_2O + NaI$$

2-Pentanol 2-Pentanone

$$CH_3CH_2CH_2C(=O)\text{–}CH_3 + 3NaOI \longrightarrow CH_3CH_2CH_2C(=O)\text{–}ONa + 2NaOH + CHI_3$$

Sodium butyrate

Polymerization. Although formaldehyde readily changes to a solid polymer (p. 75), its homologs yield high polymers only under the influence of peroxidic catalysts and high pressures. However, they do form trimers readily; when acetaldehyde is treated with a trace of acid it changes to paraldehyde.

$$3\,CH_3CH{=}O \underset{}{\overset{H^+}{\rightleftharpoons}} (CH_3CH\text{–}O)_3 \text{ (cyclic)}$$

Paraldehyde

In the pure state paraldehyde is stable, but if it is warmed with a trace of mineral acid acetaldehyde is generated. When acetaldehyde is desired in the laboratory it is made from paraldehyde in this way.

Thioaldehydes and Thioketones

The sulfur analogs of the aldehydes are unknown. Attempts to prepare them lead to trimers, similar to paraldehyde (p. 444). The simple ketones also yield trimers when treated with hydrogen sulfide and hydrogen chloride. Monomeric thioketones have been isolated in rare instances (p. 445).

$$C_6H_5\text{–}C(=O)\text{–}C_6H_5 + H_2S \xrightarrow{HCl} C_6H_5\text{–}C(=S)\text{–}C_6H_5 + H_2O$$

Benzophenone Thiobenzophenone

PROBLEMS

1. Write equations for the reaction of *n*-valeraldehyde with: (*a*) ammoniacal silver hydroxide, (*b*) hydrogen in the presence of platinum, (*c*) an alkali, (*d*) hydrogen cyanide, (*e*) sodium bisulfite, (*f*) sodium bisulfite followed by sodium cyanide, (*g*) methyl alcohol, (*h*) methyl alcohol in the presence of mineral acid, (*i*) *n*-butylmagnesium bromide, (*j*) hydroxylamine, (*k*) semicarbazide, (*l*) phenylhydrazine.
2. Which of the reagents listed above will react with acetone? with diethyl ketone? with cyclohexanone?
3. Write equations for the conversion of *n*-butyl alcohol to: (*a*) *n*-amyl alcohol, (*b*) 2-hexanol, (*c*) di-*n*-butylcarbinol, (*d*) 2-phenyl-2-hexanol, (*e*) 3-methyl-3-heptanol.
4. What deductions can be drawn concerning the structure of: (*a*) a substance that reacts with phenylhydrazine and with Benedict's solution? (*b*) a substance that reacts with phenylhydrazine but not with Benedict's solution? (*c*) a substance that does not react with phenylhydrazine but does give a yellow solid when treated with an alkaline solution of iodine?
5. Contrast the mode of attack of the carbonyl group by reagents with that of the ethylenic group.

SUGGESTED READINGS

F. Walker, "Early History of Acetaldehyde and Formaldehyde," *J. Chem. Educ.*, *10*, 546 (1933).

T. A. Geissman, "The Cannizzaro Reaction," *Org. Reactions*, *2*, 94, 1944.

E. D. Hughes, "Steric Hindrance," *Quart. Revs.*, *2*, 107 (1948)

CHAPTER 9

Carboxylic Acids and Their Derivatives

Carboxylic acids and their most important derivatives, the amides, esters, anhydrides, and acid chlorides, have in common a carbonyl group attached to an electron-rich function.

$RC(=O)-OH$	$RC(=O)-NH_2$	$RC(=O)-OR$	$RC(=O)-O-C(=O)-R$	$RC(=O)-Cl$
Acids	Amides	Esters	Acid anhydrides	Acid chlorides

The hydroxyl, amino, alkoxyl, and acyloxyl ($RC(=O)-O$) groups and the chlorine atom cede electrons to the deficient carbonyl carbon atom, becoming themselves somewhat depleted electronically. In other words a sort of *neutralization* occurs.

Neutralization is extreme in the amides, in which the deficiency of the carbonyl carbon atom is largely made up by accession of electrons from the highly basic (electron-rich) amino group. In ceding electrons to the carbonyl group the amino group loses nearly all its basic character. The electron transfer is apparent from the following resonance structures.

$$RC(=\ddot{O}:)-\ddot{N}H-H \longleftrightarrow RC(-:\ddot{O}:^-)=\overset{+}{N}H-H$$

Actually, in the carboxylic acids, the amides, the esters, and the acid chlorides, the carbonyl group is much less reactive toward the typical carbonyl reagents than in aldehydes and ketones. Similarly amides are much less basic than amines. The difference between carboxylic acids and alcohols is striking. The hydroxyl group of acids, having become electronically depleted, no longer holds the proton firmly as is the case with alcohols. Thus acids dissociate much more readily than alcohols to give hydrogen ions.

An examination of the resulting carboxylate ion shows that it is highly stabilized by resonance.

$$\mathrm{R\overset{\overset{:\!O\!:}{\|}}{C}\!-\!\ddot{\underset{\cdot\cdot}{O}}\!:^-} \longleftrightarrow \mathrm{R\overset{\overset{:\ddot{O}:^-}{|}}{C}\!=\!\ddot{\underset{\cdot\cdot}{O}}}$$

It is believed that the readiness with which an acid ionizes is due to the resonance stabilization of the carboxylate ion.

$$\mathrm{RC}\begin{matrix}\nearrow\!\!\!\!\nearrow O\\ \searrow OH\end{matrix} \rightleftharpoons \mathrm{RC}\begin{matrix}\nearrow\!\!\!\!\nearrow O\\ \searrow O^-\end{matrix} + H^+$$

Acids in which the carboxyl group is attached to a paraffin residue are sometimes called fatty acids, since certain of them can be obtained from the natural fats. The names and formulas of some of the straight-chain saturated acids are given in Table XIV. Of those containing more than six carbon atoms, only the ones with even numbers of carbon atoms are common. From the systematic names given it is evident that the ending *oic* is attached to the hydrocarbon stem in naming acids.

TABLE XIV

SATURATED STRAIGHT-CHAIN ACIDS

Name	Formula	Melting Point	Boiling Point
Formic acid (methanoic acid)	$HC(=O)-OH$	8.4°	100.7°
Acetic acid (ethanoic acid)	$CH_3C(=O)-OH$	16.6	118.1
Propionic acid (propanoic acid)	$CH_3CH_2C(=O)-OH$	−22	141.1
Butyric acid (butanoic acid)	$CH_3CH_2CH_2C(=O)-OH$	−7.9	163.5
Valeric acid (pentanoic acid)	$CH_3CH_2CH_2CH_2C(=O)-OH$	−34.5	187
Caproic acid (hexanoic acid)	$CH_3CH_2CH_2CH_2CH_2C(=O)-OH$	−2	205
Caprylic acid (octanoic acid)	$CH_3CH_2CH_2CH_2CH_2CH_2CH_2C(=O)-OH$	16	237.5
Capric acid (decanoic acid)	$CH_3(CH_2)_8C(=O)-OH$	31.5	270

TABLE XIV—*Continued*

SATURATED STRAIGHT-CHAIN ACIDS

Lauric acid (dodecanoic acid)	$CH_3(CH_2)_{10}C(=O)-OH$	44	......
Myristic acid (tetradecanoic acid)	$CH_3(CH_2)_{12}C(=O)-OH$	58	......
Palmitic acid (hexadecanoic acid)	$CH_3(CH_2)_{14}C(=O)-OH$	64	......
Stearic acid (octadecanoic acid)	$CH_3(CH_2)_{16}C(=O)-OH$	69.4	......

Aromatic acids are named as derivatives of the corresponding hydrocarbons, as shown in Table XV.

TABLE XV

AROMATIC ACIDS

Name	Formula	Melting Point
Benzoic acid	(benzene ring)$-C(=O)-OH$	122°
p-Toluic acid	CH_3-(benzene ring)$-C(=O)-OH$	179.6
o-Toluic acid	(benzene ring with $C(=O)-OH$ and ortho CH_3)	104
β-Naphthoic acid	(naphthalene ring)$-C(=O)-OH$	185

Properties of the Simple Acids

Formic acid is a colorless liquid with a sharp, pungent odor. It is very irritating to the skin; the unpleasant effect of the stings of many insects is due to formic acid. As the name implies (*formica*, ant), the acid was first obtained from ants.

Sodium formate is prepared commercially by heating sodium hydroxide with carbon monoxide under pressure. Anhydrous formic acid is obtained from the dry sodium salt by the action of concentrated sulfuric acid.

$$CO + NaOH \xrightarrow[120\ lb./sq.\ in.]{150-200^\circ} HC{\overset{\displaystyle O}{\diagup\!\!\!\diagup}}\!\!-ONa$$

$$HC{\overset{\displaystyle O}{\diagup\!\!\!\diagup}}\!\!-ONa + H_2SO_4 \longrightarrow HC{\overset{\displaystyle O}{\diagup\!\!\!\diagup}}\!\!-OH + NaHSO_4$$

Formic acid is employed in the textile, leather, and rubber industries. Since it is a relatively weak acid it can be applied safely to products, such as those indicated, which are damaged by treatment with mineral acids.

Formic acid differs from all other organic acids in having a hydrogen atom rather than an organic radical attached to the carboxyl group. It may be regarded as being at once an aldehyde and an acid. This view is in harmony with its action as a reducing agent (p. 60).

$$HC{\overset{\displaystyle O}{\diagup\!\!\!\diagup}}\!\!-OH + [O] \longrightarrow \underset{\text{Carbonic acid}}{\left[HOC{\overset{\displaystyle O}{\diagup\!\!\!\diagup}}\!\!-OH\right]} \longrightarrow CO_2 + H_2O$$

When a mixture of formic and sulfuric acids is heated the formic acid decomposes to water and carbon monoxide.

$$HC{\overset{\displaystyle O}{\diagup\!\!\!\diagup}}\!\!-OH \longrightarrow H_2O + CO$$

Acetic acid is the most important of the simple acids. As indicated above (p. 26), it is prepared by the oxidation of acetaldehyde. Since acetaldehyde may be obtained either from ethyl alcohol or from acetylene, the raw material for the commercial preparation of acetic acid may be sugar, coke, or petroleum. The acid is a liquid boiling at 118.1°. It freezes at a point just below room temperature (16.6°); hence the name glacial acetic acid is applied to the pure substance.

Acetic acid is widely used in industrial processes where a weak acid is desired. It is most valuable as a raw material for the preparation of cellulose acetate (p. 211).

Vinegar is essentially a dilute solution of acetic acid. It is obtained by the oxidation of dilute ethyl alcohol (fermented apple cider) by the oxygen of the air in the presence of "mother of vinegar" (*Bacterium aceti*).

Benzoic acid, the simplest of the aromatic acids, is a white crystalline solid. It is prepared commercially by several different methods. In one of them, phthalic acid (p. 142) is used as the raw material. In another process toluene is oxidized to benzoic acid and water. An interesting commercial preparation involves the chlorination of toluene.

The chlorine substitutes only in the side chain if the reaction is carried out under appropriate conditions (p. 47). The product, benzotrichloride, in which the side chain is completely chlorinated, can be hydrolyzed to benzoic acid. Benzoic acid, as its sodium salt, is extensively used as a preservative for foods and fruit juices.

Consideration of the boiling points of the acids reveals that they are less volatile than other substances of similar molecular weights. This leads to the supposition that the acids are associated. Indeed, measurement of the molecular weight of benzoic acid dissolved in a hydrocarbon solvent shows it to have the *dimeric* formula $(C_6H_5CO_2H)_2$. The formation of a dimer can be explained on the basis of a cyclic structure involving hydrogen bonds, as shown below.

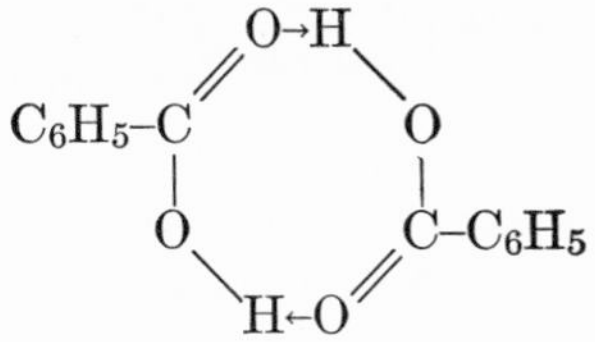

```
              O→H
            //    \
   C6H5–C          O
        |          |
        O          C–C6H5
         \        //
          H←O
```

Dimer of benzoic acid

Rings of this type, formed by a coordination process, are known as *chelate* rings (χηλή, a crab's claw) (p. 218). Other carboxylic acids likewise exist as chelate dimers.

Reactions of Carboxylic Acids

Salt Formation. A molecule containing the carboxyl group undergoes reactions to form several types of compounds. The most important of these are the salts, esters, acyl halides, acid anhydrides, and amides.

The carboxylic acids react with alkalies to form salts. Sodium acetate is obtained from acetic acid and sodium hydroxide.

$$CH_3C(=O)–OH + NaOH \longrightarrow \underset{\text{Sodium acetate}}{CH_3C(=O)–ONa} + H_2O$$

Since the carboxylic acids are stronger than carbonic acid, carbonates or bicarbonates may be used instead of hydroxides. Thus sodium acetate may also be prepared from acetic acid and sodium bicarbonate.

$$CH_3C(=O)–OH + NaHCO_3 \longrightarrow \underset{\text{Sodium acetate}}{CH_3C(=O)–ONa} + CO_2 + H_2O$$

Esterification. The reaction of alcohols with oxygen acids to give esters was mentioned earlier (p. 57). The most important esters are derived from the carboxylic acids. They are often made by the direct esterification of the acid by treatment with the alcohol in the presence of a trace of mineral acid, which acts as a catalyst. As the reaction of esterification is reversible, in order to obtain good yields it is desirable to use an excess of one of the reactants. The preparation of methyl benzoate from methyl alcohol and benzoic acid illustrates the reaction.

$$C_6H_5\text{-}C(=O)\text{-}OH + CH_3OH \overset{H^+}{\rightleftharpoons} C_6H_5\text{-}C(=O)\text{-}OCH_3 + H_2O$$

Methyl benzoate

The esterification reaction has been shown to take the following course.

$$RC(=\ddot{O}{:})\text{-}\ddot{O}\text{-}H + H^+ \rightleftharpoons \underset{(a)}{RC(=\ddot{O}^+\text{-}H)\text{-}\ddot{O}\text{-}H} \longleftrightarrow \underset{(b)}{R\overset{+}{C}(\text{-}\ddot{O}\text{-}H)\text{-}\ddot{O}\text{-}H} \overset{R'OH}{\rightleftharpoons}$$

$$\underset{(c)}{RC(\text{-}\ddot{O}\text{-}H)(\text{-}\ddot{O}\text{-}H)(\text{-}{}^+{:}O(H)\text{-}R')} \rightleftharpoons \underset{(d)}{RC(\text{-}\ddot{O}\text{-}H)(\text{-}\ddot{O}^+H_2)(\text{-}{:}\ddot{O}{:}\text{-}R')} \rightleftharpoons \underset{(e)}{R\overset{+}{C}(\text{-}\ddot{O}\text{-}H)(\text{-}O\text{-}R')} + {:}\ddot{O}(H)\text{-}H$$

$$\updownarrow$$

$$\underset{(f)}{RC(={:}\overset{+}{O}\text{-}H)\text{-}\ddot{O}\text{-}R'} \rightleftharpoons RC(={:}O{:})\text{-}\ddot{O}\text{-}R' + H^+$$

The coordination of a proton with the carbonyl oxygen atom forms a resonance-stabilized salt, the principal structures for which are the oxonium (*a*) and carbonium (*b*) structures. The carbonium structure contains a carbon atom lacking a pair of electrons. This deficiency may be satisfied by coordination with a pair of electrons from the oxygen atom of the alcohol, R′OH. By migration of a proton, the resulting oxonium salt (*c*) is transformed to *d*, which may lose a molecule of water. The resulting salt may be written in a carbonium (*e*) or an oxonium (*f*) structure. Removal of a proton from the salt gives the ester.

If a mercaptan is allowed to react with an acid a thio ester is obtained. The reaction is of particular interest because it proceeds by elimination of water rather than of hydrogen sulfide.

$$RC(=O){-}OH + R'SH \overset{H^+}{\rightleftharpoons} R{-}C(=O){-}SR' + H_2O$$

Formation of Acid Chlorides. The reagents most often employed for the preparation of acyl chlorides are phosphorus trichloride (PCl_3), phosphorus pentachloride (PCl_5), and thionyl chloride ($SOCl_2$). Equations showing the products obtained from each of these reagents are given below.

$$3CH_3C(=O){-}OH + PCl_3 \longrightarrow \underset{\text{Acetyl chloride}}{3CH_3C(=O){-}Cl} + H_3PO_3$$

$$NO_2{-}C_6H_4{-}C(=O){-}OH + PCl_5 \longrightarrow \underset{p\text{-Nitrobenzoyl chloride}}{NO_2{-}C_6H_4{-}C(=O){-}Cl} + POCl_3 + HCl$$

$$CH_3CH_2CH_2C(=O){-}OH + SOCl_2 \longrightarrow \underset{\text{Butyryl chloride}}{CH_3CH_2CH_2C(=O){-}Cl} + SO_2 + HCl$$

This type of reaction is reminiscent of the preparation of alkyl halides from alcohols (p. 55). However, as might be expected, the hydroxyl group of acids is more difficult to replace than that of alcohols. In particular, the hydrogen halides are ineffective in the conversion of acids to acid chlorides. For this change it is usual to employ the various chlorides and oxychlorides of phosphorus and sulfur. Whenever it can be used, thionyl chloride is a superior reagent for the preparation of acyl chlorides because the by-products are gases. If the chloride being prepared boils somewhat higher than thionyl chloride (b.p. 78.8°), it can often be obtained sufficiently pure simply by treating the acid with a slight excess of thionyl chloride and heating the reaction mixture on the steam bath to remove the excess reagent.

The chloride of formic acid is unknown. All attempts to prepare it have led to the formation of carbon monoxide and hydrogen chloride.

$$HC(=O){-}OH \longrightarrow \left[HC(=O){-}Cl\right] \longrightarrow HCl + CO$$

There is evidence that the decomposition of formyl chloride is reversible, since with certain reagents a mixture of hydrogen chloride and carbon monoxide gives products which may be considered derivatives of formic acid (p. 459). The instability of formyl chloride recalls the decomposition of formic acid in the presence of dehydrating agents (p. 96).

Salts

The alkali salts of organic acids resemble inorganic salts in many ways. They are soluble in water and insoluble in organic solvents such as ether and carbon tetrachloride. They are ionic substances, as is shown by the electrical conductivity of their solutions in water. Since they are salts of strong bases with relatively weak acids, their water solutions are slightly alkaline.

The organic acids can be recovered from their salts by treatment of the latter with mineral acids. The conversion of calcium benzoate to benzoic acid by treatment with hydrochloric acid, mentioned above, is an example.

Methane is obtained by heating sodium acetate with sodium hydroxide.

$$CH_3C(=O)\text{–}ONa + NaOH \xrightarrow{300°} CH_4 + Na_2CO_3$$

Since this reaction involves the removal of the carboxyl group from an acid derivative, it may be considered an indirect *decarboxylation* of the acid ($RCO_2H \longrightarrow RH$).

Acid anhydrides are sometimes prepared in the laboratory by the interaction of an acyl chloride and a salt. For example, acetic anhydride may be obtained from acetyl chloride and sodium acetate.

$$\underset{\text{Acetyl chloride}}{CH_3C(=O)\text{–}Cl} + \underset{\text{Sodium acetate}}{CH_3C(=O)\text{–}ONa} \longrightarrow \underset{\text{Acetic anhydride}}{CH_3C(=O)\text{–}O\text{–}C(=O)\text{–}CH_3} + NaCl$$

If the chloride and the salt employed are derived from different acids, a mixed anhydride is obtained.

Soaps and Detergents. The common soaps are sodium salts of fatty acids. They are usually made by boiling a fat with sodium hydroxide solution. When the saponification is complete the reaction mixture is saturated with salt, which assists in the separation of the soap by reducing its solubility (common-ion effect). The glycerol remains dissolved in the brine, from which it is separated by distillation. The following equation illustrates the saponification of a fat. The composi-

$$\begin{array}{l} CH_2OC(=O)\text{–}R \\ | \\ CHOC(=O)\text{–}R \\ | \\ CH_2OC(=O)\text{–}R \\ \text{Fat} \end{array} + 3NaOH \longrightarrow \begin{array}{l} CH_2OH \\ | \\ CHOH \\ | \\ CH_2OH \\ \text{Glycerol} \end{array} + \underset{\text{Soap}}{3RC(=O)\text{–}ONa}$$

tion of the soap depends upon the fat used in its preparation. An olive oil soap consists largely of sodium oleate; a coconut oil soap contains sodium laurate and various other salts (p. 114); and tallow soap is largely sodium palmitate and stearate. Various substances are added to the salts of the fatty acids for the preparation of soaps for different purposes. For example, naphtha soaps contain emulsified petroleum naphtha (p. 31), which is a solvent for fats, oils, and greases. Many laundry soaps contain salts of the rosin acids, which have detergent properties. The rosin acids are complex organic substances obtained from the sap of coniferous trees. Shaving soaps contain glycerol and gum to prevent rapid drying of the lather. Medicated soaps contain antiseptics, such as phenols (p. 165) and mercury salts. Most soaps contain about 15 per cent of water.

Insoluble Soaps. The fatty acid salts of the alkali metals are soluble in water, but the salts of other metals are almost completely insoluble. The difficulties attending the use of soaps in hard water are known to everyone. Hard water contains salts of iron, magnesium, and calcium. When a soap solution is prepared in such water the first soap added is precipitated as the insoluble iron, magnesium, and calcium salts. Not only is soap wasted in this process, since the insoluble salts have no detergent action, but also the precipitates formed are difficult to remove from the objects being washed. They are particularly objectionable in the textile industry, since their presence in a cloth may cause it to be dyed unevenly.

Some of the insoluble soaps are useful. Lead, copper, and mercury soaps are used in ointments and disinfectants. Zinc stearate and zinc palmitate are employed in face powders and in ointments. Aluminum soaps are incorporated into waxes and polishes. Several of the insoluble soaps are used in waterproofing textiles and leathers.

The Acyl Halides

The acyl bromides and iodides are of little importance but the chlorides are used extensively. The names, formulas, and boiling points of a few acyl chlorides are given in Table XVI.

TABLE XVI

ACYL CHLORIDES

Name	Formula	Boiling Point
Acetyl chloride	$CH_3C(=O)-Cl$	52°
Propionyl chloride	$CH_3CH_2C(=O)-Cl$	80
Butyryl chloride	$CH_3CH_2CH_2C(=O)-Cl$	102
Isobutyryl chloride	$CH_3CH(CH_3)C(=O)-Cl$	92
Valeryl chloride	$CH_3CH_2CH_2CH_2C(=O)-Cl$	128
Benzoyl chloride	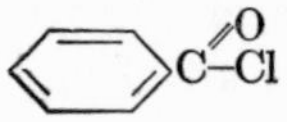 $C_6H_5C(=O)-Cl$	197
p-Bromobenzoyl chloride	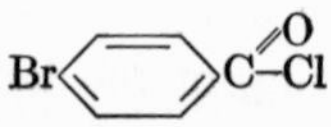 $Br-C_6H_4-C(=O)-Cl$	247 (m.p. 42°)

Reactions of Acyl Chlorides. The acyl chlorides react with many compounds containing the groups –OH and $-\overset{|}{N}-H$. Thus they react with water, alcohols, and ammonia, to give acids, esters, and amides, respectively. In each case hydrogen chloride is formed simultaneously; if ammonia is one of the reactants the hydrogen chloride is converted to ammonium chloride. The reactions are illustrated with acetyl chloride.

$$\underset{\text{Acetyl chloride}}{CH_3C(=O)-Cl} + HOH \longrightarrow \underset{\text{Acetic acid}}{CH_3C(=O)-OH} + HCl$$

$$CH_3C(=O)-Cl + CH_3CH_2OH \longrightarrow \underset{\text{Ethyl acetate}}{CH_3C(=O)-OCH_2CH_3} + HCl$$

$$CH_3C(=O)-Cl + 2NH_3 \longrightarrow \underset{\text{Acetamide}}{CH_3C(=O)-NH_2} + NH_4Cl$$

All these reactions take place very rapidly and with the evolution of heat. The acyl chlorides are thus convenient reagents for the introduction of acyl groups by reaction with compounds which have hydroxyl or amino groups.

The Friedel-Crafts Synthesis of Ketones. Acyl chlorides react with aromatic hydrocarbons in the presence of aluminum chloride to give ketones. For example, propiophenone is obtained from propionyl chloride, benzene, and aluminum chloride.

$$C_6H_6 + CH_3CH_2\overset{O}{\overset{\|}{C}}-Cl \xrightarrow{AlCl_3} C_6H_5\overset{O}{\overset{\|}{C}}-CH_2CH_3 + HCl$$

Propionyl chloride — Propiophenone

In the preparation of ketones by this method the aluminum chloride catalyst must be present in an amount equivalent to the quantity of acyl chloride used, because the ketone and the aluminum chloride form a coordination compound. It is believed to have the following structure.

$$\begin{matrix} R \\ & \rangle C{=}O{\rightarrow}AlCl_3 \\ R' \end{matrix}$$

Coordination compound from a ketone and aluminum chloride

When the reaction mixture is treated with water the coordination complex is destroyed and the ketone is obtained.

Reaction of Acyl Chlorides with Acids. When an acyl chloride is mixed with a carboxylic acid, an equilibrium of the following type is established.

$$R\overset{O}{\overset{\|}{C}}-Cl + R'\overset{O}{\overset{\|}{C}}-OH \rightleftharpoons R\overset{O}{\overset{\|}{C}}-OH + R'\overset{O}{\overset{\|}{C}}-Cl$$

The reaction is the basis of an excellent method for the preparation of certain acyl chlorides. For example, one of the most convenient laboratory preparations of acetyl chloride utilizes benzoyl chloride and acetic acid as the starting materials.

$$C_6H_5\overset{O}{\overset{\|}{C}}-Cl + CH_3\overset{O}{\overset{\|}{C}}-OH \rightleftharpoons C_6H_5\overset{O}{\overset{\|}{C}}-OH + CH_3\overset{O}{\overset{\|}{C}}-Cl$$

Benzoyl chloride (b.p. 197°)	Acetic acid (b.p. 118.1°)	Benzoic acid (b.p. 249°)	Acetyl chloride (b.p. 52°)

Since acetyl chloride is the lowest-boiling component of the equilibrium mixture it can be removed by heating the reaction mixture under a fractionating column. Removal of the product in this way forces the reaction to the right, with the result that the yield is very satisfactory.

The Acid Anhydrides

Acid anhydrides have the general formula $R\overset{O}{\overset{\|}{C}}-O-\overset{O}{\overset{\|}{C}}-R'$. In the most common anhydrides the groups R and R′ are identical. These are known as *simple* anhydrides, in contrast to the *mixed* anhydrides in which the groups are different. The simple anhydrides are named with reference to the corresponding acids, as may be seen by examination of Table XVII.

TABLE XVII

SIMPLE ACID ANHYDRIDES

Name	Formula	Boiling Point
Acetic anhydride	$CH_3C(=O)-O-C(=O)CH_3$	140°
Propionic anhydride	$CH_3CH_2C(=O)-O-C(=O)CH_2CH_3$	169.3
Butyric anhydride	$CH_3CH_2CH_2C(=O)-O-C(=O)CH_2CH_2CH_3$	198
Isobutyric anhydride	$CH_3CH(CH_3)C(=O)-O-C(=O)CH(CH_3)CH_3$	182.5
Valeric anhydride	$CH_3CH_2CH_2CH_2C(=O)-O-C(=O)CH_2CH_2CH_2CH_3$	215
Benzoic anhydride	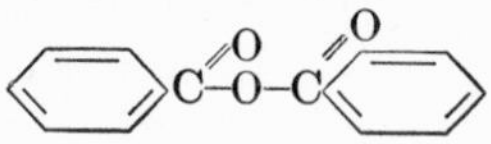 $C_6H_5C(=O)-O-C(=O)C_6H_5$	360 (m.p. 42°)

Anhydrides are also obtained by a process of interchange similar to that sometimes employed in the preparation of acyl chlorides (p. 103). One acid is treated with the anhydride of a second acid, yielding a mixture containing both acids, both simple anhydrides, and the mixed anhydride. The reaction is illustrated by the products obtained when acetic anhydride and benzoic acid are heated with a trace of phosphoric acid.

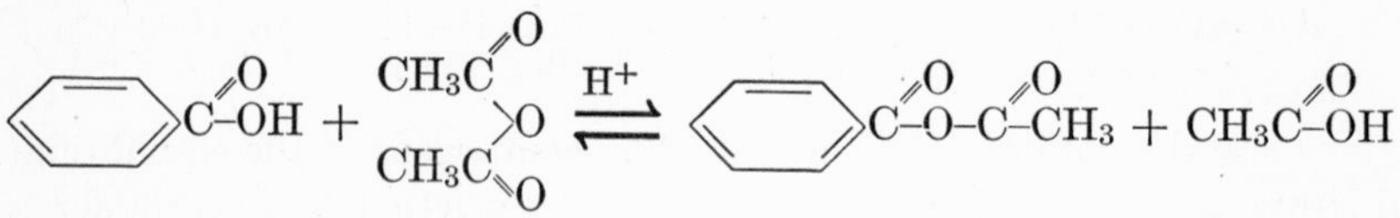

$$\underset{\text{Benzoic acid}}{C_6H_5C(=O)-OH} + \underset{\text{Acetic anhydride}}{(CH_3CO)_2O} \xrightleftharpoons{H^+} \underset{\text{Mixed anhydride}}{C_6H_5C(=O)-O-C(=O)-CH_3} + \underset{\text{Acetic acid}}{CH_3C(=O)-OH}$$

$$C_6H_5C(=O)-O-C(=O)-CH_3 + C_6H_5C(=O)-OH \xrightleftharpoons{H^+} \underset{\text{Benzoic anhydride}}{C_6H_5C(=O)-O-C(=O)C_6H_5} + CH_3C(=O)-OH$$

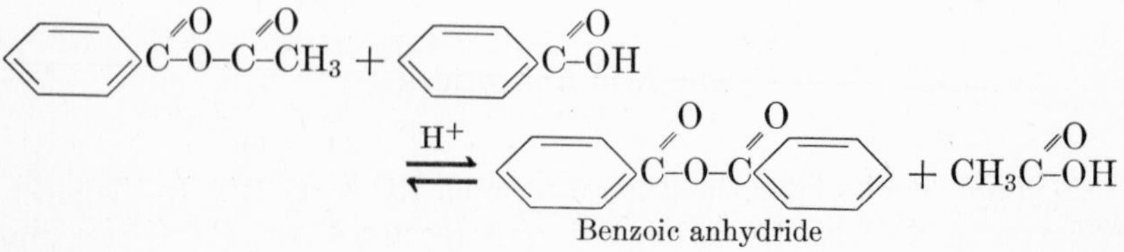

By heating the mixture under a fractionating column the acetic acid can be removed, thereby driving the reaction to the right.

The most important anhydride in industrial chemistry is acetic anhydride. It is obtained commercially from acetylene by an interesting sequence of reactions. Part of the acetylene is converted to acetic acid by hydration and oxidation (p. 26). Acetic acid and acetylene are then combined, in the presence of mercuric sulfate, to form ethylidene acetate. When the latter is heated it decomposes to acetic anhydride and acetaldehyde.

$$\underset{\text{Acetylene}}{HC{\equiv}CH} + \underset{\text{Acetic acid}}{2CH_3C(=O)\text{–}OH} \xrightarrow{HgSO_4} \underset{\text{Ethylidene acetate}}{CH_3CH(OC(=O)\text{–}CH_3)_2}$$

$$CH_3CH(OC(=O)\text{–}CH_3)_2 \xrightarrow{\text{heat}} \underset{\text{Acetaldehyde}}{CH_3C(=O)\text{–}H} + \underset{\text{Acetic anhydride}}{CH_3C(=O)\text{–}O\text{–}C(=O)\text{–}CH_3}$$

The acetaldehyde is converted to acetic acid, which is used in the first step of the process.

Acetic anhydride is manufactured on a large scale by adding acetic acid to ketene (p. 350).

Reactions of Acid Anhydrides. The acid anhydrides closely resemble the acyl chlorides in their chemical behavior. Thus, they react with water, alcohol, and ammonia to give acids, esters, and amides, respectively. The equations for the reactions of acetic anhydride with these substances are given below.

$$\underset{\text{Acetic anhydride}}{(CH_3C(=O))_2O} + H_2O \longrightarrow \underset{\text{Acetic acid}}{2CH_3C(=O)\text{–}OH}$$

$$(CH_3C(=O))_2O + CH_3CH_2OH \longrightarrow \underset{\text{Ethyl acetate}}{CH_3C(=O)\text{–}OCH_2CH_3} + \underset{\text{Acetic acid}}{CH_3C(=O)\text{–}OH}$$

$$(CH_3C(=O))_2O + 2NH_3 \longrightarrow \underset{\text{Acetamide}}{CH_3C(=O)\text{–}NH_2} + \underset{\text{Ammonium acetate}}{CH_3C(=O)\text{–}ONH_4}$$

It is to be noted that these reactions are exactly parallel to those of acetyl chloride with the same reagents. The acyl chlorides may, in fact, be considered mixed anhydrides derived from carboxylic acids and hydrochloric acid.

Acid anhydrides also react with aromatic hydrocarbons under the conditions of the Friedel-Crafts reaction. Thus, acetophenone is made from acetic anhydride, benzene, and aluminum chloride.

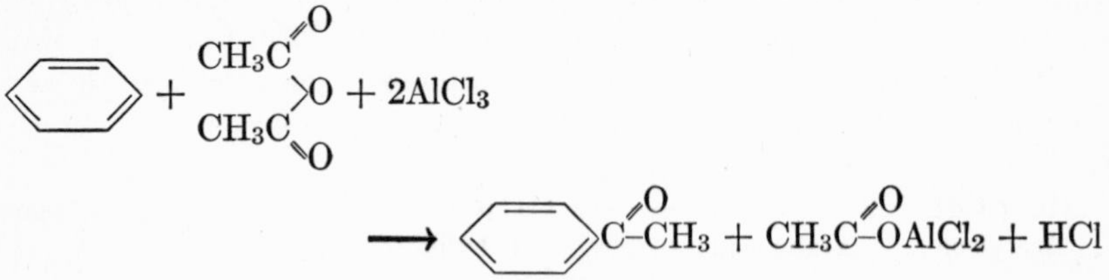

$$C_6H_6 + (CH_3CO)_2O + 2AlCl_3 \longrightarrow C_6H_5COCH_3 + CH_3COOAlCl_2 + HCl$$

Acetophenone

The reaction of an anhydride requires twice as much aluminum chloride as does that of an acyl chloride. One molecule forms a coordination compound with the ketone (p. 103), and another reacts with the organic acid to form a mixed salt.

It is of interest to note that formic anhydride, like formyl chloride, is unstable and has not been prepared. A mixed anhydride derived from acetic and formic acids can be obtained from acetic anhydride and formic acid.

$$(CH_3CO)_2O + HCOOH \longrightarrow CH_3CO\text{-}O\text{-}CHO + CH_3COOH$$

The mixed anhydride reacts with compounds containing active hydrogen atoms to introduce the formyl group. Thus it yields formamide when treated with ammonia.

$$HCO\text{-}O\text{-}COCH_3 + 2NH_3 \longrightarrow HCONH_2 + CH_3COONH_4$$

Formamide Ammonium acetate

The mixed anhydride is unstable at its boiling point at ordinary pressure, but for most purposes it is unnecessary to isolate it. One simply uses a mixture of acetic anhydride and formic acid.

Esters

An ester is named with reference to the alcohol and acid from which it is derived. A number of examples are given in Table XVIII, which also shows the boiling points of some of the common esters. A comparison of the boiling points of the lower esters with those of the acids and alcohols is interesting. For example, methyl formate (HCO_2CH_3, b.p. 31.5°) is more volatile than either the acid (HCO_2H, b.p. 100.7°) or the alcohol (CH_3OH, b.p. 65°) from which it is derived, although the ester has a higher molecular weight than either of its progenitors.

TABLE XVIII

SOME SIMPLE ESTERS

Name	Formula	Boiling Point
Methyl formate	$HC(=O)-OCH_3$	31.5°
Ethyl formate	$HC(=O)-OCH_2CH_3$	54.3
Methyl acetate	$CH_3C(=O)-OCH_3$	57.1
Ethyl acetate	$CH_3C(=O)-OCH_2CH_3$	77.1
Isopropyl acetate	$CH_3C(=O)-OCH(CH_3)CH_3$	89
n-Butyl acetate	$CH_3C(=O)-OCH_2CH_2CH_2CH_3$	126.5
n-Amyl acetate	$CH_3C(=O)-OCH_2CH_2CH_2CH_2CH_3$	148
Methyl propionate	$CH_3CH_2C(=O)-OCH_3$	79.9
n-Propyl propionate	$CH_3CH_2C(=O)-OCH_2CH_2CH_3$	123.3
Ethyl butyrate	$CH_3CH_2CH_2C(=O)-OCH_2CH_3$	121.3
Ethyl isobutyrate	$CH_3CH(CH_3)C(=O)-OCH_2CH_3$	111.7
Ethyl benzoate	$C_6H_5C(=O)-OCH_2CH_3$	212.6
Methyl *o*-toluate	o-$CH_3C_6H_4C(=O)-OCH_3$	213
Ethyl *p*-nitrobenzoate	$NO_2C_6H_4C(=O)-OCH_2CH_3$	(m.p. 57°)

The ester has no active hydrogen atom capable of forming a hydrogen bond, and thus, unlike the acid (p. 97) and alcohol (p. 50), it is a "normal" or unassociated liquid.

Hydrolysis and Saponification of Esters. As indicated by the reversibility of the esterification reaction, an ester may be hydrolyzed to regenerate the alcohol and acid. Usually it is more convenient to carry out the hydrolysis in the presence of alkali, so that the organic acid is neutralized as rapidly as it is formed. Since the acid so removed is one of the components of the equilibrium mixture (acid, alcohol, ester, and water), the reaction becomes irreversible and quantitative. Another advantage is that the reaction can be carried out in an alcohol solution containing only a little water. Many esters are nearly insoluble in water and hence are hydrolyzed by water and a trace of acid only very slowly. Addition of an alcohol as a solvent would, of course, repress hydrolysis or bring about the formation of a new ester, if the solvent alcohol were different from that involved in the ester. If alkali is added to the alcohol solution the acid is removed, as the sodium salt, as rapidly as it is formed and the ester is hydrolyzed quantitatively. The alkaline hydrolysis of esters is known as *saponification*. The term arose from the fact that soaps are made by the alkaline hydrolysis of certain esters (p. 100). The saponification of ethyl butyrate illustrates the reaction.

$$\underset{\text{Ethyl butyrate}}{CH_3CH_2CH_2C(=O){-}OCH_2CH_3} + NaOH \longrightarrow \underset{\text{Sodium butyrate}}{CH_3CH_2CH_2C(=O){-}ONa} + CH_3CH_2OH$$

Transesterification (Ester Interchange). Under appropriate conditions an ester of one alcohol reacts with a second alcohol to form a new ester. The alcohol concerned in the original ester is liberated. Because the process is reversible it is necessary to employ a large excess of the reacting alcohol to obtain good yields. The reaction of ethylene glycol diacetate with ethyl alcohol is an example.

$$\underset{\text{Ethylene glycol diacetate}}{\begin{array}{l} CH_3C(=O){-}OCH_2 \\ \qquad\qquad\quad | \\ CH_3C(=O){-}OCH_2 \end{array}} + \underset{\text{Ethyl alcohol}}{2CH_3CH_2OH} \overset{HCl}{\rightleftharpoons} \underset{\text{Ethylene glycol}}{\begin{array}{l} CH_2OH \\ | \\ CH_2OH \end{array}} + \underset{\text{Ethyl acetate}}{2CH_3C(=O){-}OCH_2CH_3}$$

As indicated in the equation, a trace of mineral acid may be used as a catalyst. Strangely enough, an alkaline catalyst also may be used; sodium methoxide ($NaOCH_3$) is often employed.

Ammonolysis of Esters. The reactions of esters described above may be considered examples of hydrolysis and alcoholysis, respectively. The reaction of an ester with ammonia follows a similar course and may be referred to as an ammonolysis. The products are an *amide* and an alcohol. Ethyl benzoate and ammonia yield benzamide and ethyl alcohol.

$$C_6H_5C(=O){-}OCH_2CH_3 + NH_3 \rightleftharpoons C_6H_5C(=O){-}NH_2 + CH_3CH_2OH$$

Ethyl benzoate — Benzamide — Ethyl alcohol

Hydrogenation of Esters. The carbonyl group of the ester linkage is capable of undergoing catalytic reduction under vigorous conditions. It is possible that the first step is addition of hydrogen to the carbon-oxygen double bond, yielding a hemiacetal; the latter dissociates to the alcohol and the aldehyde, and the aldehyde is further reduced to a primary alcohol. These steps may be represented as follows.

$$RC(=O){-}OR' + H_2 \xrightarrow{\text{catalyst}} R{-}CH(OH){-}OR'$$

$$R{-}CH(OH){-}OR' \longrightarrow R'OH + RC(=O){-}H$$

$$RC(=O){-}H + H_2 \xrightarrow{\text{catalyst}} RCH_2OH$$

The sum of these reactions may be represented as follows.

$$RC(=O){-}OR' + 2H_2 \xrightarrow{\text{catalyst}} RCH_2OH + R'OH$$

The hydrogenation of glyceryl caproate is an example of this reaction. The catalyst ordinarily used is copper chromite. The reaction is carried out at temperatures above 200° and at pressures in the neighborhood of 3000 lb. per square inch.

$$\begin{array}{l} CH_2OC(=O){-}CH_2CH_2CH_2CH_2CH_3 \\ |\\ CHOC(=O){-}CH_2CH_2CH_2CH_2CH_3 \\ | \\ CH_2OC(=O){-}CH_2CH_2CH_2CH_2CH_3 \end{array} + 6H_2 \xrightarrow{\text{catalyst}} \begin{array}{l} CH_2OH \\ | \\ CHOH \\ | \\ CH_2OH \end{array}$$

Glyceryl caproate — Glycerol

$$+\ 3CH_3CH_2CH_2CH_2CH_2CH_2OH$$

n-Hexyl alcohol

The reduction also can be effected by means of metallic sodium and alcohol. For example, lauryl alcohol may be prepared by this method.

$$\underset{\text{Ethyl laurate}}{CH_3(CH_2)_{10}\overset{O}{\overset{\|}{C}}-OCH_2CH_3} + \underset{(Na + C_2H_5OH)}{4(H)} \longrightarrow \underset{\text{Lauryl alcohol}}{CH_3(CH_2)_{10}CH_2OH} + CH_3CH_2OH$$

Reaction of Esters with the Grignard Reagent. Synthesis of Tertiary Alcohols. The addition products formed from esters and Grignard reagents are unstable. They combine with more of the Grignard reagent, either directly or after decomposing to ketones, to produce derivatives of tertiary alcohols. The various steps in the synthesis of tertiary alcohols by this method may be represented as follows.

$$R\overset{O}{\overset{\|}{C}}-OR' + R''MgX \longrightarrow \left[R\underset{R''}{\underset{|}{\overset{OMgX}{\overset{|}{C}}}}-OR' \right] \longrightarrow R\overset{O}{\overset{\|}{C}}-R'' + R'OMgX$$

$$R-\overset{O}{\overset{\|}{C}}-R'' + R''MgX \longrightarrow R-\underset{R''}{\underset{|}{\overset{OMgX}{\overset{|}{C}}}}-R''$$

$$R-\underset{R''}{\underset{|}{\overset{OMgX}{\overset{|}{C}}}}-R'' + H_2O \longrightarrow R-\underset{R''}{\underset{|}{\overset{OH}{\overset{|}{C}}}}-R'' + Mg(OH)X$$

Tertiary alcohols in which the three groups attached to the carbinol carbon atom are alike can be prepared by proper selection of the reagents. For example, triphenylcarbinol is obtained from ethyl benzoate and phenylmagnesium bromide.

$$\underset{\text{Ethyl benzoate}}{C_6H_5\overset{O}{\overset{\|}{C}}-OC_2H_5} + 2\underset{\text{Phenylmagnesium bromide}}{C_6H_5MgBr} \longrightarrow (C_6H_5)_3COMgBr + Mg(OC_2H_5)Br$$

$$(C_6H_5)_3COMgBr + H_2O \longrightarrow \underset{\text{Triphenylcarbinol}}{(C_6H_5)_3COH} + Mg(OH)Br$$

Fats

Most of the volatile esters have pleasant odors, and many of them occur in fruits and flowers. Synthetic perfumes and flavors are often mixtures of esters. Butyl acetate and isoamyl acetate have the odor of bananas. Amyl acetate is reminiscent of pears. Amyl undecanoate [$CH_3(CH_2)_9\overset{\nearrow O}{C}{-}OCH_2(CH_2)_3CH_3$] has a roselike odor.

The most important of the natural esters are those which make up the animal and vegetable fats. These will now be considered.

The animal and vegetable fats and oils are glyceryl esters of organic acids. Hydrolysis converts them to glycerol and mixtures of saturated and unsaturated acids. It is a striking fact that the acids obtained are, with very few exceptions, *straight-chain acids containing even numbers of carbon atoms.* The saturated members most frequently encountered are lauric acid [$CH_3(CH_2)_{10}\overset{\nearrow O}{C}{-}OH$], myristic acid [$CH_3(CH_2)_{12}\overset{\nearrow O}{C}{-}OH$], palmitic acid [$CH_3(CH_2)_{14}\overset{\nearrow O}{C}{-}OH$], and stearic acid [$CH_3(CH_2)_{16}\overset{\nearrow O}{C}{-}OH$]. The most common unsaturated acids have the carbon skeleton of stearic acid. Oleic acid ($C_{17}H_{33}CO_2H$) has eighteen carbon atoms with one double bond at the central point of the chain; linoleic acid ($C_{17}H_{31}\overset{\nearrow O}{C}{-}OH$) has eighteen carbons with two double bonds; and linolenic acid ($C_{17}H_{29}\overset{\nearrow O}{C}{-}OH$) has eighteen carbons with three double bonds. The ethylenic linkages in linoleic and linolenic acids are not conjugated.

$$CH_3CH_2CH_2CH_2CH_2CH_2CH_2CH_2CH{=}CHCH_2CH_2CH_2CH_2CH_2CH_2CH_2\overset{\nearrow O}{C}{-}OH$$
Oleic acid

$$CH_3CH_2CH_2CH_2CH_2CH{=}CHCH_2CH{=}CHCH_2CH_2CH_2CH_2CH_2CH_2CH_2\overset{\nearrow O}{C}{-}OH$$
Linoleic acid

$$CH_3CH_2CH{=}CHCH_2CH{=}CHCH_2CH{=}CHCH_2CH_2CH_2CH_2CH_2CH_2CH_2\overset{\nearrow O}{C}{-}OH$$
Linolenic acid

Examination of the acids produced by the hydrolysis of a typical solid fat, such as beef tallow, reveals that the substance is composed largely of the glyceryl esters of the saturated acids, palmitic and stearic acids. The glyceryl esters are known as tripalmitin and tristearin, respectively; both melt well above room temperature.

$$
\begin{array}{l}
CH_2OC(=O){-}(CH_2)_{14}CH_3 \\
| \\
CHOC(=O){-}(CH_2)_{14}CH_3 \\
| \\
CH_2OC(=O){-}(CH_2)_{14}CH_3
\end{array}
$$

Glyceryl tripalmitate
(tripalmitin)
(m.p. 65°)

$$
\begin{array}{l}
CH_2OC(=O){-}(CH_2)_{16}CH_3 \\
| \\
CHOC(=O){-}(CH_2)_{16}CH_3 \\
| \\
CH_2OC(=O){-}(CH_2)_{16}CH_3
\end{array}
$$

Glyceryl tristearate
(tristearin)
(m.p. 71°)

The acid obtained in largest quantity from olive oil is oleic acid. The chief constituent of this oil must therefore be glyceryl trioleate or triolein; this substance is a liquid at ordinary temperatures.

$$
\begin{array}{l}
CH_2OC(=O){-}(CH_2)_7CH{=}CH(CH_2)_7CH_3 \\
| \\
CHOC(=O){-}(CH_2)_7CH{=}CH(CH_2)_7CH_3 \\
| \\
CH_2OC(=O){-}(CH_2)_7CH{=}CH(CH_2)_7CH_3
\end{array}
$$

Glyceryl trioleate
(triolein)
(m.p. −6°)

This comparison illustrates the essential difference in the composition of solid and liquid fats. The solid fats contain a higher proportion of saturated glyceryl esters than do the liquid fats (oils).

Drying oils such as linseed oil and tung oil are those that change to tough solids on exposure to the air. All of them contain a large proportion of esters of the highly unsaturated acids. For example, linseed oil contains considerable quantities of trilinolein and trilinolenin.

$$
\begin{array}{l}
CH_2OC(=O){-}(CH_2)_7CH{=}CHCH_2CH{=}CH(CH_2)_4CH_3 \\
| \\
CHOC(=O){-}(CH_2)_7CH{=}CHCH_2CH{=}CH(CH_2)_4CH_3 \\
| \\
CH_2OC(=O){-}(CH_2)_7CH{=}CHCH_2CH{=}CH(CH_2)_4CH_3
\end{array}
$$

Trilinolein

$$
\begin{array}{l}
CH_2OC(=O){-}(CH_2)_7CH{=}CHCH_2CH{=}CHCH_2CH{=}CHCH_2CH_3 \\
| \\
CHOC(=O){-}(CH_2)_7CH{=}CHCH_2CH{=}CHCH_2CH{=}CHCH_2CH_3 \\
| \\
CH_2OC(=O){-}(CH_2)_7CH{=}CHCH_2CH{=}CHCH_2CH{=}CHCH_2CH_3
\end{array}
$$

Trilinolenin

Tung oil consists largely of trieleostearin. Eleostearic acid is an isomer of linolenic acid; in it the three double bonds are conjugated.

$$\begin{array}{l} CH_2OC(=O)-(CH_2)_7CH{=}CHCH{=}CHCH{=}CH(CH_2)_3CH_3 \\ | \\ CHOC(=O)-(CH_2)_7CH{=}CHCH{=}CHCH{=}CH(CH_2)_3CH_3 \\ | \\ CH_2OC(=O)-(CH_2)_7CH{=}CHCH{=}CHCH{=}CH(CH_2)_3CH_3 \end{array}$$

Trieleostearin

It has been mentioned that the most common fatty acids contain sixteen or eighteen carbon atoms. Esters of lower acids do occur, however. The mixture of acids obtained by hydrolysis of nutmeg oil contains a substantial proportion of myristic acid. Butter contains glyceryl esters of all the even-carbon saturated acids from butyric to stearic acid. In Table XIX is given the composition of the mixture of acids obtained by hydrolysis of a sample of butter. The consistency of butter is due partly to the presence of the unsaturated component and partly to the presence of esters of the lower acids.

Coconut oil is essentially saturated. Its consistency is approximately that of butter, but it is called an oil because it is a liquid in the warm regions where it is produced. The low melting point of this substance

TABLE XIX

Composition of Mixture of Acids from Hydrolysis of Butter

Fatty Acid	Formula	Per Cent in Mixture
Butyric	$CH_3(CH_2)_2C(=O)-OH$	3.2
Caproic	$CH_3(CH_2)_4C(=O)-OH$	1.4
Caprylic	$CH_3(CH_2)_6C(=O)-OH$	1.8
Capric	$CH_3(CH_2)_8C(=O)-OH$	1.8
Lauric	$CH_3(CH_2)_{10}C(=O)-OH$	6.9
Myristic	$CH_3(CH_2)_{12}C(=O)-OH$	22.6
Palmitic	$CH_3(CH_2)_{14}C(=O)-OH$	22.6
Stearic	$CH_3(CH_2)_{16}C(=O)-OH$	11.4
Oleic	$C_{17}H_{33}C(=O)-OH$	27.4
		99.1

is to be ascribed largely to the presence of esters of lower acids. The composition of the acid mixture from coconut oil is given in Table XX. It is of interest to note that lauric acid is the chief component.

TABLE XX

Composition of Mixture of Acids from Hydrolysis of Coconut Oil

Fatty Acid	Formula	Per Cent in Mixture
Caproic	$CH_3(CH_2)_4CO_2H$	0.2
Caprylic	$CH_3(CH_2)_6CO_2H$	8.0
Capric	$CH_3(CH_2)_8CO_2H$	7.0
Lauric	$CH_3(CH_2)_{10}CO_2H$	48.0
Myristic	$CH_3(CH_2)_{12}CO_2H$	17.5
Palmitic	$CH_3(CH_2)_{14}CO_2H$	8.8
Stearic	$CH_3(CH_2)_{16}CO_2H$	2.0
Oleic	$C_{17}H_{33}CO_2H$	6.0
Linoleic	$C_{17}H_{31}CO_2H$	2.5
		100.0

Castor oil is unique in that it consists of the glyceryl ester of a hydroxy acid. It is largely glyceryl triricinoleate. Ricinoleic acid may be considered a hydroxyoleic acid.

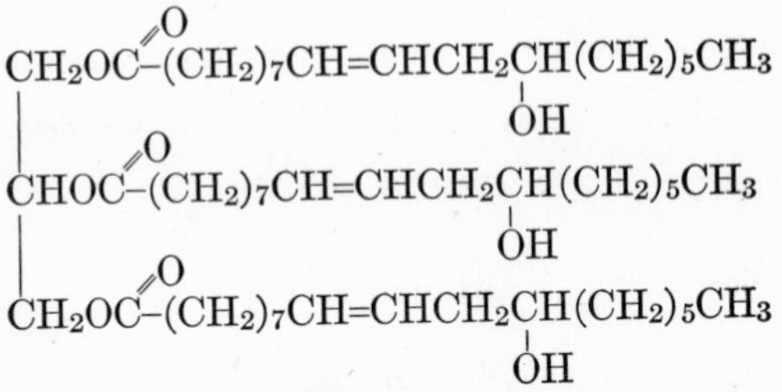

$$
\begin{array}{l}
CH_2OC(=O)-(CH_2)_7CH{=}CHCH_2CH(OH)(CH_2)_5CH_3 \\
|\\
CHOC(=O)-(CH_2)_7CH{=}CHCH_2CH(OH)(CH_2)_5CH_3 \\
|\\
CH_2OC(=O)-(CH_2)_7CH{=}CHCH_2CH(OH)(CH_2)_5CH_3
\end{array}
$$

Triricinolein

Compounds such as triolein and tristearin are considered *simple* glyceryl esters; that is, the three acid radicals in such an ester are identical. The naturally occurring fats and oils also contain *mixed* glyceryl esters, in which two or three different acid radicals are present in the molecules. An ester of one molecule of glycerol, two molecules of stearic acid, and one molecule of palmitic acid, called palmitodistearin, occurs in beef tallow. Two formulas for such an ester are possible, as shown below.

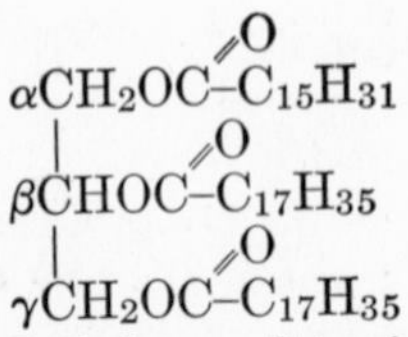

$$
\begin{array}{l}
\alpha CH_2OC(=O)-C_{15}H_{31} \\
\beta CHOC(=O)-C_{17}H_{35} \\
\gamma CH_2OC(=O)-C_{17}H_{35}
\end{array}
\qquad
\begin{array}{l}
\alpha CH_2OC(=O)-C_{17}H_{35} \\
\beta CHOC(=O)-C_{15}H_{31} \\
\gamma CH_2OC(=O)-C_{17}H_{35}
\end{array}
$$

α-Palmito-β,γ-distearin　　β-Palmito-α,γ-distearin

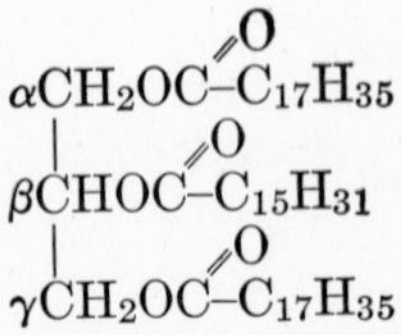

Mixed glyceryl esters derived from three different fatty acids may exist in three isomeric forms. The general formulas for such isomers are given below.

$$\begin{array}{lll} CH_2OC(=O)\text{–}R & CH_2OC(=O)\text{–}R' & CH_2OC(=O)\text{–}R \\ | & | & | \\ CHOC(=O)\text{–}R' & CHOC(=O)\text{–}R & CHOC(=O)\text{–}R'' \\ | & | & | \\ CH_2OC(=O)\text{–}R'' & CH_2OC(=O)\text{–}R'' & CH_2OC(=O)\text{–}R' \end{array}$$

Isomeric mixed glyceryl esters

Because of the existence of isomeric mixed esters the natural fats contain many more components than is indicated by the analysis of the mixture of acids obtained by hydrolysis.

The Hardening of Vegetable Oils. Vegetable oils such as cottonseed oil and soybean oil find extensive use in the preparation of cooking fats. As indicated above, these oils are characterized by the presence of esters of unsaturated acids. In order to change them to solids it is necessary only to hydrogenate them. This is accomplished by treating the oils with hydrogen in the presence of nickel. The reaction may be considered as involving the change of triolein to tristearin.

$$\begin{array}{l} CH_2OC(=O)\text{–}(CH_2)_7CH{=}CH(CH_2)_7CH_3 \\ | \\ CHOC(=O)\text{–}(CH_2)_7CH{=}CH(CH_2)_7CH_3 \\ | \\ CH_2OC(=O)\text{–}(CH_2)_7CH{=}CH(CH_2)_7CH_3 \end{array} + 3H_2 \xrightarrow[200^\circ]{Ni} \begin{array}{l} CH_2OC(=O)\text{–}(CH_2)_{16}CH_3 \\ | \\ CHOC(=O)\text{–}(CH_2)_{16}CH_3 \\ | \\ CH_2OC(=O)\text{–}(CH_2)_{16}CH_3 \end{array}$$

Triolein (m.p. −6°) Tristearin (m.p. 71°)

If the oil is allowed to react with enough hydrogen to effect complete saturation, the product is a hard, waxy solid. By interrupting the reaction before saturation is complete, a fat of the proper consistency for use as a substitute either for butter or for lard may be obtained. If it is to be used as a butter substitute it is churned with skimmed milk and otherwise flavored to increase its resemblance to butter. Pure vitamins or vitamin extracts may also be added. If the product is to be marketed in the summer it is made a little "harder" than that intended for winter use. The principal difference between natural butter and such substitutes is that the substitutes do not contain esters of the lower fatty acids. There is no difference in calorific value.

The Alkyl Sulfate Detergents. Several detergents which are free from the disadvantages of soap used with hard water are available. Most of them are salts of organic derivatives of sulfuric acid. Some are sodium alkyl sulfates of the general formula $ROSO_3Na$. The long-chain alcohols needed for their preparation are obtained by the hydrogenation (p. 109) of coconut oil.

$$\begin{array}{l} CH_2OC(=O)-R \\ | \\ CHOC(=O)-R \\ | \\ CH_2OC(=O)-R \end{array} + 6H_2 \xrightarrow{\text{catalyst}} \begin{array}{l} CH_2OH \\ | \\ CHOH \\ | \\ CH_2OH \end{array} + 3RCH_2OH$$

Coconut oil — Glycerol — Primary alcohols

The product is a mixture of glycerol and the primary alcohols corresponding to coconut oil acids (p. 114). These are separated by distillation, and the lauryl alcohol is used in the preparation of the detergent. *n*-Hexyl, *n*-octyl, and *n*-decyl alcohols are by-products. The lauryl alcohol is treated with sulfuric acid, and the resulting acid ester is neutralized.

$$\underset{\text{Lauryl alcohol}}{CH_3(CH_2)_{10}CH_2OH} + HOSO_2OH \longrightarrow \underset{\text{Laurylsulfuric acid}}{CH_3(CH_2)_{10}CH_2OSO_2OH} + H_2O$$

$$CH_3(CH_2)_{10}CH_2OSO_2OH + NaOH \longrightarrow \underset{\text{Sodium laurylsulfate}}{CH_3(CH_2)_{10}CH_2OSO_2ONa} + H_2O$$

Another product is prepared in a similar way from monoesters derived from glycerol and the fatty acids. These are obtained by ester interchange (p. 108) from coconut oil and glycerol.

$$\begin{array}{l} CH_2OC(=O)-R \\ | \\ CHOC(=O)-R \\ | \\ CH_2OC(=O)-R \end{array} + 2\begin{array}{l} CH_2OH \\ | \\ CHOH \\ | \\ CH_2OH \end{array} \longrightarrow 3RC(=O)-O-CH_2\underset{OH}{\underset{|}{C}H}CH_2OH$$

Coconut oil — Glycerol mono-esters

$$RC(=O)-OCH_2\underset{OH}{\underset{|}{C}H}CH_2OH + HOSO_2OH \longrightarrow RC(=O)-OCH_2\underset{OH}{\underset{|}{C}H}CH_2OSO_2OH + H_2O$$

$$RC(=O)-OCH_2\underset{OH}{\underset{|}{C}H}CH_2OSO_2OH + NaOH \longrightarrow RC(=O)-OCH_2\underset{OH}{\underset{|}{C}H}CH_2OSO_2ONa + H_2O$$

The iron, calcium, and magnesium salts derived from either of these detergents are soluble in water; hence either can be used in untreated hard water. For certain purposes they have a further advantage in that they can be used in weakly acidic solutions.

Both the synthetic detergents mentioned above are, like the soaps, manufactured from fats and oils. Many other detergents are made from the products of coal tar or petroleum refining. One of the principal types of ionic detergents can be represented by the formula R–Ar–SO_3Na. These substances are the sodium salts of *sulfonic* acids. Like the sodium salts of the alkyl*sulfuric* acids mentioned above, they are comprised of a large hydrophobic residue (the hydrocarbon portion of the molecule) attached to a strongly hydrophilic function (the sulfonate or sulfate salt function). They are manufactured in large quantity. A number of different processes are employed; the steps include an alkylation of an aromatic hydrocarbon, usually benzene or naphthalene, with an olefin having eight carbon atoms or more, or with an alkyl chloride or a mixture of chlorinated hydrocarbons of about the same number of carbon atoms, followed by sulfonation and neutralization of the sulfonic acids formed. Such products are, of course, complex mixtures of isomeric and homologous compounds. Sodium salts of alkanesulfonic acids (RSO_3Na) of the proper molecular weight also are excellent detergents, and several products of this type are marketed.

In the soaps and the synthetic detergents mentioned above, the hydrophilic portion of the molecule is an anionic residue ($-CO_2^-$, $-OSO_3^-$, or $-SO_3^-$). It is also possible to produce *cationic* detergents in which the organic residue is attached to a positively charged nitrogen atom; salts of high-molecular-weight amines such as laurylamine (p. 120) have detergent properties.

Finally, the hydrophilic portion of a detergent molecule can be a neutral function, in which case the substance is classified as a non-ionic detergent. Among commercial materials of this type are the products obtained by the condensation of fatty acids with ethylene oxide.

$$RCO_2H + \underbrace{CH_2{-}CH_2}_{\diagdown O \diagup} \longrightarrow R\overset{\displaystyle /\!\!/ O}{C}{-}OCH_2CH_2OH + (x+1)\underbrace{CH_2{-}CH_2}_{\diagdown O \diagup}$$

$$\longrightarrow R\overset{\displaystyle /\!\!/ O}{C}{-}OCH_2CH_2(OCH_2CH_2)_xOCH_2CH_2OH$$

Among the advantages of detergents of this type is the lower sudsing tendency.

Drying Oils. Linseed oil, tung oil (China wood oil), and certain fish oils contain glyceryl esters of highly unsaturated fatty acids (p. 111).

On exposure to air they change to tough, hard solids. The "dried" products are polymeric, so the drying must involve oxidation by the air and polymerization of the oxidation products. The process is catalyzed by metal oxides. Thus linseed oil as it is obtained from flaxseed changes only very slowly when spread out in the air, but if it is first heated with lead oxide it hardens within a few hours. These are the "raw" and "boiled" linseed oils of commerce.

Soybean oil dries in the air, but the film is softer than that from linseed oil. When mixed in suitable proportions with linseed oil it can be used in paints. An interesting substitute for tung oil is derived from castor oil. The latter is dehydrated to yield the glyceryl ester of 9,11-octadecadienoic acid.

$$\begin{array}{l} CH_2OC(=O)-(CH_2)_7CH=CHCH_2CH(OH)(CH_2)_5CH_3 \\ | \\ CHOC(=O)-(CH_2)_7CH=CHCH_2CH(OH)(CH_2)_5CH_3 \\ | \\ CH_2OC(=O)-(CH_2)_7CH=CHCH_2CH(OH)(CH_2)_5CH_3 \end{array}$$

Triricinolein

$$\xrightarrow{\text{dehydration}} \begin{array}{l} CH_2OC(=O)-(CH_2)_7CH=CHCH=CH(CH_2)_5CH_3 \\ | \\ CHOC(=O)-(CH_2)_7CH=CHCH=CH(CH_2)_5CH_3 \\ | \\ CH_2OC(=O)-(CH_2)_7CH=CHCH=CH(CH_2)_5CH_3 \end{array} + 3H_2O$$

Oil paints are made by suspending finely ground pigments in a drying oil. Varnishes contain resins which increase the gloss. Both paints and varnishes contain "driers," metal salts which catalyze the reactions involved in the drying.

Oilcloth is made by impregnating cloth with boiled linseed oil and allowing it to dry. Linoleum is made from a mixture of ground cork and boiled linseed oil which has been dried to a transparent jelly.

Waxes contain esters derived from long-chain alcohols and long-chain acids. Beeswax is largely myricyl palmitate; carnauba wax contains myricyl cerotate; and spermaceti (from the head of the sperm whale) is mostly cetyl palmitate.

$$C_{15}H_{31}C(=O)-OC_{31}H_{63} \qquad C_{25}H_{51}C(=O)-OC_{31}H_{63} \qquad C_{15}H_{31}C(=O)-OC_{16}H_{33}$$

Myricyl palmitate — Myricyl cerotate — Cetyl palmitate

Some waxes also contain high-molecular-weight hydrocarbons, alcohols, and ketones. The waxes are not digestible. They find uses in the preparation of polishes, candles, and pharmaceuticals.

The Amides

The amides ($RC(=O)-NH_2$) may be regarded as acyl derivatives of ammonia. From the consideration that the acyl derivatives ($RC(=O)-OH$) of the neutral substance, water, are acids it would be predicted that the amides are more acid (less basic) than ammonia. It happens that the acidifying influence of the acyl groups just neutralizes the basic properties of ammonia, for the amides are neutral substances.

Of the simple amides, all but formamide are solids. The names, formulas, melting points, and boiling points of some of them are given in Table XXI.

TABLE XXI

AMIDES

Name	Formula	Melting Point	Boiling Point
Formamide	$HC(=O)-NH_2$	2.5°	195°
Acetamide	$CH_3C(=O)-NH_2$	81	222
Propionamide	$CH_3CH_2C(=O)-NH_2$	79	213
Butyramide	$CH_3CH_2CH_2C(=O)-NH_2$	116	216
Valeramide	$CH_3CH_2CH_2CH_2C(=O)-NH_2$	106	...
Benzamide	$C_6H_5C(=O)-NH_2$	130	...
α-Naphthamide	$C_{10}H_7C(=O)-NH_2$	202	...

The formation of amides from esters (p. 109), acyl chlorides (p. 102), and anhydrides (p. 105) has been mentioned. All these reactions are used in the laboratory as preparative methods. Amides are also obtained by dehydration of ammonium salts and by hydration of nitriles. The relationship between ammonium salts, amides, and nitriles is shown by the following equation.

$$\underset{\text{Ammonium salt}}{RC(=O)-ONH_4} \underset{\text{hydration}}{\overset{\text{dehydration}}{\rightleftharpoons}} \underset{\text{Amide}}{RC(=O)-NH_2} \underset{\text{hydration}}{\overset{\text{dehydration}}{\rightleftharpoons}} \underset{\text{Nitrile}}{R-C \equiv N}$$

The dehydration of ammonium salts to amides is often effected by heating. For example, acetamide is made conveniently by heating ammonium acetate.

$$\underset{\text{Ammonium acetate}}{CH_3C(=O)-ONH_4} \rightleftharpoons \underset{\text{Acetamide}}{CH_3C(=O)-NH_2} + H_2O$$

The reduction of amides provides a method for transforming an acid to a primary amine of the same number of carbon atoms. The conversion of lauric acid to laurylamine is an example.

$$\underset{\text{Lauric acid}}{CH_3(CH_2)_{10}C(=O)-OH} \xrightarrow[\text{heat}]{NH_3} \underset{\text{Lauramide}}{CH_3(CH_2)_{10}C(=O)-NH_2}$$

$$\xrightarrow{4[H]} \underset{\text{Laurylamine}}{CH_3(CH_2)_{10}CH_2NH_2} + H_2O$$

The same result could be achieved by dehydrating the amide to the nitrile and reducing the latter.

Nitriles

Nitriles, although they do not possess a carbonyl group, are closely related to the acids. They can be made from the acids by way of the amides (p. 119), and they yield acids when hydrolyzed. Nitriles are generally prepared from alkyl (p. 69) or aryl halides (p. 121); they are important intermediates in the synthesis of acids of one more carbon atom than the parent halide. Thus phenylacetic acid is obtained from benzyl chloride.

$$\underset{\text{Benzyl chloride}}{C_6H_5CH_2Cl} + NaCN \longrightarrow \underset{\text{Benzyl cyanide}}{C_6H_5CH_2CN} + NaCl$$

$$C_6H_5CH_2CN + 2H_2O + H_2SO_4$$

$$\longrightarrow \underset{\text{Phenylacetic acid}}{C_6H_5CH_2C(=O)-OH} + (NH_4)HSO_4$$

Aryl halides are inert to aqueous solutions of alkali cyanides. However, they do react with anhydrous cuprous cyanide in the presence of an organic base such as pyridine (C_5H_5N, p. 496). α-Naphthoic acid may be prepared from α-bromonaphthalene by this method.

$$\text{C}_{10}\text{H}_7\text{Br} + \text{CuCN} \xrightarrow[200^\circ]{C_5H_5N} \text{C}_{10}\text{H}_7\text{C}\equiv\text{N} \xrightarrow{H_2O} \text{C}_{10}\text{H}_7\text{CO}_2\text{H}$$

α-Naphthonitrile α-Naphthoic acid

Nitriles can be reduced to primary amines, either by hydrogen and a catalyst or by sodium and alcohol. The reduction of nitriles enables one to prepare primary amines from alkyl halides and at the same time add one carbon atom to the chain. An example is the preparation of β-phenylethylamine from benzyl chloride by way of benzyl cyanide.

$$C_6H_5CH_2Cl \xrightarrow{NaCN} C_6H_5CH_2C\equiv N \xrightarrow{4[H]} C_6H_5CH_2CH_2NH_2$$

PROBLEMS

1. Give equations for the conversion of isobutyl alcohol to: (*a*) isobutyric acid, (*b*) isovaleric acid, (*c*) isobutyl isovalerate, (*d*) isovaleryl chloride, (*e*) isovaleric anhydride, (*f*) isovaleramide, (*g*) isovalerophenone.

2. Give equations to illustrate the following terms: (*a*) esterification, (*b*) ammonolysis, (*c*) saponification, (*d*) transesterification, (*e*) Friedel-Crafts synthesis of hydrocarbons, (*f*) Friedel-Crafts synthesis of ketones.

3. Compare the formulas of stearic, oleic, linoleic, linolenic, ricinoleic, and eleostearic acids. Write equations for the conversion of each of the last five acids to stearic acid.

4. Compare the structural formulas of the sulfate detergents with that of a soap. What structural features appear to be necessary in a compound which is to be used as a detergent?

5. Assume that *n*-butyric acid, but not the chloride or anhydride, is available in the laboratory and *n*-butyrophenone is desired. Would you convert the acid to the chloride or to the anhydride in order to prepare the ketone? Explain.

SUGGESTED READING

C. P. Reidig and A. B. Hersberger, "Organic Synthetic Detergents," *Chem. Eng. News*, *30*, 3610 (1952).

CHAPTER 10

Amines

The amines may be regarded as derivatives of ammonia in which one, two, or three of the hydrogen atoms have been replaced by alkyl or aryl radicals. The amines are classified according to the number of

TABLE XXII

AMINES

Name	Class	Formula	Boiling Point
Methylamine	Primary	CH_3NH_2	−6.5°
Dimethylamine	Secondary	$(CH_3)_2NH$	7.4
Trimethylamine	Tertiary	$(CH_3)_3N$	3.5
Ethylamine	Primary	$CH_3CH_2NH_2$	16.6
Diethylamine	Secondary	$(CH_3CH_2)_2NH$	55.5
Triethylamine	Tertiary	$(CH_3CH_2)_3N$	89.5
n-Butylamine	Primary	$CH_3CH_2CH_2CH_2NH_2$	77.8
Aniline	Primary	$C_6H_5NH_2$	184.4
p-Toluidine	Primary	$CH_3C_6H_4NH_2$	200 (m.p. 45°)
Methylaniline	Secondary	$C_6H_5NHCH_3$	195.7
Dimethylaniline	Tertiary	$C_6H_5N(CH_3)_2$	193.5
Diethylaniline	Tertiary	$C_6H_5N(C_2H_5)_2$	215.5
α-Naphthylamine	Primary	$C_{10}H_7NH_2$	301 (m.p. 50°)

such radicals present. Those in which only one organic residue is attached to the nitrogen atom are known as primary amines (RNH_2). Secondary amines $\left(\begin{matrix}R\\ \quad\end{matrix}\!\!>\!NH\right.$ $\left.\begin{matrix}\\R\end{matrix}\right)$ have two organic radicals on the nitrogen atom and tertiary amines $\left(R_2\!>\!N\!-\!R\right)$ have three.

In Table XXII the names, classes, formulas, and boiling points of a number of amines are given.

Preparation of Amines

Amines can be made in a great variety of ways, but scarcely any of the methods are generally applicable. That of Hofmann (p. 69) is perhaps the most general. The reduction of nitro compounds (p. 411) and of nitriles (p. 120) furnishes primary amines.

Other methods for the preparation of primary amines, and of secondary and tertiary amines, are discussed later.

Reactions of Amines

Hydration. Amines are more soluble in water than are the alcohols of corresponding molecular weights. Certain tertiary amines exhibit the peculiar behavior of being more soluble in cold than in hot water. These observations indicate that the amines form unstable hydrates which are more soluble than the amines. The hydration undoubtedly involves coordination between the nitrogen atom and a hydrogen atom of water.

$$\underset{\text{Amine}}{R_3N:} + H:\ddot{\underset{..}{O}}:H \rightleftharpoons \underset{\text{Amine hydrate}}{R_3N:H:\ddot{\underset{..}{O}}:H} \rightleftharpoons \underset{\text{Substituted ammonium hydroxide}}{R_3N:H^+ \;\; :\ddot{\underset{..}{O}}:H^-}$$

Ionization of the hydrate accounts for the basic properties of the amine. In this connection it is interesting to consider the basicity of quaternary ammonium hydroxides. These can be made from quaternary halides and silver oxide.

$$2R_4N^+X^- + Ag_2O + H_2O \longrightarrow \underset{\text{Quaternary ammonium hydroxide}}{2R_4N^+OH^-} + 2AgX$$

Here the hydroxyl group must remain as an ion, since the cation has no hydrogen atom capable of coordinating with it. As a consequence the quaternary hydroxides are extremely strong bases, comparable to the alkali hydroxides.

Salts. Most of the reagents which attack ammonia also react with the amines. The outstanding characteristic of ammonia and amines is basicity. The basic character of ammonia may be attributed to its tendency to donate its unshared pair of electrons to a deficient atom or ion. In the formation of ammonium salts from ammonia and acids the pair is accepted by a hydrogen ion.

$$\begin{array}{c}H\\ H:\ddot{\underset{\cdot\cdot}{N}}:\\ H\end{array} + H^+:\ddot{\underset{\cdot\cdot}{Cl}}:^- \longrightarrow \begin{array}{c}H\\ H:\ddot{\underset{\cdot\cdot}{N}}:H^+\\ H\end{array} \quad :\ddot{\underset{\cdot\cdot}{Cl}}:^-$$

Ammonium chloride

Primary, secondary, and tertiary amines react to form substituted ammonium salts. Methylammonium chloride, dimethylammonium chloride, and trimethylammonium chloride are obtained from methylamine, dimethylamine, and trimethylamine, respectively.

$$\begin{array}{c}H\\ CH_3:\ddot{\underset{\cdot\cdot}{N}}:\\ H\end{array} + H^+:\ddot{\underset{\cdot\cdot}{Cl}}:^- \longrightarrow \begin{array}{c}H\\ CH_3:\ddot{\underset{\cdot\cdot}{N}}:H^+\\ H\end{array} \quad :\ddot{\underset{\cdot\cdot}{Cl}}:^-$$

Methylammonium chloride

$$\begin{array}{c}CH_3\\ CH_3:\ddot{\underset{\cdot\cdot}{N}}:\\ H\end{array} + H^+:\ddot{\underset{\cdot\cdot}{Cl}}:^- \longrightarrow \begin{array}{c}CH_3\\ CH_3:\ddot{\underset{\cdot\cdot}{N}}:H^+\\ H\end{array} \quad :\ddot{\underset{\cdot\cdot}{Cl}}:^-$$

Dimethylammonium chloride

$$\begin{array}{c}CH_3\\ CH_3:\ddot{\underset{\cdot\cdot}{N}}:\\ CH_3\end{array} + H^+:\ddot{\underset{\cdot\cdot}{Cl}}:^- \longrightarrow \begin{array}{c}CH_3\\ CH_3:\ddot{\underset{\cdot\cdot}{N}}:H^+:\ddot{\underset{\cdot\cdot}{Cl}}:^-\\ CH_3\end{array}$$

Trimethylammonium chloride

In order to simplify the writing of formulas, these products are ordinarily represented as $CH_3NH_2 \cdot HCl$, $(CH_3)_2NH \cdot HCl$, and $(CH_3)_3N \cdot HCl$, respectively. To emphasize their relationship to the amines from which they are derived the salts are usually referred to as methylamine hydrochloride, dimethylamine hydrochloride, etc.

Amides. Primary and secondary amines react with derivatives of acids to yield amides. The most convenient laboratory methods of preparing amides employ acyl chlorides and acid anhydrides for the introduction of the acyl group. With chlorides of aliphatic acids it is necessary to employ two molecules of amine for each molecule of amide produced because the hydrochloric acid liberated from the reagent neutralizes one molecule of the amine. The preparation of N-methylvaleramide is an example.

$$CH_3CH_2CH_2CH_2C(=O)\text{-}Cl + 2CH_3NH_2$$

Valeryl chloride Methylamine

$$\longrightarrow CH_3CH_2CH_2CH_2C(=O)\text{-}NHCH_3 + CH_3NH_2 \cdot HCl$$

N-Methylvaleramide Methylamine hydrochloride

Acetanilide is prepared in a similar manner from aniline and acetyl chloride.

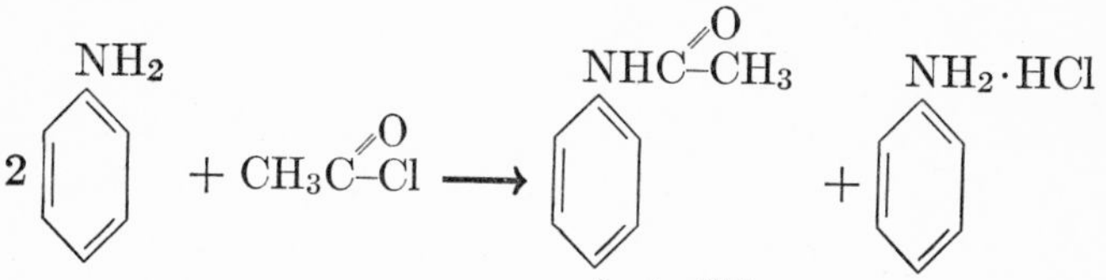

$$2\, C_6H_5NH_2 + CH_3C(=O)\text{-}Cl \longrightarrow C_6H_5NHC(=O)\text{-}CH_3 + C_6H_5NH_2 \cdot HCl$$

Acetanilide

Acetanilide is useful in combating fever and is sold for this purpose under the name Antifebrin.

When the chlorides of aromatic acids or sulfonic acids are employed, it is possible to run the reaction in the presence of water and alkali. These chlorides react with amines much more rapidly than with water. The alkali combines with the hydrochloric acid, thus making it possible to convert all the amine to the amide. The process is known as the Schotten-Baumann reaction. The preparations of benzanilide and N-methylbenzenesulfonamide are examples.

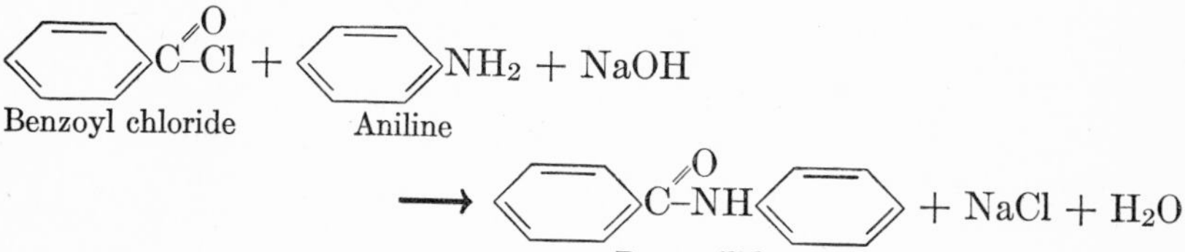

$$C_6H_5C(=O)\text{-}Cl + C_6H_5NH_2 + NaOH$$

Benzoyl chloride Aniline

$$\longrightarrow C_6H_5C(=O)\text{-}NHC_6H_5 + NaCl + H_2O$$

Benzanilide

$$C_6H_5SO_2Cl + CH_3NH_2 + NaOH$$

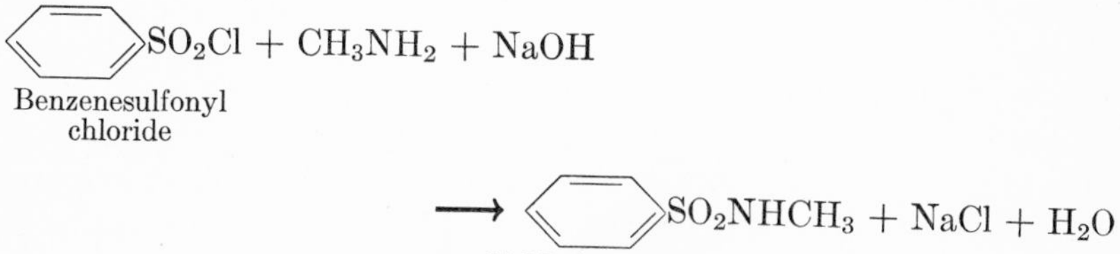

Benzenesulfonyl chloride

$$\longrightarrow C_6H_5SO_2NHCH_3 + NaCl + H_2O$$

N-Methylbenzenesulfonamide

Reactions of Amines with Nitrous Acid

Aliphatic amines can be classified on the basis of their reactions with nitrous acid. Primary aliphatic amines are converted to alcohols by this reagent.

$$RNH_2 + HON{=}O \longrightarrow ROH + N_2 + H_2O$$

The reaction is of little value in the synthesis of alcohols from amines because of the tendency toward *rearrangement* during the replacement of the amino group by the hydroxyl group. Thus, treatment of *n*-propylamine with nitrous acid yields a mixture of propyl alcohol and isopropyl alcohol in a ratio of about 1 to 5. Propylene is also formed as the product of a side reaction.

$$CH_3CH_2CH_2NH_2 + HON{=}O \begin{cases} \nearrow CH_3CH_2CH_2OH \text{ (expected product, 7\%)} \\ \longrightarrow CH_3CH(OH)CH_3 \text{ (rearrangement product, 32\%)} \\ \searrow CH_3CH{=}CH_2 \text{ (side reaction product, 28\%)} \end{cases}$$

In testing an unknown aliphatic amine in this way the evolution of nitrogen gas is taken as an indication of the presence of a primary amine.

Secondary aliphatic amines react with nitrous acid to give nitrosamines.

$$R_2NH + HON{=}O \longrightarrow \underset{\text{A nitrosamine}}{R_2NN{=}O} + H_2O$$

The nitrosamines are really amides of nitrous acid and as such would be expected to be neutral compounds. They usually separate from the test solution as neutral oils, insoluble in either acid or base.

Tertiary aliphatic amines react with nitrous acid to give unstable salts.

$$R_3N + HON{=}O \rightleftharpoons \underset{\text{An amine nitrite}}{R_3N \cdot HON{=}O}$$

The free tertiary amine can be recovered from the nitrite by the addition of alkali.

Aromatic amines behave differently toward nitrous acid. Tertiary amines, such as dimethylaniline, react readily with nitrous acid to form *p*-nitroso derivatives.

$$\underset{\text{Dimethylaniline}}{C_6H_5N(CH_3)_2} + HON{=}O \longrightarrow \underset{p\text{-Nitrosodimethylaniline}}{O{=}N\text{-}C_6H_4\text{-}N(CH_3)_2} + H_2O$$

This reaction affords an illustration of the ease with which aromatic amines undergo substitution in the *ortho* and *para* positions of the ring. The amino group greatly alters the properties of the aromatic system Dimethylaniline reacts with nitrous acid in water solution at room temperature, whereas the reaction of benzene with the more vigorous reagent, nitric acid, requires a higher temperature, a nearly anhydrous reagent, and a catalyst (H_2SO_4).

Secondary aromatic amines react with nitrous acid to form nitrosamines, just as do the aliphatic analogs. For example, methylaniline yields N-nitrosomethylaniline.

$$C_6H_5NHCH_3 + HON{=}O \longrightarrow C_6H_5N(CH_3)N{=}O + H_2O$$

N-Nitrosomethylaniline

The importance of primary aromatic amines in industrial and laboratory syntheses depends largely on their reaction with nitrous acid. Primary aromatic amines are converted to *diazonium salts* by treatment with nitrous acid in the presence of a mineral acid. The *diazotization* of aniline is an example.

$$C_6H_5NH_2 \cdot HCl + HON{=}O \xrightarrow{0\text{–}5°} [C_6H_5N{\equiv}N]^+Cl^- + 2H_2O$$

Aniline hydrochloride — Benzenediazonium chloride

Since nitrous acid is unstable, sodium nitrite is added to an acid solution of the amine salt. The reaction is very rapid. An aqueous solution of sodium nitrite is added slowly until starch-potassium iodide paper indicates an excess of nitrous acid. In general, it is unwise to over-run the end point since free nitrous acid acts as an oxidizing agent.

If the diazotization is carried out in alcoholic solution by adding an alkyl nitrite, the pure diazonium salt may be isolated. It can be thrown out of alcohol solution by the addition of ether. The pure salts are colorless, explosive solids. They are rarely isolated, but are used in aqueous solutions. On account of their instability, their solutions must be kept cold. Their instability seems to be due to the tendency of the two nitrogen atoms to separate as molecular nitrogen.

The reactions of diazonium salts can be classified in three general types, replacement of the diazonium group by other atoms or groups, coupling reactions, and reduction.

Replacement Reactions. If an aqueous solution of a diazonium salt is warmed, a *phenol* is produced. Benzenediazonium chloride yields phenol.

$$C_6H_5N^+(\equiv N)Cl^- + H_2O \longrightarrow C_6H_5OH + N_2 + HCl$$

Phenol

The diazonium group can be replaced by a halogen atom by warming a diazonium halide with a solution of cuprous halide and halogen acid. This is the *Sandmeyer reaction.* It is illustrated by the formation of *p*-chlorotoluene from diazotized *p*-toluidine.

$$CH_3C_6H_4N^+(\equiv N)Cl^- \xrightarrow[HCl]{CuCl} CH_3C_6H_4Cl + N_2$$

p-Toluenediazonium chloride — *p*-Chlorotoluene

The *Gattermann* method differs by the use of metallic copper as the catalyst. The diazonium group can be replaced by bromine by treating the diazonium bromide or sulfate with cuprous bromide and hydrobromic acid. Replacement by iodine can be effected by treating the diazonium sulfate with iodine and potassium iodide in the absence of a catalyst.

Replacement of the diazonium group by the cyanide group is effected in much the same way. A diazonium chloride or sulfate is treated with a solution of cuprous cyanide. The preparation of *o*-tolunitrile from diazotized *o*-toluidine is an example.

$$o\text{-}CH_3C_6H_4N^+(\equiv N)Cl^- + CuCN \longrightarrow o\text{-}CH_3C_6H_4C{\equiv}N + CuCl + N_2$$

o-Toluenediazonium chloride — *o*-Tolunitrile

The diazonium group is replaced by a hydrogen atom when a diazonium salt is treated with a reducing agent such as ethyl alcohol in the presence of copper powder. The reaction is of value because it enables one to introduce an amino group and make use of its directive influence, and then remove the amino group. The synthesis of *m*-bromotoluene is illustrative. This compound can be obtained only in slight amount by the bromination of toluene and its synthesis would at first appear difficult. However, both *o*- and *p*-nitrotoluene can be obtained in the pure state from the nitration of toluene. From them both *o*- and *p*-toluidine are available by reduction. If it were possible to brominate *p*-toluidine the bromine would enter the ring *ortho* to the amino group (*meta* to the methyl group). Removal of the amino group, by diazotization and treatment with alcohol, would then produce *m*-bromotoluene.

In practice one modification of this scheme is found necessary. If *p*-toluidine is brominated directly both the positions *ortho* to the amino group are attacked, because of the powerful effect of the amino group in activating the *ortho* and *para* positions toward substitution (p. 41). If the amine is first acetylated the bromination can be controlled, and the acetyl group can be removed by hydrolysis. The various steps in the synthesis of *m*-bromotoluene from *p*-toluidine are as follows:

$$CH_3C_6H_4NH_2 \xrightarrow{(CH_3CO)_2O} CH_3C_6H_4NHCOCH_3 \xrightarrow{Br_2} CH_3C_6H_3(Br)NHCOCH_3 \xrightarrow{H_2O} CH_3C_6H_3(Br)NH_2$$

$$\xrightarrow[H_2SO_4]{HONO} CH_3C_6H_3(Br)N^+{\equiv}N\ HSO_4^- \xrightarrow[Cu]{C_2H_5OH} CH_3C_6H_4Br + CH_3CHO + H_2SO_4 + N_2$$

m-Bromotoluene

A side reaction which attends the use of alcohol and copper for the removal of the diazonium group is the formation of an ether. With benzenediazonium chloride the ether, phenetole, is the major product.

$$C_6H_5N^+{\equiv}N\ Cl^- + C_2H_5OH \xrightarrow{Cu} C_6H_5OC_2H_5 + N_2 + HCl$$

Phenetole

In many syntheses it is desirable to bring about the replacement of the diazonium group by hydrogen under the influence of reducing agents other than alcohol. The best reagents appear to be hypophosphorous acid and alkaline formaldehyde.

Coupling Reactions. When a diazonium salt is treated with an aromatic amine in the presence of a mild alkali, an azo compound is produced. The formation of *p*-dimethylaminoazobenzene from diazotized aniline, dimethylaniline, and potassium acetate is an example.

$$C_6H_5N^+{\equiv}N\ Cl^- + C_6H_5N(CH_3)_2 + CH_3CO_2K$$

$$\longrightarrow C_6H_5N{=}NC_6H_4N(CH_3)_2 + KCl + CH_3CO_2H$$

p-Dimethylaminoazobenzene

Phenols also couple with diazonium salts. The hydroxyl group of the phenols has an effect similar to that of the amino group in facilitating substitution in the *ortho* and *para* positions. Phenol, benzenediazonium chloride, and sodium acetate yield *p*-hydroxyazobenzene.

$$C_6H_5N^+Cl^-(\equiv N) + C_6H_5OH + CH_3CO_2Na$$

$$\longrightarrow C_6H_5N{=}NC_6H_4OH + NaCl + CH_3CO_2H$$

p-Hydroxyazobenzene

Azo compounds are colored. The coupling reaction finds many important applications in the synthesis of dyes (p. 508). It is also used in the laboratory as part of a test for primary aromatic amines. The unknown amine is subjected to the action of nitrous acid and the resulting solution is added to an alkaline solution of β-naphthol. Since only primary aromatic amines can be diazotized, the appearance of a dye in the last step is proof that the unknown amine is a primary aromatic amine.

Reduction of diazonium compounds produces arylhydrazines. Phenylhydrazine is made by reducing benzenediazonium chloride with sodium sulfite.

$$C_6H_5N^+Cl^-(\equiv N) + 4[H](Na_2SO_3) \longrightarrow C_6H_5NHNH_2 \cdot HCl$$

Phenylhydrazine hydrochloride

$$C_6H_5NHNH_2 \cdot HCl + NaOH$$

$$\longrightarrow C_6H_5NHNH_2 + NaCl + H_2O$$

Phenylhydrazine

PROBLEMS

1. Suggest useful syntheses of the following: (*a*) α-naphthylamine, (*b*) *n*-amylamine (from *n*-butyl alcohol), (*c*) *n*-octylamine (from caprylic acid).

2. Write equations for the reaction of aniline with: (*a*) acetic anhydride, (*b*) hydrochloric acid, (*c*) hydrochloric acid and sodium nitrite, (*d*) benzoyl chloride and aqueous sodium hydroxide.

3. Give equations to represent: (*a*) diazotization, (*b*) the Sandmeyer reaction, (*c*) coupling reaction.

4. By means of equations, show how toluene may be converted to: (*a*) *p*-nitrotoluene, (*b*) *p*-toluidine, (*c*) *p*-tolunitrile, (*d*) *p*-toluic acid, (*e*) *p*-iodotoluene.

CHAPTER 11

Polyfunctional Acids

Carbonic Acid and Its Derivatives

Aqueous solutions of carbon dioxide are weakly acidic. From such solutions derivatives of carbonic acid can be prepared, although the acid itself never has been isolated because of the ease with which it decomposes to carbon dioxide and water.

$$O{=}C{=}O + H_2O \rightleftharpoons HO{-}C({=}O){-}OH$$

Carbonic acid is unique in containing two hydroxyl groups attached to the same carbonyl group. It is a dibasic acid, both hydrogen atoms being replaceable.

Carbonic acid forms two series of salts, the bicarbonates and the carbonates. Either may be obtained from an aqueous solution of carbon dioxide and an alkali. The formulas of the sodium salts are given as examples.

$$\underset{\text{Sodium bicarbonate}}{NaO{-}C({=}O){-}OH} \qquad \underset{\text{Sodium carbonate}}{NaO{-}C({=}O){-}ONa}$$

Other derivatives of carbonic acid, such as the chloride, esters, and the amide, are usually obtained from sources other than the acid. For example, the chloride, $COCl_2$, known as phosgene, is prepared from carbon monoxide and chlorine.

$$C{\equiv}O + Cl_2 \xrightarrow{\text{catalyst}} \underset{\text{Phosgene}}{ClC({=}O){-}Cl}$$

Light can be used as the catalyst, hence the name phosgene (light-generated). Phosgene is an extremely poisonous gas (b.p. 8°) and has been used for military purposes. It has been said that inhalation for one-half hour of air containing as little as five parts per million of phosgene (by volume) may be fatal.

Another route to phosgene consists in the treatment of carbon tetrachloride with fuming sulfuric acid. The sulfur trioxide attacks the carbon tetrachloride, being itself converted to pyrosulfuryl chloride. Under suitable conditions the yield is very high.

$$CCl_4 + SO_3 \longrightarrow COCl_2 + S_2O_5Cl_2$$

Phosgene is formed in small quantities when chloroform is exposed to air and light.

$$HCCl_3 + [O] \longrightarrow [HOCCl_3] \longrightarrow HCl + COCl_2$$

Phosgene has the chemical properties of an acyl chloride. It reacts with water, ammonia, and alcohol to form the acid, amide, and ester, respectively.

$$ClC(=O){-}Cl + 2H_2O \longrightarrow \left[HOC(=O){-}OH\right] + 2HCl$$
$$\downarrow$$
$$CO_2 + H_2O$$

$$ClC(=O){-}Cl + 4NH_3 \longrightarrow \underset{\text{Urea}}{H_2NC(=O){-}NH_2} + 2NH_4Cl$$

$$ClC(=O){-}Cl + 2C_2H_5OH \longrightarrow \underset{\text{Ethyl carbonate}}{C_2H_5OC(=O){-}OC_2H_5} + 2HCl$$

The reaction of the chloride with alcohol can be arrested at an earlier stage, yielding ethyl chlorocarbonate (also called ethyl chloroformate).

$$ClC(=O){-}Cl + C_2H_5OH \longrightarrow \underset{\text{Ethyl chlorocarbonate}}{ClC(=O){-}OC_2H_5} + HCl$$

Ethyl chlorocarbonate is at once an acyl chloride and an ester. It reacts with ammonia to give an amido-ester, ethyl carbamate.

$$ClC(=O){-}OC_2H_5 + 2NH_3 \longrightarrow \underset{\text{Ethyl carbamate (urethan)}}{H_2NC(=O){-}OC_2H_5} + NH_4Cl$$

Carbamic acid ($H_2NC(=O){-}OH$) is unstable but many of its salts and esters are well known. The ethyl ester is sometimes called urethan. It has been used in medicine as a hypnotic and sedative. Many of its derivatives in which organic groups are present on the nitrogen atom have similar properties. They can be made by treating amines with ethyl chlorocarbonate. Phenylurethan (or ethyl phenylcarbamate), for example, is obtained from aniline and the chlorocarbonate.

$$C_6H_5NH_2 + ClC(=O)OC_2H_5 \longrightarrow C_6H_5NHC(=O)OC_2H_5 + HCl$$

Phenylurethan

Urea, the diamide of carbonic acid, is of great historical interest as the first organic compound to be synthesized from inorganic substances. It is the end product of protein metabolism in man. Ammonia liberated from the proteins is combined with carbon dioxide in the liver, and the urea so formed is eliminated in the urine. Urea is now produced commercially for use as a special fertilizer and in the preparation of plastics and drugs. It is made from carbon dioxide and ammonia. These react to give ammonium carbamate, which can be converted to urea and water by heating.

$$CO_2 + 2NH_3 \longrightarrow \underset{\text{Ammonium carbamate}}{H_2NC(=O)ONH_4} \xrightarrow{\text{heat}} \underset{\text{Urea}}{H_2NC(=O)NH_2} + H_2O$$

Unlike the simple amides, urea is a weak base. This might be expected from the consideration that two ammonia nitrogen atoms are attached to a single carbonyl group (p. 119). The salts of urea with strong acids are stable only in the presence of an excess of the acid or in the dry state. In contact with water they are hydrolyzed completely. Urea nitrate is an example.

$$H_2NC(=O)NH_2 + HNO_3 \rightleftharpoons \underset{\text{Urea nitrate}}{H_2NC(=O)NH_2 \cdot HNO_3}$$

When urea nitrate is added to cold sulfuric acid it is dehydrated to nitrourea.

$$\underset{\text{Urea nitrate}}{H_2NC(=O)NH_2 \cdot HNO_3} \xrightarrow{H_2SO_4} \underset{\text{Nitrourea}}{H_2NC(=O)NHNO_2} + H_2O$$

Semicarbazide, a reagent for aldehydes and ketones (pp. 81, 82), is prepared by the electrolytic reduction of nitrourea.

$$H_2NC(=O)NHNO_2 + 6[H] \longrightarrow \underset{\text{Semicarbazide}}{H_2NC(=O)NHNH_2} + 2H_2O$$

Urea undergoes hydrolysis in the same manner as other amides. The products are carbon dioxide and ammonia.

$$\underset{\text{Urea}}{H_2NC(=O)NH_2} \xrightarrow{H_2O} \underset{\text{Ammonium carbamate}}{H_2NC(=O)ONH_4} \xrightarrow{H_2O} \underset{\text{Ammonium carbonate}}{H_4NOC(=O)ONH_4}$$

$$\longrightarrow CO_2 + 2NH_3 + H_2O$$

One of the principal uses of urea is in the manufacture of urea-formaldehyde resins. It is possible that the reaction involves the addition of urea to formaldehyde to give hydroxymethylurea and that the latter combines with itself by elimination of water to form a polymer. These reactions are shown in the following equations.

$$HC(=O)H + H_2NC(=O)NH_2 \longrightarrow \underset{\text{Hydroxymethylurea}}{HOCH_2NHC(=O)NH_2}$$

$$HOCH_2NHC(=O)NH_2 + HOCH_2NHC(=O)NH_2 + HOCH_2NHC(=O)NH_2, \text{ etc.}$$

$$\longrightarrow HOCH_2NHC(=O)NH(CH_2NHC(=O)NH)_xCH_2NHC(=O)NH_2 + (x+1)H_2O$$

The formation of the plastic involves the further reaction of the long polymeric chains with more formaldehyde. Some of the NH groups add to formaldehyde, forming $\underset{|\atop CH_2OH}{-N-}$ groups at points along the chain. When the material is heated in the mold these groups react with free NH groups in adjacent chains. The long chains thus become tied together and the molecule is built up in three dimensions. The linking of the chains can be illustrated as follows:

$$\begin{array}{c} -CH_2-N-C(=O)-NH- \\ | \\ CH_2 \\ | \\ -CH_2-N-C(=O)-NH- \end{array}$$

A polymer formed by a reaction which also produces a small molecule such as water or hydrogen chloride is known as a *condensation polymer*. The polymerization of hydroxymethylurea is illustrative. When polymerization is accompanied by the linking together of the long chains the polymer is said to be *cross linked*.

Cyanamide. The dehydration of urea yields cyanamide, $H_2NC{\equiv}N$, which may be regarded as the nitrile of carbamic acid ($H_2NC({=}O){-}OH$). The most important derivative of cyanamide is calcium cyanamide. It is prepared from calcium carbide and nitrogen.

$$CaC_2 + N_2 \xrightarrow{\text{heat}} \underset{\text{Calcium cyanamide}}{CaNC{\equiv}N} + C$$

Calcium cyanamide is used in the fertilizer industry. It is also a raw material for the preparation of sodium cyanide and other chemicals.

Guanidine may be prepared by the addition of ammonia to cyanamide.

$$H_2NC{\equiv}N + NH_3 \longrightarrow \underset{\text{Guanidine}}{H_2NC({=}NH){-}NH_2}$$

Guanidine bears a formal resemblance to urea, but the third nitrogen atom greatly increases the basic strength. The basicity of guanidine is approximately that of the amines. Guanidine is very easily hydrolyzed to urea, particularly in the presence of bases.

$$H_2N{-}C({=}NH){-}NH_2 + H_2O \longrightarrow H_2NC({=}O){-}NH_2 + NH_3$$

Cyanic Acid, Isocyanic Acid, and Fulminic Acid. When urea is heated with zinc chloride it loses ammonia and forms a gas which is called cyanic acid. The latter spontaneously changes to the trimer, known as cyanuric acid.

$$(H_2N)(H{-}NH)C{=}O \xrightarrow[220^\circ]{ZnCl_2} NH_3 + \underset{\text{Cyanic acid}}{HNCO} \longrightarrow \underset{\text{Cyanuric acid}}{(HNCO)_3}$$

Cyanuric acid is depolymerized by heating and so may serve as a source of cyanic acid.

If cyanic acid is dissolved in water the resulting solution is strongly acid. For this reason the solution is believed to contain a substance of the formula $HOC{\equiv}N$, since this would be expected to be more acidic than the alternate structure, $O{=}C{=}NH$. On the other hand, its formation from urea and most of its reactions are more easily explained on the basis of the latter formula. It seems likely that the substance is actually a mixture of both forms in equilibrium.

$$\underset{\text{(Cyanic formula)}}{HOC{\equiv}N} \rightleftharpoons \underset{\text{(Isocyanic formula)}}{O{=}C{=}NH}$$

Cyanic acid

As indicated above, the reactions of cyanic acid are best represented on the basis of the isocyanic structure. Water, alcohols, ammonia, and amines react, as shown in the equations below.

$$O{=}C{=}NH + H_2O \longrightarrow \underset{\text{Carbamic acid}}{\left[HOC({=}O){-}NH_2\right]} \longrightarrow NH_3 + CO_2$$

$$O{=}C{=}NH + CH_3CH_2OH \longrightarrow \underset{\substack{\text{Urethan} \\ \text{(ethyl carbamate)}}}{CH_3CH_2OC({=}O){-}NH_2}$$

$$O{=}C{=}NH + NH_3 \longrightarrow \underset{\text{Urea}}{H_2NC({=}O){-}NH_2}$$

$$O{=}C{=}NH + CH_3CH_2NH_2 \longrightarrow \underset{\text{Ethylurea}}{CH_3CH_2NHC({=}O){-}NH_2}$$

It is often convenient to carry out reactions of alcohols or amines with cyanic acid by heating the reagent with urea. The urea slowly decomposes to ammonia and cyanic acid, and the latter reacts with the reagent. It is possible that the formation of biuret ($H_2NC({=}O){-}NHC({=}O){-}NH_2$) occurs in this way. It is formed along with ammonia when urea is heated alone. On the basis of the intermediate formation of cyanic acid the reaction would be represented as follows:

$$H_2NC({=}O){-}NH_2 \xrightarrow{\text{heat}} NH_3 + HN{=}C{=}O \xrightarrow{H_2NC({=}O){-}NH_2} \underset{\text{Biuret}}{H_2NC({=}O){-}NHC({=}O){-}NH_2}$$

Organic derivatives of the isocyanic type are well known. One of the most useful is phenyl isocyanate, prepared from aniline and phosgene.

$$C_6H_5NH_2 + ClC({=}O){-}Cl \longrightarrow C_6H_5NHC({=}O){-}Cl$$

$$\xrightarrow{\text{heat}} \underset{\text{Phenyl isocyanate}}{C_6H_5N{=}C{=}O} + HCl$$

Its reactions resemble those of cyanic acid. For example, it reacts with alcohol to give phenylurethan and with aniline to give diphenylurea.

$$C_6H_5N{=}C{=}O + C_2H_5OH \longrightarrow C_6H_5NHC(=O){-}OC_2H_5$$

Phenylurethan

$$C_6H_5N{=}C{=}O + C_6H_5NH_2 \longrightarrow C_6H_5NHC(=O){-}NHC_6H_5$$

Diphenylurea

This and other isocyanates are used in the laboratory to convert amines and alcohols to solid derivatives.

Fulminic acid is an isomer of cyanic acid. Its structure is HONC, showing it to be related to the isocyanides (p. 217). The electronic formula is shown below.

$$H:\ddot{\underset{..}{O}}:N\vdots C: \quad \text{or} \quad HON{\equiv}C$$

Fulminic acid

The mercury salt of fulminic acid is obtained from mercuric nitrate, nitric acid, and alcohol. Mercury fulminate is a powerful explosive, and because it detonates under a slight shock it is used in priming caps.

Ethyl Orthocarbonate. Carbon tetrachloride may be regarded as the chloride of the hypothetical orthocarbonic acid $C(OH)_4$. Esters of this acid are well known. They are usually made from chloropicrin and sodium alkoxides. The preparation of the ethyl ester is an example.

$$\underset{\text{Chloropicrin}}{NO_2CCl_3} + 4NaOC_2H_5 \longrightarrow \underset{\text{Ethyl orthocarbonate}}{C(OC_2H_5)_4} + NaNO_2 + 3NaCl$$

Similarly, chloroform may be considered the chloride of orthoformic acid. Orthoformic esters are made from chloroform and sodium alkoxides.

$$HCCl_3 + 3NaOC_2H_5 \longrightarrow \underset{\text{Ethyl orthoformate}}{HC(OC_2H_5)_3} + 3NaCl$$

Higher orthoesters have the general formula $RC(OR')_3$. As the formulas indicate they are more closely related to the acetals than to the normal esters.

The Dicarboxylic Acids

In Table XXIII are given the names, formulas, and melting points of the simpler acids containing two carboxyl groups. It is interesting to note that they are all solids and that any aliphatic member containing an even number of carbon atoms melts higher than the neighboring odd-carbon members.

TABLE XXIII

Name	Formula	Melting Point
Aliphatic Dibasic Acids		
Oxalic	$HOC(=O){-}C(=O){-}OH$	189°
Malonic	$HOC(=O)CH_2C(=O){-}OH$	136
Succinic	$HOC(=O)CH_2CH_2C(=O){-}OH$	181
Glutaric	$HOC(=O)CH_2CH_2CH_2C(=O){-}OH$	98
Adipic	$HOC(=O)CH_2CH_2CH_2CH_2C(=O){-}OH$	153
Pimelic	$HOC(=O)(CH_2)_5C(=O){-}OH$	105
Suberic	$HOC(=O)(CH_2)_6C(=O){-}OH$	144
Azelaic	$HOC(=O)(CH_2)_7C(=O){-}OH$	106
Sebacic	$HOC(=O)(CH_2)_8C(=O){-}OH$	134
Aromatic Dibasic Acids		
Phthalic (*o*-phthalic)	$C_6H_4(C(=O){-}OH)_2$ (1,2)	208 (dec.)
Isophthalic (*m*-phthalic)	$C_6H_4(C(=O){-}OH)_2$ (1,3)	330
Terephthalic	$C_6H_4(C(=O)OH)_2$ (1,4)	(sublimes at 300°)

Preparation of the Dibasic Acids. Most of the simpler dibasic acids are prepared by special methods rather than by adaptations of the general methods for the introduction of the carboxyl group.

Sodium oxalate is prepared commercially by heating sodium formate. The reaction is a peculiar one involving the formation of hydrogen gas and the linking of the two carboxyl groups.

$$2HC(=O){-}ONa \xrightarrow{200^\circ} H_2 + NaOC(=O){-}C(=O){-}ONa$$

Sodium formate — Sodium oxalate

The free acid is obtained by converting the sodium salt to the calcium salt and treating the latter with just enough sulfuric acid to precipitate the calcium as calcium sulfate. Evaporation of the resulting aqueous solution yields oxalic acid dihydrate. Salts of oxalic acid can also be made by fusing sawdust (cellulose) with alkalies.

Oxalic acid is very easily oxidized to carbon dioxide and water. Even as mild an agent as a ferric salt (represented as ferric oxide in the equation) brings about the oxidation.

$$HOC(=O){-}C(=O){-}OH + Fe_2O_3 \longrightarrow 2CO_2 + H_2O + 2FeO$$

The use of oxalic acid in laundries for the removal of iron stains and ink spots depends on its reduction of ferric salts to soluble ferrous salts. Oxalic acid is also used in calico printing, in dyeing, and as a reagent in chemical analysis.

Malonic acid is prepared commercially from acetic acid by way of chloroacetic and cyanoacetic acids. The equations for the reactions are as follows:

$$CH_3C(=O){-}OH + Cl_2 \longrightarrow ClCH_2C(=O){-}OH + HCl$$

Chloroacetic acid

$$ClCH_2C(=O){-}OH + NaOH \longrightarrow ClCH_2C(=O){-}ONa + H_2O$$

Sodium chloroacetate

$$ClCH_2C(=O){-}ONa + NaCN \longrightarrow N{\equiv}CCH_2C(=O){-}ONa + NaCl$$

Sodium cyanoacetate

$$N{\equiv}CCH_2C(=O){-}ONa + 2H_2O + 2HCl \longrightarrow HOC(=O){-}CH_2C(=O){-}OH + NH_4Cl + NaCl$$

Malonic acid

Malonic acid is less important as an industrial chemical than its ethyl ester. The latter is used extensively in synthesis (p. 161) and in the preparation of certain drugs (p. 162). It is prepared from cyanoacetic acid by the action of ethyl alcohol and sulfuric acid.

$$N{\equiv}CCH_2C(=O)OH + 2C_2H_5OH + H_2SO_4$$
Cyanoacetic acid

$$\longrightarrow C_2H_5OC(=O){-}CH_2C(=O){-}OC_2H_5 + NH_4HSO_4$$
Ethyl malonate

It should be noted that this conversion of the nitrile group to the ester group in a single operation is generally applicable and usually gives better yields than can be obtained by hydrolysis followed by isolation and esterification of the acid.

Succinic acid is most conveniently obtained by catalytic hydrogenation of maleic acid.

$$\begin{matrix} H{-}C{-}CO_2H \\ \| \\ H{-}C{-}CO_2H \end{matrix} + H_2 \xrightarrow{\text{catalyst}} \begin{matrix} CO_2H \\ | \\ CH_2 \\ | \\ CH_2 \\ | \\ CO_2H \end{matrix}$$

Maleic acid — Succinic acid

Maleic acid is available commercially from the catalytic oxidation of benzene (p. 155).

One method of preparing glutaric acid in the laboratory utilizes trimethylene glycol as the starting material. The bromide is prepared from the glycol and converted to the dinitrile by the action of a cyanide. Hydrolysis of the dinitrile yields the acid.

$$HOCH_2CH_2CH_2OH + 2HBr \xrightarrow{H_2SO_4} BrCH_2CH_2CH_2Br + 2H_2O$$
Trimethylene glycol — Trimethylene bromide

$$BrCH_2CH_2CH_2Br + 2NaCN \longrightarrow N{\equiv}CCH_2CH_2CH_2C{\equiv}N + 2NaBr$$
Glutaronitrile

$$N{\equiv}CCH_2CH_2CH_2C{\equiv}N + 4H_2O + 2HCl$$

$$\longrightarrow HOC(=O){-}CH_2CH_2CH_2C(=O){-}OH + 2NH_4Cl$$
Glutaric acid

Adipic acid, as an intermediate in the manufacture of nylon (p. 148), is one of the most valuable dibasic acids. It is prepared by oxidation of cyclohexane or cyclohexanol, which are obtained by the hydrogenation of benzene and phenol (p. 37), respectively.

$$\text{Phenol} + 3H_2 \xrightarrow{\text{catalyst}} \text{Cyclohexanol}$$

$$\begin{array}{c} CH_2 \\ / \quad \backslash \\ CH_2 \quad CHOH \\ | \qquad | \\ CH_2 \quad CH_2 \\ \backslash \quad / \\ CH_2 \end{array} + 4(O) \longrightarrow \begin{array}{c} CH_2 \\ / \quad \backslash \\ CH_2 \quad C(=O)OH \\ | \\ CH_2 \quad C(=O)OH \\ \backslash \quad / \\ CH_2 \end{array} + H_2O$$

Adipic acid

The higher dibasic acids are much less common than those discussed above, and their individual preparations will not be considered in detail. Pimelic acid is obtained from cyclohexanone by a series of reactions described later (p. 329). Suberic and azelaic acids are prepared by the oxidation of castor oil. Sebacic acid is obtained by heating castor oil with alkali. Still higher members may be made by the Kolbe electrolysis of the potassium salt of an acid ester. For example, the ethyl ester of 1,18-octadecanedioic acid is made from potassium ethyl sebacate.

$$2C_2H_5OC(=O)\text{–}(CH_2)_8\,C(=O)\text{–}O^- \longrightarrow 2CO_2 + C_2H_5OC(=O)\text{–}(CH_2)_{16}C(=O)\text{–}OC_2H_5$$

Ethyl 1,18-octadecanedioate

Another general method consists in the hydrogenation (p. 109) of an ester of a dibasic acid to yield a glycol which is converted to the dibasic acid of two more carbon atoms by the nitrile synthesis. The method is illustrated by the scheme outlined below.

$$C_2H_5OC(=O)\text{–}(CH_2)_xC(=O)\text{–}OC_2H_5 + 4H_2 \xrightarrow{\text{catalyst}} HOCH_2(CH_2)_xCH_2OH + 2C_2H_5OH$$

$$HOCH_2(CH_2)_xCH_2OH \longrightarrow BrCH_2(CH_2)_xCH_2Br \longrightarrow N{\equiv}CCH_2(CH_2)_xCH_2C{\equiv}N$$

$$N{\equiv}CCH_2(CH_2)_xCH_2C{\equiv}N \longrightarrow HOC(=O)\text{–}CH_2(CH_2)_xCH_2C(=O)\text{–}OH$$

Of the aromatic dibasic acids, only phthalic acid is common. Its anhydride is prepared in large quantities by the catalytic oxidation of naphthalene.

$$2\,C_{10}H_8 + 9O_2 \xrightarrow[\text{(air)}]{V_2O_5} 2\,C_6H_4(CO)_2O + 4CO_2 + 4H_2O$$

Naphthalene   Phthalic anhydride

The acid is prepared by hydrolysis of the anhydride.

$$C_6H_4(CO)_2O + H_2O \longrightarrow C_6H_4(COOH)_2$$

Phthalic anhydride   Phthalic acid

When naphthalene is oxidized with alkaline permanganate, phthalonic acid is formed.

$$C_{10}H_8 \xrightarrow{(O)} C_6H_4(COCOOH)(COOH) \xrightarrow{-CO_2} C_6H_4(CHO)(COOH)$$

Phthalonic acid   Phthalaldehydic acid

The latter compound can be decarboxylated easily and is thereby converted into phthalaldehydic acid.

Behavior of Dibasic Acids on Heating. The dibasic acids exhibit several different types of thermal decomposition. The distance between the carboxyl groups determines the nature of the reaction. If the carboxyl groups are in the 1,2 and 1,3 positions with respect to each other the dibasic acid easily undergoes decarboxylation. Thus, oxalic acid is converted to carbon dioxide and formic acid by heating at its melting point (189°). Formic acid is partly decomposed to water and carbon monoxide at this temperature, so the products actually obtained from oxalic acid are water, carbon monoxide, carbon dioxide, and formic acid.

$$HOOC{-}COOH \xrightarrow{\text{heat}} HCOOH + CO_2$$

$$HCOOH \xrightarrow{\text{heat}} H_2O + CO$$

The decomposition occurs at lower temperatures when oxalic acid is heated with sulfuric acid. The products are then water, carbon monoxide, and carbon dioxide.

Malonic acid likewise loses carbon dioxide on heating to 150° or higher.

$$HO\overset{O}{\overset{\|}{C}}CH_2\overset{O}{\overset{\|}{C}}{-}OH \xrightarrow{\text{heat}} CH_3\overset{O}{\overset{\|}{C}}{-}OH + CO_2$$

The monobasic acids undergo decarboxylation only under much more vigorous conditions. The carboxyl groups in oxalic and malonic acids activate each other. It will be seen later that other unsaturated groups have a similar activating influence on the carboxyl group when they are in the α or β position with respect to it.

When the two carboxyl groups are in the 1,4 or 1,5 positions, the characteristic reaction is one of *dehydration.* The product is a cyclic anhydride containing five or six members in the ring. Both succinic and glutaric acids are converted to their anhydrides by heating to temperatures in the neighborhood of their melting points.

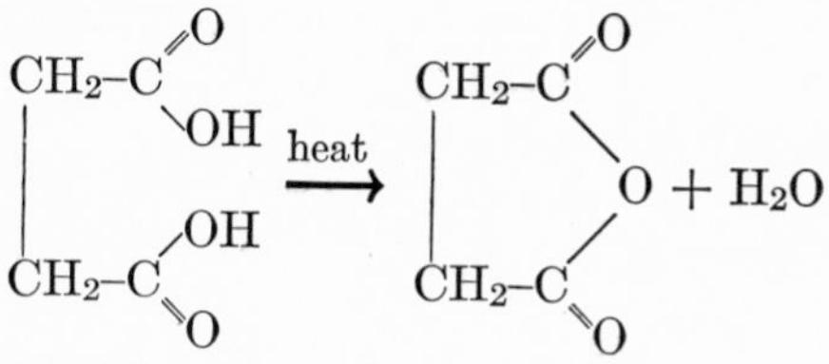

```
CH2-C//O                  CH2-C//O
|    \OH     heat         |     \
|            --->         |      O + H2O
|    /OH                  |     /
CH2-C\\O                  CH2-C\\O
Succinic acid           Succinic anhydride

   CH2-C//O                  CH2-C//O
  /     \OH     heat        /       \
CH2             --->     CH2         O + H2O
  \     /OH                 \       /
   CH2-C\\O                  CH2-C\\O
Glutaric acid            Glutaric anhydride
```

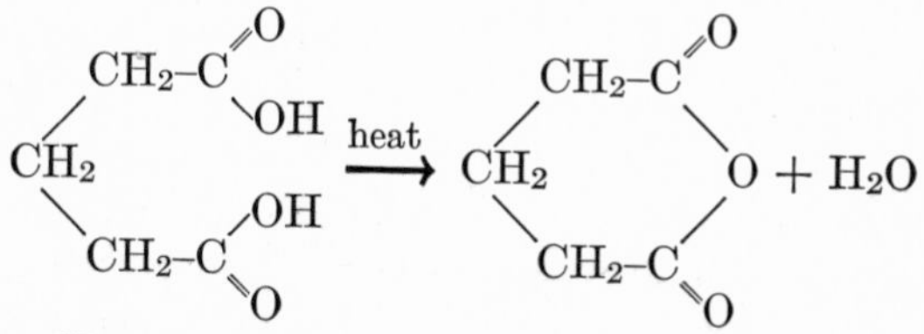

The ease with which these anhydrides are formed may be ascribed to the fact that the two carboxyl groups approach each other very closely. Models constructed from tetrahedral carbon atoms possess zigzag carbon chains; rotation of each carbon atom with respect to those to which it is joined (by thermal energy in the actual molecule) causes the hydroxyl groups of models of succinic and glutaric acids to collide. It is recommended that the student examine models for a demonstration of this point.

When the carboxyl groups of a dibasic acid are in more remote positions cyclic anhydrides are not readily formed. When adipic acid is heated with a dehydrating agent it forms a *polymeric anhydride* by loss of water between carboxyl groups of *different molecules*. The reaction can be illustrated as follows:

$$HO{-}\overset{\overset{O}{\|}}{C}(CH_2)_4\overset{\overset{O}{\|}}{C}{-}OH + HO{-}\overset{\overset{O}{\|}}{C}(CH_2)_4\overset{\overset{O}{\|}}{C}{-}OH + HO{-}\overset{\overset{O}{\|}}{C}(CH_2)_4\overset{\overset{O}{\|}}{C}{-}OH$$

$$\xrightarrow{\text{dehydration}} HO\overset{\overset{O}{\|}}{C}(CH_2)_4\overset{\overset{O}{\|}}{C}{-}O{-}\overset{\overset{O}{\|}}{C}(CH_2)_4\overset{\overset{O}{\|}}{C}{-}O{-}\overset{\overset{O}{\|}}{C}(CH_2)_4\overset{\overset{O}{\|}}{C}{-}OH + 2H_2O$$

The polymer actually obtained has a molecular weight of several thousand; it can be represented by the following formula.

$$HO\overset{\overset{O}{\|}}{C}(CH_2)_4\overset{\overset{O}{\|}}{C}{-}O\left(\overset{\overset{O}{\|}}{C}(CH_2)_4\overset{\overset{O}{\|}}{C}{-}O\right)_n\overset{\overset{O}{\|}}{C}(CH_2)_4\overset{\overset{O}{\|}}{C}{-}OH$$

Polyadipic anhydride

When adipic acid is heated in the presence of certain metallic oxides, such as barium oxide and thorium oxide, it undergoes loss of carbon dioxide and water to form cyclopentanone. The reaction is used for the laboratory preparation of the cyclic ketone.

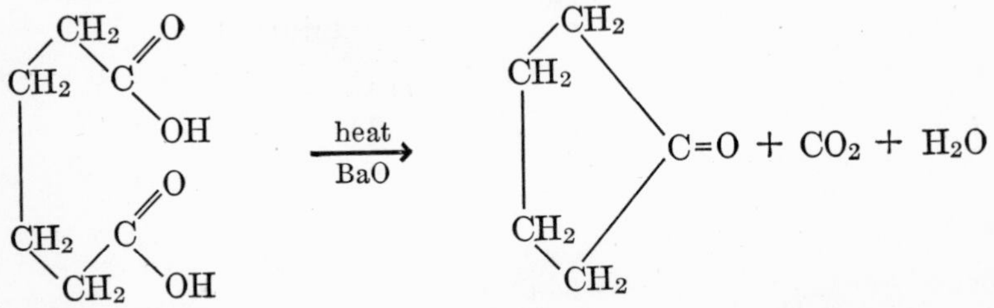

$$\underset{\text{Adipic acid}}{HOOC{-}CH_2CH_2CH_2CH_2{-}COOH} \xrightarrow[\text{BaO}]{\text{heat}} \underset{\text{Cyclopentanone}}{\text{(CH}_2)_4\text{C=O (ring)}} + CO_2 + H_2O$$

Pimelic acid is converted to cyclohexanone in good yields by this method, but the reaction is of no preparative value, since cyclohexanone is available from the reduction of phenol (p. 165).

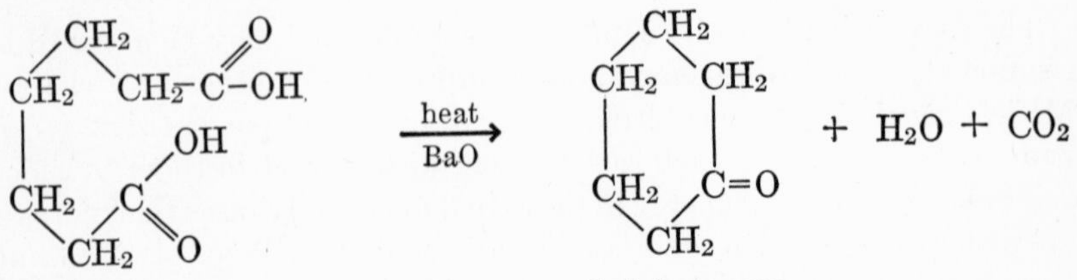

$$\underset{\text{Pimelic acid}}{HOOC{-}CH_2CH_2CH_2CH_2CH_2{-}COOH} \xrightarrow[\text{BaO}]{\text{heat}} \underset{\text{Cyclohexanone}}{\text{(CH}_2)_5\text{C=O (ring)}} + H_2O + CO_2$$

Cyclic ketones containing larger rings also may be obtained from the appropriate dibasic acids. However, the preparations are much less successful, from the standpoint of yields, than those of cyclopentanone and cyclohexanone. It is to be noted that in the preparation of both cyclic anhydrides and cyclic ketones the yields are best when the product contains a five- or six-membered ring. It is generally true that rings of this size are more readily formed than larger or smaller ones.

Derivatives of Dibasic Acids

The carboxyl groups in the dibasic acids are capable of undergoing all the transformations described in connection with the monobasic acids. Thus, these acids yield esters, amides, chlorides, salts, and anhydrides. Since two carboxyl groups are present it is possible to prepare mixed derivatives, such as acid esters, amido acids, and amido esters. A few such derivatives of succinic acid are listed below.

$$\begin{array}{l} CH_2C(=O)\text{–}OH \\ | \\ CH_2C(=O)\text{–}OK \end{array}$$

Potassium acid succinate

$$\begin{array}{l} CH_2C(=O)\text{–}OH \\ | \\ CH_2C(=O)\text{–}OCH_2CH_3 \end{array}$$

Ethyl acid succinate

$$\begin{array}{l} CH_2C(=O)\text{–}NH_2 \\ | \\ CH_2C(=O)\text{–}OH \end{array}$$

Succinamic acid

$$\begin{array}{l} CH_2C(=O)\text{–}NH_2 \\ | \\ CH_2C(=O)\text{–}OCH_2CH_3 \end{array}$$

Ethyl succinamate

Cyclic Imides. Those dibasic acids which easily form cyclic anhydrides can be converted readily to imides. Imides are closely related to amides; they contain a nitrogen atom joined to two acyl groups. Succinimide can be obtained by heating succinamide, much as the anhydride can be obtained from the acid.

$$\begin{array}{l} CH_2C(=O)\text{–}NH_2 \\ | \\ CH_2C(=O)\text{–}NH_2 \end{array} \xrightarrow{\text{heat}} \begin{array}{l} CH_2\text{–}C(=O) \\ | \qquad\quad \diagdown \\ | \qquad\qquad NH \\ | \qquad\quad \diagup \\ CH_2\text{–}C(=O) \end{array} + NH_3$$

Succinamide → Succinimide

Glutarimide and phthalimide may be prepared in the same manner.

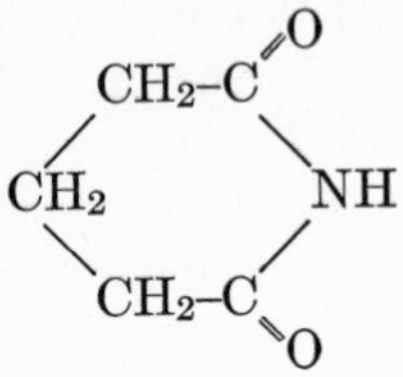

$CH_2–C(=O)$, CH_2, NH, $CH_2–C(=O)$

Glutarimide

O, C, NH, C, O

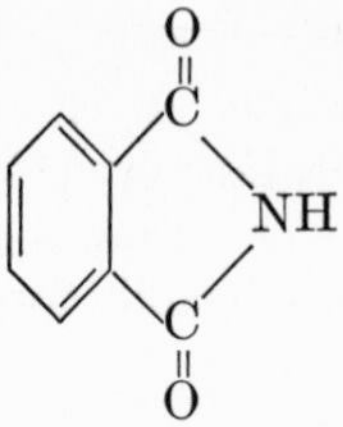

Phthalimide

The most interesting property of imides is their acidity. It will be recalled that the amides, which contain one acyl group attached to a basic nitrogen atom, are neutral. The presence of the second acyl group on the nitrogen atom makes the imide a weak acid. The imides yield sodium or potassium salts on treatment with the corresponding alkali hydroxides.

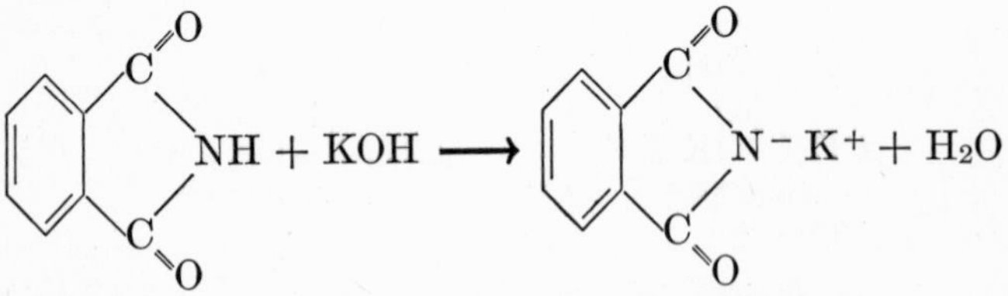

$$NH + KOH \longrightarrow N^-K^+ + H_2O$$

Phthalimide — Potassium phthalimide

Since the imides behave as extremely weak acids such salts are decomposed by carbon dioxide.

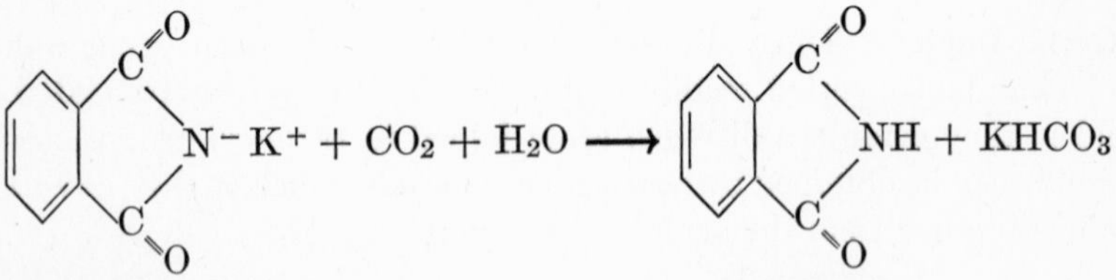

$$N^-K^+ + CO_2 + H_2O \longrightarrow NH + KHCO_3$$

Potassium phthalimide — Phthalimide

Polyesters Derived from Dibasic Acids. When a polybasic acid is allowed to react with a polyhydroxy alcohol the product may be either a cyclic ester or a polymeric ester. As might be predicted (p. 143), cyclic esters form when five- or six-membered rings are possible. Such cases are rare, since the simplest glycol and the simplest dicarboxylic acid yield a six-membered cyclic diester.

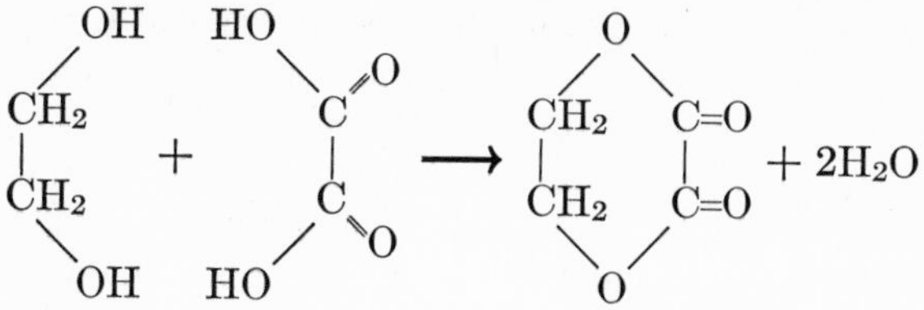

$$\begin{array}{c}\text{OH}\\ |\\ \text{CH}_2\\ |\\ \text{CH}_2\\ |\\ \text{OH}\end{array} + \begin{array}{c}\text{HO}\diagdown \\ \text{C}{=}\text{O}\\ |\\ \text{C}{=}\text{O}\\ \text{HO}\diagup\end{array} \longrightarrow \begin{array}{c}\text{O}\\ \text{CH}_2 \quad \text{C=O}\\ | \qquad\quad |\\ \text{CH}_2 \quad \text{C=O}\\ \text{O}\end{array} + 2H_2O$$

Ethylene glycol   Oxalic acid   Ethylene oxalate

The products are usually polyesters. Ethylene glycol and succinic acid, for example, react to give a linear condensation polymer.

$$HOCH_2CH_2OH \quad HO{-}\overset{O}{\overset{\|}{C}}{-}CH_2CH_2\overset{O}{\overset{\|}{C}}{-}OH \quad HOCH_2CH_2OH$$

$$HO{-}\overset{O}{\overset{\|}{C}}{-}CH_2CH_2\overset{O}{\overset{\|}{C}}{-}OH, \text{ etc.}$$

$$\longrightarrow HOCH_2CH_2O\left(\overset{O}{\overset{\|}{C}}{-}CH_2CH_2\overset{O}{\overset{\|}{C}}{-}OCH_2CH_2O\right)_n\overset{O}{\overset{\|}{C}}CH_2CH_2\overset{O}{\overset{\|}{C}}{-}OH$$

A polyester

If glycerol is used in place of ethylene glycol the polymerization proceeds in all directions, yielding a three-dimensional polymer instead of a linear polymer. The most important polymers derived from glycerol are known as Glyptal resins; as the name indicates, they are formed from glycerol and phthalic anhydride. An idea of their structure can be gained from the following diagram:

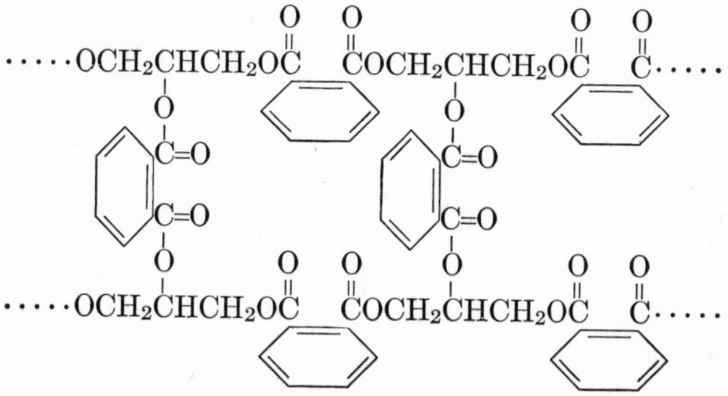

$$\cdots\cdots OCH_2CHCH_2O\overset{O}{\overset{\|}{C}}\;\;\overset{O}{\overset{\|}{C}}OCH_2CHCH_2O\overset{O}{\overset{\|}{C}}\;\;\overset{O}{\overset{\|}{C}}\cdots\cdots$$

(each pair of adjacent C=O groups joined through a benzene ring; the central CH of each glycerol unit bears –O–, linked through C=O / C=O of a phthalic ring to the CH of the chain below)

$$\cdots\cdots OCH_2\overset{|}{C}HCH_2O\overset{O}{\overset{\|}{C}}\;\;\overset{O}{\overset{\|}{C}}OCH_2\overset{|}{C}HCH_2O\overset{O}{\overset{\|}{C}}\;\;\overset{O}{\overset{\|}{C}}\cdots\cdots$$

This section of the structure of a glycerol phthalic anhydride polymer shows one way in which the long chains (the horizontal ones) are tied together through esterification of the third hydroxyl group of the glycerol residue. In the same way each of the horizontal chains is tied to others on all sides, giving the polymer three dimensions. If glycerol and phthalic anhydride are used alone the product is an insoluble, infusible, brittle substance. These properties are characteristic of *cross-linked* polymers (p. 134). To prevent the formation of the three-dimensional polymer an aliphatic acid is added in amount sufficient to esterify one of the three hydroxyl groups of the glycerol. Products so obtained are known as modified Glyptals. One of the most interesting is modified by addition of a fatty acid obtained from a drying oil, yielding an air-drying resin which is used in the preparation of high-grade enamels.

Polyamides—Nylon. When a dibasic acid is caused to react with a diamine under conditions suitable for amide formation, a condensation polymer is produced. Nylon is a polymer of this type, obtained from adipic acid and hexamethylenediamine. The latter is prepared from adipic acid by conversion to the amide and reduction of the amide or nitrile. Adipic acid is prepared from cyclohexanol, which in turn is made from phenol (p. 141). The equations for the preparation of nylon from adipic acid are as follows:

$$\underset{\text{Adipic acid}}{HO\overset{O}{\overset{\|}{C}}(CH_2)_4\overset{O}{\overset{\|}{C}}\text{–}OH} + 2NH_3 \xrightarrow[\text{pressure}]{\text{heat}} \underset{\text{Adipamide}}{H_2N\overset{O}{\overset{\|}{C}}(CH_2)_4\overset{O}{\overset{\|}{C}}\text{–}NH_2} + 2H_2O$$

$$H_2N\overset{O}{\overset{\|}{C}}(CH_2)_4\overset{O}{\overset{\|}{C}}\text{–}NH_2 + 4H_2 \xrightarrow{\text{catalyst}} \underset{\text{Hexamethylenediamine}}{H_2NCH_2(CH_2)_4CH_2NH_2} + 2H_2O$$

$$HO\overset{O}{\overset{\|}{C}}(CH_2)_4\overset{O}{\overset{\|}{C}}\text{–}OH + H_2N(CH_2)_6NH_2 + HO\overset{O}{\overset{\|}{C}}(CH_2)_4\overset{O}{\overset{\|}{C}}\text{–}OH + H_2N(CH_2)_6NH_2, \text{ etc.}$$

$$\longrightarrow HO\overset{O}{\overset{\|}{C}}(CH_2)_4\overset{O}{\overset{\|}{C}}\text{–}\left[NH(CH_2)_6NH\overset{O}{\overset{\|}{C}}(CH_2)_4\overset{O}{\overset{\|}{C}}\right]_n NH(CH_2)_6NH_2$$

The molten polyamide is extruded in the form of fine filaments that are stretched by winding them from one reel onto another which rotates at a higher speed. The stretching process is believed to cause the long molecules, which are in random arrangement in the newly formed filament, to line up end to end and side by side. The strength and elasticity of the filament are greatly increased by the stretching. The filaments are then gathered together and made into a yarn. The textile obtained resembles silk but is superior to it in certain respects.

The polyamide is also produced in strands of fairly large diameter suitable for bristles.

The Hydroxy Acids

The hydroxy acids contain an alcoholic hydroxyl group as well as a carboxyl group. In general, they have all the properties of alcohols as well as those of acids. In addition they have certain special properties which vary with the distance between the two functional groups. Those in which the hydroxyl and carboxyl groups are on the same carbon atom are known as α-hydroxy acids. The use of the Greek letters in naming substituted acids is evident from the names of the hydroxybutyric acids.

$$\overset{\gamma}{C}H_3\overset{\beta}{C}H_2\underset{OH}{\overset{\alpha}{C}H}\overset{O}{\overset{\|}{C}}{-}OH \quad \alpha\text{-Hydroxybutyric acid}$$

$$CH_3\underset{OH}{CH}CH_2\overset{O}{\overset{\|}{C}}{-}OH \quad \beta\text{-Hydroxybutyric acid}$$

$$\underset{OH}{CH_2}CH_2CH_2\overset{O}{\overset{\|}{C}}{-}OH \quad \gamma\text{-Hydroxybutyric acid}$$

α-Hydroxy acids are sometimes made from the corresponding α-halo acids. Thus glycolic acid may be obtained by treating chloroacetic acid with water in the presence of calcium carbonate.

$$CH_3\overset{O}{\overset{\|}{C}}{-}OH + Cl_2 \longrightarrow \underset{\text{Chloroacetic acid}}{ClCH_2\overset{O}{\overset{\|}{C}}{-}OH} + HCl$$

$$ClCH_2\overset{O}{\overset{\|}{C}}{-}OH + HOH \longrightarrow \underset{\text{Glycolic acid}}{HOCH_2\overset{O}{\overset{\|}{C}}{-}OH} + HCl$$

Glycolic acid is manufactured by the condensation of formaldehyde, carbon monoxide, and water in the presence of a catalyst such as sulfuric acid dissolved in an organic acid such as acetic acid. The condensation takes place under pressure and at a temperature of 160–170°.

$$CO + CH_2O + H_2O \longrightarrow \underset{OH}{CH_2}CO_2H$$

If the water is replaced by methanol the product is methyl glycolate (p. 233).

A very convenient synthesis of α-hydroxy acids makes use of the cyanohydrins derived from aldehydes and certain ketones. Mandelic acid and α-hydroxyisobutyric acid are made in this way from benzaldehyde and acetone, respectively.

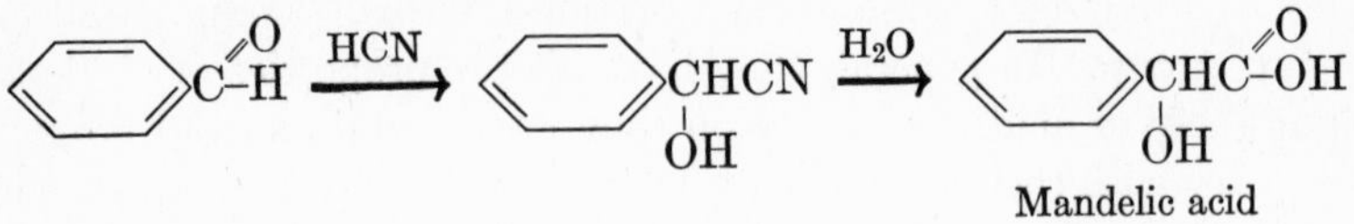

$$C_6H_5C(=O){-}H \xrightarrow{HCN} C_6H_5\underset{\displaystyle OH}{\underset{|}{C}}HCN \xrightarrow{H_2O} C_6H_5\underset{\displaystyle OH}{\underset{|}{C}}HC(=O){-}OH$$

Mandelic acid

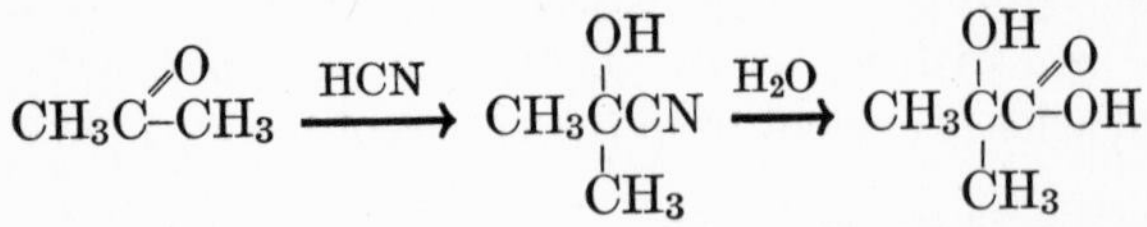

$$CH_3C(=O){-}CH_3 \xrightarrow{HCN} CH_3C(OH)(CH_3)CN \xrightarrow{H_2O} CH_3C(OH)(CH_3)C(=O){-}OH$$

α-Hydroxyisobutyric acid

The most important α-hydroxy acids are those obtainable from natural sources. The commonest of these is lactic acid, $CH_3CH(OH)C(=O){-}OH$. It is intimately associated with certain of the chemical processes of life and is present in the blood and tissues, particularly in muscle tissue. It is formed from the sugar lactose in the souring of milk, hence the name lactic acid.

Since lactic acid is at once an alcohol and an acid it might be expected to react with itself to form an ester. Actually, when a water solution of the acid is evaporated to a concentration of 50 per cent or higher, part of the acid is converted to the dimeric ester, lactide.

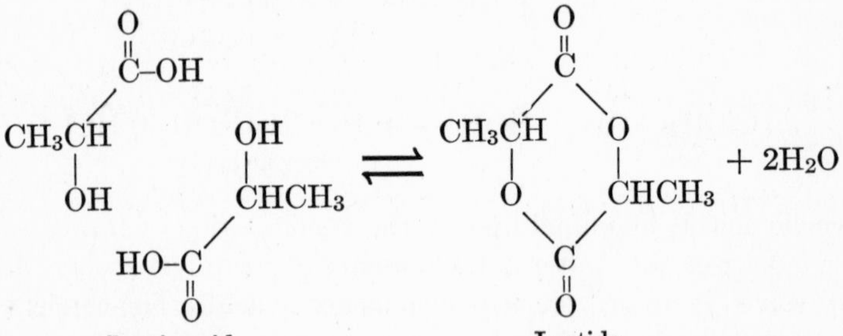

$$2\ CH_3CH(OH)C(=O){-}OH \rightleftharpoons \text{lactide (cyclic } {-}CH(CH_3){-}C(=O){-}O{-}CH(CH_3){-}C(=O){-}O{-}) + 2H_2O$$

Lactic acid — Lactide

Other α-hydroxy acids behave in the same way when subjected to dehydration.

Malic acid occurs in maple sap, in apples, and in other fruits. Tartaric acid, as the potassium acid salt, is obtained from argol or wine lees which are formed in the preparation of wine. Citric acid is a constituent of all citrus fruits. It is extracted from lemons and is also prepared by the action of molds on sugar solutions.

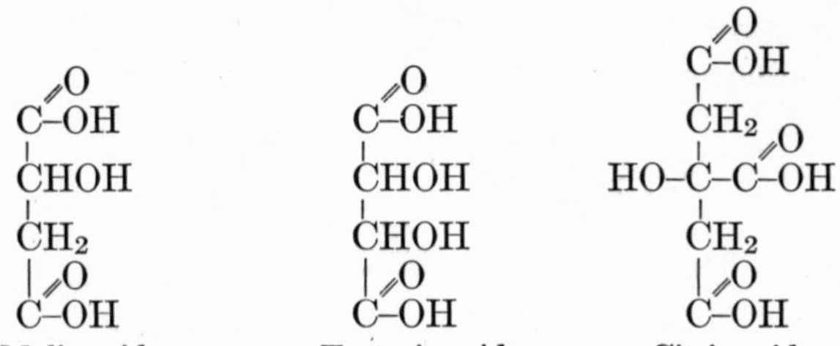

$$\begin{array}{c}COOH\\ |\\ CHOH\\ |\\ CH_2\\ |\\ COOH\end{array}$$
Malic acid

$$\begin{array}{c}COOH\\ |\\ CHOH\\ |\\ CHOH\\ |\\ COOH\end{array}$$
Tartaric acid

$$\begin{array}{c}COOH\\ |\\ CH_2\\ |\\ HO-C-COOH\\ |\\ CH_2\\ |\\ COOH\end{array}$$
Citric acid

Lactic, malic, and tartaric acids each occur in isomeric forms which differ in their action on polarized light and are said to be optical isomers. This phenomenon is discussed in Chapter 13.

β-Hydroxy acids usually are obtained by reduction of the corresponding ketonic acids or by means of the Reformatsky reaction (p. 296). β-Hydroxybutyric acid is made by the careful oxidation of aldol (p. 87). β-Hydroxypropionic acid can be obtained from ethylene chlorohydrin.

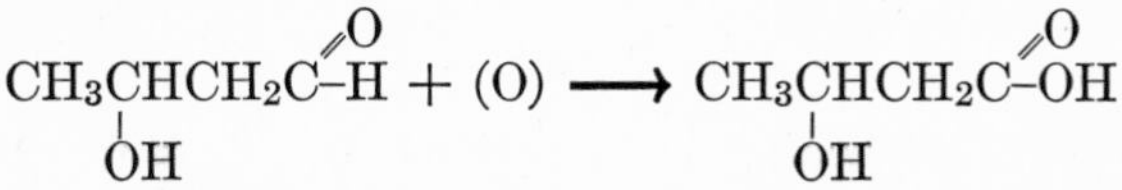

$$\underset{\text{Aldol}}{CH_3CH(OH)CH_2C(=O)H} + (O) \longrightarrow \underset{\beta\text{-Hydroxybutyric acid}}{CH_3CH(OH)CH_2C(=O)OH}$$

$$\underset{\text{Ethylene chlorohydrin}}{HOCH_2CH_2Cl} \xrightarrow{KCN} \underset{\text{Ethylene cyanohydrin}}{HOCH_2CH_2CN} \xrightarrow{H_2O} \underset{\beta\text{-Hydroxypropionic acid}}{HOCH_2CH_2C(=O)OH}$$

The β-hydroxy acids which contain a hydrogen atom on the α-carbon atom are rather unstable. On heating they lose the elements of water, forming unsaturated acids. β-Hydroxypropionic acid, for example, yields acrylic acid.

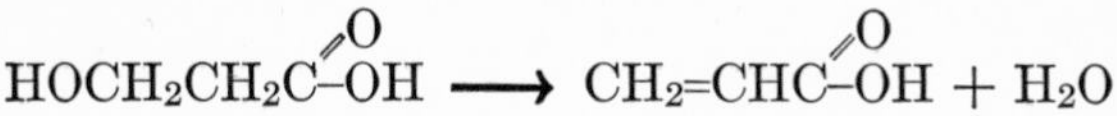

$$HOCH_2CH_2C(=O)OH \longrightarrow \underset{\text{Acrylic acid}}{CH_2{=}CHC(=O)OH} + H_2O$$

Tartaric acid, when heated with sodium hydrogen sulfate, not only suffers the loss of water but also undergoes decarboxylation. The product is the simplest keto acid pyruvic acid.

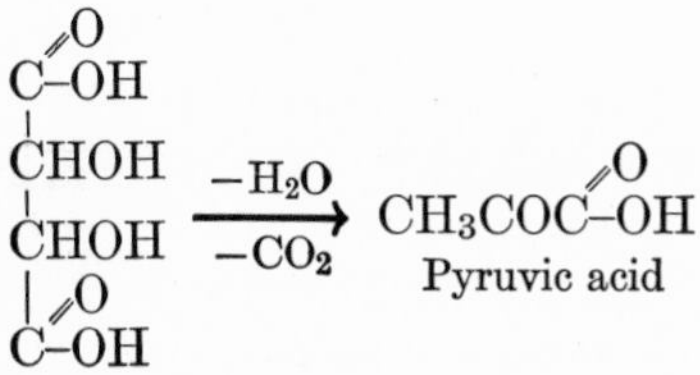

$$\begin{array}{c}COOH\\ |\\ CHOH\\ |\\ CHOH\\ |\\ COOH\end{array} \xrightarrow[-CO_2]{-H_2O} \underset{\text{Pyruvic acid}}{CH_3COC(=O)OH}$$

Citric acid also loses water at higher temperatures. The product is the corresponding unsaturated acid, aconitic acid.

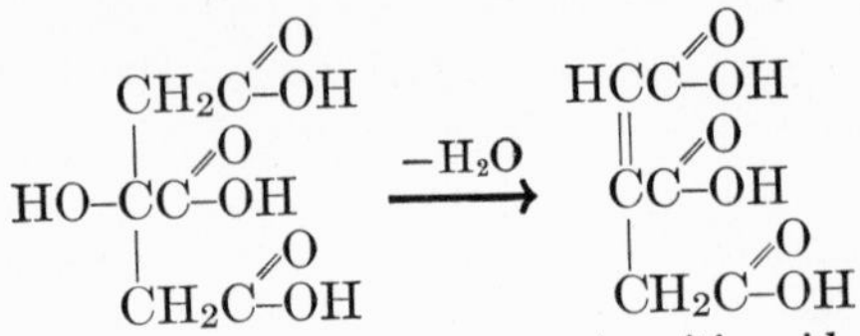

$$\begin{array}{l} CH_2C(=O)\text{–}OH \\ | \\ HO\text{–}CC(=O)\text{–}OH \\ | \\ CH_2C(=O)\text{–}OH \end{array} \xrightarrow{-H_2O} \begin{array}{l} HCC(=O)\text{–}OH \\ \| \\ CC(=O)\text{–}OH \\ | \\ CH_2C(=O)\text{–}OH \end{array}$$

Citric acid — Aconitic acid

If the decomposition is carried out by rapid distillation of the acid, decarboxylation occurs also, and the product is a mixture of the anhydrides of itaconic and citraconic acids.

$$\begin{array}{l} CH_2C(=O)\text{–}OH \\ | \\ CH_2{=}CC(=O)\text{–}OH \end{array} \qquad \begin{array}{l} CH_3CC(=O)\text{–}OH \\ \| \\ HCC(=O)\text{–}OH \end{array}$$

Itaconic acid — Citraconic acid

When citric acid is heated with sulfuric acid it loses water and carbon monoxide and yields acetonedicarboxylic acid.

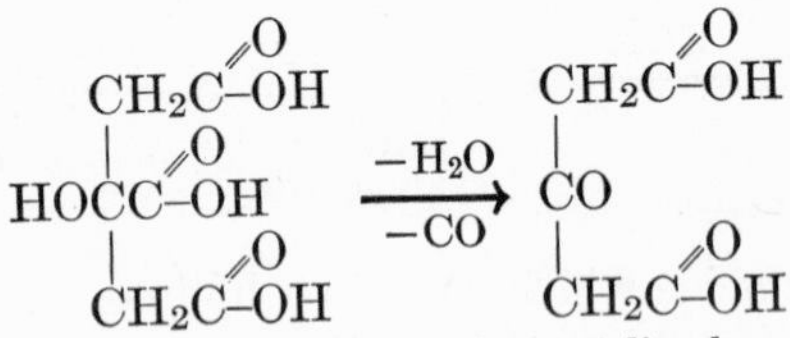

$$\begin{array}{l} CH_2C(=O)\text{–}OH \\ | \\ HOCC(=O)\text{–}OH \\ | \\ CH_2C(=O)\text{–}OH \end{array} \xrightarrow[-CO]{-H_2O} \begin{array}{l} CH_2C(=O)\text{–}OH \\ | \\ CO \\ | \\ CH_2C(=O)\text{–}OH \end{array}$$

Acetonedicarboxylic acid

Loss of carbon monoxide and water is characteristic of α-hydroxy acids.

γ-Hydroxy acids are difficult to prepare. They lose water spontaneously to form inner esters known as lactones. For example, reduction of the keto acid levulinic acid (p. 194) yields γ-hydroxyvaleric acid, which readily forms γ-valerolactone.

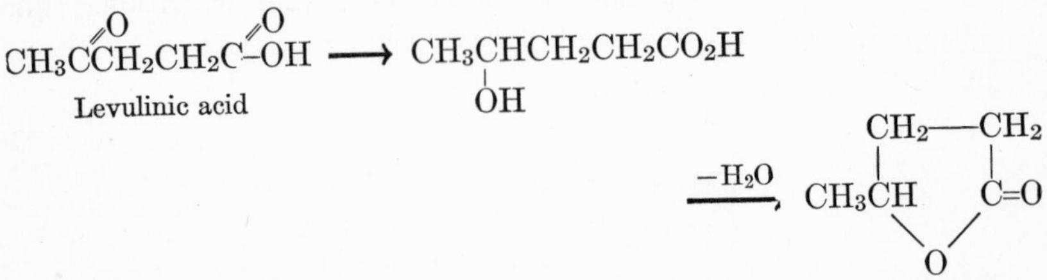

$$CH_3C(=O)CH_2CH_2C(=O)\text{–}OH \longrightarrow CH_3CH(OH)CH_2CH_2CO_2H$$

Levulinic acid

$$\xrightarrow{-H_2O} \begin{array}{ccc} & CH_2\text{——}CH_2 & \\ & | \qquad\quad | & \\ CH_3CH & & C{=}O \\ & \diagdown \ \diagup & \\ & O & \end{array}$$

γ-Valerolactone

Unsaturated Acids

The most common unsaturated acids are those which have the double bond between the α- and β-carbon atoms. They are called α,β-unsaturated acids. The simplest member of the series is acrylic acid, whose preparation from β-hydroxypropionic acid has been mentioned. It may also be obtained by the careful oxidation of allyl alcohol or acrolein.

$$\underset{\text{Allyl alcohol}}{CH_2{=}CHCH_2OH} \xrightarrow{[O]} \underset{\text{Acrolein}}{CH_2{=}CHC{\overset{\displaystyle /\!\!/O}{-}}H}$$

$$CH_2{=}CHC{\overset{\displaystyle /\!\!/O}{-}}H \xrightarrow{[O]} \underset{\text{Acrylic acid}}{CH_2{=}CHC{\overset{\displaystyle /\!\!/O}{-}}OH}$$

Crotonic acid may be prepared by the oxidation of crotonaldehyde (p. 87).

$$CH_3CH{=}CHC{\overset{\displaystyle /\!\!/O}{-}}H \xrightarrow{[O]} CH_3CH{=}CHCO_2H$$

There are two isomeric crotonic acids. One is a solid melting at 72° and the other a liquid of melting point 15°. Hydrogenation of either yields n-butyric acid, and ozonization of either gives acetaldehyde, so there can be no question but that the abbreviated structural formula given above represents each of them. The difference between the two isomers can be understood readily by constructing models with tetrahedral carbon atoms. It is found that the inclusion of a double bond results in a rigid structure and that it is impossible for one of the two atoms so joined to rotate with respect to the other. If the two groups attached to each unsaturated carbon atom are different from each other it becomes possible to make two models as shown in the diagram. The isomer in which the two like groups are on the same side is called the *cis* form, and that in which they are on opposite sides, the *trans* form. The two crotonic acids are such a pair; their formulas can be represented as follows:

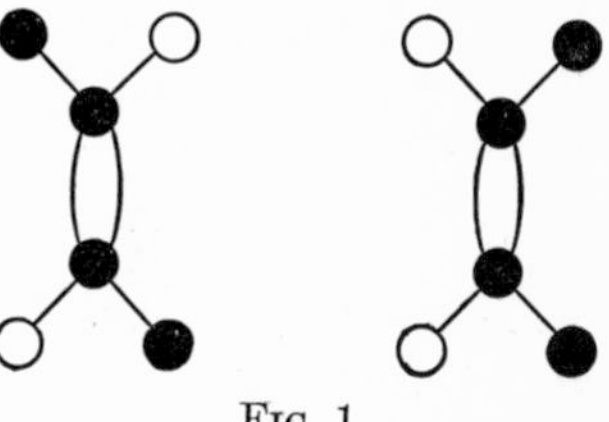

Fig. 1.

$$\begin{array}{c} H{-}C{-}CO_2H \\ \| \\ CH_3{-}C{-}H \end{array} \qquad\qquad \begin{array}{c} H{-}C{-}CO_2H \\ \| \\ H{-}C{-}CH_3 \end{array}$$

Crotonic acid, m.p. 72° (*trans*)   Isocrotonic acid, m.p. 15° (*cis*)

It is interesting to note that here the *trans* form is the higher melting. This is generally true of *cis-trans* pairs.

cis-trans-Isomerism is also called geometrical isomerism. It is a type of stereoisomerism (space isomerism), that is, the *cis* and *trans* forms differ in the space relationships within the molecules.

Methacrylic acid, $CH_2{=}C(CH_3)C({=}O){-}OH$, is one of the most important unsaturated acids. It cannot exist in *cis-trans* modifications, since one of the unsaturated carbon atoms bears two identical groups (hydrogen atoms). The methyl ester is prepared from acetone cyanohydrin by treatment with methyl alcohol and sulfuric acid (p. 85). Methyl methacrylate is of value because it polymerizes readily.

$$CH_3C(CH_3){=}O \xrightarrow{HCN} CH_3{-}C(OH)(CH_3){-}CN \xrightarrow[H_2SO_4]{CH_3OH} \underset{\text{Methyl methacrylate}}{CH_2{=}C(CH_3)C({=}O){-}OCH_3} + NH_4HSO_4$$

$$(n+2)CH_2{=}C(CH_3)(CO_2CH_3) \xrightarrow{\text{catalyst}} \underset{\text{Polymethyl methacrylate}}{{-}CH_2C(CH_3)(CO_2CH_3){-}\left(CH_2C(CH_3)(CO_2CH_3){-}\right)_n{-}CH_2C(CH_3)(CO_2CH_3){-}}$$

The conversion of methyl methacrylate to polymethyl methacrylate can be accomplished by heat, by ultraviolet light, or by the action of organic peroxides. The polymer is more transparent than glass. It softens on heating and so can be molded. Because of its toughness, transparency, and lightness it is used in the windows of airplanes. Because it can be molded easily it finds many other uses, as in lenses, decorative fixtures, and even in dentures. It is sold under the trade names Lucite and Plexiglas.

Polymethyl methacrylate has the peculiar property of conducting light along a curved path. Thus, when a flashlight is held against one end of a U-shaped rod of the material, the beam emerges from the other end, traveling in a direction opposite to its original course. Certain dental and surgical instruments make application of this phenomenon.

Methyl acrylate also polymerizes readily. It is made from ethylene chlorohydrin by way of the cyanohydrin.

$$\underset{\text{Ethylene chlorohydrin}}{HOCH_2CH_2Cl} + NaCN \longrightarrow \underset{\text{Ethylene cyanohydrin}}{HOCH_2CH_2CN} + NaCl$$

$$HOCH_2CH_2CN \xrightarrow[\text{heat}]{H_2SO_4,\ CH_3OH} \underset{\text{Methyl acrylate}}{CH_2{=}CHC({=}O){-}OCH_3}$$

The polymer of methyl acrylate is much softer than that of methyl methacrylate. It is used in the finishing of textiles and leathers.

Maleic and fumaric acids are isomeric unsaturated dibasic acids. Maleic acid is the *cis* isomer and fumaric acid is the *trans* form. In this case it is easy to distinguish between the two isomers, since maleic acid readily forms an anhydride.

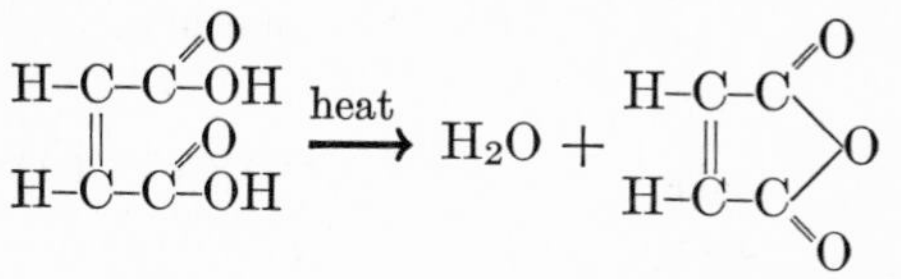

$$\underset{\text{Maleic acid}}{\begin{matrix} H{-}C{-}C({=}O){-}OH \\ \| \\ H{-}C{-}C({=}O){-}OH \end{matrix}} \xrightarrow{\text{heat}} H_2O + \underset{\text{Maleic anhydride}}{\begin{matrix} H{-}C{-}C{=}O \\ \| \quad\quad \rangle O \\ H{-}C{-}C{=}O \end{matrix}}$$

Fumaric acid is converted to an anhydride only under much more vigorous conditions. When heated to high temperatures it isomerizes to maleic acid and the latter yields maleic anhydride.

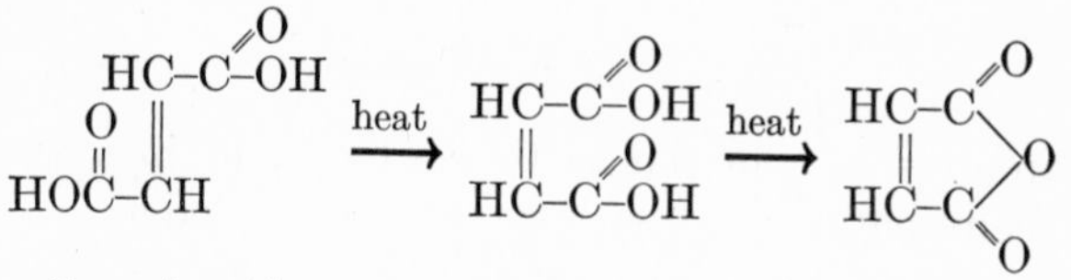

$$\underset{\text{Fumaric acid}}{\begin{matrix} HC{-}C({=}O){-}OH \\ \| \\ HOC({=}O){-}CH \end{matrix}} \xrightarrow{\text{heat}} \underset{\text{Maleic acid}}{\begin{matrix} HC{-}C({=}O){-}OH \\ \| \\ HC{-}C({=}O){-}OH \end{matrix}} \xrightarrow{\text{heat}} \underset{\text{Maleic anhydride}}{\begin{matrix} HC{-}C{=}O \\ \| \quad\quad \rangle O \\ HC{-}C{=}O \end{matrix}}$$

Maleic anhydride is prepared commercially by the catalytic oxidation of benzene.

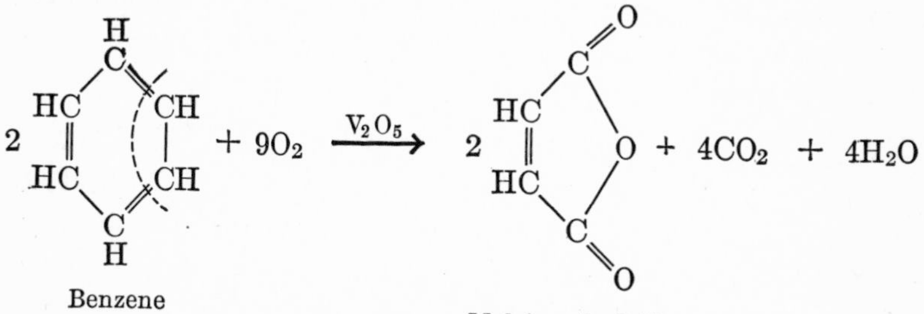

$$2\ \underset{\text{Benzene}}{C_6H_6} + 9O_2 \xrightarrow{V_2O_5} 2\ \underset{\text{Maleic anhydride}}{\begin{matrix} HC{-}C{=}O \\ \| \quad\quad \rangle O \\ HC{-}C{=}O \end{matrix}} + 4CO_2 + 4H_2O$$

The acid is prepared by hydrolysis of the anhydride.

Fumaric acid is made by isomerization of maleic acid. Among the catalysts which bring about the change are sulfur and bromine.

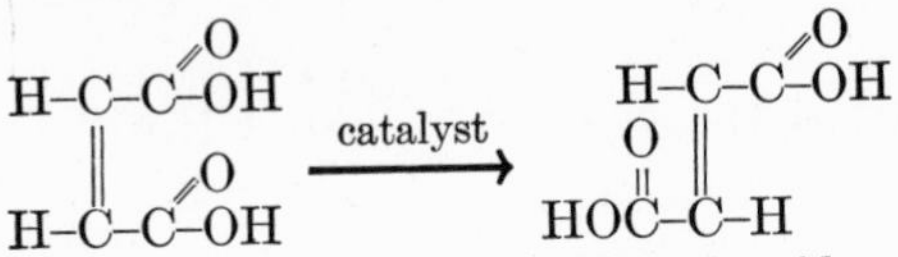

$$\begin{array}{c} \text{H-C-C}\overset{\nearrow O}{}\text{-OH} \\ \| \\ \text{H-C-C}\overset{\nearrow O}{}\text{-OH} \\ \text{Maleic acid} \end{array} \xrightarrow{\text{catalyst}} \begin{array}{c} \text{H-C-C}\overset{\nearrow O}{}\text{-OH} \\ \| \\ \text{HO}\overset{O}{\overset{\|}{C}}\text{-C-H} \\ \text{Fumaric acid} \end{array}$$

Fumaric acid is found in many plants and is present in muscle tissue. The fact that fumaric acid is nontoxic and even occurs in living organisms, whereas maleic acid is a poison, affords a striking illustration of the differences which may exist in the physiological properties of *cis-trans* isomers.

Acetylenic acids are known also. Propiolic acid and acetylenedicarboxylic acid are examples.

$$\underset{\text{Propiolic acid}}{HC{\equiv}CCO_2H} \qquad \underset{\text{Acetylenedicarboxylic acid}}{HO_2CC{\equiv}CCO_2H}$$

Neither of these compounds exists in *cis-trans* modifications. The reason may be seen by examination of the following diagram of an acetylenic compound:

a b

FIG. 2.

The four atoms shown in the acetylene model lie in a straight line; there are no alternative positions for the groups *a* and *b*.

Keto Acids—Tautomerism

Ethyl acetoacetate is the ester of a β-keto acid. It has been known for many years as the product obtained by the action of sodium on ethyl acetate.

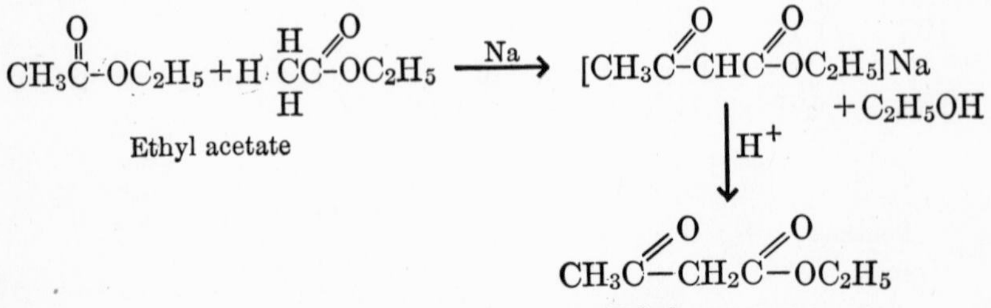

$$\underset{\text{Ethyl acetate}}{CH_3\overset{O}{\overset{\|}{C}}\text{-}OC_2H_5 + H\text{-}\underset{H}{\overset{H}{C}}C\overset{\nearrow O}{}\text{-}OC_2H_5} \xrightarrow{Na} [CH_3\overset{\nearrow O}{C}\text{-}CH\overset{\nearrow O}{C}\text{-}OC_2H_5]Na + C_2H_5OH$$

$$\downarrow H^+$$

$$\underset{\text{Ethyl acetoacetate}}{CH_3\overset{\nearrow O}{C}\text{—}CH_2\overset{\nearrow O}{C}\text{—}OC_2H_5}$$

The ethyl alcohol reacts with the sodium to form sodium ethoxide. The latter appears to be the actual catalyst. Presumably, when sodium is used a small amount of sodium ethoxide is produced from a trace of alcohol present in the ethyl acetate. The reaction then starts, and more of the catalyst is produced from the alcohol formed. In reactions of this type it is frequently desirable to add a little alcohol, if sodium is being used, or to use dry sodium ethoxide as the catalyst. The reaction is known as the acetoacetic ester condensation. It is generally applicable to esters of the formula $RCH_2C(=O)-OC_2H_5$, yielding β-keto esters of the type $RCH_2C(=O)-CH(R)C(=O)-OC_2H_5$.

Acetoacetic acid is rarely prepared. It is unstable and undergoes decarboxylation to yield acetone and carbon dioxide.

$$CH_3COCH_2C(=O)-OH \longrightarrow CH_3COCH_3 + CO_2$$

This type of reaction is characteristic of β-keto acids. The formation of pyruvic acid from tartaric acid (p. 151) probably involves a β-keto acid as an intermediate. The steps in this interesting transformation appear to be the following:

$$HO-C(=O)-CHOH-CHOH-C(=O)-OH \xrightarrow{-H_2O} HO-C(=O)-CH{=}COH-C(=O)-OH \longrightarrow HO-C(=O)-CH_2-C{=}O-C(=O)-OH \xrightarrow{-CO_2} CH_3COC(=O)-OH$$

Ethyl acetoacetate, commonly known as acetoacetic ester, has properties which were puzzling to the chemists who first investigated it. As a keto ester, it would be expected to show the properties of ketones as well as those of esters. And, indeed, it does form carbonyl derivatives such as a sodium bisulfite addition product (p. 83) and also gives the reactions typical of esters, such as hydrolysis to an acid.

$$CH_3C(=O)-CH_2C(=O)-OC_2H_5 + NaHSO_3 \longrightarrow CH_3C(SO_3Na)(OH)CH_2C(=O)-OC_2H_5$$

Sodium bisulfite addition product of acetoacetic ester

$$CH_3C(=O)-CH_2C(=O)-OC_2H_5 + H_2O \rightleftharpoons CH_3C(=O)-CH_2C(=O)-OH + C_2H_5OH$$

Acetoacetic acid

The curious fact is that a sample of the same lot of ester which gives the above reactions also behaves as a hydroxyl compound. For example, it gives a color with ferric chloride, a test which is characteristic of phenols (p. 165), and it can be converted to a sodium derivative by the action of sodium or sodium ethoxide.

$$CH_3C(=O)-CH_2C(=O)-OC_2H_5 + NaOC_2H_5$$

$$\longrightarrow \left[CH_3C(=O)-CHC(=O)-OC_2H_5\right]^- Na^+ + C_2H_5OH$$

Sodioacetoacetic ester

In order to account for all these reactions it was proposed that ordinary acetoacetic ester is a mixture of two compounds, called the *keto* and *enol* forms.

$$\underset{\text{(keto form)}}{CH_3C(=O)-CH_2C(=O)-OC_2H_5} \rightleftharpoons \underset{\text{(enol form, classical formula)}}{CH_3C(O\text{-}H)=CH-C(=O)-OC_2H_5}$$

Acetoacetic ester

If it is postulated that the two forms are in equilibrium, then it is possible to explain all the reactions. A reagent, such as sodium ethoxide, which attacks the enol form causes the equilibrium to shift until all the material has been converted to an enol derivative. A carbonyl reagent shifts the equilibrium in the other direction so that the sample behaves as if it contained only the keto form. The phenomenon of reversible interconversion between isomeric forms has been named *tautomerism.* The forms in mobile equilibrium are said to be tautomers of each other. Thus, the enol form of acetoacetic ester is a tautomer of the keto form.

The sodio derivative was formerly considered to have a structure, corresponding to that of the enol, in which the hydrogen atom of the hydroxyl group is replaced by a sodium atom. Since the sodio derivative is an ionic salt this representation cannot be strictly correct. If the sodium is written as a cation, then the remainder must be written as an anion and the question of the location of the negative charge arises. It may be carried by the oxygen atom or by the carbon atom or it may be divided between them. For this reason the formula just shown will be used in the sequel, and no attempt to show the actual location of the negative charge will be made.

The correctness of the hypothesis with respect to the tautomeric forms of acetoacetic ester has been demonstrated by their separation. This can be accomplished by careful distillation in quartz apparatus. Glass apparatus is to be avoided because alkali, always present in traces on the surface of glass, catalyzes the interchange of the two forms. The pure enol form has been found to possess all the chemical properties to be expected on the basis of the formula given above. It gives the enol reactions rapidly but does not react as a ketone except as it slowly tautomerizes. Likewise the pure keto form reacts readily as a carbonyl compound but responds only slowly to enol reagents. Either of the pure forms slowly changes to ordinary acetoacetic ester on standing. In the presence of a trace of alkali the change is rapid. The equilibrium mixture obtained from either form contains about 10 per cent of the enol.

In the separation of the tautomeric forms of acetoacetic ester by distillation the enol form was found to be the lower boiling. At the time, this was a surprising observation, since ketones ordinarily boil lower than alcohols of similar structure (acetone, b.p. 56.1°; isopropyl alcohol, b.p. 82.3°). However, when it is recalled that the boiling points of alcohols are "abnormal" because of association (p. 51), a glance at the formula of the enol is sufficient to explain the apparent anomaly. The hydrogen atom of the hydroxyl group is so near the carbonyl oxygen of the ester group that coordination occurs between them, forming a chelate ring (p. 97).

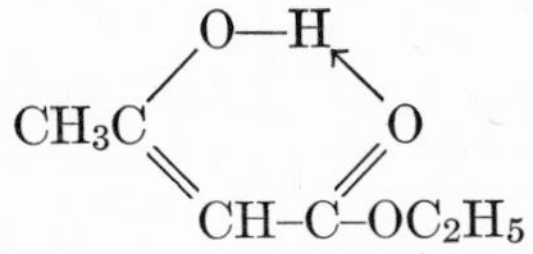

$$\begin{array}{ccccc} & & O\!-\!H & \leftarrow & \\ & / & & & \searrow \\ CH_3C & & & & O \\ & \backslash\backslash & & // & \\ & & CH\!-\!C\!-\!OC_2H_5 & & \end{array}$$

Enol of acetoacetic ester

The hydrogen atom of the hydroxyl group is thus not available for coordination with an oxygen atom of another molecule and consequently association does not occur. It is believed that chelation tends to stabilize the enol form. This would account for the fact that enols which are incapable of chelation, such as the hypothetical vinyl alcohol $CH_2{=}CHOH$ (p. 26), have not been isolated.

The Use of Acetoacetic Ester and Malonic Ester in Synthesis

As indicated above, acetoacetic ester is readily converted to its sodio derivative. The latter can be *alkylated* by treatment with alkyl halides; either one or two alkyl groups can be introduced. The following general equations are illustrative.

$$CH_3\overset{\displaystyle O}{\overset{/\!/}{C}}\!-\!CH_2\overset{\displaystyle O}{\overset{/\!/}{C}}\!-\!OC_2H_5 \xrightarrow[\text{alcohol solution}]{NaOC_2H_5} \left[CH_3\overset{\displaystyle O}{\overset{/\!/}{C}}\!-\!CH\overset{\displaystyle O}{\overset{/\!/}{C}}\!-\!OC_2H_5\right]^- Na^+$$

$$\left[CH_3\overset{O}{\overset{\|}{C}}-CH\overset{O}{\overset{\|}{C}}-OC_2H_5\right]^- Na^+ + RBr \xrightarrow[\text{solution}]{\text{alcohol}} CH_3\overset{O}{\overset{\|}{C}}-\underset{R}{\underset{|}{C}}H\overset{O}{\overset{\|}{C}}-OC_2H_5 + NaBr$$

$$CH_3\overset{O}{\overset{\|}{C}}-\underset{R}{\underset{|}{C}}H\overset{O}{\overset{\|}{C}}-OC_2H_5 \xrightarrow{NaOC_2H_5} \left[CH_3\overset{O}{\overset{\|}{C}}-\underset{R}{\underset{|}{C}}-\overset{O}{\overset{\|}{C}}-OC_2H_5\right]^- Na^+$$

$$\left[CH_3\overset{O}{\overset{\|}{C}}-\underset{R}{\underset{|}{C}}\overset{O}{\overset{\|}{C}}-OC_2H_5\right]^- Na^+ + R'Br \longrightarrow CH_3\overset{O}{\overset{\|}{C}}-\underset{R}{\overset{R'}{\overset{|}{\underset{|}{C}}}}-\overset{O}{\overset{\|}{C}}-OC_2H_5 + NaBr$$

The value of these reactions in synthesis lies in the fact that the substituted acetoacetic esters may be converted to either ketones or monobasic acids. If a ketone is desired the substituted ester is saponified by mild treatment with alkali. Acidification of the reaction mixture yields the substituted acetoacetic acid. On heating, the latter undergoes decarboxylation to a ketone.

$$CH_3\overset{O}{\overset{\|}{C}}-\underset{R}{\overset{R'}{\overset{|}{\underset{|}{C}}}}-\overset{O}{\overset{\|}{C}}-OC_2H_5 \longrightarrow CH_3\overset{O}{\overset{\|}{C}}-\underset{R}{\overset{R'}{\overset{|}{\underset{|}{C}}}}-\overset{O}{\overset{\|}{C}}-OH \longrightarrow CH_3\overset{O}{\overset{\|}{C}}-\underset{R}{\underset{|}{C}}HR' + CO_2$$

In practice, this synthesis of disubstituted ketones is of little value; the hydrolysis of the dialkylated ester requires such strenuous conditions that the acid cleavage predominates.

If the substituted acetoacetic ester is heated with strong alkali, cleavage between the α- and β-carbon atoms occurs. The products are the sodium salts of acetic acid and a higher acid.

$$CH_3\overset{O}{\overset{\|}{C}}-\underset{R}{\overset{R'}{\overset{|}{\underset{|}{C}}}}-\overset{O}{\overset{\|}{C}}\vdots OC_2H_5 \quad NaO\vdots H \longrightarrow CH_3\overset{O}{\overset{\|}{C}}\vdots-\underset{R}{\overset{R'}{\overset{|}{\underset{|}{C}}}}-\overset{O}{\overset{\|}{C}}-ONa \quad NaO\vdots H \longrightarrow CH_3\overset{O}{\overset{\|}{C}}-ONa + \begin{matrix}R\\ \ \ \diagdown\\ \ \ \diagup\\ R\end{matrix}CH\overset{O}{\overset{\|}{C}}-ONa$$

Both the ketone cleavage and the acid cleavage may be carried out on monoalkyl acetoacetic esters. It is thus evident that from acetoacetic ester and alkyl halides one may prepare mono- and dialkylacetones and mono- and dialkylacetic acids. In the dialkyl derivatives the substituents are attached to the same carbon atom and may be alike or different. These various products may be represented as follows.

$$CH_3C(=O)\text{-}CH_2R \qquad CH_3C(=O)\text{-}CHR(R') \qquad CH_3C(=O)\text{-}CHR(R)$$

$$RCH_2C(=O)\text{-}OH \qquad (R)(R')\!>\!CHC(=O)\text{-}OH \qquad (R)(R)\!>\!CHC(=O)\text{-}OH$$

In actual laboratory work it is more convenient to prepare the *acids* from malonic ester. Like acetoacetic ester, malonic ester yields a sodio derivative which reacts with alkyl halides.

$$\underset{\text{Malonic ester}}{C_2H_5O\overset{O}{\overset{\|}{C}}CH_2C(=O)\text{-}OC_2H_5} + NaOC_2H_5 \longrightarrow \underset{\text{Sodio malonic ester}}{\left[C_2H_5O\overset{O}{\overset{\|}{C}}CHC(=O)\text{-}OC_2H_5\right]^-} Na^+ + C_2H_5OH$$

$$\left[C_2H_5O\overset{O}{\overset{\|}{C}}CHC(=O)\text{-}OC_2H_5\right]^- Na^+ + RBr \longrightarrow C_2H_5O\overset{O}{\overset{\|}{C}}\underset{R}{\underset{|}{C}}HC(=O)\text{-}OC_2H_5 + NaBr$$

$$\left[C_2H_5O\overset{O}{\overset{\|}{C}}\underset{R}{\underset{|}{C}}HC(=O)\text{-}OC_2H_5\right] + NaOC_2H_5 \longrightarrow \left[C_2H_5O\overset{O}{\overset{\|}{C}}\underset{R}{\underset{|}{C}}C(=O)\text{-}OC_2H_5\right]^- Na^+ + C_2H_5OH$$

$$\left[C_2H_5O\overset{O}{\overset{\|}{C}}\underset{R}{\underset{|}{C}}C(=O)\text{-}OC_2H_5\right]^- Na^+ + R'Br \longrightarrow C_2H_5O\overset{O}{\overset{\|}{C}}\overset{R'}{\overset{|}{\underset{R}{\underset{|}{C}}}}C(=O)\text{-}OC_2H_5 + NaBr$$

Cleavage of the substituted malonic ester yields only the substituted acid. It is usually accomplished by saponification of the ester followed by isolation and decarboxylation of the malonic acid.

$$C_2H_5O\overset{O}{\overset{\|}{C}}-\overset{R'}{\overset{|}{\underset{R}{\underset{|}{C}}}}-\overset{O}{\overset{\|}{C}}OC_2H_5 \longrightarrow H\ O\overset{O}{\overset{\|}{C}}-\overset{R'}{\overset{|}{\underset{R}{\underset{|}{C}}}}-\overset{O}{\overset{\|}{C}}OH \longrightarrow \begin{matrix}R'\\ \quad\diagdown\\ \quad\diagup\\ R\end{matrix}CHCO_2H + CO_2$$

The substituted acetic acids so obtained are identical with those that can be prepared from acetoacetic ester. The advantage in the use of malonic ester lies in the fact that the yields are usually better, since the ketone cleavage which occurs as a side reaction in the acid cleavage of a substituted acetoacetic ester cannot occur in the corresponding malonic ester.

Aryl halides do not react with the sodio derivatives of acetoacetic and malonic esters and hence cannot be used in the syntheses indicated above. Among the alkyl halides those which are primary usually give excellent yields. Good results are obtained with secondary halides, but the yields from tertiary halides are negligible.

Barbituric Acid and Its Derivatives. When malonic ester and urea are brought together in the presence of sodium ethoxide they react by elimination of alcohol to form a cyclic substance known as barbituric acid.

```
     O                                          O
     ‖                                          ‖
    C–OC2H5   H2N                              C—NH
   /              \            NaOC2H5        /     \
CH2                C=O   ─────────→     CH2          C=O + 2C2H5OH
   \              /                           \     /
    C–OC2H5   H2N                              C—NH
     ‖                                          ‖
     O                                          O
```

Barbituric acid

It will be noted that this compound is not a carboxylic acid. Its acidic property may be attributed to the presence of the two imide groups, or to the existence of an enol form.

```
        O                          OH
        ‖                          |
       C–NH                       C–N
      /    \                     //   \\
   CH2      C=O   ⇌    H–C              C–OH
      \    /                     \    /
       C–NH                       C=N
        ‖                          |
        O                          OH
   (keto form)                 (enol form)
```

Barbituric acid

Barbituric acid is a hypnotic and a sedative but in medicine it has been displaced by derivatives which are more effective. A great variety of derivatives have been prepared by alkylating malonic ester before condensing it with urea. For example, barbital (diethylbarbituric acid) is prepared from ethyl diethylmalonate and urea.

$$
\begin{array}{lll}
 & \overset{\displaystyle O}{\overset{\|}{C}}\text{–}OC_2H_5 & H_2N \diagdown \\
C_2H_5 \diagdown \; C \diagup & & \qquad C{=}O \\
C_2H_5 \diagup \; \diagdown & & \\
 & \underset{\displaystyle O}{\underset{\|}{C}}\text{–}OC_2H_5 & H_2N \diagup
\end{array}
$$

$$
\xrightarrow{NaOC_2H_5}
\begin{array}{lcl}
 & \overset{\displaystyle O}{\overset{\|}{C}}\text{–}NH & \\
C_2H_5 \diagdown \; C & & C{=}O + 2C_2H_5OH \\
C_2H_5 \diagup & & \\
 & \underset{\displaystyle O}{\underset{\|}{C}}\text{–}NH &
\end{array}
$$

Barbital

Other common barbiturates are amytal (isoamylethylbarbituric acid), alurate (allylisopropylbarbituric acid), and phenobarbital (phenylethylbarbituric acid), the formulas of which appear below.

$$
\begin{array}{lcl}
 & \overset{\displaystyle O}{\overset{\|}{C}}\text{–}NH & \\
CH_3CH_2 \diagdown \; C & & C{=}O \\
(CH_3)_2CHCH_2CH_2 \diagup & & \\
 & \underset{\displaystyle O}{\underset{\|}{C}}\text{–}NH &
\end{array}
$$

Amytal

$$
\begin{array}{lcl}
 & \overset{\displaystyle O}{\overset{\|}{C}}\text{–}NH & \\
CH_2{=}CHCH_2 \diagdown \; C & & C{=}O \\
CH_3\underset{\displaystyle CH_3}{\underset{|}{CH}} \diagup & & \\
 & \underset{\displaystyle O}{\underset{\|}{C}}\text{–}NH &
\end{array}
$$

Alurate

$$
\begin{array}{lcl}
 & \overset{\displaystyle O}{\overset{\|}{C}}\text{–}NH & \\
C_6H_5 \diagdown \; C & & C{=}O \\
CH_3CH_2 \diagup & & \\
 & \underset{\displaystyle O}{\underset{\|}{C}}\text{–}NH &
\end{array}
$$

Phenobarbital

PROBLEMS

1. Give equations for commercial preparations of the following substances from coal, petroleum, and inorganic substances: (*a*) oxalic acid, (*b*) malonic acid, (*c*) succinic acid, (*d*) adipic acid, (*e*) urea, (*f*) nylon, (*g*) barbituric acid, (*h*) phthalic acid.

2. By means of formulas or equations, illustrate the following: (*a*) condensation polymerization, (*b*) lactone, (*c*) lactide, (*d*) tautomers, (*e*) *cis-trans* isomers, (*f*) imide, (*g*) cross linking, (*h*) polyester, (*i*) chelation, (*j*) enolization, (*k*) ketonization.

3. Give equations for the preparation of the following from acetoacetic ester, malonic ester, ethyl alcohol, and *n*-butyl alcohol: (*a*) caproic acid, (*b*) methyl *n*-amyl ketone, (*c*) di-*n*-butylacetic acid, (*d*) 2-ethylhexanoic acid.

4. Predict the effect of heating on: (*a*) methylmalonic acid, (*b*) phthalic acid, (*c*) α-hydroxycaproic acid, (*d*) β-hydroxycaproic acid, (*e*) γ-hydroxycaproic acid, (*f*) δ-hydroxycaproic acid, (*g*) ε-hydroxycaproic acid, (*h*) β-ketocaproic acid, (*i*) succinamic acid.

SUGGESTED READING

E. K. Bolton, "The Development of Nylon" (Chemical Industry Medal Address), *Ind. Eng. Chem.*, *34*, 53 (1942).

CHAPTER 12

Phenols

The properties of compounds containing a hydroxyl group directly attached to an aromatic ring are altogether different from those of the alcohols. For this reason, these substances constitute a separate class of organic compounds. They are called phenols, after the name of the simplest member.

Phenol itself occurs in coal tar, but the supply so available has long been augmented by the commercial synthesis of the substance. The oldest industrial preparation, one which is still in use, is the alkali fusion of sodium benzenesulfonate. The raw materials are benzene, sulfuric acid, and sodium hydroxide.

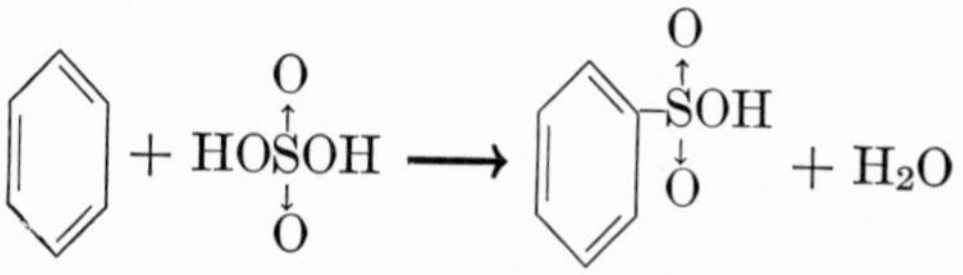

$$C_6H_6 + HOSO_2OH \longrightarrow C_6H_5SO_2OH + H_2O$$

Benzenesulfonic acid

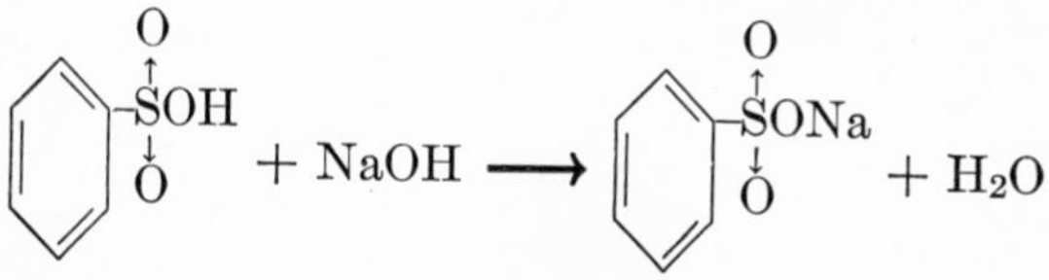

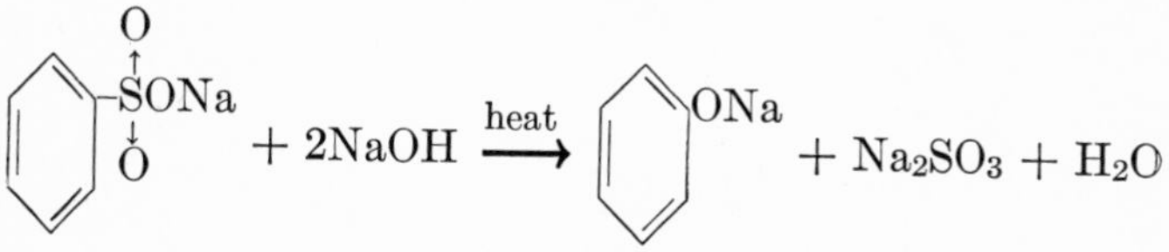

$$C_6H_5SO_2OH + NaOH \longrightarrow C_6H_5SO_2ONa + H_2O$$

$$C_6H_5SO_2ONa + 2NaOH \xrightarrow{\text{heat}} C_6H_5ONa + Na_2SO_3 + H_2O$$

Sodium phenoxide

$$2\,C_6H_5ONa + H_2SO_4 \longrightarrow 2\,C_6H_5OH + Na_2SO_4$$

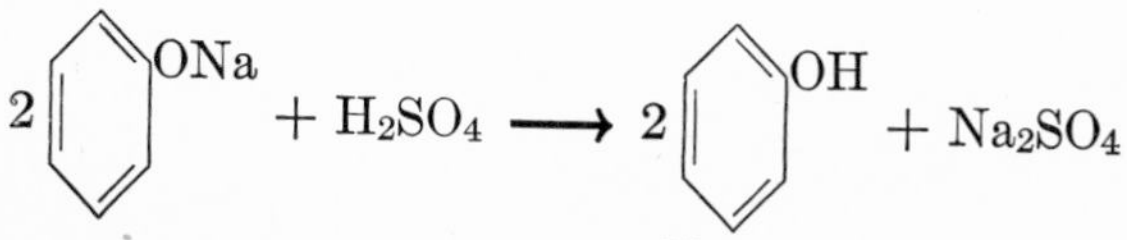

Phenol
(m.p. 41°; b.p. 182°)

The more recent methods involve the hydrolysis of chlorobenzene. Aromatic halides are ordinarily very resistant to hydrolysis, and drastic conditions are required to effect the reaction. In one process chlorobenzene is heated under pressure with sodium hydroxide to give sodium phenoxide and sodium chloride. The chlorobenzene may be prepared by chlorination, so the raw materials are benzene, chlorine, and sodium hydroxide.

$$C_6H_6 + Cl_2 \xrightarrow{FeCl_3} C_6H_5Cl + HCl$$

$$C_6H_5Cl + 2NaOH \xrightarrow{heat} C_6H_5ONa + NaCl + H_2O$$

Sodium phenoxide

$$C_6H_5ONa + HCl \longrightarrow C_6H_5OH + NaCl$$

Phenol

The Raschig process (p. 247) is similar.

In the newest method phenol is made from cumene (p. 46) in a process that also produces acetone. The steps involved are oxidation with air and decomposition of the resulting hydroperoxide.

$$C_6H_5CH(CH_3)_2 + O_2 \rightarrow C_6H_5C(CH_3)_2\text{–OOH} \xrightarrow{H^+} C_6H_5OH + CH_3COCH_3$$

Cumene hydroperoxide

Cumene, having a tertiary C–H linkage which is also in the α-position of a side chain, is peculiarly susceptible to autoxidation. The phenol and acetone, produced in the second step, are easily separated from each other and from unchanged cumene, which is recycled. Since cumene is made by the Friedel-Crafts reaction (p. 44) the process permits the conversion of benzene and propylene to phenol and acetone.

The cresols and naphthols are important phenols related to toluene and naphthalene, respectively. The cresols are present in coal tar and are obtained by extraction of the middle oil. For most purposes a mixture of the three is used. The naphthols are made by alkali fusion of the corresponding naphthalenesulfonic acids (p. 48). The formulas of the cresols and naphthols are given below.

CH_3, OH	CH_3, OH	CH_3, OH	OH	OH
o-Cresol (m.p. 31°; b.p. 191°)	*m*-Cresol (m.p. 10°; b.p. 203°)	*p*-Cresol (m.p. 35°; b.p. 201°)	α-Naphthol (m.p. 96°)	β-Naphthol (m.p. 122°)

Other phenols of importance in commerce are picric acid (2,4,6-trinitrophenol) and the dihydroxybenzenes, catechol (pyrocatechol), resorcinol, and hydroquinone. The preparations of these compounds are given later. Their structures are as follows:

OH, NO_2, NO_2, NO_2	OH, OH	OH, OH	OH, OH
Picric acid (m.p. 122°)	Catechol (m.p. 104°)	Resorcinol (m.p. 110°)	Hydroquinone (m.p. 169°)

In the laboratory, phenols are usually prepared by the alkali fusion of sulfonates or by the hydrolysis of diazonium salts (p. 128).

From the melting points (given under the formulas) it can be seen that most of the phenols are solids. Phenol and *o*- and *p*-cresols are often encountered as liquids because a small amount of water, taken up from the air, is sufficient to lower their melting points to values below room temperature.

Reactions of Phenols

The common name for phenol, "carbolic acid," originates from the fact that phenols are weakly acidic. Most of them are only slightly soluble in water, but they dissolve readily in aqueous sodium hydroxide because of the conversion to salts. The formation of sodium phenoxide is an example.

$$C_6H_5OH + NaOH \rightleftharpoons C_6H_5ONa + H_2O$$

Sodium phenoxide

Since the phenols are very weak acids, solutions of their salts are alkaline. Addition of a slightly stronger acid, such as carbon dioxide (carbonic acid), liberates the free phenol. This property can be used in the laboratory to distinguish phenols from carboxylic acids, for the latter are not displaced from their salts by carbon dioxide.

Most phenols give highly colored compounds when added to aqueous ferric chloride. This property is often used as a qualitative test for phenols; enols (p. 158) also give colors.

It will be recalled that the alcohols are neutral substances. In the phenols the hydroxyl group is attached to an unsaturated carbon atom, and the compounds are more closely related structurally to the enols (p. 158) than to the alcohols. As in the case of carboxylic acids (p. 94), removal of the proton of the hydroxyl group leaves an anion which is resonance-stabilized. Resonance stabilization of the phenoxide ion causes it to form readily, i.e., renders phenol acidic.

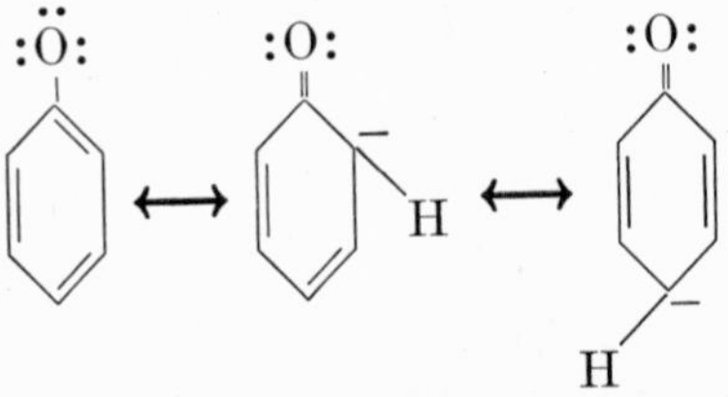

:Ö: ⟷ :O: H ⟷ :O: H

In most of their chemical properties the phenols show little resemblance to alcohols. For example, they do not react with halogen acids to form halides. In some instances the hydroxyl group of a phenol can be replaced by halogen by treatment with phosphorus halides, but the reaction is of little value in synthesis (p. 417). Phenols cannot be esterified by the direct action of an organic acid, the process most often used in the preparation of esters of alcohols. Esters can be obtained by the action of acyl chlorides or anhydrides on phenols. The preparation of *p*-cresyl acetate is an example.

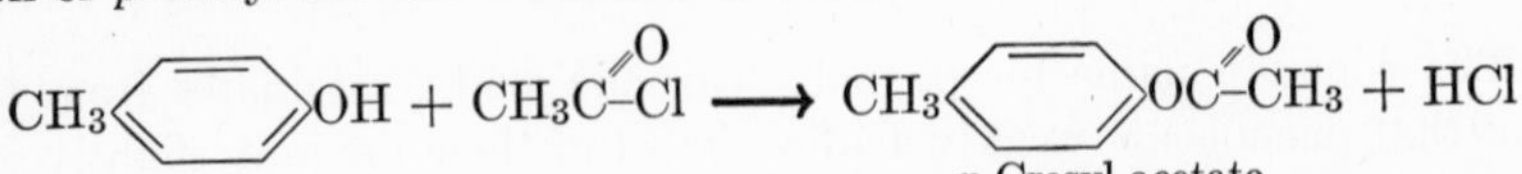

$$CH_3C_6H_4OH + CH_3C(=O)Cl \longrightarrow CH_3C_6H_4OC(=O)CH_3 + HCl$$

p-Cresyl acetate

Alkyl ethers of phenols are easily obtained by treating sodium salts of phenols with alkyl halides or alkyl sulfates. For example, anisole is made from sodium phenoxide and methyl sulfate.

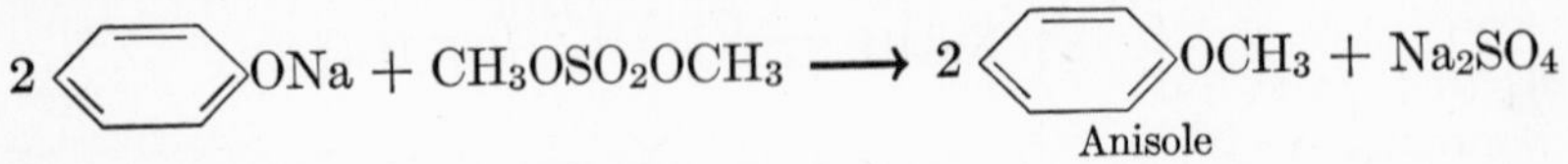

$$2\,C_6H_5ONa + CH_3OSO_2OCH_3 \longrightarrow 2\,C_6H_5OCH_3 + Na_2SO_4$$

Anisole

Diaryl ethers can be made from aryl halides and salts of phenols, but, because of the low reactivity of aryl halides, drastic conditions are required.

The properties generally considered most characteristic of phenols, aside from their acidity, are those involving reactions of the aromatic ring. The presence of the hydroxyl group greatly modifies the properties of the ring. In particular, substitution reactions occur with remarkable ease. For example, cold dilute nitric acid (15 per cent) converts phenol to a mixture of *o*- and *p*-nitrophenols, whereas the nitration of benzene requires treatment with a hot mixture of concentrated nitric and sulfuric acids (p. 39).

$$C_6H_5OH + HONO_2 \longrightarrow H_2O + o\text{-}NO_2C_6H_4OH \text{ and } p\text{-}NO_2C_6H_4OH$$

o-Nitrophenol *p*-Nitrophenol

Another example of the enhanced reactivity of the aromatic ring in phenols is the coupling of diazonium salts with these compounds (p. 130). In general, with respect to the ease of substitution the phenols are to be compared to the aromatic amines (p. 126).

When heated with carbon dioxide, the sodium salts of phenols give a peculiar reaction in which a carboxyl group is introduced into the aromatic ring. This is the *Kolbe synthesis*, which is very useful for the preparation of phenolic acids. An example is the synthesis of salicylic acid from sodium phenoxide.

$$C_6H_5ONa + CO_2 \xrightarrow{140^\circ} o\text{-}HOC_6H_4C(=O)\text{-}ONa$$

Sodium salicylate

$$o\text{-}HOC_6H_4C(=O)\text{-}ONa + HCl \longrightarrow o\text{-}HOC_6H_4C(=O)\text{-}OH + NaCl$$

Salicylic acid

Some *p*-hydroxybenzoic acid also is produced in the reaction. This reaction is carried out on a large scale industrially because of the value of various derivatives of salicylic acid in medicine. The most common of these is aspirin (acetyl salicylic acid), made by treatment of salicylic acid with acetic anhydride. It may be regarded as a substituted phenyl acetate. Aspirin is consumed in the United States at a rate which approximates 10,000,000 lb. per year. Salol is the phenyl ester of salicylic acid. It is used as an intestinal antiseptic. It is made from a mixture of salicylic acid, phenol, and phosphorus oxychloride. Methyl salicylate, known as oil of wintergreen, is applied externally for the relief of rheumatic pains. It is made by the direct esterification of salicylic acid with methyl alcohol. The formulas of these drugs are shown below.

Aspirin (acetyl salicylic acid) — Salol (phenyl salicylate) — Oil of wintergreen (methyl salicylate)

The *Reimer-Tiemann* reaction provides a method for the synthesis of phenolic aldehydes. The sodium (or potassium) salt of a phenol is heated with chloroform in the presence of aqueous alkali to give products containing the aldehyde group in positions *ortho* and *para* to the hydroxyl group. The synthesis of salicylaldehyde and *p*-hydroxybenzaldehyde from sodium phenoxide illustrates the process.

$$C_6H_5ONa + CHCl_3 + NaOH \longrightarrow NaCl + H_2O + o\text{-}CHCl_2C_6H_4ONa \text{ and } p\text{-}CHCl_2C_6H_4ONa$$

$$o\text{-}CHCl_2C_6H_4ONa \text{ and } p\text{-}CHCl_2C_6H_4ONa + 2NaOH \longrightarrow 2NaCl + H_2O + o\text{-}HC(=O)C_6H_4ONa \text{ and } p\text{-}HC(=O)C_6H_4ONa$$

$$o\text{-}HC(=O)C_6H_4ONa \text{ and } p\text{-}HC(=O)C_6H_4ONa + HCl \longrightarrow NaCl + o\text{-}HC(=O)C_6H_4OH \text{ and } p\text{-}HC(=O)C_6H_4OH$$

Salicylaldehyde — *p*-Hydroxybenzaldehyde

It is believed that the reaction involves the formation of the intermediate dichloro compounds shown in the equations.

Industrial Uses of Phenols

The simple phenols are very poisonous and find many uses in the preparation of antiseptics, germicides, and disinfectants. Phenol, the cresols, and resorcinol are present in many such preparations. Phenol is also an important raw material for the manufacture of many dyes and drugs (e.g., the salicylates). The naphthols are extensively used in dye manufacturing. Catechol and hydroquinone are photographic developers. At the present time most of the phenol produced is consumed in the manufacture of synthetic resins. Bakelite, an important example, is prepared from phenol and formaldehyde in the presence of a trace of catalyst. The reaction proceeds by addition of phenol to formaldehyde and loss of water between the product and another similar molecule. It can be illustrated as follows.

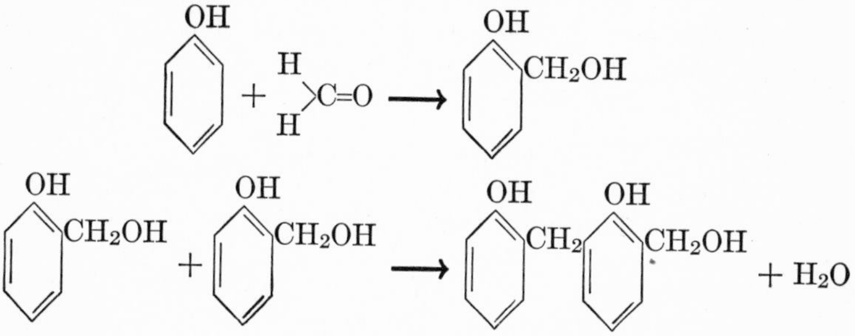

OH
H
$+ \quad {>}C{=}O \longrightarrow$
H
OH
CH_2OH

OH OH OH OH
$CH_2OH \quad + \quad CH_2OH \quad \longrightarrow \quad CH_2 \quad CH_2OH \quad + H_2O$

At the same time, reaction occurs in the positions *para* to the hydroxyl group. This leads to the following type of linkage in the final product.

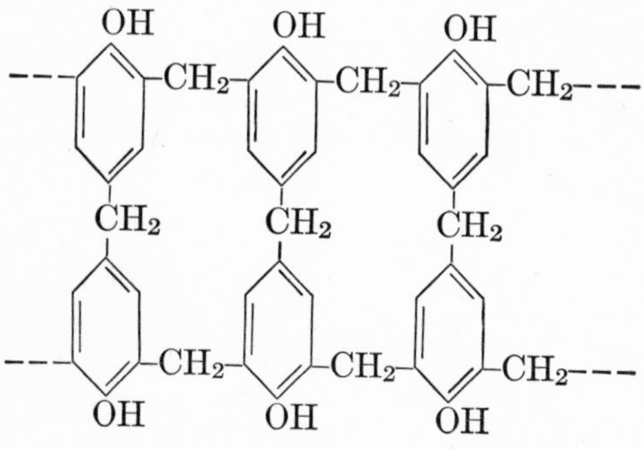

OH OH OH
$---\,CH_2-\,CH_2-\,CH_2---$
$CH_2 \quad CH_2 \quad CH_2$
$---\,CH_2-\,CH_2-\,CH_2---$
OH OH OH

Bakelite is thus a *cross-linked, condensation* polymer.

PROBLEMS

1. Give equations for the conversion of toluene to: (*a*) *p*-cresol, (*b*) *p*-cresyl acetate, (*c*) 2-hydroxy-5-methylbenzaldehyde, (*d*) ethyl *p*-cresyl ether, (*e*) 2-hydroxy-5-methylbenzoic acid.

2. Suggest a method for obtaining salicylaldehyde (prepared by the Reimer-Tiemann method) entirely free from phenol.

CHAPTER 13

Optical Isomerism

It has been mentioned earlier that lactic acid and certain other hydroxy acids exist in isomeric forms. The fundamental difference between these isomers is in their behavior toward plane polarized light. It is therefore desirable to consider briefly the nature of plane polarized light.

It is a familiar fact that light involves a wave motion. The different colors of light, for example, differ in *wavelength*. The waves which constitute a beam of ordinary light have *all the possible planes of vibration.* This fact can be made clear by reference to Fig. 3, which represents a beam of light traveling toward the eye. It contains waves vibrating in the plane A, others vibrating in the plane B, *and still others vibrating in all the intermediate planes.*

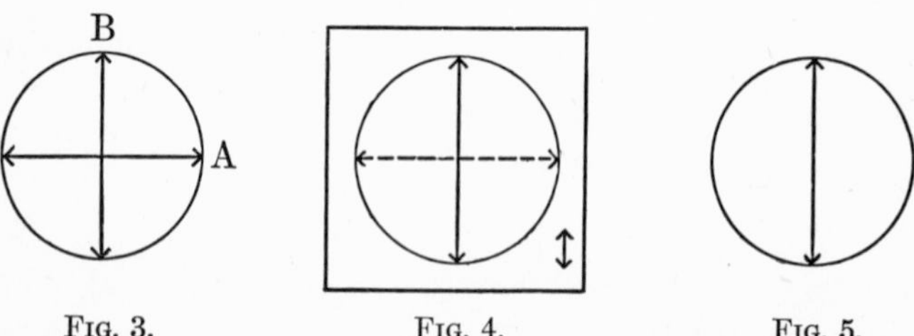

FIG. 3. FIG. 4. FIG. 5.

A lens made of certain materials, such as tourmaline or Polaroid, has the peculiar property of transmitting only those waves which have planes of vibration in a certain direction called the axis of the lens. Figure 4 shows the effect of such a lens on ordinary light. If the lens is placed in the path of a beam of light with axis of the lens in the vertical position, only those waves which have vibrations in the vertical plane can pass through. The emergent light is plane polarized (Fig. 5). It is possible, then, to define plane polarized light as *light in which all waves vibrate in parallel planes.*

The polarization of light can be proved by a simple experiment using two tourmaline lenses. If these are held between the eye and a light source in positions such that their axes are parallel, then all the light which passes through the first lens also passes through the second, and the latter appears completely transparent (Fig. 6). If one of the lenses is rotated so that its axis is perpendicular to that of the other, then all the light transmitted by the first lens is absorbed by the second and the latter appears completely opaque (Fig. 7).

The *polarimeter* is an instrument which is used in studying the effect of liquids or solutions on plane polarized light. In its simplest form it consists of a tube, with glass caps, placed between two tourmaline lenses. A light source is placed near one of the lenses, and this lens is held in a fixed position. It is called the polarizer, since it polarizes the light entering the tube. The lens at the other end of the tube is mounted so that it can be rotated. It is called the analyzer, because it enables one to determine whether the plane of the polarized light is altered as the light passes through the tube. If the polarizer is arranged with its axis in the vertical position and the polarimeter tube is filled with water, ethyl alcohol, acetone, or ether, it is found that the maximum amount of light passes through the analyzer when its axis is also in the vertical position. This means that the liquids mentioned have no effect on plane polarized light.

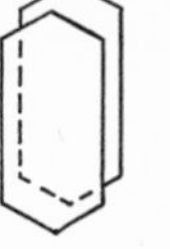

FIG. 6.

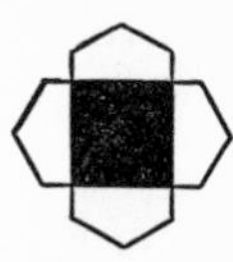

FIG. 7.

However, if the polarimeter tube contains the lactic acid obtained from muscle tissue, it is found that the maximum light transmission

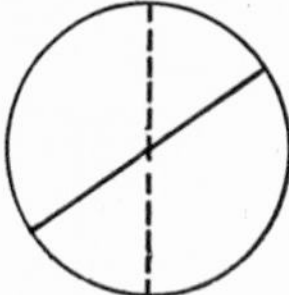

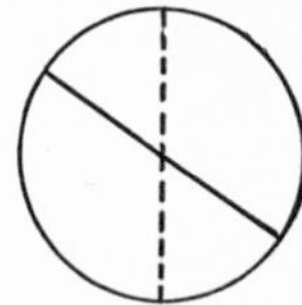

FIG. 8.

by the analyzer occurs when the latter is rotated to the right. This lactic acid must, therefore, rotate the plane of polarized light to the right. It is called *dextro-rotatory* lactic acid. If the tube is now filled with lactic acid obtained by a special fermentation of sugar it will be found to rotate the plane of the light to the left. This lactic acid is called *levo-rotatory* lactic acid. If the two samples are of the same degree of purity and if the amount of rotation by each is measured carefully, it will be found that the number of degrees of rotation to the right effected by the first lactic acid is exactly the same as the rotation to the left caused by the second. Figure 8 shows the results of the above experiment. The dotted line represents the plane of the polarized light entering the liquid and the solid line shows the plane of the light as it leaves the sample.

If a sample of lactic acid prepared by a laboratory synthesis is examined in the polarimeter it is found to have no effect on plane polarized light. This lactic acid is said to be *optically inactive,* in contrast to those mentioned above which are said to be *optically active.* A careful examination of the properties of the two active acids shows them to be identical in all physical properties, such as melting point, boiling point, solubility, density, *with the single exception of their effect on polarized light.* They also have identical chemical properties. It follows, then, that they have the same structure and that they are equally correctly represented by the formula $CH_3\underset{|}{C}HCO_2H$ (with OH on the second carbon). However, since there are two of them, this structure must be capable of existing in two forms.

By the use of tetrahedral atomic models it is indeed found that two models corresponding to the formula $CH_3\overset{*}{C}HCO_2H$ (with OH on the starred carbon) can be constructed. These are shown in Fig. 9. The tetrahedron represents the carbon atom

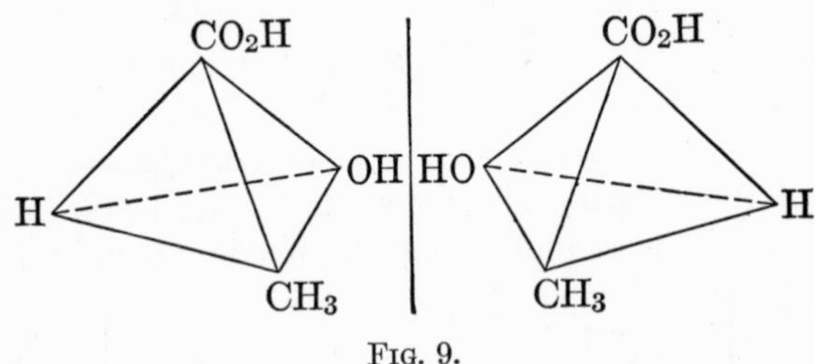

FIG. 9.

marked by an asterisk in the formula just given. These two models bear the same relationship to each other as do the right and left hands. One is the mirror image of the other, but they are not superimposable. They have the same structure, that is, each has a methyl group, a carboxyl group, a hydroxyl group, and a hydrogen atom attached to a carbon atom, but they differ in the order in which these groups are attached, just as the fingers of the left hand may be considered as attached in an order which is the reverse of that of the right hand. The models are said to differ in *configuration.* If one of them is taken to represent dextro-rotatory lactic acid, the other must represent levo-rotatory lactic acid. The two molecules are called *enantiomorphs* or *optical antipodes.*

These models provide a satisfactory explanation for the existence of the two optically active lactic acids. The inactive lactic acid, usually called *racemic* lactic acid, has been found to consist of equal parts of the active acids. Racemic lactic acid is without optical activity because the two active forms exactly neutralize each other.

Lactic acid contains one carbon atom which carries *four different groups.* Such an atom is said to be *asymmetric.* The investigation of a great many substances has shown that those which have one or more asymmetric carbon atoms are invariably capable of existing in optically active forms. The number of possible optical isomers increases rapidly with the number of asymmetric atoms. It will be instructive to examine a few compounds which have more than one asymmetric atom.

Two Unlike Asymmetric Carbon Atoms. Consider the structure $CH_3\underset{\beta}{\overset{*}{C}}HOH\underset{\alpha}{\overset{*}{C}}HOHCO_2H$. The carbon atoms marked with asterisks are asymmetric, and the substituents on the α-atom are not identical with those on the β-atom. In constructing a model, it would be possible to select the α-atom in the D configuration and add the β-atom in either the D or L form, or to start with the α-atom as L and add the β-atom in either D or L configuration. This leads to four forms (Fig. 10).

CO_2H				
αCHOH	D	D	L	L
βCHOH	D′	L′	D′	L′
CH_3	1	2	3	4

FIG. 10. Two unlike asymmetric carbon atoms.

Forms 2 and 3 will each be optically active since the two asymmetric carbon atoms are unlike and their rotations will not exactly neutralize each other. Forms 1 and 4 are enantiomorphs (mirror images) and will form a racemic modification. Forms 2 and 3 will form a second racemic modification. Form 1 is *not* an enantiomorph of 2 or 3, however. This is an extremely important consideration because optical isomers which are not enantiomorphs have different physical properties and hence can be separated by the usual methods such as crystallization. Optical isomers which are not mirror images are called *diastereoisomers.* If the compound in question were synthesized in the laboratory two products would be obtained. These are the two racemic mixtures (1,4 and 2,3). If the racemic modifications were *resolved* into the active components (p. 178) then four optically active forms would be obtained.

From a similar examination of a compound with three unlike asymmetric carbon atoms it is seen that *eight* active forms are possible. An example is given in Fig. 11.

CO_2H								
CHOH	D	D	D	D	L	L	L	L
CHOH	D′	D′	L′	L′	D′	D′	L′	L′
CHOH	D″	L″	D″	L″	D″	L″	D″	L″
CH_3	1	2	3	4	5	6	7	8

FIG. 11. Three unlike asymmetric carbon atoms.

It will be noted that in this case four racemic modifications are possible (1,8; 2,7; 3,6; 4,5). A laboratory synthesis would yield these four racemic forms and separation of each would give the eight active forms.

From the three examples considered it is evident that the addition of a new, different asymmetric carbon doubles the number of active forms. The number of active forms can be predicted from the equation below, in which n represents the number of unlike asymmetric carbon atoms.

$$\text{Number of active forms} = 2^n$$

Two Similar Asymmetric Carbon Atoms. Tartaric acid presents an interesting case, since it has two asymmetric carbon atoms which have identical groups attached. If the two possibilities for each carbon atom are considered as was done above, the forms 1, 2, 3, and 4 (Fig. 12) might be written. However, when it is remembered that the asymmetric carbon atoms are alike it will be seen that forms 2 and 3 are identical. Moreover, the form in which the two identical asymmetric atoms have opposite configurations will be optically inactive. The dextro-rotatory effect of the one atom will be exactly neutralized by the levo-rotatory effect of the other. This is not a racemic form since the neutralization is *within* the molecule, whereas in a racemic form neutralization occurs *between* molecules. The internally neutralized isomer is said to be a *meso* form. Thus there are three individual tartaric acids, dextro-rotatory tartaric, levo-rotatory tartaric, and meso-tartaric acids. Racemic tartaric acid is, of course, a mixture of the two active forms.

CO_2H				
CHOH	D	D	L	L
CHOH	D	L	D	L
CO_2H	1	2	3	4

Fig. 12.

Projection Formulas. It is possible to represent the various optical isomers with plane formulas by the aid of certain conventions. Consider the models of the two lactic acids (Fig. 13). If it is agreed that in writing plane formulas of the lactic acids the carboxyl group shall always be placed at the top of the formula and the methyl group at the bottom, then the difference between the two isomers can be shown by the formulas below the models.

These plane formulas are called projection formulas; they may be regarded as the shadows cast by the three-dimensional models. With their aid it is possible to represent on paper even very complicated cases of optical isomerism. They must be used by the beginner with caution and with frequent reference to the three-dimensional models, however. For instance, a student occasionally inquires how the two projection formulas of the lactic acids can be different when he can make them coincide by folding the paper between them. If he keeps in mind the three-dimensional models just above the formulas, he will see that the two models do not coincide during this operation.

It has been found that many of the derivatives of *dextro-rotatory* lactic acid are *levo-rotatory*. If the acid is dissolved in water and neutralized with a metallic hydroxide, for example, the rotation changes from a plus value to a minus value. If an equivalent amount of a mineral acid is now added to regenerate the acid the rotation changes in the reverse

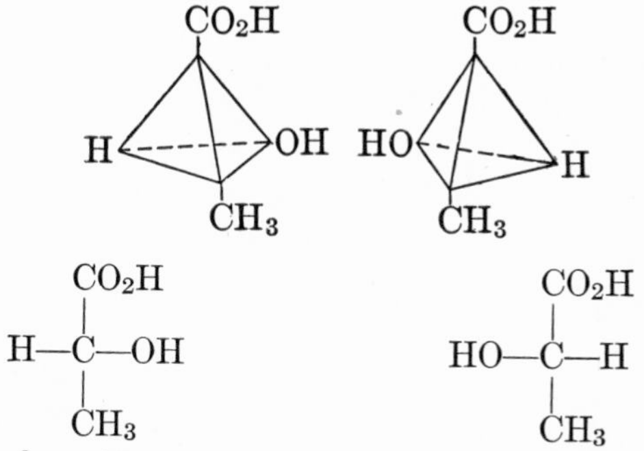

levo-rotatory Lactic acid

dextro-rotatory Lactic acid

FIG. 13.

manner. It is desirable to have some notation to show that these levo-rotatory salts are related to the dextro-rotatory acid. This has been done by making *dextro-rotatory* glyceraldehyde the standard of reference. It was agreed that the *dextro configuration*, for any carbon atom, shall be defined as that corresponding to the configuration of the asymmetric carbon atom in *dextro-rotatory* glyceraldehyde. An enantiomorph in which the asymmetric carbon atom has this configuration shall be considered as a member of the dextro series, regardless of the direction of its rotation. When desired, the rotation is specified by including in the name a plus sign or a minus sign. *Dextro-rotatory* glyceraldehyde has been found to be related to *levo-rotatory* lactic acid. This lactic acid is therefore written as D(−)lactic acid. Other examples of this very convenient system are shown in the projection formulas and names below.

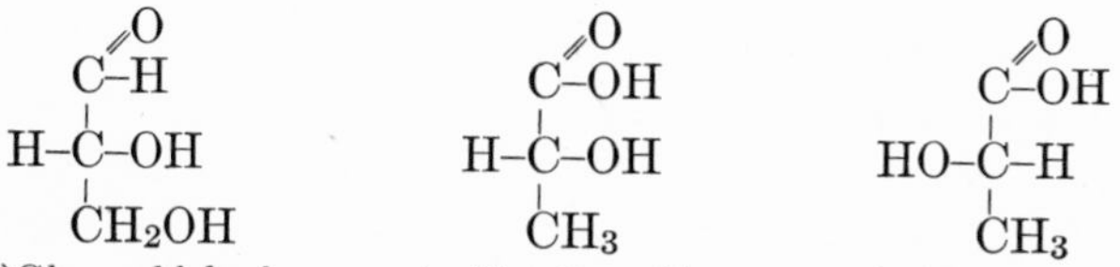

D(+)Glyceraldehyde D(−)Lactic acid L(+)Lactic acid

$$\begin{array}{c} \overset{\displaystyle O}{\overset{\|}{\text{C--ONa}}} \\ | \\ \text{HO--C--H} \\ | \\ \text{CH}_3 \end{array} \qquad\qquad \begin{array}{c} \overset{\displaystyle O}{\overset{\|}{\text{C--OH}}} \\ | \\ \text{H}_2\text{N--C--H} \\ | \\ \text{CH}_3 \end{array}$$

Sodium L(−)lactate L(+)Alanine

In each case the letter indicates the *absolute configuration* of the asymmetric *carbon atom* and the sign indicates the direction of rotation of the *compound.* This notation has been extended to apply to compounds with many asymmetric carbon atoms (p. 196). Unfortunately, it has not invariably been followed, so that in the use of the chemical literature one must determine for each author whether the expression D isomer is used to indicate absolute configuration or direction of rotation.

Resolution of Racemic Modifications. There are three general methods of separating a racemic modification into its active components. They are the mechanical, the biological, and the chemical methods.

Mechanical Resolution. Occasionally the two substances which constitute a racemic modification crystallize separately. If the two types of crystals can be distinguished from each other they can be separated with the aid of a magnifying glass. The first resolution was accomplished by Pasteur in this manner. The method has the disadvantage that it is rarely applicable, and when it can be used it is extremely tedious.

Biological Resolution. If the racemic substance is acted upon by a bacterium, a yeast, or a mold, one of the active forms will be utilized more rapidly than the other. Often one form is completely unaffected. The difficulties with this method are that it may not be easy to find the appropriate biological agent, the resolution may be incomplete, and at best only one of the two active forms can be obtained.

Chemical Method. The most satisfactory method of resolution consists in treating the racemic compound with an optically active reagent. Two diastereoisomeric products are formed. These are separated and purified by recrystallization, and each is treated with a reagent which will regenerate the starting material. The resolution of lactic acid by the aid of L-strychnine is an example.

DL-Lactic acid + L-Strychnine

⟶ L-Strychnine D-lactate + L-Strychnine L-lactate

The two L-strychnine lactates are not mirror images, and they can be separated because of their different solubilities. Each salt is purified and treated with hydrochloric acid.

L-Strychnine D-lactate + HCl ⟶ L-Strychnine chloride + D-lactic acid

L-Strychnine L-lactate + HCl ⟶ L-Strychnine chloride + L-lactic acid

Because naturally occurring compounds are nearly always produced in optically active forms, if optical activity is possible, a large number of active acids, bases, alcohols, etc., are available as resolving agents.

The role of optically active compounds in physiological chemistry is of great interest. Not only do plants and animals usually synthesize compounds which have asymmetric carbon atoms as the individual active forms, but also often only one of the active forms is utilized in metabolic processes. The pronounced effect of many substances, such as vitamins and hormones, is often characteristic of only one of the optical isomers. Such differences in physiological effects can be explained on the assumption that the substances act on the body by combining with some optically active compound already present. In this way the "natural" and "unnatural" enantiomorphs would yield two diastereoisomers which would have different physical properties and hence different physiological effects.

It is not nearly so easy to understand how optically active forms are synthesized in nature. An idea of the problem here can be gained from a consideration of the reduction of pyruvic acid ($CH_3\overset{O}{\overset{\|}{C}}-\overset{O}{\overset{\|}{C}}-OH$) to lactic acid. In Fig. 14 the ketone carbon atom is represented by the tetrahedron.

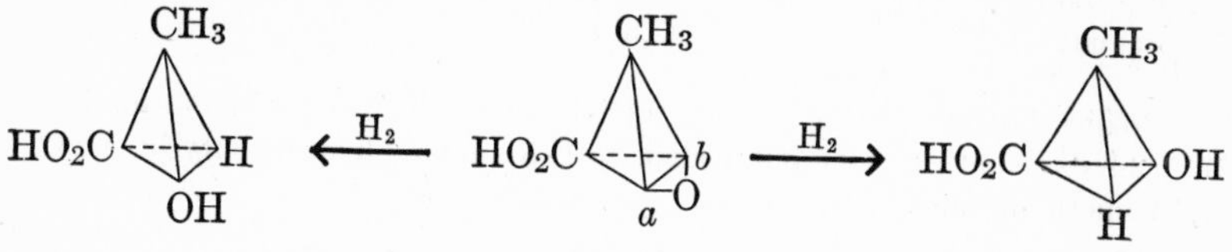

CH_3 / HO_2C / H / OH $\xleftarrow{H_2}$ CH_3 / HO_2C / b / O / a $\xrightarrow{H_2}$ CH_3 / HO_2C / OH / H

Fig. 14.

The two bonds *a* and *b* which connect the carbon and oxygen atoms are identical. If the reduction is carried out in the laboratory these two bonds are broken at exactly the same rate, and the product is racemic lactic acid. However, if the reaction occurs as part of a biological process, then it will take only one of the two possible courses and the product will be an active lactic acid. No completely satisfactory theory of the specificity of such reactions in nature has yet been advanced.

The optical rotation of a natural substance is often of great value in identification and analytical work. In order to measure it accurately, very sensitive polarimeters have been devised. Because the actual rotation of a substance varies with the solvent, the concentration, the length of the column of substance through which the polarized light passes, the temperature, and the wavelength of light employed, the results are usually calculated to "specific rotations" by the aid of one of the following formulas.

For pure liquids $[\alpha]_D^{25} = \frac{a}{ld}$

For solutions $[\alpha]_D^{25} = \frac{100a}{lc}$

a = observed rotation at 25°.
l = length of polarimeter tube expressed in decimeters.
d = density.
c = concentration (grams per 100 cc. of solution).
$[\alpha]_D^{25}$ = specific rotation at 25° with respect to light of a sodium lamp (D line of sodium spectrum).

When the second equation is used the solvent and concentration must be reported along with the calculated rotation. For example, the specific rotation of L(+)tartaric acid is recorded as "+11.98° in 20 per cent aqueous solution."

PROBLEMS

1. Define and illustrate the following terms: (*a*) plane polarized light, (*b*) asymmetric carbon atom, (*c*) dextro-rotatory form, (*d*) configuration, (*e*) D configuration, (*f*) racemic form, (*g*) *meso* form, (*h*) enantiomorphs, (*i*) diastereoisomers, (*j*) resolution.

2. Predict the number of optically active forms of: (*a*) α-amino-*n*-caproic acid, (*b*) 1,2-butanediol, (*c*) 2,3-butanediol, (*d*) α-amino-β-hydroxybutyric acid, (*e*) 2,3,4-trimethylhexane.

CHAPTER 14

Amino Acids and Proteins

Compounds containing both a carboxyl group and an amino group are known as amino acids. They are usually classified as α-, β-, γ-, etc., amino acids, depending on the distance between the two functional groups. Each type has, in general, the properties of the amines as well as those of the acids. Each type also has certain special properties, depending on the influence of the two functional groups on each other. Only these special properties are discussed in this chapter.

The behavior of the amino acids on heating closely parallels that of the hydroxy acids (p. 150). For example, α-amino acids lose water to form diketopiperazines, compounds which may be regarded as the nitrogen analogs of the lactides (p. 150).

$$2\ RCH(NH_2)C(=O)OH \xrightarrow{\text{heat}} \text{diketopiperazine (ring: } HN-CH(R)-C(=O)-NH-CH(R)-C(=O)-) + 2H_2O$$

α-Amino acid — Diketopiperazine

In practice, the diketopiperazines are best obtained from esters of α-amino acids.

β-Amino acids decompose on heating to form ammonia and an unsaturated acid. The reaction resembles the dehydration of β-hydroxy acids.

$$RCH(NH_2)CH_2C(=O)OH \xrightarrow{\text{heat}} RCH{=}CHC(=O)OH + NH_3 \longrightarrow RCH{=}CHC(=O)ONH_4$$

γ- and δ-Amino acids lose water to form cyclic amides known as lactams. Their formation recalls the production of lactones from hydroxy acids (p. 152).

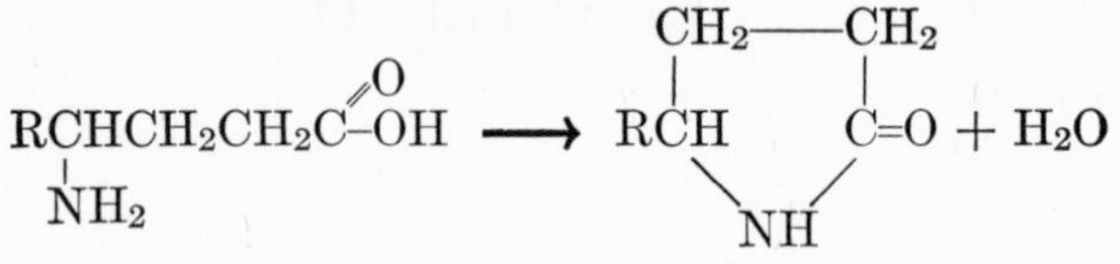

$$\underset{\text{γ-Amino acid}}{\underset{\displaystyle NH_2}{RCH}CH_2CH_2\overset{\displaystyle O}{\overset{\|}{C}}{-}OH} \longrightarrow \underset{\text{γ-Lactam}}{\begin{array}{ccc} CH_2 & — & CH_2 \\ | & & | \\ RCH & & C{=}O \\ & \diagdown\ \ NH\ \ \diagup & \end{array}} + H_2O$$

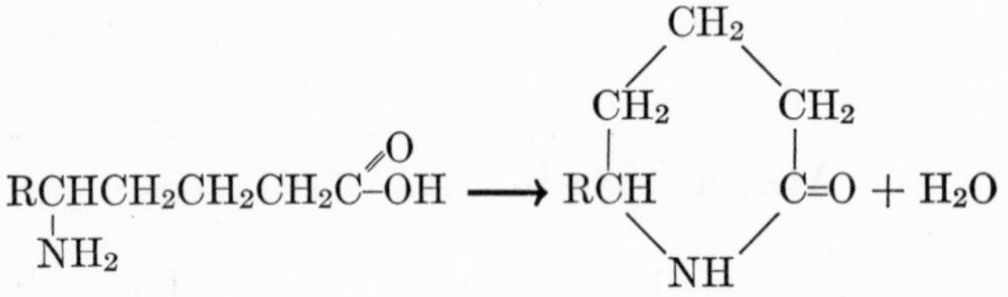

$$\underset{\text{δ-Amino acid}}{\underset{\displaystyle NH_2}{RCH}CH_2CH_2CH_2\overset{\displaystyle O}{\overset{\|}{C}}{-}OH} \longrightarrow \underset{\text{δ-Lactam}}{\begin{array}{ccc} & CH_2 & \\ \diagup & & \diagdown \\ CH_2 & & CH_2 \\ | & & | \\ RCH & & C{=}O \\ & \diagdown\ \ NH\ \ \diagup & \end{array}} + H_2O$$

The Proteins

The proteins are organic materials which are present in all living organisms. In the plants, only the seeds contain appreciable quantities of proteins. Animals, however, are constructed largely of proteins. Hair, nails, feathers, horns, hoofs, skin, muscles, tendons, and nerve tissues are essentially proteins. The albumen of egg-white, the casein of milk, and the hemoglobin of the blood are examples of individual proteins.

The properties of proteins show them to be polymeric. The molecular weights have been estimated to vary from 12,000 for insulin to as high as 50,000,000 for the tobacco mosaic protein (p. 371). Knowledge of the structure of these extremely complex compounds has been gained largely by the study of their hydrolysis products. All proteins are converted to mixtures of α-amino acids by hydrolysis. Examination of the hydrolysis products of a great variety of proteins has revealed the presence of only twenty-three different α-amino acids. Their names and formulas are given in Table XXIV. It is possible that other α-amino acids may also be involved in proteins. Several which do not appear in the table have been isolated from natural sources, but they have not been shown to occur generally as products of protein hydrolysis.

The natural amino acids fall into three groups, the neutral amino acids, the acidic amino acids, and the basic amino acids (Groups I, II, and III of Table XXIV). Of the neutral compounds all but tryptophan possess one amino group for each carboxyl group. These compounds actually have many of the properties of salts and are, perhaps, better represented by the inner salt ("zwitterion") formula as follows.

$$\begin{array}{l} \quad\;\; {}^{\nearrow O} \\ RCHC{-}O^- \\ \;\,| \\ \;NH_3{}^+ \end{array}$$

Inner salt formula of an amino acid

Tryptophan, although it has two amino groups, is classed as a neutral amino acid because the secondary amino group is attached to two unsaturated carbon atoms and hence is practically neutral (compare with diphenylamine, p. 419). The members of the second class have two carboxyl groups for each amino group. Those of the last type have a preponderance of basic groups.

It will be noted that each of the natural amino acids, except glycine, has at least one asymmetric carbon atom and is, therefore, capable of existing in two or more optical isomeric forms. Careful hydrolysis of proteins invariably yields optically active amino acids, never racemic modifications. It is a striking fact that the α-carbon atoms of all these active forms have the same (L) configuration (p. 177).

When a protein is ingested it is hydrolyzed in the digestive tract to the component amino acids. It has been found that dietary protein can be replaced by mixtures of pure amino acids. Only nine of the twenty-three known amino acids are necessary to support growth in young animals. If any one of these nine is absent from the diet the animal fails to grow and may even die. These nine are called essential amino acids; they are marked with asterisks in Table XXIV. The protein of an animal fed only the nine essential amino acids is found to contain many of the others. This means that the animal body is capable of synthesizing some of the amino acids and the nine essential ones are those which cannot be synthesized in the animal and so must be obtained from external sources, ultimately plants. Another curious fact is that some of the essential amino acids are utilized in either form (D or L configuration of the α-carbon atom) but others must be supplied in the natural (L) configuration. This indicates that, in some cases, the animal can convert one optical isomer into its enantiomorph.

Thyroxine occupies a unique place among amino acids. It is found only in the hydrolysis products of the hormone thyroglobulin, a protein produced by the thyroid gland. Hormones are substances secreted internally by the endocrine (ductless) glands and carried by the blood or lymph to other portions of the body, the functions or structures of which are thereby altered. The thyroid hormone is a protein in which thyroxine and a number of other amino acids are combined. The activity of the hormone is due to the thyroxine present in the protein. Thyroxine contains a high percentage of iodine, and in regions where the water is deficient in this element the diet of the inhabitants may be so low in

TABLE XXIV

NATURAL AMINO ACIDS

Name	Formula
I *Neutral amino acids*	
Glycine	$H_2NCH_2CO_2H$
Alanine	$CH_3CH(NH_2)CO_2H$
Valine *	$CH_3CH(CH_3)-CH(NH_2)CO_2H$
Leucine *	$CH_3CH(CH_3)CH_2CH(NH_2)CO_2H$
Isoleucine *	$CH_3CH_2CH(CH_3)-CH(NH_2)CO_2H$
Serine	$HOCH_2CH(NH_2)CO_2H$
Threonine *	$CH_3CH(OH)-CH(NH_2)CO_2H$
Cysteine	$HSCH_2CH(NH_2)CO_2H$
Cystine	$S-CH_2CH(NH_2)CO_2H$ / $S-CH_2CH(NH_2)CO_2H$ (S–S linked)
Methionine *	$CH_3SCH_2CH_2CH(NH_2)CO_2H$
Proline	CH_2-CH_2, CH_2 and $CHCO_2H$ joined by NH (ring)
Hydroxyproline	$HOCH-CH_2$, CH_2 and $CHCO_2H$ joined by NH (ring)
Citrulline	$H_2NC(=O)NHCH_2CH_2CH_2CH(NH_2)CO_2H$

* Essential amino acid (p. 183).

TABLE XXIV (*Continued*)

Name	Formula
I *Neutral amino acids* (*Continued*)	
Phenylalanine *	$C_6H_5CH_2CH(NH_2)CO_2H$
Tyrosine	$HOC_6H_4CH_2CH(NH_2)CO_2H$
Diiodotyrosine	$HOC_6H_2I_2CH_2CH(NH_2)CO_2H$
Thyroxine	$HOC_6H_2I_2OC_6H_2I_2CH_2CH(NH_2)CO_2H$
Tryptophan *	C_6H_4–$C(=CH$–$NH)$–$CH_2CH(NH_2)CO_2H$ (indole ring)
II *Acidic amino acids*	
Aspartic acid	$HO_2CCH_2CH(NH_2)CO_2H$
Glutamic acid	$HO_2CCH_2CH_2CH(NH_2)CO_2H$
III *Basic amino acids*	
Lysine *	$H_2NCH_2CH_2CH_2CH_2CH(NH_2)CO_2H$
Arginine	$H_2NC(=NH)$–$NHCH_2CH_2CH_2CH(NH_2)CO_2H$
Histidine *	$CH=CCH_2CH(NH_2)CO_2H$ with ring N–CH–NH (imidazole)

* Essential amino acid (p. 183).

iodine that insufficient thyroxine is produced by the thyroid gland. This leads to various disorders of which endemic goiter is the best known. Extracts of thyroid glands obtained from slaughtered cattle are used in treating such disorders, as is also pure synthetic thyroxine.

It is known that the proteins are built up of amino acid units joined together by amide linkages. Such amides are known as peptides. The general formulas of dipeptides, tripeptides, and polypeptides are as follows.

$$\mathrm{RCH(NH_2)C(=O)\!-\!NHCH(R)C(=O)\!-\!OH} \qquad \text{Dipeptide}$$

$$\mathrm{RCH(NH_2)C(=O)\!-\!NHCH(R)\!-\!C(=O)\!-\!NHCH(R)C(=O)\!-\!OH} \qquad \text{Tripeptide}$$

$$\mathrm{RCH(NH_2)C(=O)\!-\!\left(NHCH(R)\!-\!C(=O)\right)_n\!-\!NHCH(R)C(=O)\!-\!OH} \qquad \text{Polypeptide}$$

The sequence of the various amino acid units in a protein chain is difficult to ascertain. The sequence of the peptide linkages of insulin, however, has been almost completely elucidated.

The synthesis of peptides of known structure for comparison with the natural materials is a difficult task. Suppose, for example, it is desired to prepare a dipeptide from two different amino acids. The problem might be regarded as merely the synthesis of an amide from an acid and an amine, and it might be supposed that it is only necessary to convert one amino acid to the acyl chloride and cause it to react with the other. However, the chlorides of the amino acids are extremely unstable, inasmuch as they contain two functional groups which readily react with each other ($-C(=O)-Cl$ and $-NH_2$). It is therefore necessary to "protect" the amino group by converting it to a more stable derivative before preparing the acyl chloride. One of the best methods consists in treating the amino acid with benzyl chlorocarbonate ($C_6H_5CH_2OC(=O)-Cl$, also called benzyl chloroformate) thereby converting the amino group to the carbobenzoxy derivative ($-NHC(=O)-OCH_2C_6H_5$). After the synthesis is complete the carbobenzoxy group is removed by catalytic reduction

$(-NHC(=O)-OCH_2C_6H_5 + H_2 \xrightarrow{Pt} -NH_2 + CO_2 + CH_3C_6H_5)$. The use of this scheme in making a dipeptide is illustrated below. The benzyl chlorocarbonate is prepared in the same way as ethyl chlorocarbonate (p. 132).

$$\underset{\text{Benzyl alcohol}}{C_6H_5CH_2OH} + ClC(=O)-Cl \longrightarrow \underset{\text{Benzyl chlorocarbonate}}{C_6H_5CH_2OC(=O)-Cl} + HCl$$

$$H_2NCH(R)C(=O)-OH + C_6H_5CH_2OC(=O)-Cl \longrightarrow C_6H_5CH_2OC(=O)-NHCH(R)C(=O)-OH + HCl$$

$$C_6H_5CH_2OC(=O)-NHCH(R)C(=O)-OH + SOCl_2 \longrightarrow C_6H_5CH_2OC(=O)-NHCH(R)C(=O)-Cl + SO_2 + HCl$$

$$C_6H_5CH_2OC(=O)-NHCH(R)-C(=O)-Cl + H_2NCH(R')C(=O)-OH \longrightarrow C_6H_5CH_2OC(=O)-NHCH(R)C(=O)-NHCH(R')C(=O)-OH + HCl$$

$$C_6H_5CH_2OC(=O)-NHCH(R)C(=O)-NHCH(R')C(=O)-OH + H_2 \xrightarrow{Pt} \underset{\text{Dipeptide}}{H_2NCH(R)C(=O)-NHCH(R')C(=O)-OH} + C_6H_5CH_3 + CO_2$$

Treatment of the dipeptide with the carbobenzoxy derivative of an amino acid chloride followed by reduction yields a tripeptide.

Polypeptide chains of molecular weights above 12,000 have been produced by allowing the anhydrides of N-carboxy-α-amino acids to react with water. The reaction proceeds in the following way.

$$H_2O + \underset{\text{(A)}}{\overbrace{C(=O)-CH(R)NHC(=O)}^{\text{ring closed through }-O-}} \longrightarrow HOC(=O)-CH(R)NHC(=O)OH \xrightarrow{-CO_2}$$

$$HOC(=O)-CH(R)NH_2 \xrightarrow{+A} HOC(=O)-CH(R)NHC(=O)-CH(R)NHC(=O)OH$$

$$\xrightarrow{-CO_2} HOC(=O)-CH(R)NHC(=O)-CH(R)NH_2 \xrightarrow{+A} \text{etc.}$$

These synthetic polypeptides, with molecular weights in some cases as high as those of the smaller proteins, have some of the properties of proteins.

The amphoteric nature of most proteins results from the presence of both acidic and basic amino acid units in the protein molecule. A protein composed exclusively of neutral amino acids would have but one free amino group and one free carboxylic group at either end of the chain, and these could hardly be expected to exert an appreciable influence on so large a molecule. However, if units of acidic and basic amino acids are scattered at various points along the chain, then the molecule will have a number of free acid and basic groups and will be amphoteric. Some proteins have the power to react with more equivalents of base than of acid, whereas others consume a larger amount of acid than of base. Examination of the hydrolysis products of a protein of the former type reveals a preponderance of acidic amino acids as compared with the basic amino acids, whereas the reverse is true of the hydrolysis products of proteins of the second group.

The presence of charged groups at points along a protein chain also may have an important influence in causing the chains to associate. Some such association may account for the enormous molecular weights of certain proteins. For example, physical measurements which indicated the molecular weight of a sample of a protein (hemocyanin) to be 6,740,000 gave values which were successively one-half, one-eighth, and one-sixteenth of this figure as the acidity of the solution was changed. By restoring the acidity to its original value the initial molecular weight was again indicated. With certain other proteins the apparent molecular weights has been found to be affected by the concentration of salt in the aqueous solution of the protein.

It was mentioned above that ingested protein is hydrolyzed to the constituent amino acids during digestion. The hydrolysis is brought about by the proteolytic enzymes of the stomach and intestine. The individual amino acids pass through the intestinal wall into the blood stream, and some of them are combined in the various body proteins. If the foreign protein or its partial hydrolysis products, known as proteoses and peptones, find their way into the blood stream they act as violent poisons. Idiosyncrasies of individuals to certain foods are believed to be due to permeability of the intestinal wall to proteins of the food. The allergies, such as asthma and hay fever, are ascribed to conditions in which foreign protein enters the body. The venoms of certain reptiles are proteins which are poisonous because they are injected into the blood stream without preliminary hydrolysis. Serum sickness is caused by traces of protein carried over from the animal from which the serum was taken.

The above facts indicate that each protein has its own individuality; similar proteins taken from different species are not identical. This has been demonstrated chemically in the case of hemoglobins from various animals. By hydrolyzing weighed samples of proteins and analyzing the hydrolysate it is possible to determine quite accurately the amounts of some of the amino acids. From the analytical result the ratios of these amino acids in the protein can be calculated. When this was done with hemoglobin from the horse, the sheep, the cow, and the dog, it was found that arginine, histidine, and lysine were present in the ratio 12 to 32 to 36. However, the figure for cysteine was 2 for horse hemoglobin, 3 for sheep and cattle hemoglobins, and 4 for dog hemoglobin. This demonstrates a definite difference in the amino acid make-up of the hemoglobin of either the horse or dog as compared to that of the cow and sheep. It is also possible that they differ in the order in which the amino acid units are joined together, much as words differ in the order in which their letters are grouped. If this possibility is admitted there is no limit to the number of proteins which may exist.

It can be concluded that present knowledge of the structures of proteins indicates that they are polypeptides, but that much remains to be learned about the detailed arrangements within the giant molecules.

Classification of Proteins. Proteins which give only α-amino acids upon hydrolysis are known as simple proteins. These are further classified as albumins, globulins, glutelins, and others on the basis of their solubilities in various salt solutions and acidic or basic solutions. Conjugated proteins yield on hydrolysis α-amino acids plus some other compound which may be a pigment (such as hemin from hemoglobin), a sugar, a derivative of phosphoric acid, or other substance. The products obtained from proteins by the action of heat and the chemical reagents mentioned in the next paragraph are known as derived proteins.

Coagulation and Precipitation of Proteins. An important property of soluble proteins is their tendency to form insoluble precipitates, known as *coagulated proteins*, under the influence of heat, ultraviolet light, or alcohol. The hardening of egg albumen and casein on heating are facts familiar to everyone. The mild action of acids or bases on proteins brings about a less profound change. The products are said to be *denatured proteins;* they do not dissolve in neutral solutions but are soluble in acids and bases. Certain heavy metal salts and tannic acid convert proteins into insoluble compounds. The poisonous nature of salts of mercury, lead, and silver has been attributed to the conversion of body proteins into insoluble compounds. In the preparation of *leather*, chromic salts and tannic acid are employed to change the protein of the skin into insoluble materials. Formaldehyde converts soluble proteins into tough, hard, insoluble materials. Such products from casein and formaldehyde have long been used as substitutes for ivory, horn, and hard rubber, and for waterproofing of paper and textiles. In some countries artificial wool is prepared from casein and formaldehyde. It is possible to use other soluble proteins, such as that from soybean, in similar applications.

Tests for Proteins. Many color reactions are characteristic of proteins and are used in testing for their presence. Biuret (p. 136) gives a violet color in the presence of dilute sodium hydroxide and a copper salt. Other substances containing two or more $-\overset{\displaystyle O}{\overset{\|}{C}}-\underset{|}{N}H$ links, notably the proteins, yield similar colors. The test is known as the biuret test, but its widest application is in connection with proteins, as, for instance, in determining when the hydrolysis of a protein has proceeded to a stage where only α-amino acids are present. Proteins which contain amino acid units with aromatic groups give a yellow color with nitric acid. The coloring of the skin by nitric acid is familiar to every chemist. This test is known as the xanthoproteic test. Many proteins contain one or more of the sulfur-containing amino acids and hence give a black precipitate (lead sulfide) when heated with a solution of a lead salt.

Useful quantitative analyses in connection with proteins are the determination of total nitrogen, usually by the Kjeldahl method, and the determination of amino nitrogen in amino acid mixtures, such as protein hydrolysates, by the Van Slyke method. This method consists in bringing the sample in contact with nitrous acid and measuring the volume of nitrogen gas produced. The reaction is that of a primary amine with nitrous acid (p. 126), as shown by the following equation.

$$\underset{\displaystyle NH_2}{RCH}\overset{O}{\overset{\|}{C}}-OH + HNO_2 \longrightarrow \underset{\displaystyle OH}{RCH}\overset{O}{\overset{\|}{C}}-OH + N_2 + H_2O$$

Amino acids are sometimes titrated after treatment with formaldehyde. The formaldehyde destroys the basicity of the amino group, so that the carboxyl group is easily titrated. The reaction may be that shown in the following equation.

$$\underset{\displaystyle NH_2}{RCH}\overset{O}{\overset{\|}{C}}-OH + H_2CO \longrightarrow \underset{\displaystyle \overset{\displaystyle N}{\|}\atop CH_2}{RCH}\overset{O}{\overset{\|}{C}}-OH + H_2O$$

A superior test for amino acids is provided by the "ninhydrin" reaction, in which triketohydrindene hydrate reacts with an amino acid to give ammonia, carbon dioxide, and an aldehyde, the triketone being reduced.

$$\text{C}_6\text{H}_4(\text{C{=}O})_2\text{C{=}O} + \underset{\displaystyle |\atop \displaystyle NH_2}{RCHCO_2H} + H_2O \longrightarrow \text{C}_6\text{H}_4(\text{C{=}O})_2\text{CHOH} + RCHO + NH_3 + CO_2$$

The triketone and its reduction product then combine with ammonia to give the blue compound which is responsible for the color that characterizes a positive test.

$$\text{C}_6\text{H}_4\text{(CONH}_4\text{)(C{=}O)C—N{=}C(C{=}O)}_2\text{C}_6\text{H}_4$$

If the evolved carbon dioxide is measured, the test serves as a quantitative determination of α-amino acids.

The Synthesis of Amino Acids

From the foregoing discussion it will be realized that great interest attaches to methods of synthesis of α-amino acids. A number of processes have been developed, and only a few of them can be described here. One very useful method is the Strecker synthesis of an amino acid from an aldehyde with one less carbon atom. When an aldehyde is treated with ammonium cyanide it forms the cyanohydrin and ammonia. These react to give the amino nitrile, which is then hydrolyzed to the amino acid. The synthesis of DL alanine serves as an example.

$$\underset{\text{Acetaldehyde}}{CH_3C(=O)H} + \underset{(NH_4Cl\,+\,NaCN)}{NH_4CN} \longrightarrow \underset{\text{A cyanohydrin}}{CH_3C(H)(OH)CN} + NH_3$$

$$\longrightarrow \underset{\text{An aminonitrile}}{CH_3CH(NH_2)CN} + H_2O$$

$$CH_3CH(NH_2)CN + 2H_2O + 2HCl \longrightarrow \underset{\text{DL-Alanine hydrochloride}}{CH_3CH(NH_2\cdot HCl)C(=O)OH} + NH_4Cl$$

$$2CH_3CH(NH_2\cdot HCl)C(=O)\text{–}OH + Pb(OH)_2 \longrightarrow 2CH_3CH(NH_2)C(=O)\text{–}OH + PbCl_2 + 2H_2O$$

DL-Alanine

Another method involves the reaction of an α-bromo acid with ammonia. Sometimes the α-bromo acid can be obtained by direct bromination of the acid (Hell-Volhard-Zelinsky bromination, p. 319) as in the synthesis of DL-leucine. The isocaproic acid required in this preparation is made from isoamyl alcohol (p. 232). The equations for the reactions are given below.

$$(CH_3)_2CHCH_2CH_2C(=O)\text{–}OH + Br_2 \xrightarrow{PBr_3} (CH_3)_2CHCH_2CH(Br)C(=O)\text{–}OH + HBr$$

Isocaproic acid — α-Bromoisocaproic acid

$$(CH_3)_2CHCH_2CH(Br)C(=O)\text{–}OH + 2NH_3 \longrightarrow (CH_3)_2CHCH_2CH(NH_2)C(=O)\text{–}OH + NH_4Br$$

Leucine

If the acid used in the synthesis is prepared by the malonic ester method, the substituted malonic acid is sometimes brominated before decarboxylation. This is done in the synthesis of DL-isoleucine, which is made from *sec*-butyl bromide by the following reactions.

$$CH_3CH_2CH(Br)CH_3 + \left[C_2H_5OC(=O)CHC(=O)\text{–}OC_2H_5\right]^- Na^+$$

sec-Butyl bromide — Sodio malonic ester

$$\longrightarrow CH_3CH_2CH(CH_3)CH(CO_2C_2H_5)_2$$

Ethyl *sec*-butylmalonate

$$CH_3CH_2CH(CH_3)CH(CO_2C_2H_5)_2 \longrightarrow CH_3CH_2CH(CH_3)CH(CO_2H)_2$$

sec-Butylmalonic acid

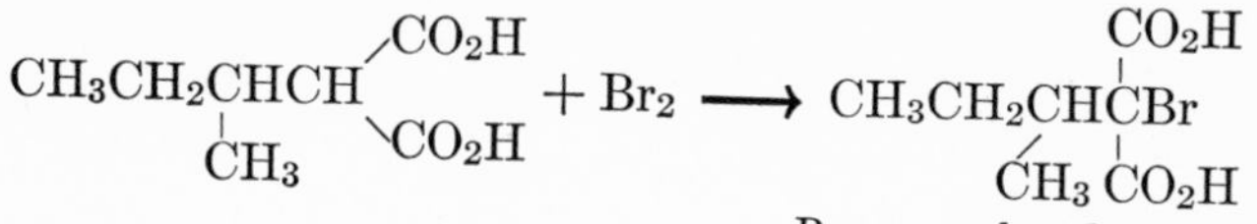

$$CH_3CH_2CH(CH_3)CH(CO_2H)_2 + Br_2 \longrightarrow CH_3CH_2CH(CH_3)CBr(CO_2H)_2$$

α-Bromo-*sec*-butylmalonic acid

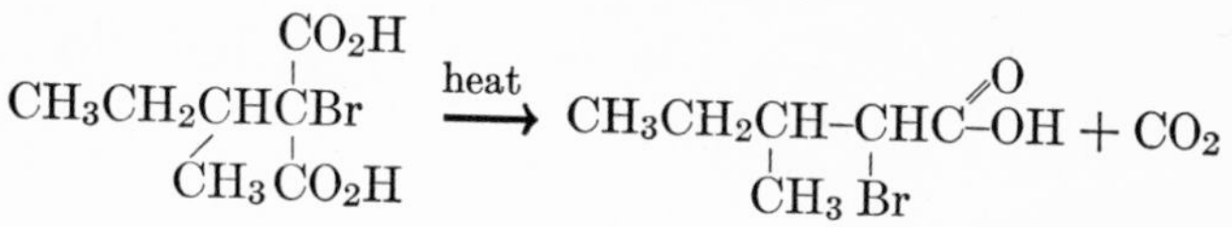

$$CH_3CH_2CH(CH_3)CBr(CO_2H)_2 \xrightarrow{\text{heat}} CH_3CH_2CH(CH_3)\text{–}CHBrC(=O)\text{–}OH + CO_2$$

α-Bromo-*sec*-butylacetic acid

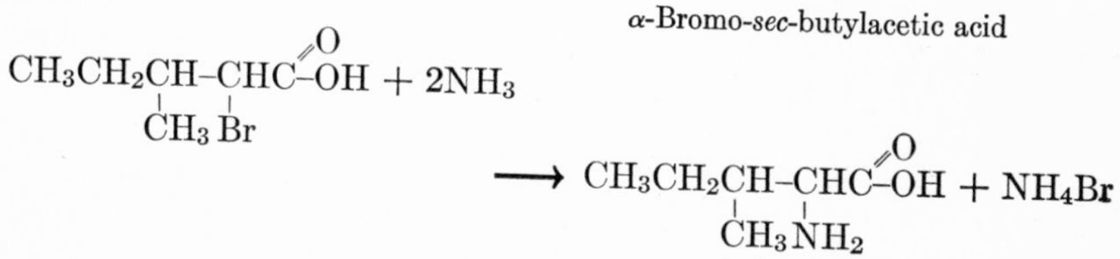

$$CH_3CH_2CH(CH_3)\text{–}CHBrC(=O)\text{–}OH + 2NH_3$$

$$\longrightarrow CH_3CH_2CH(CH_3)\text{–}CH(NH_2)C(=O)\text{–}OH + NH_4Br$$

DL-Isoleucine

When the malonic ester method is used it is also possible to aminate the bromomalonic acid before decarboxylation. One synthesis of DL-methionine is run in this way. The desired malonic acid is made from malonic ester and β-chloroethyl methyl sulfide prepared from ethylene chlorohydrin by the following scheme.

$$ClCH_2CH_2OH \xrightarrow{CH_3SNa} CH_3SCH_2CH_2OH \xrightarrow{SOCl_2} CH_3SCH_2CH_2Cl$$

β-Hydroxyethyl methyl sulfide; β-Chloroethyl methyl sulfide

The β-chloroethyl methyl sulfide is condensed with malonic ester, and the substituted malonic acid is obtained by hydrolysis. This is converted to the bromomalonic acid, then to the aminomalonic acid, and finally to DL methionine. The reactions are represented by the following scheme.

$$CH_3SCH_2CH_2Cl \xrightarrow[\text{malonic ester}]{\text{sodio-}} CH_3SCH_2CH_2CH(CO_2C_2H_5)_2$$

$$\xrightarrow{\text{hydrolysis}} CH_3SCH_2CH_2CH(CO_2H)_2$$

$$\xrightarrow{Br_2} CH_3SCH_2CH_2CBr(CO_2H)_2 \xrightarrow{NH_3} CH_3SCH_2CH_2C(NH_2)(CO_2H)_2$$

$$\xrightarrow{\text{heat}} CH_3SCH_2CH_2CH(NH_2)CO_2H$$

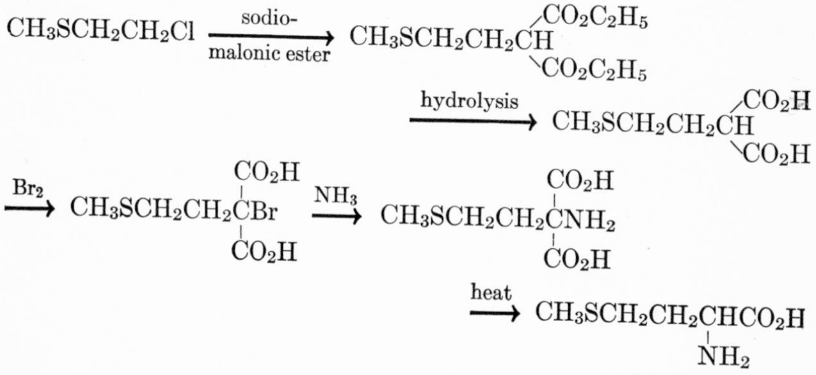

DL-Methionine

DL-Methionine is prepared commercially by a modification of the Strecker synthesis with β-methylthiopropionaldehyde. The sulfur-containing aldehyde is formed by the conjugate addition of methylmercaptan to acrolein, as shown in the accompanying equation.

$$CH_2{=}CHCH{=}O + CH_3SH \xrightarrow{Cu^{++}} CH_3SCH_2CH_2CHO$$

β-Amino acids are most conveniently prepared by addition of ammonia to α,β-unsaturated esters. This is an example of 1,4 addition (p. 341). The process is illustrated by the general equation below.

$$RCH{=}CHC(=O){-}OC_2H_5 + NH_3 \longrightarrow RCH(NH_2)CH_2C(=O){-}OC_2H_5$$

Part of the amino ester may react with more ammonia to give the amide, but hydrolysis converts either product to the amino acid.

There are no general methods for the preparation of γ- and δ-amino acids. When the corresponding keto acids are available they can be converted to the amino acids by reduction of the phenylhydrazones. γ-Aminovaleric acid is made from levulinic acid by this method.

$$\underset{\text{Levulinic acid}}{CH_3C(=O){-}CH_2CH_2C(=O){-}OH} \longrightarrow \underset{\text{Phenylhydrazone of levulinic acid}}{CH_3C(=NNHC_6H_5)CH_2CH_2C(=O){-}OH}$$

$$\xrightarrow[\text{aluminum amalgam}]{4[H]} \underset{\gamma\text{-Aminovaleric acid}}{CH_3CH(NH_2)CH_2CH_2C(=O){-}OH}$$

Aromatic amino acids having an amino group attached to the aromatic ring are often prepared by reduction of the nitro acids. The synthesis of *p*-aminobenzoic acid (p. 412) is an example.

PROBLEMS

1. Define and illustrate the following: (*a*) dipeptide, (*b*) polypeptide, (*c*) neutral amino acid, (*d*) basic amino acid, (*e*) simple protein, (*f*) derived protein, (*g*) essential amino acid.

2. Give equations for the preparation of DL norleucine by means of (*a*) the Strecker synthesis, (*b*) the malonic ester synthesis, (*c*) another method.

3. Write the formula of a neutral tripeptide, of a basic tripeptide, of an acidic tripeptide. Explain why soluble proteins are amphoteric.

CHAPTER 15

Carbohydrates

Plants are composed largely of organic materials called carbohydrates. It has been mentioned that seeds of plants contain proteins and fats, sometimes in rather large amounts. The substances which constitute other parts of plants, the roots, stems, leaves, bark, etc., are almost wholly carbohydrate. The name derives from the formulas of the first of these materials to be examined, which could be written as $C_mH_{2n}O_n$ or $C_m(H_2O)_n$ and were therefore thought to be hydrates of carbon. This supposition proved to be false, for the compounds are not hydrates and many of them do not even correspond to these general formulas. The name carbohydrate has been retained, nevertheless; a modern definition is given later (p. 204).

The carbohydrates are classified as monosaccharides, disaccharides, and polysaccharides. It is convenient to begin the discussion with the simplest members, the monosaccharides.

Monosaccharides

Glucose, also known as dextrose or corn sugar, is the commonest of the monosaccharides. It has the formula $C_6H_{12}O_6$. It is an optically active, neutral, solid substance, extremely soluble in water. It is oxidized by copper or silver oxides (p. 77) to an acid of the formula $C_6H_{12}O_7$. This shows that glucose is an aldehyde. When glucose is treated with acetic anhydride it yields an ester whose formula [$C_{16}H_{22}O_{11}$ or $C_6H_7O(OCOCH_3)_5$] shows it to be a pentaacetate. Thus glucose must be a pentahydroxyaldehyde. Since the substance is not easily dehydrated no two of the hydroxyl groups can be attached to the same carbon atom (p. 79), and it can be said that, of the six carbon atoms in the molecule, one is part of a carbonyl (aldehyde) group and the other five each carry one hydroxyl group. The question remaining, then, is whether the six carbon atoms form a straight or branched chain. Since glucose is reduced by phosphorus and hydrogen iodide to a mixture of *straight*-chain iodohexanes, the carbon atoms must be in a straight chain. The formula of glucose can then be written as follows.

```
     O
    //
1  C-H
   |
2  CHOH
   |
3  CHOH
   |
4  CHOH
   |
5  CHOH
   |
6  CH2OH
```

Glucose

In this formula there are four unlike asymmetric carbon atoms, so it should represent 2^4 or 16 different optical isomers. These are all known; they fall into eight pairs of enantiomorphs. The configuration of each carbon atom in glucose and its optical isomers is known. By the use of the conventions developed for representing optically isomeric substances with projection formulas (p. 176), it is possible to show the differences between these isomers, and this is done below (Fig. 15). It will be recalled that the configuration of an asymmetric carbon atom is assigned on the basis of its relationship to the asymmetric carbon atom in D(+)glycerose, and not on the basis of the rotation of the compound in question (p. 177). In order to have a system of naming enantiomorphic pairs in the sugar series it has been agreed that the asymmetric carbon atom nearest the primary hydroxyl group, that is, carbon atom number 5 in the usual scheme of numbering the atoms in the carbon chains of the sugars, shall be taken as the point of reference. Of each pair of enantiomorphs, that one in which carbon atom number 5 has the same configuration as the asymmetric atom of D(+)glycerose shall be referred to as the D isomer, regardless of its optical rotation. This system is illustrated in Fig. 15. The formulas of only the D compounds are given. The projection formula of any of the L isomers can be written by reversing the positions of the hydrogen atom and the hydroxyl group on each asymmetric carbon atom of the corresponding D isomer.

The six-carbon atom monosaccharides are called hexoses. Monosaccharides containing the aldehyde group are known as aldoses. It is convenient to combine the two names and to designate glucose and its optical isomers as the aldohexoses.

As indicated in Fig. 15, the correct designation of ordinary glucose is D(+)glucose. Since L(−)glucose does not occur in natural products many writers use only the word glucose for the ordinary material. Others employ the term D-glucose. In the sequel the letters D and L will be used to denote configuration only; when it is desired to indicate direction of rotation, the plus or minus sign will be used.

The fact that reactions of D(+)glucose often lead to mixtures of two isomeric products may well have been distressing to early carbohydrate

O C–H	O C–H	O C–H	O C–H
HCOH	HOCH	HCOH	HOCH
HOCH	HOCH	HCOH	HCOH
HCOH	HCOH	HCOH	HCOH
HCOH	HCOH	HCOH	HCOH
CH_2OH	CH_2OH	CH_2OH	CH_2OH
D(+) Glucose	D(+) Mannose	D(+) Allose	D(+) Altrose

O C–H	O C–H	O C–H	O C–H
HCOH	HOCH	HCOH	HOCH
HOCH	HOCH	HCOH	HCOH
HOCH	HOCH	HOCH	HOCH
HCOH	HCOH	HCOH	HCOH
CH_2OH	CH_2OH	CH_2OH	CH_2OH
D(+) Galactose	D(+) Talose	D(−) Gulose	D(−) Idose

Fig. 15. The D aldohexoses.

chemists. However, when the spontaneous reaction of an alcohol with an aldehyde (p. 82) is recalled, the reason becomes clear. D(+)Glucose contains an aldehyde group and several hydroxyl groups, and so it might be expected to form a cyclic hemiacetal (sometimes called a lactol) containing either a five- or six-membered ring. It has been shown that in most cyclic D(+)glucose derivatives the ring has six members. When ring formation occurs, the carbonyl carbon atom changes to the *asymmetric* hemiacetal carbon atom. This new asymmetric carbon atom may take either the D or L configuration, so there *must be two diastereoisomeric hemiacetal* (*lactol*) *forms of* D(+)*glucose*. The three forms of D(+)glucose can then be represented as follows.

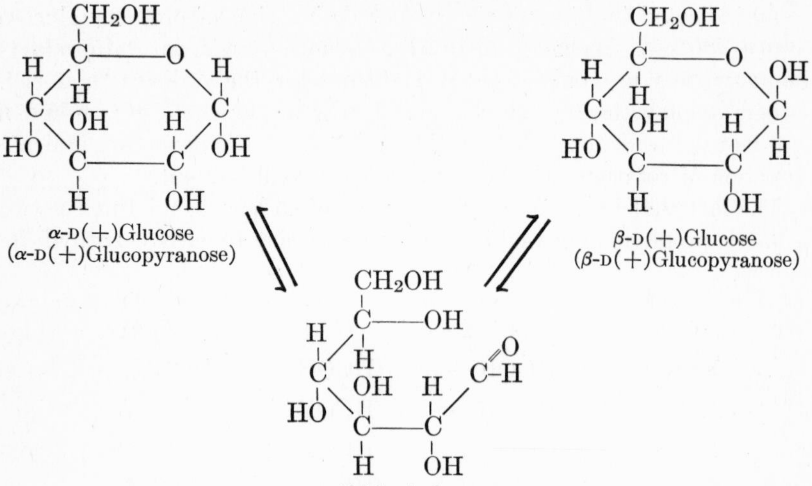

α-D(+)Glucose
(α-D(+)Glucopyranose)

β-D(+)Glucose
(β-D(+)Glucopyranose)

Aldehyde form
D(+)Glucose

In some cyclic derivatives of sugars five-membered rings are present. It is therefore desirable to have a method of indicating, in the name, whether a cyclic sugar contains a five- or six-membered ring. This is done by naming those with five-membered rings furanoses and those with six-membered rings pyranoses. Examples of this system of naming are used above in parentheses. The names are derived from furan and pyran, cyclic compounds of five- and six-membered rings, respectively, each including one oxygen atom.

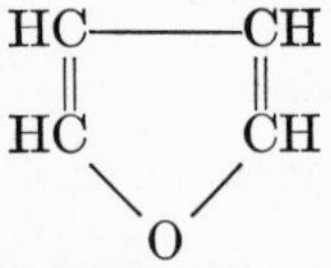

Furan

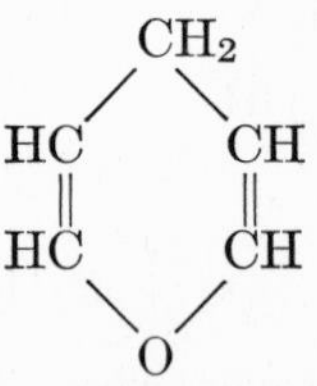

Pyran

Since hemiacetal formation is reversible it is to be predicted that a solution of D(+)glucose contains all three forms. Reagents that convert glucose to two isomeric products are those that attack the hemiacetal forms, whereas a substance that reacts with the open-chain form yields a single product.

The equilibrium between the three forms also accounts for the *mutarotation* of D(+)glucose. Two pure crystalline forms of D(+)glucose have been isolated. One of them has a specific rotation of +113.4° in a freshly prepared solution, but, as the solution stands, the rotation drops until it becomes constant at +52.2°. The other form shows an initial specific rotation of +19°, but this value slowly increases and becomes constant at +52.2°. The isomer of initial rotation +113.4° is α-D(+)glucose; in solution it changes to the open-chain form, and this changes to both the α and β forms. When equilibrium between the three forms is established the rotation is +52.2°. The same equilibrium is established when pure β-D(+)glucose (rotation +19°) is dissolved.

It is a singular fact that the pure aldehyde form of D(+)glucose has not been isolated. It is believed that only traces of it exist in solution in equilibrium with the cyclic forms and that the glucose of commerce (corn sugar) is a mixture of approximately the same composition as the equilibrium mixture. This view is not in contradiction with the fact that D(+)glucose behaves as an aldehyde toward certain reagents. As the reagent combines with the trace of aldehyde form present, more of the latter is produced from the cyclic forms until eventually all the D(+)-glucose has been consumed.

Fructose. Fructose, also called levulose or fruit sugar, is widely distributed in nature. It is levo-rotatory, hence the name levulose; the specific rotation is −93°. Fructose has the same molecular formula ($C_6H_{12}O_6$) as the aldohexoses. By methods similar to those used in the study of the structure of D(+)glucose it has been found that fructose is a pentahydroxy ketone (a ketohexose). The ketone group has been located at the position second from the end of the chain, and it has been found that each asymmetric carbon atom in fructose has the same configuration as the corresponding one in D(+)glucose. The projection formula of fructose can then be written as follows.

```
   CH2OH
    |
    C=O
    |
 HOCH
    |
  HCOH
    |
  HCOH
    |
   CH2OH
```

D(−)Fructose

From the relationship to D(+)glucose it is evident that ordinary fructose is a member of the D series and is correctly designated as D(−)-fructose.

Although the simple ketones do not react with alcohols (p. 82), this reaction does occur with hydroxy ketones when the two functional groups are so situated that a five- or six-membered ring may be formed. It would be predicted, therefore, that D(−)fructose should exhibit the phenomenon of mutarotation, and this is found to be true. The α and β forms which have been isolated are pyranoses, but in its most important derivative D(−)fructose exists in a furanose form. The five forms of D fructose are, then, the following.

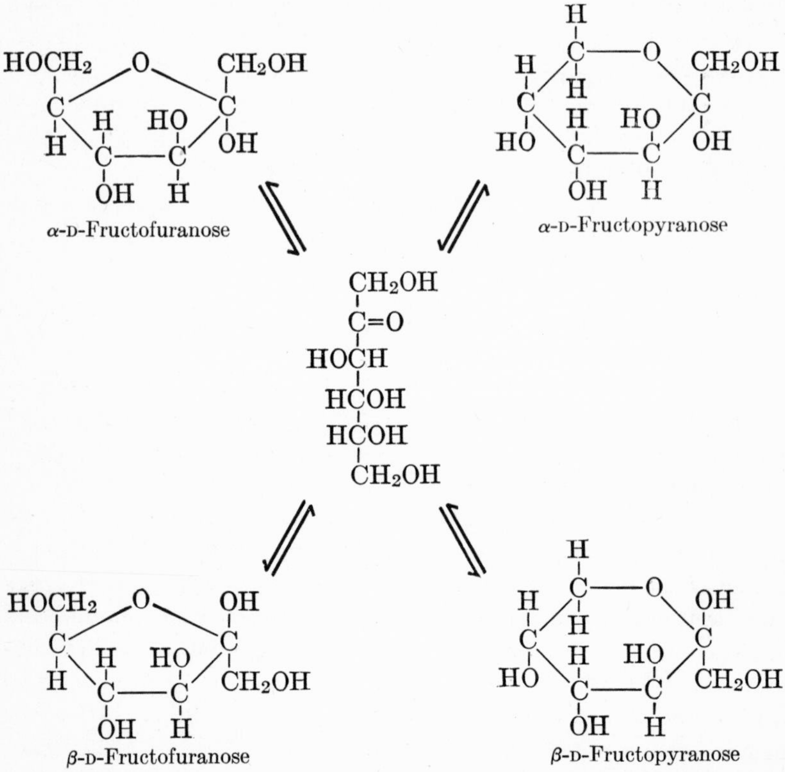

α-D-Fructofuranose

α-D-Fructopyranose

$$\begin{array}{c} CH_2OH \\ | \\ C{=}O \\ | \\ HOCH \\ | \\ HCOH \\ | \\ HCOH \\ | \\ CH_2OH \end{array}$$

β-D-Fructofuranose

β-D-Fructopyranose

The Aldopentoses. The aldopentoses have one less >CHOH group than aldohexoses have. The number of asymmetric carbons is three, and, consequently, there should be four pairs of optical antipodes. These are all known and are shown in Fig. 16. The formulas of only the D forms are given.

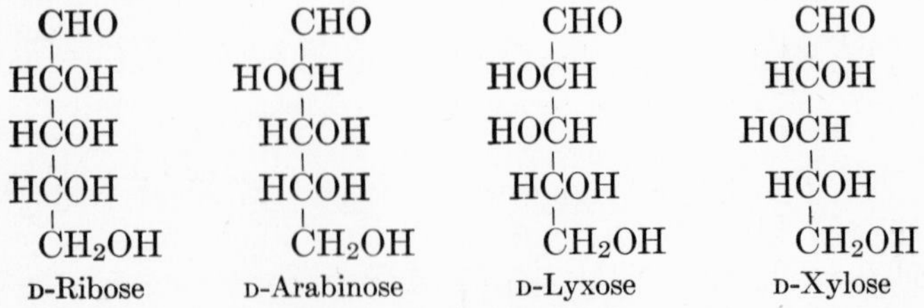

D-Ribose	D-Arabinose	D-Lyxose	D-Xylose
CHO	CHO	CHO	CHO
HCOH	HOCH	HOCH	HCOH
HCOH	HCOH	HOCH	HOCH
HCOH	HCOH	HCOH	HCOH
CH_2OH	CH_2OH	CH_2OH	CH_2OH

FIG. 16. The aldopentoses.

Reactions of the Monosaccharides

The Benedict Test. All the monosaccharides are mild reducing agents, and all give positive tests with Benedict's or Fehling's solution (p. 76). It is not surprising that the aldoses respond to mild oxidizing agents, since the test is characteristic of aldehydes. The oxidation of a ketose by these reagents must, however, involve a reaction of a somewhat different type. Actually, it has been found that α-hydroxy ketones in which the alcohol group is primary or secondary are oxidized to keto aldehydes or diketones under very mild conditions $(-\underset{\text{OH}}{\underset{|}{\text{CH}}}-\underset{\text{O}}{\underset{\|}{\text{C}}}- + [\text{O}] \longrightarrow -\underset{\text{O}}{\underset{\|}{\text{C}}}-\underset{\text{O}}{\underset{\|}{\text{C}}}-)$. All ketoses are capable of this type of oxidation.

Sugars which reduce Fehling's or Benedict's solutions are known as *reducing sugars*. This class includes all the monosaccharides and most of the common disaccharides (p. 204). Reducing sugars are sometimes determined quantitatively by these reagents. In the quantitative procedure the cuprous oxide is separated, dried, and weighed.

Formation of Osazones. All reducing sugars react with phenylhydrazine to give products known as *osazones*. The reaction proceeds in three steps. In the first, the aldehyde or ketone group of the sugar reacts in the normal fashion to give a phenylhydrazone. The phenylhydrazone then reduces a second molecule of phenylhydrazine (to aniline and ammonia) with the formation of a new carbonyl group in the phenylhydrazone molecule. In the last step the newly formed carbonyl group reacts to give a second phenylhydrazone linkage. The product is the osazone, which is usually insoluble in water and crystallizes from the hot reaction mixture. Osazone formation is illustrated by the accompanying equations for the reactions of D-glucose and D-fructose with phenylhydrazine. The osazones are of great value in the laboratory study of carbohydrates for several reasons. Because of their low solubility they are usually easily isolated and purified, whereas many of the sugars are extremely soluble in water and crystallize with great difficulty. Different sugars are converted to osazones at different rates, and different osazones crystallize in definite, characteristic patterns. Consequently, it is often possible to identify a sugar by converting it to the osazone, noting the time required for the reaction and observing the melting point and crystal form of the product. Hydrolysis of osazones yields dicarbonyl compounds known as *osones*.

The fact that dextro-rotatory glucose and levo-rotatory fructose are

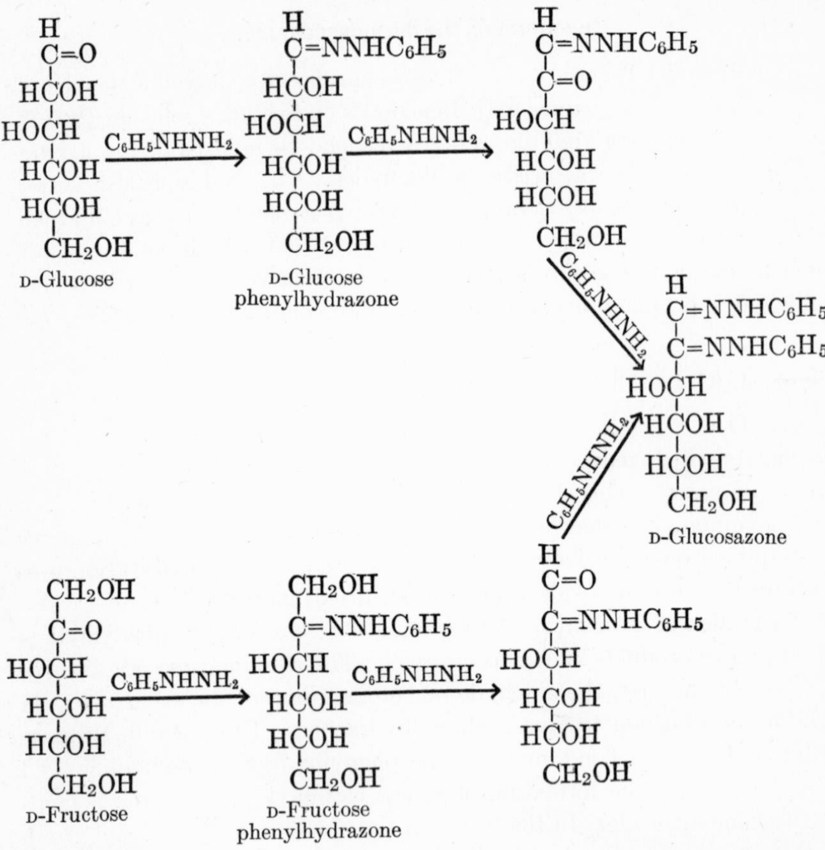

D-Glucose

D-Glucose phenylhydrazone

D-Glucosazone

D-Fructose

D-Fructose phenylhydrazone

converted to the *same* osazone (see equations) is of unusual interest. Once the configuration of the asymmetric carbon atoms in D-glucose had been established, this single observation was sufficient to show that the three asymmetric atoms in D-fructose have the same configurations as the corresponding three in D-glucose. If this were not true, then two diastereoisomeric osazones would be produced. From the same reasoning, it can be seen that, once it is known that D-glucose is a member of the D series, then ordinary fructose must be D-fructose.

A similar relationship obtains between ribose and arabinose; their osazones are identical. Lyxose and xylose also yield osazones that are the same.

Ascorbic Acid. One of the most important derivatives of xylose is ascorbic acid or vitamin C. A deficiency of this substance in the diet causes scurvy. The vitamin occurs in fruits and vegetables, notably in citrus fruits, tomatoes, and fresh peppers. It has been synthesized from L-xylose by the following sequence of transformations.

```
     CHO            HC=NNHC6H5            HC=O
     |              |                     |
 HOCH               C=NNHC6H5             C=O
     |              |          H2O        |           HCN
   HCOH    ——→    HCOH         ——→      HCOH         ——→
     |              |                     |
 HOCH             HOCH                  HOCH
     |              |                     |
   CH2OH           CH2OH                 CH2OH
 L-Xylose        L-Xylosazone        L-Xylose osone

   CN              CO2H                        HO        OH
   |               |                            |         |
   CHOH            CHOH                    OH   C=========C
   |               |                        |   |         |
   C=O    H2O      C=O     -H2O    HOCH2-C——CH        C=O
   |      ——→      |       ——→           H     \     /
  HCOH            HCOH                          O
   |               |                      Ascorbic acid
 HOCH            HOCH
   |               |
   CH2OH           CH2OH
```

Ascorbic acid is the enol form of a keto lactone. The group –C(OH)=C(OH)– is known as the enediol group. The acidity of the compound is due to the hydroxyl group in the *beta* position.

Glycosides. Reduction and osazone formation are reactions of the *carbonyl* forms of the monosaccharides. The most important derivatives of the cyclic hemiacetal or lactol forms are the acetals. In this connection it should be recalled that simple hemiacetals react with alcohols to give acetals (p. 82). The hemiacetal forms of the sugars react in the same way, yielding acetals which are known by the class name of *glycoside*. Particular compounds of this type are named after the sugars from which they are derived. Thus glycosides obtained from glucose are glucosides, and those from fructose are fructosides. If it is desired to make the names still more specific, to show the size of the rings, this is done by incorporating the stems furan and pyran (p. 198) in the names.

Examples of glycosides are the two methyl glucosides obtained from D-glucose and methyl alcohol in the presence of an acid catalyst. Their formulas are given below.

```
          CH2OH                               CH2OH
          |                                   |
          C————O                              C————O
    H\  / |      \    /H              H\  /  |      \    /OCH3
      C   H       C                     C    H        C
 HO/  \  OH   H  /  \OCH3          HO/  \  OH    H  /  \H
        \|     | /                        \|      | /
          C————C                            C—————C
          |    |                            |     |
          H    OH                           H     OH
   α-Methyl D-glucoside              β-Methyl D-glucoside
(α-methyl D-glucopyranoside)     (β-methyl D-glucopyranoside)
```

The chemical properties of the glycosides are widely different from those of the simple sugars. Because hemiacetal formation is readily reversible the monosaccharides have the properties of aldehydes or ketones, and, as already seen, mutarotation, reducing properties, and osazone formation all depend on the spontaneous change of hemiacetal forms of sugars to the carbonyl forms. Acetal formation, however, is *not* spontaneously reversible. Only on heating with water and acid do the acetals regenerate the parent aldehyde and alcohol. In consequence, the glycosides are quite stable substances. They do not exhibit mutarotation, nor do they react with phenylhydrazine or mild oxidizing agents. This is an important consideration, because the more complex sugars, the disaccharides and polysaccharides, are glycosides derived from two or more molecules of monosaccharide.

Classification and Definitions. From what has been said of glucose and fructose, it is seen that the monosaccharides are polyhydroxy aldehydes or ketones. Other carbohydrates can be hydrolyzed to monosaccharides in the presence of acids. It is possible to define carbohydrates as those substances which are polyhydroxy aldehydes or ketones or which upon hydrolysis yield only polyhydroxy aldehydes or ketones. According to this definition a glycoside involving one molecule of monosaccharide and one molecule of a non-sugar, such as α-methyl D-glucoside, is to be regarded as a carbohydrate *derivative.*

The Disaccharides

The disaccharides have compositions which indicate that they are formed from two molecules of monosaccharide by elimination of one molecule of water. Under the influence of acids or digestive enzymes they take up one molecule of water and yield two molecules of monosaccharide. The common disaccharides are derived from the hexoses and so have the formula $C_{12}H_{22}O_{11}$. The two molecules of monosaccharide formed by hydrolysis may be alike or different. Thus maltose yields a single monosaccharide, while lactose and sucrose yield mixtures.

$$\text{Maltose} + H_2O \longrightarrow \text{D-Glucose} + \text{D-Glucose}$$

$$\text{Lactose} + H_2O \longrightarrow \text{D-Glucose} + \text{D-Galactose}$$

$$\text{Sucrose} + H_2O \longrightarrow \text{D-Glucose} + \text{D-Fructose}$$

The Structure of Maltose. Maltose, which yields two molecules of D-glucose upon acid hydrolysis, is a reducing sugar. It exhibits the phenomenon of mutarotation, and it can be converted to an osazone. Analysis of the osazone shows that only one of the two glucose units present is involved in osazone formation. These facts indicate that the two monosaccharide units are linked in such a way that *the hemiacetal group of one is converted to an acetal linkage, but the hemiacetal group of the other remains unchanged.* In other words, maltose must be a glycoside derived from two molecules of glucose, one acting as a hemiacetal, the other as an alcohol. It has been found that the glucose unit fixed as the glucoside is an α-D-glucose residue and that it is connected to the second D-glucose molecule through the hydroxyl group of the fourth carbon atom of the latter. The formulas of α-maltose and β-maltose are the following.

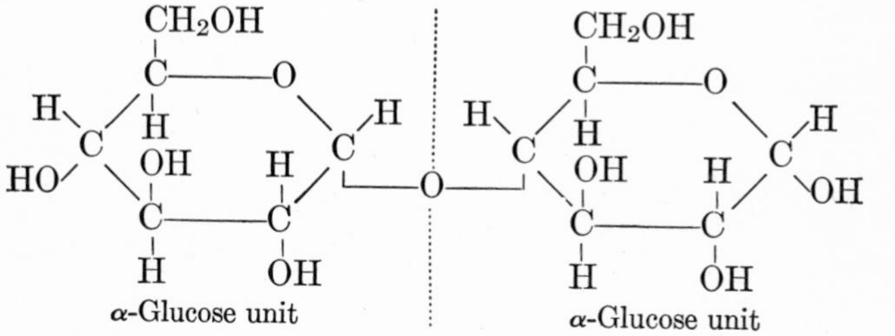

α-Glucose unit | α-Glucose unit

α-Maltose

α-Glucose unit | β-Glucose unit

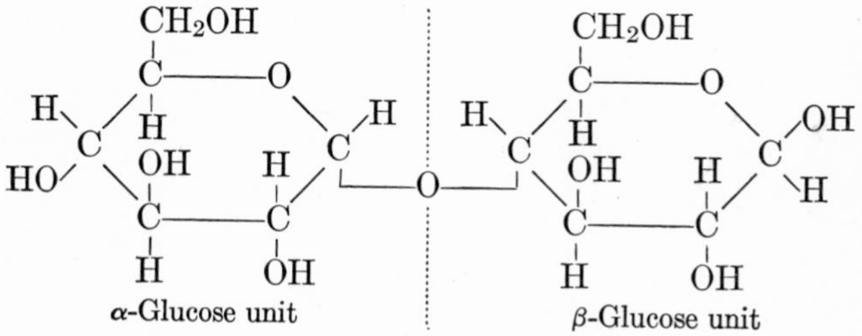

β-Maltose

Lactose, or milk sugar, is also a reducing disaccharide. It undergoes mutarotation and forms an osazone. It must, then, have a structure similar to that of maltose except that the monosaccharides concerned are galactose (p. 197) and glucose. It has been found to differ from maltose only in that it is a β-galactoside rather than an α-glucoside. The formulas of α- and β-lactoses are as follows.

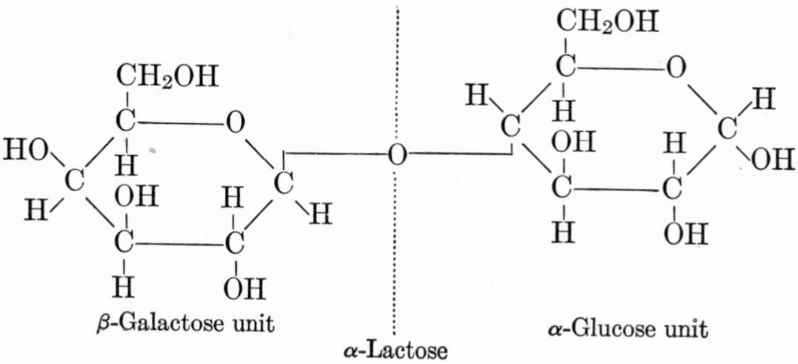

β-Galactose unit | α-Glucose unit

α-Lactose

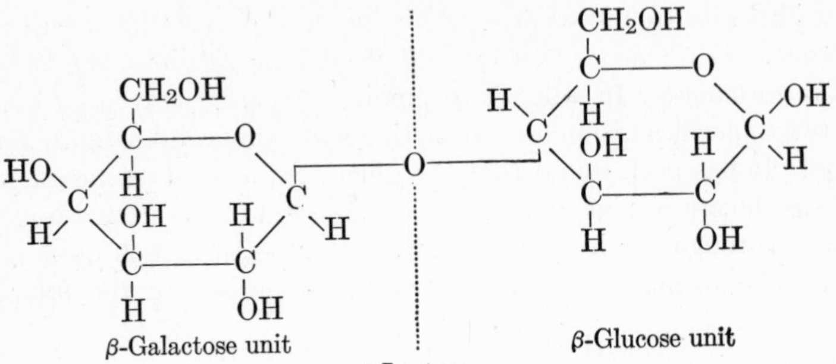

β-Galactose unit | β-Glucose unit

β-Lactose

Sucrose. Maltose and lactose, having reducing properties, are known as reducing disaccharides. The only important member of the other possible class, the non-reducing disaccharides, is *sucrose,* or the ordinary sugar obtained from the sugar cane and the sugar beet. Sucrose yields one molecule each of D-glucose and D-fructose upon hydrolysis in the presence of acids. Since sucrose is not oxidized by Benedict's reagent, does not mutarotate, and does not form an osazone, the two monosaccharide units must be combined in such a way that neither residue retains a hemiacetal linkage. *It must be at once a glucoside and a fructoside.* It has been found that the glucose residue is present as an α-glucoside and that the fructose is combined as a β-fructofuranoside (p. 198). Its formula is the following and has been confirmed by synthesis.

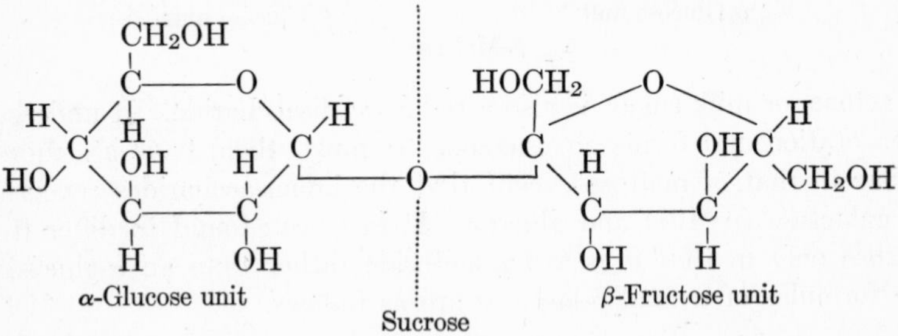

α-Glucose unit | β-Fructose unit

Sucrose

Sucrose is dextro-rotatory ($[\alpha]_D^{20} = +66.4°$). On hydrolysis it yields equal amounts of dextro-rotatory glucose ($[\alpha]_D^{20} = +52.2°$) and levo-rotatory fructose ($[\alpha]_D^{20} = -93°$). When hydrolysis is complete the solution is levo-rotatory, the rotation being the algebraic sum of the rotations of the two monosaccharides ($[\alpha]_D^{20} = -40.8°$). Because of the change in sign the process is called *inversion,* and a mixture of equal parts of glucose and fructose prepared in this way is known as *invert sugar.* Honey is largely invert sugar.

Polysaccharides

Starch. The cereal grains are composed essentially of starch. Certain roots also contain high percentages of starch; the potato contains about 18 per cent of this component. The granules of starch produced by different plants vary in size and shape, and so it is possible to determine the source of a sample of starch by examination under a microscope. In their chemical properties the purified starches from different sources are identical.

Two varieties of starch are known. One of them, called amylose, is soluble in water; the other, called amylopectin, does not dissolve in water.

The analysis of starch shows that it has the composition $(C_6H_{10}O_5)_n$. As hydrolysis by enzymes or acids converts starch into D-glucose, it is evident that the unit $C_6H_{10}O_5$ is a D-glucose residue. Maltose is among the products of incomplete hydrolysis, indicating that the glucose units are linked together in the α-glucoside form. From these and other observations of the chemical behavior of starch the following structure has been deduced.

```
      CH2OH                     CH2OH                      CH2OH
       |                  /      |                  \       |
       C----O            |       C----O              |      C----O
 H    / H    \     H   H |     / H    \      H     H |    / H     \     H
  \  C   |    C   /     \|   C   |     C   /        \|  C   |      C   /
HO  / \ OH  H  \ C       |  /  \ OH  H  \ C          |  / \ OH  H   \ C
       \ |   |  /  \--O--|-/    \ |   |  /  \--O-----|-/    \ |  |  /  \OH
        C----C           |       C----C              |       C----C
        |    |            \      |    |             /n       |    |
        H    OH                  H    OH                     H    OH
```

Formerly it was believed that the starch molecule consisted of 24 to 30 α-glucose units joined together as shown in the above formula ($n = 22$ to 28). However, it is now evident that the molecule is much larger. It appears that in amylopectin the chains of about 25 glucose residues are united by a linkage different from that which joins the glucose units in the chains. The number of chains composing the starch molecule is unknown, but it is likely that the molecule contains hundreds, perhaps thousands, of glucose units rather than about twenty-five. The branching of the molecules appears to be through linkages involving hydroxyl groups at positions 3 and 6 in the formula shown above (the acetal carbon atom is given the number 1).

Because of its high molecular weight amylopectin does not give a true solution in water. However, it does give colloidal dispersions, ranging from jellies to mobile liquids as the concentration of starch is diminished. These "solutions" of starch do not respond to the Benedict or Fehling test. This indicates that the chains of glucose units are combined in the starch molecule in such a way that the hemiacetal group at the end of each chain is involved.

The soluble starch, amylose, is believed to be a linear polymer. It can be represented by the formula above, the value of n probably being between 60 and 300. Its solubility results partly from its lower molecular weight, as compared to amylopectin, and partly from its shape. In the linear molecule a much higher proportion of the hydroxyl groups are exposed to the solvent than in the branched molecule of amylopectin.

Partial hydrolysis of starch converts it into smaller molecules known as dextrins. Dextrins are also obtained by heating starch to 200–250°; the gloss of starched cloth is due to the formation of dextrins when the cloth is ironed. Dextrins are used in the preparation of mucilages.

Continued hydrolysis converts starch into maltose and finally into glucose. Under the influence of the enzyme diastase, obtained from sprouted barley, the hydrolysis product is maltose. The commercial hydrolysis of starch is usually carried out in the presence of very dilute hydrochloric acid. After hydrolysis has proceeded to the desired stage the acid is neutralized and the solution is evaporated to give a thick syrup which contains dextrins, maltose, and glucose. This syrup, usually known as "corn syrup" since the starch is obtained from corn, is widely used as a sweetening agent. Pure D-glucose is also prepared commercially by the complete hydrolysis of starch.

A deep blue color is produced when iodine is added to a solution of starch. This is the basis of a very sensitive test for either starch or iodine. With dextrins the result may be a color ranging from violet to red or no color at all, depending upon the degree of degradation. Maltose and glucose do not give colors.

The normal human diet contains more of carbohydrate than of fat and protein combined, and the greater part of the carbohydrate is starch. Digestion of starch consists in its hydrolysis to glucose. The saliva contains the enzymes ptyalin, which catalyzes the hydrolysis of starch to maltose, and maltase, which converts maltose to glucose. The gastric juice contains no starch-splitting enzyme, but digestion of carbohydrate in the stomach continues under the influence of the salivary enzymes. Several amylases (the general name for starch-splitting enzymes) and maltases are present in the pancreatic and intestinal juices, as are also certain enzymes which bring about the hydrolysis of disaccharides such as sucrose and lactose. Thus practically all the starch and sugar ingested is converted to monosaccharides. These are absorbed through the intestinal wall and are carried to the liver by the blood stream. In the liver glucose is recombined to form *glycogen*, a polysaccharide very similar to ordinary starch but apparently of lower molecular weight. Hydrolysis of glycogen converts it wholly to glucose. However, the liver produces it from all the hexoses normally liberated in the small intestine (glucose, fructose, and galactose). The glycogen stored in the liver is a reserve supply of carbohydrate for the body. When sugar is required by other parts of the body, liver glycogen is hydrolyzed to glucose, and the glucose is discharged into the blood stream. The muscles remove glucose from the blood and convert it to muscle glycogen. The energy required for muscular work is obtained by a complex process involving the indirect oxidation of glycogen. Also, the energy required for maintenance of body temperature is obtained in part from the oxidation of glycogen.

The dextrans are polysaccharides containing only α-glucose units. They differ from starch and glycogen in having a high proportion of the α-glucose units incorporated through linkages at the 1 and 6 positions. The molecules appear to be branched, a glucose unit at a branch point having an additional linkage which may involve the 2, 3, or 4 position. Dextrans are formed when organisms of the *Leuconostoc* class grow in solutions of sucrose. Dextran fractions of certain molecular-weight range are of interest as plasma substitutes.

Cellulose. Cellulose, which constitutes the greater portion of plants, is a polysaccharide which can be represented by the formula $(C_6H_{10}O_5)_n$. This is identical with the empirical formula of starch, and cellulose, like starch, is converted to D-glucose by hydrolysis in the presence of acids. However, there are two important differences in the structures of the two polysaccharides. In the first place, the monosaccharide unit of cellulose is β-glucose, rather than α-glucose as in starch. Secondly, the molecular weight of cellulose is much greater than that of starch. It appears that several thousand β-glucose units are involved in the linear molecule.

Linkage of β-glucose units in cellulose

Hydrolysis of cellulose under severe conditions and in the presence of acids produces glucose, as mentioned above. If the hydrolysis is incomplete the reaction mixture is found to contain cellobiose, a disaccharide which differs from maltose only in that it is a β-glucosido-glucose. In the condensed formula for a cellulose chain given above, the unit enclosed by the brackets is a cellobiose residue. The human digestive system provides no enzymes capable of splitting cellulose, but certain animals are able to utilize part of the ingested cellulose.

Natural cotton is one of the purest forms of cellulose. The fibers of raw cotton are covered with a waxy substance which acts as a sizing, making the fibers waterproof. Absorbent cotton is made by extracting the natural sizing with organic solvents. Linen, made from flax, is also essentially cellulose; it is not so pure as cotton.

Wood contains cellulose and lignin, a substance of high molecular weight, whose structure is not yet definitely known. The manufacture of paper is an important cellulose industry. The raw material is usually wood, and the principal operation in converting it to paper is the removal of lignin. The wood is first shredded to separate the fibers and then heated with a solution of some chemical, such as sodium sulfite, to extract the lignin. The purified cellulose is collected on screens, rolled, and dried. Various additional processes are required, depending on the type of paper desired. For instance, bleaching is necessary to produce a white paper. Writing paper is impregnated with sizes, such as rosin, glue, starch, and silicates. Parchment paper is prepared by immersing the sheets in cold, concentrated sulfuric acid. This treatment renders the surface waterproof. The best grades of paper are made from cotton rags, that is, from quite pure cellulose. Some paper is made from straw.

Cellulose Derivatives

Cellulose Nitrate. From the structural formula written above for a portion of the cellulose molecule it can be seen that three alcohol groups are present in each glucose unit. These show many of the reactions of ordinary alcohols. For example, treatment of cellulose with a mixture of sulfuric and nitric acids produces the nitrate, $[C_6H_7O_2(ONO_2)_3]_x$, in which each hydroxyl group has been esterified by nitric acid. This product is known as cellulose trinitrate or guncotton. It is a high explosive of great military value. If the reaction with nitric acid is carried out under milder conditions a mixture of mono- and dinitrates is formed. This material, known as pyroxylin, finds many uses. *Smokeless powder* is a mixture of pyroxylin and guncotton. *Celluloid* is a mixture of camphor and pyroxylin. *Collodion* is a solution of pyroxylin in alcohol and ether. Certain *lacquers* are essentially solutions of pyroxylin in butyl acetate or other solvents. The pyroxylin is first treated with dilute alkali, a process which makes it more soluble in organic solvents and renders the solutions less viscous. The lacquer must also contain coloring materials, resins, and certain very high-boiling liquids (plasticizers) which increase the elasticity of the dry lacquer film. It is to be noted that the drying of lacquers involves only the evaporation of a solvent, whereas the "drying" of oil paints depends on chemical reactions initiated by the oxygen of the air.

Cellulose Acetate. Acetic anhydride converts cellulose to the triacetate $[C_6H_7O_2(OCOCH_3)_3]_x$. Cellulose acetate is soluble in various solvents, and it can be obtained in the form of thin sheets by evaporation of its solutions. Cellulose acetate is much less inflammable than pyroxylin and has supplanted it in certain products which are subjected to fire hazards. When mixed with suitable plasticizers the acetate can be molded. Cellulose acetate has been widely used as the bonding sheet in safety glass.

The acetate process for making fibers employs a solution of cellulose acetate in a volatile organic solvent. The solution is spun into a heated chamber so that the solvent evaporates, leaving a filament of cellulose acetate.

Rayon. It has been found that the difference in the appearance of silk and cotton materials depends on the fact that the silk fibers are long, smooth, tubular threads, whereas those of cotton are short and irregular. The first process developed for improving the appearance of cotton fabrics was mercerization, which is a brief treatment with alkali. It imparts a sheen to the cloth, but since it affects only the surface of the fibers the appearance of the product is still quite different from that of silk. In making rayon, cellulose is converted into a soluble derivative, and a solution of the derivative is forced through fine holes into a medium which alters the derivative that a filament is formed. These processes are designed to give filaments of *regenerated cellulose*. The most extensively used is the viscose process, in which cellulose is converted into the soluble cellulose xanthate. The xanthate solution is spun into a bath of acid, which decomposes the xanthate and precipitates cellulose. The formation and decomposition of a xanthate can be illustrated with a simple alcohol. The reagents are sodium hydroxide and carbon disulfide.

$$CH_3CH_2OH + CS_2 + NaOH \longrightarrow \underset{\text{Sodium ethyl xanthate}}{CH_3CH_2OC(=S)SNa} + H_2O$$

$$CH_3CH_2OC(=S)SNa + HCl \longrightarrow CH_3CH_2OH + CS_2 + NaCl$$

In the preparation of cellulose xanthate the cellulose is first treated with alkali. The "sodium cellulose" so obtained is a somewhat degraded cellulose probably containing both adsorbed and combined alkali. On treatment with carbon disulfide the xanthate is formed. Colloidal dispersions of cellulose xanthate are extremely viscous, hence the name viscose. In the preparation of cellophane the xanthate solution is forced through narrow slits into the regenerating bath.

The cuprammonium process makes use of the soluble derivative formed when cellulose is treated with an ammoniacal solution of a copper salt (Schweitzer's reagent). The derivative is decomposed by acids to regenerate the cellulose.

In the practical application of these processes a number of modifications are necessary. Various substances are added to the solutions of the cellulose derivatives to improve the spinning properties and increase the flexibility of the filaments. Glycerol and glucose are among the substances added. A number of washings of the filaments are required to remove the various chemicals used in each process, and bleaching is necessary. In the preparation of cellophane numerous washing and rolling operations are required, and the product is finally coated with a lacquer to make it waterproof.

An idea of the industrial importance of rayons may be gained from the consideration that the annual production in the United States is approaching *400,000 tons*. In the early development of the industry, low-grade cotton was used as the raw material. With the improvement in methods of processing wood, more and more of the cellulose is being obtained from this source.

SUGGESTED READING

G. H. Bixler, G. E. Hines, R. M. McGhee, and R. A. Shurter, "Dextran," *Ind. Eng. Chem.*, *45*, 692 (1953).

PROBLEMS

1. Define and illustrate the following terms: (*a*) aldopentose, (*b*) ketohexose, (*c*) reducing sugar, (*d*) lactol, (*e*) mutarotation, (*f*) invert sugar, (*g*) glycoside, (*h*) glucoside, (*i*) osazone, (*j*) pyranose, (*k*) furanose, (*l*) polysaccharide, (*m*) dextrin, (*n*) glycogen.

2. A new sugar is found to exhibit mutarotation; predict its behavior toward: (*a*) Benedict's solution, (*b*) methyl alcohol and hydrochloric acid, (*c*) phenylhydrazine.

3. By means of equations, show the reactions involved in the preparation of rayon, gunpowder, lacquers, cellophane, and edible sugars from cellulose.

4. Compare the structures of α-methyl D-glucoside, maltose, dextrin, and starch. Compare the structure of starch with that of cellulose.

CHAPTER 16

Valence

Since the time of Kekule many theories have been developed regarding the nature of valence. The most successful of these is the electronic theory of valence originated by Kossel and Lewis. It grew out of the experiments and speculations of Werner and others and was later amplified by Langmuir and interpreted by Sidgwick.

The chief practical value of the electronic theory is that it provides an explanation of the different kinds of valence, for valence had come to mean to the organic chemist something very different from the classical concept of the inorganic chemist. Inorganic compounds are generally salts, acids, or bases—compounds possessing polar properties. Organic compounds, on the other hand, are generally nonpolar in character. The contrast between these two classes of substances is seen best by reference to their physical properties. Some of these are listed below.

Nonpolar Compounds	Polar Compounds
Volatile	Nonvolatile
Low melting points	High melting points
Insoluble in water	Soluble in water
Soluble in organic solvents	Insoluble in organic solvents
Un-ionized in solution	More or less completely ionized in solution
Fixed bonds which permit structural isomerism	No isomerism
Reactions slow	Reactions rapid

These properties represent the extreme cases of polar and nonpolar substances. Most compounds fall somewhere between the two extremities of the series, and all gradations are observed.

An example of an extremely polar compound is sodium chloride. Most inorganic salts belong in this category. Saturated hydrocarbons such as methane exemplify the extremely nonpolar group.

TYPES OF VALENCE

Any theory of valence must be able to account for the great difference in these two groups. The electronic theory does this by providing a means of representing *different kinds* of valence. This theory assumes that a bond is formed by a pair of electrons shared between two atoms.

Each atom except those of the inert gases has one or more electrons available for bond formation. These are known as valence electrons, and the number is related to the position of the element in the periodic table. Thus sodium has one, magnesium two, aluminum three, carbon four, nitrogen five, oxygen six, and chlorine seven.

It is postulated that in a nonpolar compound a valence bond is formed by two electrons—one from each of the atoms involved. Such a bond is called covalent or nonpolar and is highly localized; it has a fixed direction. Thus the hydrogen molecule is represented as H:H. Similarly, methane is

$$\begin{array}{c} H \\ \cdot\cdot \\ H:C:H \\ \cdot\cdot \\ H \end{array}$$

Ethylene and acetylene are written in the following manner:

$$\begin{array}{cc} H & H \\ \cdot\cdot & \cdot\cdot \\ C & ::C \\ \cdot\cdot & \cdot\cdot \\ H & H \end{array} \qquad\qquad H:C:::C:H$$

Ethylene Acetylene

It is evident that these representations differ from the line formulas commonly used by organic chemists only in that a pair of dots has replaced a line. Clearly in such cases the electronic formulas offer as yet little or no practical advantage over the line formulas.

The case of sodium chloride is very different. Here an electron has passed from the sodium atom to the chlorine atom and the formula is Na^+Cl^-. In other words, the two ions are held together only by electrostatic forces. This relationship, characteristic of polar compounds, is generally spoken of as electrovalence. The binding force is not localized but is exerted in all directions and affects all ions of the opposite charge which happen to be near.

This type of linkage is not ordinarily formed by carbon but is found in salts of organic acids and amines.

$$[RCO_2]^- Na^+ \qquad [R_2NH_2]^+ Cl^-$$
$$[RSO_3]^- K^+ \qquad [R_4N]^+ I^-$$

Amino acids have saltlike or polar characteristics and may be represented as inner salts.

$$\begin{array}{l} RCHCO_2^- \\ \;\;| \\ \;\;NH_3^+ \end{array} \qquad \overset{+}{N}H_3\text{—}C_6H_4\text{—}SO_3^-$$

These are known as zwitterions (p. 182).

Compounds whose properties are intermediate between those of the extreme polar and nonpolar categories are supposed to have one or more bonds in which the electron pair is *shared unequally* by the two atoms. Thus methyl alcohol may be pictured as follows: $\begin{array}{c}H\\ H:\ddot{\underset{..}{C}}:\ddot{\underset{..}{O}}:H\\ H\end{array}$. The electron pair joining the hydrogen atom to the oxygen atom is represented as being predominantly in the possession of the oxygen atom. This distribution of the electrons creates a dipole approaching the truly polar type in which the electrical charges are entirely separate. This explains why methyl alcohol is more polar than methane and why sugars—with many such hydroxyl groups—show a marked polar character in many of their physical properties.

The Coordinate Covalence

A special type of covalent linkage known as the coordinate covalence (also called semipolar) bond occurs frequently. It is present, for example, in the nitro group. The accepted formula for nitrobenzene is represented by *a*.

(*a*) (*b*)

Here it will be observed that both oxygen atoms as well as the nitrogen atom have shells of eight electrons. Structure *b*, which corresponds to the line formula $C_6H_5{-}N\begin{smallmatrix}\nearrow\!\!\!\!\nearrow O\\ \searrow\!\!\!\!\searrow O\end{smallmatrix}$, is seen to be unlikely because it violates the octet rule, the nitrogen atom having a shell of ten electrons. Most negative atoms tend to acquire electrons and reach a saturation point at eight. It follows that the maximum valence of these elements is four. In *a* the nitrogen atom holds four electron pairs and thus is tetravalent.

It will be noticed, however, that the single bond between nitrogen and oxygen is peculiar in that both of the electrons of the bonding pair come from one atom. This is true of all coordinate covalent bonds. The atom furnishing the electron pair is called the *donor;* the other atom is known as the *acceptor*. In sharing the pair the nitrogen atom virtually gives up one electron to the oxygen atom. The nitrogen atom will, accordingly, carry a positive charge. The oxygen atom, on the other hand, will possess a negative charge. This is a typical coordinate covalent linkage.

The formula might be written $\mathrm{C_6H_5{-}\underset{\underset{O}{\|}}{N^+}{-}O^-}$ or $\mathrm{C_6H_5{:}\underset{\underset{:\ddot{O}:}{\cdot\cdot}}{N^+}{:}\overset{\cdot\cdot}{\underset{\cdot\cdot}{O}}{:}^-}$ to show this. The notation generally used is $\mathrm{C_6H_5{-}\underset{\underset{O}{\|}}{N}{\rightarrow}O}$. That is, the coordinate covalent bond is represented by an arrow pointing from the *donor* to the *acceptor*.

Ammonium chloride offers a striking illustration of types of valence. Consider the reaction between ammonia and hydrogen ion.

$$\mathrm{H{:}\overset{\overset{H}{\cdot\cdot}}{\underset{\underset{H}{\cdot\cdot}}{N}}{:} + H^+ \longrightarrow \left[H{:}\overset{\overset{H}{\cdot\cdot}}{\underset{\underset{H}{\cdot\cdot}}{N}}{:}H\right]^+}$$

The nitrogen atom in ammonia is trivalent but has in addition an unshared pair of electrons which permits it to form a linkage with the proton, giving rise to the ammonium ion. Thus, in ammonium chloride the chloride ion is held by an electrovalence.

$$\mathrm{NH_4{}^+Cl^-}$$

Amine oxides (p. 423), formerly written $\mathrm{R{-}\overset{\overset{R}{|}}{\underset{\underset{R}{|}}{N}}{=}O}$, are now represented as $\mathrm{R{:}\overset{\overset{R}{\cdot\cdot}}{\underset{\underset{R}{\cdot\cdot}}{N}}{:}\overset{\cdot\cdot}{\underset{\cdot\cdot}{O}}{:}}$ or $\mathrm{R{-}\overset{\overset{R}{|}}{\underset{\underset{R}{|}}{N}}{\rightarrow}O}$, the oxygen atom being joined to the nitrogen atom by a coordinate covalent bond.

Free Radicals

Another very great advantage gained by the use of two dots for a valence bond is that the bond can be separated into two parts. Thus the dissociation of hexaphenylethane into the free radical, triphenylmethyl, can be pictured as follows.

$$\mathrm{(C_6H_5)_3C{:}C(C_6H_5)_3 \rightleftharpoons 2(C_6H_5)_3C\cdot}$$

In general free radicals may be represented as having a trivalent carbon atom with one additional (unshared) electron. In liquid sulfur dioxide the dissociation is ionic and can be indicated as follows.

$$\mathrm{(C_6H_5)_3C\cdot \rightleftharpoons (C_6H_5)_3C^+ + \ominus}$$

This means that in sulfur dioxide solution the free radical is in equilibrium with the triphenylmethyl cation and an electron. Both the ion and the electron are believed to be solvated by the sulfur dioxide. Here are seen examples of trivalent carbon with no extra electrons (positive ion) and with one extra electron (free radical). The electronic theory enables one to represent these satisfactorily whereas the line formulas furnished no adequate means of notation for such instances.

"Divalent" Carbon Atoms

Carbon monoxide and certain other molecules long supposed to contain divalent carbon atoms can also be clearly represented by use of electron bonds. Carbon monoxide is now believed to have the structure $:\mathrm{C}\overset{:}{\underset{:}{:}}\mathrm{O}:$. The carbon atom is therefore not divalent but trivalent. Nevertheless, the valence state is again different from any of the three examples of trivalent carbon just considered in connection with free radicals. In carbon monoxide the carbon atom and the oxygen atom have five electrons each (one pair and half of three pairs) and therefore are joined not only by two nonpolar or covalent bonds but also by a coordinate covalent linkage as well. The formula may be written

$$:\overset{-}{\mathrm{C}}\overset{:}{\underset{:}{:}}\overset{+}{\mathrm{O}}: \quad \text{or} \quad \mathrm{C}\overset{\leftarrow}{=}\mathrm{O}$$

The isonitriles (isocyanides) can be represented similarly.

$$\mathrm{R}:\mathrm{N}\overset{:}{\underset{:}{:}}\mathrm{C}: \quad \text{or} \quad \mathrm{RN}\overset{\rightarrow}{=}\mathrm{C}$$

It is interesting to compare the cyanide ion with nitrogen and carbon monoxide. All have the same valence arrangement.

$$:\mathrm{C}\overset{:}{\underset{:}{:}}\mathrm{O}: \quad :\mathrm{N}\overset{:}{\underset{:}{:}}\mathrm{N}: \quad \left[:\mathrm{C}\overset{:}{\underset{:}{:}}\mathrm{N}:\right]^{-}$$

The union of the cyanide ion with a positively charged alkyl radical is a coördination and may take place in either of two ways, producing in the one instance a nitrile and in the other an isonitrile.

$$\mathrm{R} + :\mathrm{C}\overset{:}{\underset{:}{:}}\mathrm{N}: \begin{array}{l} \nearrow \ \mathrm{R}:\mathrm{C}\overset{:}{\underset{:}{:}}\mathrm{N}: \quad \text{Nitrile} \\ \searrow \ :\mathrm{C}\overset{:}{\underset{:}{:}}\mathrm{N}:\mathrm{R} \quad \text{Isonitrile} \end{array}$$

The Hydrogen Bond

It has been shown that a hydrogen atom can form a bridge between two other atoms if they are very electronegative. Oxygen, fluorine, and nitrogen may be joined in this way. As would be expected, the link between two fluorine atoms is the most stable. It exists in potassium hydrogen fluoride (KHF_2), the formula of which is written $K^+[:\ddot{\underset{..}{F}}:H:\ddot{\underset{..}{F}}:]^-$.

The association of water and other hydroxyl-containing compounds has been ascribed to the formation of a hydrogen bridge between two oxygen atoms.

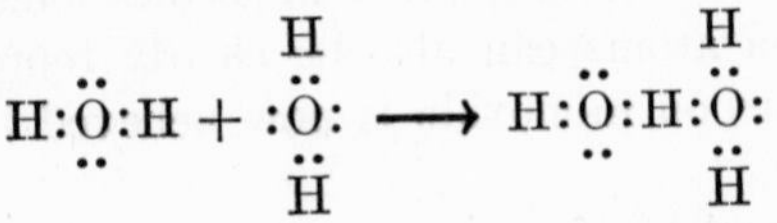

$$H:\ddot{\underset{..}{O}}:H + :\overset{H}{\ddot{\underset{\underset{H}{..}}{O}}}: \longrightarrow H:\overset{H}{\ddot{\underset{..}{O}}}:H:\ddot{\underset{\underset{H}{..}}{O}}:$$

Chelate Rings

This type of linkage is believed to exist in many *ortho* disubstituted benzene derivatives. For example, *o*-nitrophenol and salicylaldehyde may be written as follows.

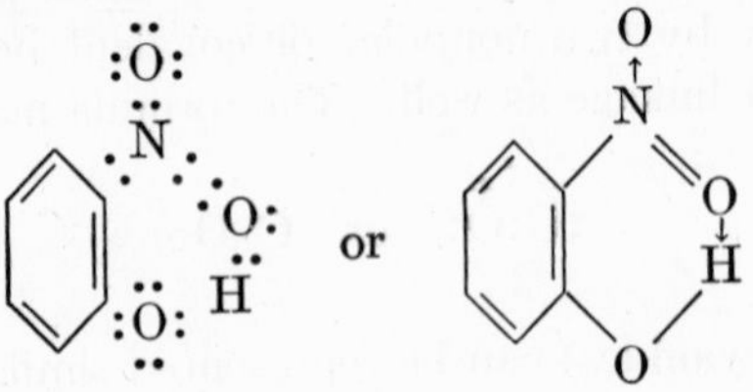

o-Nitrophenol

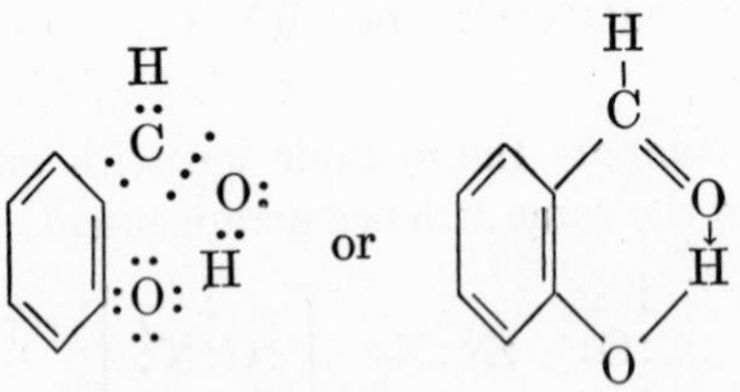

Salicylaldehyde

Nearly all enols can be formulated as ring compounds in which the ring is closed through a hydrogen bond. Acetoacetic ester will serve as an example.

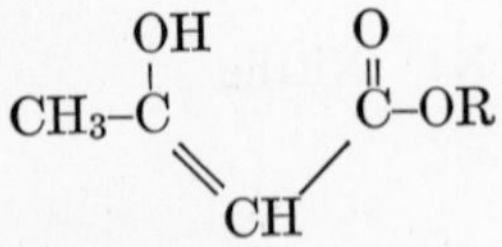

Classical formula

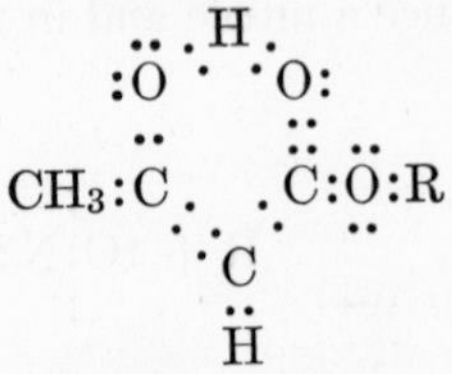

Chelated structure

Such rings are known as chelate rings and are often represented in the following way.

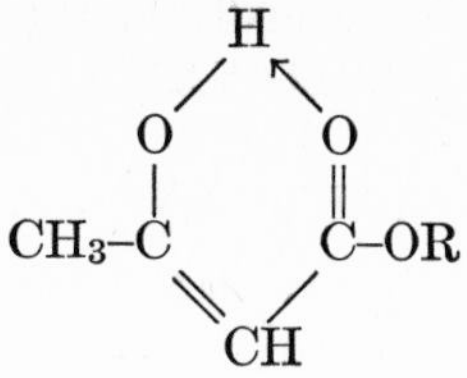

```
            H
          /   ↖
        O       O
        |       ‖
  CH3–C         C–OR
         ⧹⧹   /
           CH
```

INFRARED AND ULTRAVIOLET ABSORPTION SPECTRA

A great deal can be learned about the valence forces in an organic molecule, and hence about its structure, from an examination of its infrared and ultraviolet spectra.

The infrared spectra have proved especially valuable to the organic chemist. An empirical study of the spectra of many related organic compounds has revealed the presence of characteristic absorption bands corresponding to various structural elements. Those listed in Table XXV are illustrative. The frequencies are expressed in reciprocal centi-

TABLE XXV

CHARACTERISTIC INFRARED ABSORPTION BANDS

Structural Unit	Range ($cm.^{-1}$)
O–H (free)	3730–3520
(associated)	3520–3100
≡C–H (acetylenic)	3310–3200
$=CH_2$ (ethylenic)	3090–3070
$-\overset{\vert}{\underset{\vert}{C}}-H$	2890
–C=C– (unconjugated)	1650–1600
(conjugated)	1610–1580
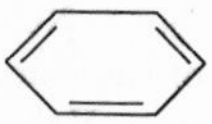	1625–1575
C≡N	2400–2100
C=O (aldehyde)	1730–1675
C=O (ketone, unconjugated)	1720–1705
(ketone, α, β-conjugated)	1700–1665
$-CO_2H$	1740–1650
$-NO_2$	2500–2400

meters. The complexity of the spectra generally makes their interpretation difficult, and their use in structural determination is usually a complement to chemical methods rather than a substitute for them.

Ultraviolet spectra, although not as widely applicable as infrared spectra, are also of great value to the organic chemist in determining the structure of compounds especially of those containing conjugated systems of multiple linkages. Table XXVI shows a few of the ultraviolet

TABLE XXVI

CHARACTERISTIC ULTRAVIOLET ABSORPTION VALUES

System	Example	γ_{max}	ϵ_{max}
–C=C–	3-Octene	185	8,000
–C=N–	Acetoxime	190	5,000
–C=O	Acetone	188	900
C=C–C=C	1,3-Butadiene	217	20,900
C=C=C	Ethylallene	170	4,000
	Benzene	260	250
	Cyclopentadiene	244	2,500
	Pyridine	250	2,000

absorption values (described by giving γ_{max}, the wavelength at the absorption maximum, and ϵ_{max}, the molecular extinction coefficient at this wavelength) associated with structural units in organic molecules.

PROBLEM

Write electronic formulas for the following substances.

a. SO_2
b. CH_3
c. R_3C
d. RSO_2NH_4
e. CO
f. H_2O_2
g. KNO_3
h. CH_3CO_2H
i. R_3SI
j. RIO_2

SUGGESTED READINGS

J. R. Johnson, "Modern Electronic Concepts of Valence," Gilman's *Organic Chemistry*, Vol. II, Second Ed., Chapter 25, John Wiley & Sons, New York, 1943.

L. Pauling, "The Significance of Resonance to the Nature of the Chemical Bond and the Structure of Molecules," Gilman's *Organic Chemistry*, Vol. II, Second Ed., Chapter 26, John Wiley & Sons, New York, 1943.

L. P. Hammett, *Physical Organic Chemistry*, McGraw-Hill Book Company, New York, 1940.

L. N. Ferguson, "Relationships between Absorption Spectra and Chemical Constitution," *Chem. Revs.*, *43*, 385 (1948).

F. A. Miller, "Applications of Infrared and Ultraviolet Spectra to Organic Chemistry," Gilman's *Organic Chemistry*, Vol. III, p. 122, John Wiley & Sons, New York, 1953.

CHAPTER 17

Isomerism

Isomerism is characteristic of complex molecules held together by fixed or covalent bonds and is, therefore, confined primarily to carbon compounds. Isomers have the same molecular formula but differ in at least one of their chemical or physical properties. The difference is, of course, due to a difference in the arrangement of the atoms in the molecule. Following are the principal types of isomerism.

TYPES OF ISOMERISM

Simple Structural Isomerism

The difference between isomers of this group can be expressed by simple structural formulas. Ordinary planar or two-dimensional formulas are sufficient.

Nucleus or Chain Isomers. Nucleus or chain isomers differ in the arrangement of the carbon atoms. Examples of this are the three pentanes:

$$CH_3\text{–}CH_2\text{–}CH_2\text{–}CH_2\text{–}CH_3 \qquad CH_3\text{–}\overset{\displaystyle CH_3}{\overset{|}{C}}H\text{–}CH_2\text{–}CH_3 \qquad CH_3\text{–}\underset{\displaystyle CH_3}{\underset{|}{\overset{\displaystyle CH_3}{\overset{|}{C}}}}\text{–}CH_3$$

n-Pentane Isopentane Neopentane

Position Isomers. Position isomers have the same carbon skeleton but differ in the position of some atom or group attached to it. Examples are *o*-, *m*-, and *p*-dichlorobenzene and 1- and 2-butanol.

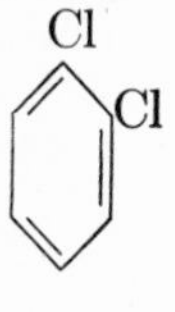

[benzene ring with Cl at positions 1,2] *o*-Dichlorobenzene [benzene ring with Cl at positions 1,3] *m*-Dichlorobenzene [benzene ring with Cl at positions 1,4] *p*-Dichlorobenzene

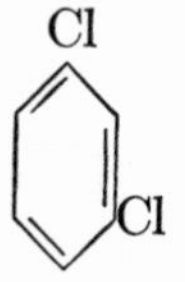

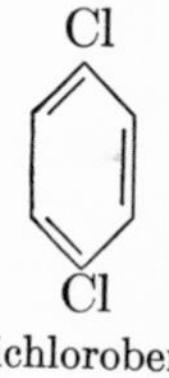

$$CH_3CH_2CH_2CH_2OH \qquad CH_3CH_2\underset{\displaystyle OH}{\underset{|}{C}}HCH_3$$

1-Butanol 2-Butanol

Functional Group Isomers. Functional group isomers have different functional groups. Ethyl alcohol and methyl ether are examples.

CH_3CH_2OH	Ethyl alcohol
CH_3OCH_3	Methyl ether

Chain, position, and functional group isomerism often occur together.

Tautomerism is really a type of functional group isomerism but is often classified separately because of its unusual nature and its profound theoretical importance. In this type of isomerism two forms occur and are characterized by the fact that they are directly and readily interconvertible. The classical example is acetoacetic ester. The *enol* and *keto* modifications form an equilibrium mixture (p. 158).

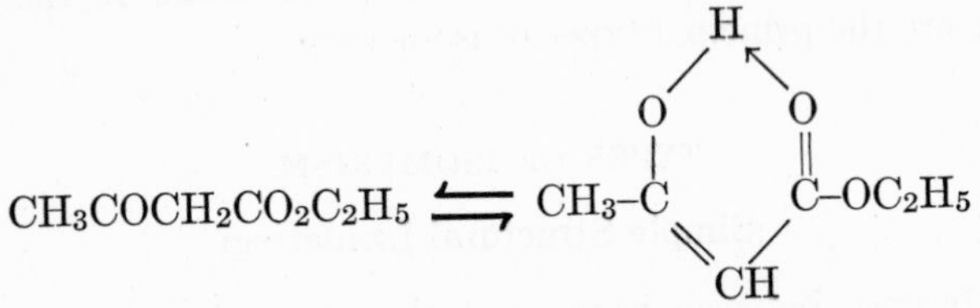

$$CH_3COCH_2CO_2C_2H_5 \rightleftharpoons CH_3\text{–}C(\text{–O–H}\cdots O\text{=})\text{=CH–}C\text{–}OC_2H_5$$

Stereoisomerism

Stereoisomerism depends on differences in the three-dimensional space relations in molecules. There are two principal types: optical isomerism and *cis-trans* or geometrical isomerism.

Optical Isomers. Optical isomerism occurs in molecules which are asymmetric. In other words, any molecule which is not superimposable upon its mirror image may exist in two forms. These isomers have identical properties except for the effect on plane polarized light. The common elements of symmetry which must be absent from such a molecule are (*a*) a plane of symmetry and (*b*) a center of symmetry.

Most of the known optically active compounds owe their molecular asymmetry to the presence of an asymmetric carbon atom. The carbon atom is said to be asymmetric when it holds four different atoms or groups of atoms. α-Amino acids illustrate this type.

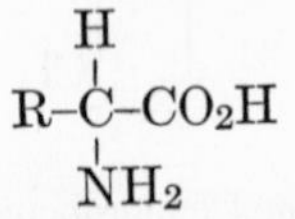

$$R\text{–}CH(NH_2)\text{–}CO_2H$$

Optical activity may be due also to asymmetric atoms other than carbon. The resolvable sulfinic esters are examples (p. 446).

The number of optical isomers to be expected for a given structure is equal to 2^n, where n is the number of *dissimilar* asymmetric atoms present. Each of the following structures, for example, calls for four isomers —two DL pairs.

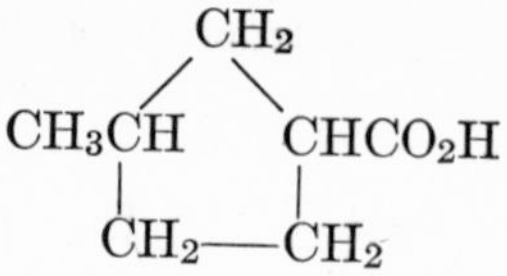

$$\begin{array}{ccc} & CH_2 & \\ CH_3CH & & CHCO_2H \\ | & & | \\ CH_2 & — & CH_2 \end{array}$$

$C_6H_5CHBrCHBrCO_2H$

$$\begin{array}{l} RCHCO_2CHCH_2CH_3 \\ \;\;|\quad\quad\;\;\; | \\ NH_2 \quad CH_3 \end{array}$$

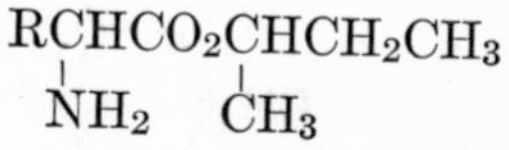

A compound containing two similar asymmetric atoms may exist in three forms: dextro, levo, and meso. Examples of this type are the following.

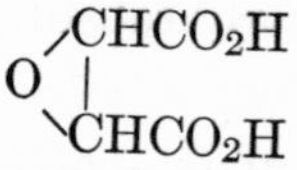

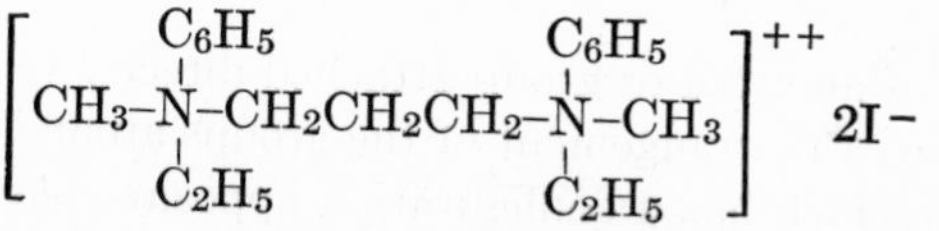

$$\begin{array}{l} \;\;/CHCO_2H \\ O\;\;| \\ \;\;\backslash CHCO_2H \end{array}$$

$$\left[\begin{array}{ccc} C_6H_5 & & C_6H_5 \\ CH_3-N- & CH_2CH_2CH_2 & -N-CH_3 \\ C_2H_5 & & C_2H_5 \end{array}\right]^{++} 2I^-$$

The last compound is of particular interest because it contains asymmetric nitrogen atoms. A number of similar salts in which the nitrogen atom is tetravalent have been resolved. From the knowledge that sulfinic esters are capable of existence in optically active forms, it would be expected that tertiary amines of the type

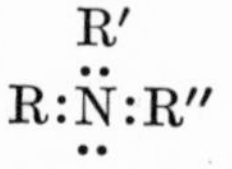

$$\begin{array}{c} R' \\ \cdot\cdot \\ R:\!N\!:R'' \\ \cdot\cdot \end{array}$$

could be resolved. The following are a few of the many tertiary amines whose resolution has been unsuccessfully attempted.

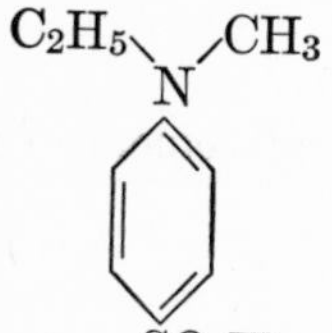

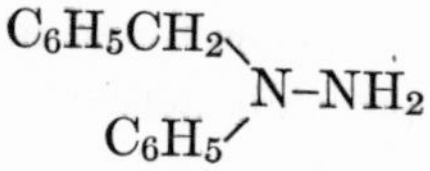

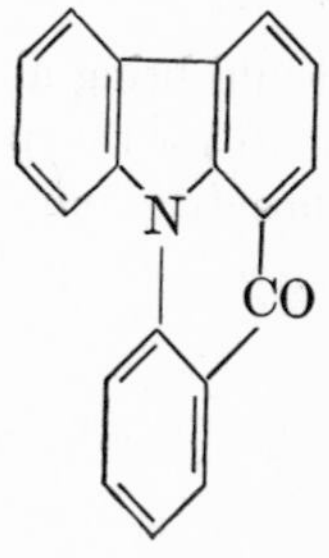

$C_2H_5(CH_3)N-C_6H_4-SO_3H$ $\qquad$ $(C_6H_5CH_2)(C_6H_5)N-NH_2$ $\qquad$ [carbazole N-linked to benzene ring bridged by CO]

A condensation product of *p*-toluidine and formaldehyde, known as Troeger's base, has been resolved into enantiomorphic forms. This result, however, hardly bears on the problem of the resolution of tervalent nitrogen compounds since it is to be ascribed to molecular asymmetry made possible by the very rigid structure of the molecule.

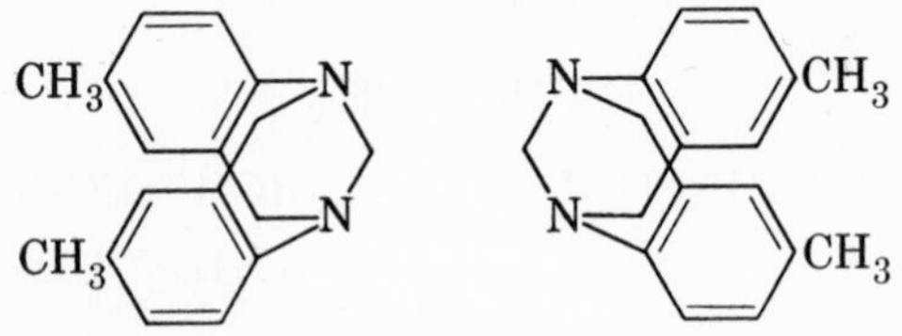

Selenium, tellurium, tin, germanium, phosphorus, arsenic, boron, beryllium, copper, zinc, and a number of other elements may give rise to optical activity when properly substituted.

The Walden Inversion

Replacement of an atom or group attached directly to an asymmetric atom often causes a rearrangement of the groups around the latter, giving a derivative which has a configuration opposite that of the original molecule. This phenomenon was discovered by Walden and is known as the Walden inversion.

This inversion has attracted much attention, primarily because of its bearing on the problem of the mechanism of substitution in general. A suggestion that has proved very helpful is that the entering atom approaches the face of the tetrahedron opposite to the atom which is displaced.

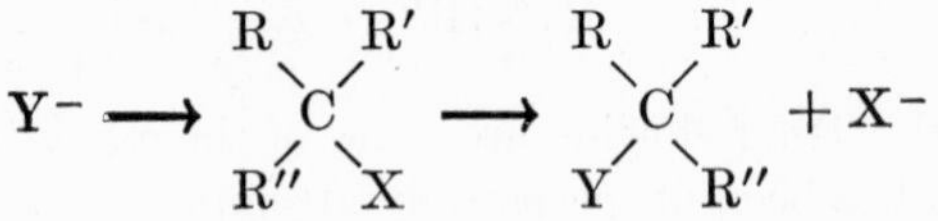

$$Y^- \longrightarrow \begin{array}{c} R \quad R' \\ \diagdown\diagup \\ C \\ \diagup\diagdown \\ R'' \quad X \end{array} \longrightarrow \begin{array}{c} R \quad R' \\ \diagdown\diagup \\ C \\ \diagup\diagdown \\ Y \quad R'' \end{array} + X^-$$

This would bring about inversion.

Support for this proposal has been found in the replacement of iodine by radioactive iodine in an optically active iodide.

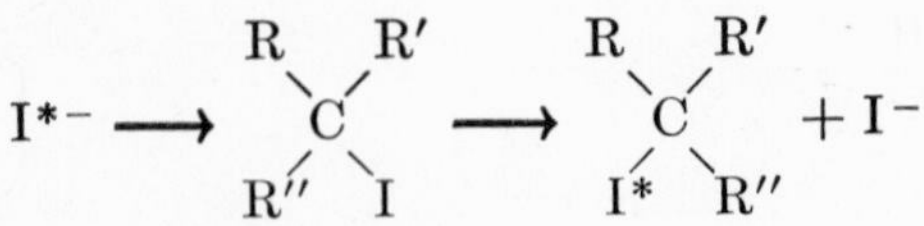

$$I^{*-} \longrightarrow \begin{array}{c} R \quad R' \\ \diagdown\diagup \\ C \\ \diagup\diagdown \\ R'' \quad I \end{array} \longrightarrow \begin{array}{c} R \quad R' \\ \diagdown\diagup \\ C \\ \diagup\diagdown \\ I^* \quad R'' \end{array} + I^-$$

The rate of inversion, as measured by the rate of racemization, of the original iodide is the same as the rate at which the iodide becomes radioactive.

Optically Active Compounds Which Do Not Contain an Asymmetric Atom. For a long time it was believed that the presence of an asymmetric atom was necessary if a molecule was to be optically active. This view has changed, however, with the discovery of numerous optically active substances whose structures contain no asymmetric atom. These fall into several distinct groups, each of which will now be examined briefly.

The Inositol Type. Inositol is a hexahydroxycyclohexane and exists in eight different forms, two of which are represented here.

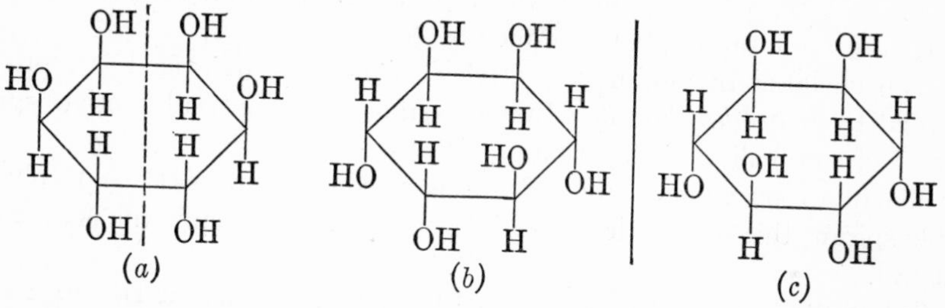

(*a*) (*b*) (*c*)

Seven of these isomers have one or more planes of symmetry and are optically inactive; an example is represented by figure *a*, whose plane of symmetry is indicated by the dotted line. The eighth form of inositol, however, has no plane of symmetry or center of symmetry. Furthermore, it has no asymmetric carbon atom. Yet it exists in D and L forms as shown in figures *b* and *c*.

The Allene Type. Early in the development of stereochemistry it was recognized that properly substituted allenes should be asymmetric molecules and, therefore, should be resolvable into D and L forms. Although many chemists have sought to obtain such optically active allenes it was only comparatively recently that success was achieved. The first allene to be resolved was the following.

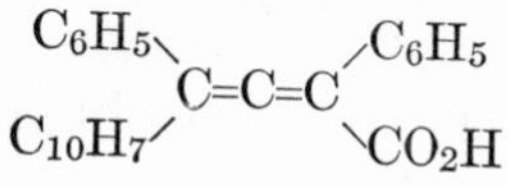

$$\begin{matrix} C_6H_5 \diagdown & & \diagup C_6H_5 \\ & C{=}C{=}C & \\ C_{10}H_7 \diagup & & \diagdown CO_2H \end{matrix}$$

The Spirans. These are very similar to the allenes. Following are three which have been resolved into D and L forms.

```
H\   /CH2\   /CH2\   /CO2H
   C       C       C
HO2C/  \CH2/   \CH2/   \H
```

(*a*)

```
     C6H5                       C6H5
       \                        /
        C—O               O—C
       //    \          /     \\
     CH        Be          CH
       \     ↗    ↖       /
        C=O          O=C
       /                \
     CO2H               CO2H
```

(*b*)

```
⎡C6H5\   /CH2CH2\   /CH2CH2\   /CO2C2H5⎤+
⎢      C          N          C         ⎥   Br−
⎣  H/   \CH2CH2/   \CH2CH2/   \H       ⎦
```

(*c*)

Figure *a* represents a spiran which differs from an allene in that the rings are four- rather than two-membered.

The chelated beryllium derivative of benzoylpyruvic acid is represented by figure *b*. The fact that this molecule is optically active is a proof of the reality of chelation.

The quaternary ammonium salt represented by figure *c* is also a resolvable spiran; this proves that the nitrogen atom in this molecule is tetrahedral.

Substituted Biphenyls and Related Compounds. Restricted rotation about the central bond in certain substituted biphenyls may also cause molecular asymmetry. The following is an example.

```
          CH3   CH3
CH3<ring>———<ring>—CH3
   NH2 CH3   CH3    NH2
```

Such molecules are asymmetric only when each ring is unsymmetrically substituted. A similar case has been observed in the naphthalene series.

```
C6H5SO2NCH2CO2H
   NO2 |
  (naphthalene ring)
```

Here the free rotation about the amido nitrogen atom is prevented by the interference of the nitro group.

***cis-trans* Isomerism.** *cis-trans* Isomerism (p. 153) may occur in a molecule having a structure so rigid that its parts are not free to rotate with respect to each other. The simplest type includes all olefins having the structure abC=Cab. This structure may exist in two forms known as *cis* and *trans*.

```
 a a           a b
 | |           | |
 C=C           C=C
 | |           | |
 b b           b a
```

cis Form　　　*trans* Form

The best-known examples of this type of isomerism are maleic and fumaric acids.

```
H–C–CO2H          HO2C–C–H
  ||                   ||
H–C–CO2H             H–C–CO2H
```

Maleic acid　　　Fumaric acid

In fact, *cis* and *trans* forms are often called, respectively, *malenoid* and *fumaroid*. In general, the *cis* form is lower melting and more soluble than the corresponding *trans* form. For example, maleic acid melts at 130° whereas fumaric acid sublimes at 286°. Also, maleic acid is 100 times as soluble in water as is fumaric acid.

Oximes and many similar types of nitrogen compounds also may exist in *cis* and *trans* forms. These are often called, respectively, *syn* and *anti* forms.

```
R               R OH
|               | |
C=N             C=N
| |             |
H OH            H
```

syn Form　　　*anti* Form

cis-trans Isomerism may also occur in ring compounds in which the rigidity of the ring structure serves to prevent rotation. 1,3-Cyclopentanedicarboxylic acids illustrate this type.

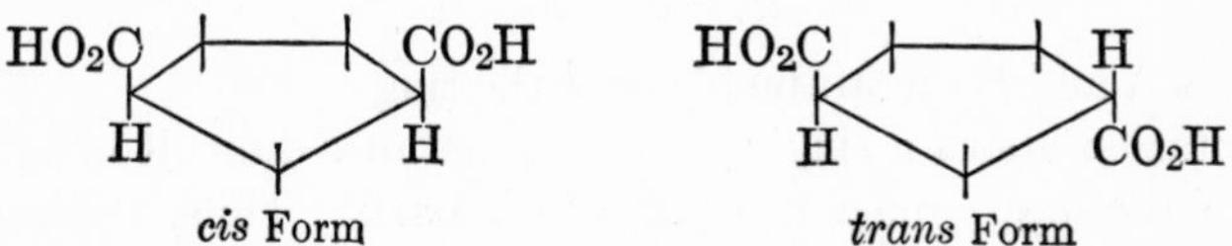

cis Form　　　*trans* Form

An extremely significant example of this type is presented by the disulfoxide of dithiane. Its two forms are represented below (see p. 446).

```
   CH2–CH2                CH2–CH2  O
  /       \              /        \||
 S         S            S           S
 ||\      /||           ||\        /
 O  CH2–CH2 O           O  CH2–CH2
```

cis Form　　　*trans* Form

The existence of these forms shows that the bonds of the sulfur atom in a sulfoxide do not lie in the same plane. This fact proves that there is an important difference between the structures of ketones and sulfoxides, which appear to be very similar on the basis of the sulfur-oxygen double bond (p. 446) shown in the formulas above, for the bonds attached to the carbon atom of a carbonyl group are coplanar.

Cyclic compounds of the above type may exhibit both *cis-trans* and optical isomerism if asymmetric atoms are present. For example, 1,3-cyclopentanedicarboxylic acid has two similar asymmetric carbon atoms and should exist in a racemic and meso form (p. 176).

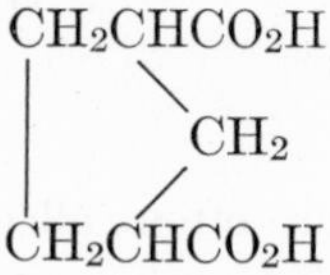

CH_2CHCO_2H

CH_2

CH_2CHCO_2H

Because of the rigidity of the ring structure, it should exist in *cis* and *trans* forms. The *cis* form has a plane of symmetry and, thus, is the meso form; the *trans* acid is racemic (p. 227).

It is to be noted that *cis-trans* isomerism *due to a double bond* is not possible when the double bond is part of a ring system. This is evident from a consideration of a model of a 1,2-disubstituted-1-cyclohexene.

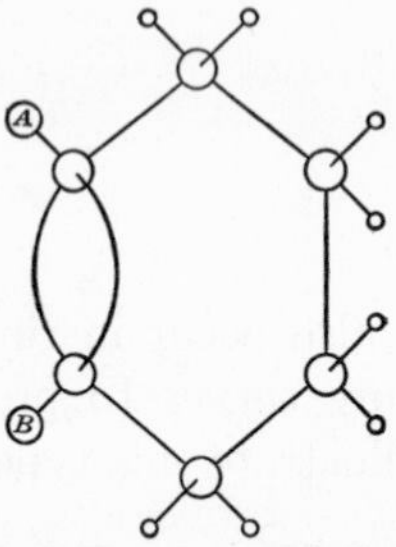

A

B

The groups A and B are in the plane of the ring.

Free rotation about a single bond is sometimes difficult or impossible because of the interference of the rotating parts. Thus, as we have already seen, biphenyl derivatives which have substituents in positions *ortho* to the central linkage may be incapable of rotation about this bond. This may give rise to geometrical isomerism as well as optical isomerism. An example is shown below.

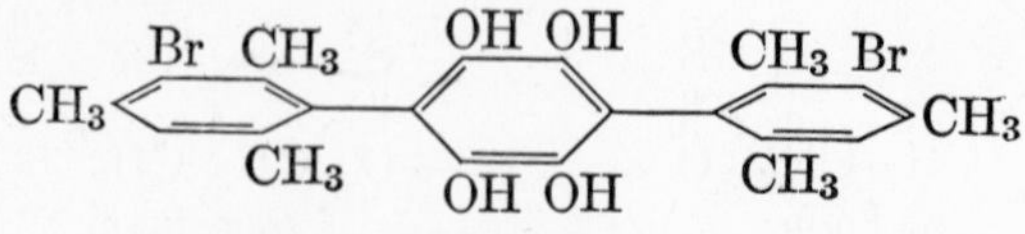

Br CH_3 OH OH CH_3 Br

CH_3 CH_3

CH_3 OH OH CH_3

cis Form

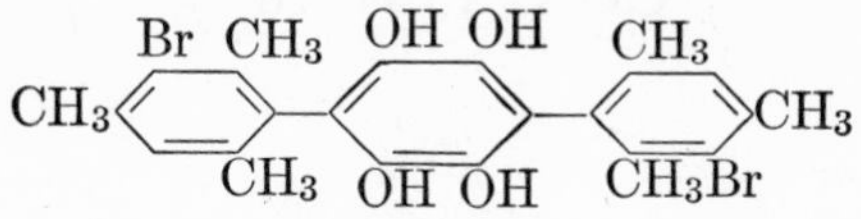

trans Form

In this case neither form is capable of optical activity; the *cis* form has a plane of symmetry and the *trans* form has a center of symmetry.

PROBLEM

Indicate the number and type of stereoisomers to be expected of the following structures.

a. $C_6H_5CH{=}CHC_6H_5$

b. 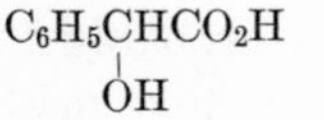

c. 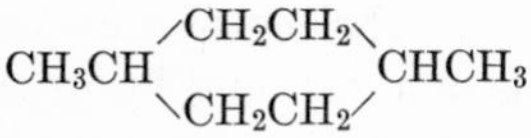

d. 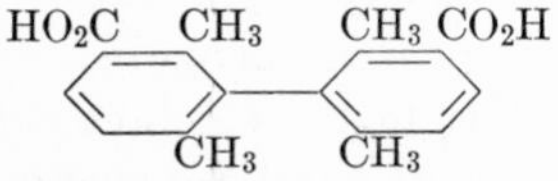

e. 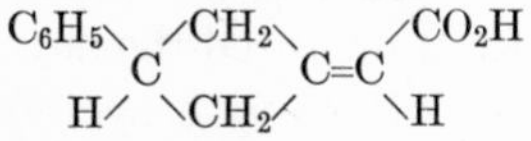

f. 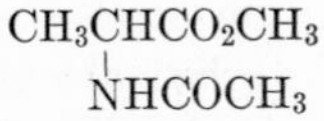

g. 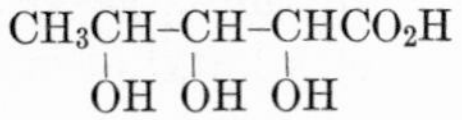

h. 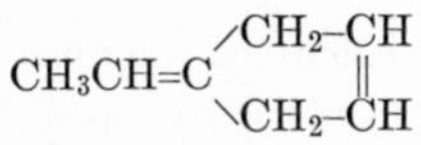

i. 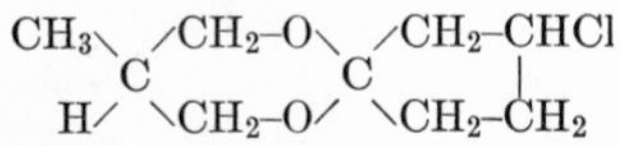

j. 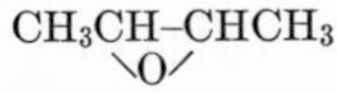

k. 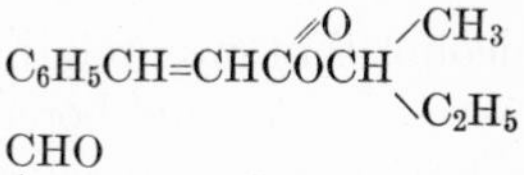

l. 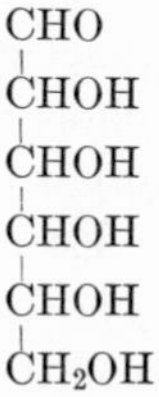

m. 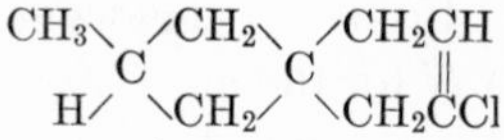

n. 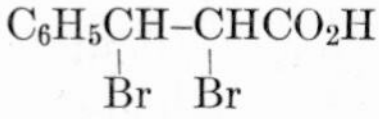

o. 

p. 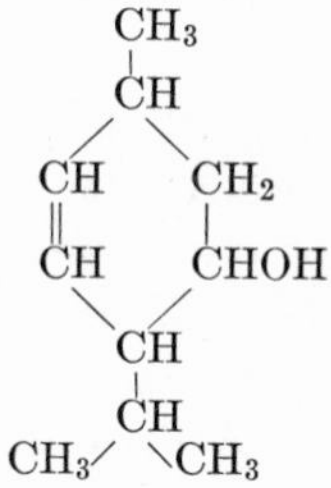

SUGGESTED READINGS

R. L. Shriner, R. Adams, and C. S. Marvel, "Stereoisomerism," Gilman's *Organic Chemistry*, Vol. I, Second Ed., p. 150, John Wiley & Sons, New York, 1943.

R. L. Bent, "Aspects of Isomerism and Mesomerism," *J. Chem. Educ.*, *30*, 220 (1953).

CHAPTER 18

Industrial Alcohols

In 1930 the only alcohols that were obtainable in quantity were methyl alcohol, made by the distillation of wood, and ethyl alcohol, obtained by fermentation of sugar with yeast. A by-product of the latter process was fusel oil, which consists of a mixture of amyl alcohols. No dihydroxy alcohol was on the market, and glycerol was the only polyhydroxy alcohol that was relatively cheap. Today the alcohols available commercially are numbered by the score. This is probably the most important advance that modern industrial chemists have made, for not only are these alcohols adapted to a wide variety of uses but also they serve as raw materials for the synthesis of a vast and imposing array of useful derivatives. Ethers, esters, acids, aldehydes, and ketones in great variety are available from the new inexpensive alcohols.

The events which led up to the manufacture of "higher alcohols" are absorbing. Probably the war-time (1914–1918) demand for acetone paved the way for the most important of these, for it nurtured the development of Weizmann's fermentation of starch (p. 54) to give acetone. This change is brought about by the bacterium *Clostridium acetobutylicum*. The organic products are acetone (30 per cent), ethyl alcohol (10 per cent), and *n*-butyl alcohol (60 per cent). In the large-scale manufacture of acetone, accordingly, vast quantities of *n*-butyl alcohol were made.

The story of *n*-butyl alcohol is one of the most interesting in the annals of the science. This little-known and apparently useless by-product proved to be the foundaton stone for the modern lacquer industry. For a long time the Weizmann process was operated to produce the alcohol, and the ketone was regarded as a by-product. However, the demand for acetone has increased to such an extent as to be comparable to that for *n*-butyl alcohol.

Another product of Weizmann's fermentation is a gas which contains carbon dioxide (55 per cent) and hydrogen (45 per cent). This too has found a use. Part of the carbon dioxide is removed and the residual mixture subjected to high temperature and pressure in the presence of a suitable catalyst. Methanol is formed.

$$CO_2 + 3H_2 \longrightarrow CH_3OH + H_2O$$

However, the importance of this synthesis of methanol is relatively insignificant when compared to that based on the hydrogenation of carbon monoxide. The latter process has made methanol as cheap as ethyl alcohol. It consists in the treatment of carbon monoxide with hydrogen in the presence of a zinc chromite catalyst at about 450° and 3000 lb. pressure.

By changes in the catalyst the methanol synthesis may be made to give a variety of higher alcohols. It is possible that the higher alcohols are derived from the lower ones by a condensation similar to the Guerbet reaction which is also a high-pressure process and consists in the interaction of an alcohol with an alcoholate.

$$RONa + RCH_2CH_2OH \longrightarrow \underset{\displaystyle R}{RCHCH_2OH} + NaOH$$

Another method of making alcohols is hydration of olefins. The latter are available in vast amounts from the petroleum industry and yield an extensive collection of alcohols. Except for ethyl alcohol these are all secondary or tertiary alcohols.

The Carbide and Carbon Chemicals Corporation produces a series of alcohols which appear to be derived from acetaldehyde by condensation and hydrogenation.

$$2CH_3CHO \longrightarrow CH_3CH_2CH_2CH_2OH$$

$$CH_3CHO + CH_3CH_2CH_2CHO \longrightarrow \begin{cases} CH_3(CH_2)_4CH_2OH \\ (CH_3CH_2)_2CHCH_2OH \end{cases}$$

$$2CH_3CH_2CH_2CHO \longrightarrow CH_3CH_2CH_2CH_2\underset{\displaystyle C_2H_5}{CH}CH_2OH$$

The Sharples Corporation makes certain amyl alcohols from pentanes by chlorination and hydrolysis of the chloropentanes.

The most important alcohols which are commercially available are listed in Table XXVII. The sources of the alcohols are indicated by the following abbreviations.

O = hydration of olefins
G = Guerbet reaction
C = Carbide and Carbon Chemicals Corporation's method
F = fermentation
H = hydrolysis of the corresponding chlorides
P = from carbon monoxide

TABLE XXVII

INDUSTRIAL ALCOHOLS

Methanol	CH_3OH	*P*
Ethanol	CH_3CH_2OH	*F O P*
1-Propanol	$CH_3CH_2CH_2OH$	*P*
2-Propanol	$(CH_3)_2CHOH$	*O*
1-Butanol	$CH_3(CH_2)_2CH_2OH$	*F*
2-Butanol	$CH_3CH_2CH(OH)CH_3$ (OH on the third carbon)	*O*
Isobutyl alcohol	$(CH_3)_2CHCH_2OH$	*P*
t-Butyl alcohol	$(CH_3)_3COH$	*O*
n-Amyl alcohol	$CH_3(CH_2)_3CH_2OH$	*H*
2-Methyl-1-butanol	$CH_3CH_2CH(CH_3)CH_2OH$	*F P H*
Isoamyl alcohol	$(CH_3)_2CHCH_2CH_2OH$	*F H*
2-Pentanol	$CH_3CH_2CH_2CH(OH)CH_3$	*O H*
3-Pentanol	$(CH_3CH_2)_2CHOH$	*H*
t-Amyl alcohol	$(CH_3)_2C(OH)CH_2CH_3$	*O*
n-Hexyl alcohol	$CH_3(CH_2)_4CH_2OH$	*C*
2-Methyl-1-pentanol	$CH_3CH_2CH_2CH(CH_3)CH_2OH$	*P G*
2-Ethyl-1-butanol	$(CH_3CH_2)_2CHCH_2OH$	*C*
4-Methyl-2-pentanol	$(CH_3)_2CHCH_2CH(OH)CH_3$ (Hydrogenation of mesityl oxide?)	
1-Heptanol	$CH_3(CH_2)_5CH_2OH$ (Hydrogenation of *n*-heptaldehyde)	
Diisopropylcarbinol	$(CH_3)_2CHCH(OH)CH(CH_3)_2$	*P*
2,4-Dimethyl-1-pentanol	$(CH_3)_2CHCH_2CH(CH_3)CH_2OH$	*P*
4-Methyl-1-hexanol	$CH_3CH_2CH(CH_3)CH_2CH_2CH_2OH$	*P*
2-Octanol	$CH_3(CH_2)_5CH(OH)CH_3$ (From castor oil)	
2-Ethyl-1-hexanol	$CH_3(CH_2)_3CH(C_2H_5)CH_2OH$	*C G?*
Lauryl alcohol	$CH_3(CH_2)_{10}CH_2OH$	
Palmityl alcohol (cetyl alcohol)	$CH_3(CH_2)_{14}CH_2OH$	

By the catalytic hydrogenation of fats, lauryl, myristyl, palmityl, and stearyl alcohols are made. These are important because the sodium alkylsulfates (RCH_2OSO_3Na) derived from them are excellent detergents (p. 116). Cyclohexanol is made by catalytic hydrogenation of phenol and by the oxidation of cyclohexane.

A hydrogenation process has also been developed for the production of ethylene glycol from methyl glycolate.

$$\underset{\text{Methyl glycolate}}{\begin{matrix} CH_2OH \\ | \\ CO_2CH_3 \end{matrix}} + 2H_2 \longrightarrow \begin{matrix} CH_2OH \\ | \\ CH_2OH \end{matrix} + CH_3OH$$

The most interesting feature of this method is the high-pressure synthesis of the glycolic ester. It is accomplished by condensation of carbon monoxide, formaldehyde, and methanol.

$$CO + CH_2O + CH_3OH \longrightarrow HOCH_2CO_2CH_3$$

Glycerol as stated earlier (p. 100) has long been available as a by-product of soap manufacture.

$$\begin{array}{l} CH_2OCOR \\ | \\ CHOCOR \\ | \\ CH_2OCOR \end{array} + 3NaOH \longrightarrow 3RCO_2Na + \begin{array}{l} CH_2OH \\ | \\ CHOH \\ | \\ CH_2OH \end{array}$$

Much of the supply is converted into glyceryl trinitrate or "nitroglycerine" (p. 62) which is used extensively as an explosive. During World War I a fermentation method was developed to meet the excessive demand for glycerol. A maximum yield is obtained when the fermentation is conducted within the pH range of 7.0 to 8.8. Ethyl alcohol, on the other hand, is formed in a markedly acid medium with a pH approaching 4.5.

At best, the production of glycerol from sugar can only be a war-time expedient, for the cost is great. The synthetic method involves the chlorination of propylene to give allyl chloride (p. 67). The latter is converted to glycerol through glycerol α,γ-dichlorohydrin.

About one-fourth of the annual output of glycerol is used in dynamite. Enormous amounts also go into the tobacco industry; glycerol is added to tobacco as a softening agent and to facilitate the maintenance of the desired moisture content as well as to give sweetness and improved flavor.

Paints, varnishes, lacquers, and molded plastics require large amounts of glycerol. The manufacture of viscose uses about 20,000,000 lb. of glycerol annually.

PROBLEMS

1. Make a list of the more important derivatives of (*a*) ethylene, (*b*) acetylene.
2. What important organic compounds can be made from castor oil?
3. What influence has the use of high-pressure technic had on the development of organic chemistry?

SUGGESTED READINGS

A. H. Levey, "The Production and Economics of Synthetic Glycerol," *Ind. Eng. Chem., News Ed.*, *16*, 326 (1938).

E. E. Ayres, "Amyl Alcohols from the Pentanes," *Ind. Eng. Chem.*, *21*, 899 (1929).

CHAPTER 19

Reactions of Halogen Compounds

Alkyl halides are attacked by many nucleophilic reagents in processes which result in the replacement of halogen by other groups. Thus they react with water to give alcohols, with ammonia to give amines, with inorganic cyanides to give nitriles, with sodium hydrosulfide to give mercaptans, and with sodium alkoxides to give ethers. These are only a few of many such reactions of great value in the synthesis of organic compounds. Simple aryl halides undergo many of the same transformations, but they are less reactive and require more strenuous experimental conditions.

The reactivity of halogen compounds toward nucleophilic reagents results from the tendency of the carbon atom of the carbon-halogen bond to assume a positive character. In some reactions carbonium ions (R^+) formed by ionization of the molecules ($RBr \longrightarrow R^+ + Br^-$) take part in the transformations. Other reactions are initiated by the attraction of the positive end of the carbon-halogen dipole ($C^+–X^-$) for the electron-rich reagent, and the transformations occur without the formation of carbonium ions.

Halogen compounds also can react with electrophilic reagents of great electronic deficiency. Thus they donate electrons to aluminum chloride in taking part in the Friedel-Crafts reaction. Here again the transformations that occur result from the formation of carbonium ions ($RX + AlCl_3 \longrightarrow R^+ + AlCl_3X^-$). Finally, some reactions of halides appear to proceed by way of free-radical intermediates, like the coupling of diphenylbromomethane to tetraphenylethane by the action of mercury (p. 260).

Mechanisms of Nucleophilic Displacements

The mechanisms by which nucleophilic displacements of halogen occur have been the subject of intensive study. The types of processes that occur differ principally according to the kinetic order of the reaction concerned. For many years it was believed that the most important mechanisms were those that followed first- and second-order kinetics, respectively; in the first-order process the rate of the reaction depends only on the concentration of the halide; in the second-order process the rate depends on the concentration of the nucleophilic reagent as well as on that of the halogen compound. The two displacement mechanisms apply to reactions of substances other than halogen compounds, and since they are often referred to they have been given the abbreviations S_N1 and S_N2 (substitution, nucleophilic, first order; and substitution, nucleophilic, second order, respectively). It now appears that a third-order mechanism also is of general importance; in reactions that follow this course the rate may be dependent on the concentrations of the halide, the nucleophilic reagent, and the solvent, for example.

When an alkyl halide enters into an S_N1 process the occurrence of the reaction depends upon the ionization of the carbon halogen bond. The ionization is the slow (rate-controlling) step and is followed by a rapid combination of the organic cation with the reagent. Thus the alkaline hydrolysis of tertiary butyl chloride can be represented in a simplified fashion as follows.

$$(CH_3)_3CCl \longrightarrow (CH_3)_3C^+ + Cl^- \qquad \text{(slow)}$$
$$(CH_3)_3C^+ + OH^- \longrightarrow (CH_3)_3COH \qquad \text{(fast)}$$

Reactions of this kind are most likely to occur when the carbonium ion that forms as an intermediate is stabilized by resonance and hence is of more than usual stability. In the example just cited the *tert*-butyl carbonium ion owes its stability to hyperconjugation. In the similar hydrolysis of α-phenylethyl chloride $(C_6H_5\underset{\substack{|\\ Cl}}{C}HCH_3)$ the intermediate α-phenylethyl carbonium is stabilized by resonance involving the benzene ring.

All the available evidence indicates that the carbonium ion is always *planar*. Hence it is symmetrical, and an S_N1 process occurring at the asymmetric center of an optically active molecule would be expected to give a *racemic* product. In the representation below, the hydroxyl ion is as likely to approach the carbonium ion from above as from below, and so equal numbers of D and L alcohol molecules are formed.

$$\begin{array}{c} X \\ | \\ C \\ /\;|\;\backslash \\ R\;\;R'\;\;R'' \end{array} \xrightarrow{-X^-} \begin{array}{c} \quad R'' \\ \quad / \\ R\text{–}\overset{+}{C} \\ \quad \backslash \\ \quad R' \end{array} \xrightarrow{+OH^-} \begin{array}{c} OH \\ | \\ C \\ /\;|\;\backslash \\ R\;\;R'\;\;R'' \end{array} \quad \text{and} \quad \begin{array}{c} R\;\;R''\;\;R' \\ \backslash\;|\;/ \\ C \\ | \\ OH \end{array}$$

It is a general rule that S_N1 reactions are accompanied by extensive *racemization*, and the assignment of an S_N1 mechanism to a reaction often is made on the basis of experimental observation of racemization when the process occurs at an asymmetric center.

In an S_N2 reaction of an alkyl halide with a nucleophilic reagent the carbon atom of the carbon halogen bond is attacked by the electron-rich reagent at the face of the tetrahedron *opposite the halogen atom* (the so-called *rearward approach*). The reagent comes into the sphere of influence of the carbon atom and establishes a bond with it, the halogen atom being pushed away as a halide ion. At an intermediate stage the carbon atom may be bound equally to the halogen and to the entering group; it is never in the carbonium ion state. The alkaline hydrolysis of methyl bromide occurs by the S_N2 mechanism and can be represented as shown. It is to be noted that in such a process the entering group

$$\mathrm{H\bar{O}} \quad \mathrm{CH_3Br} \longrightarrow \left[\mathrm{HO\cdots CH_3\cdots Br}\right]^- \longrightarrow \mathrm{HO{-}CH_3} + \mathrm{Br^-}$$

takes a position on the carbon atom *opposite* that previously occupied by the group which is displaced. This means that if the reaction occurs at the asymmetric center of an optically active molecule the product will have a *configuration opposite that of the reacting substance.* This is the mechanism by which the *Walden inversion* occurs; a process occurring by an S_N2 mechanism may be said to proceed *with inversion,* and the mechanism frequently is assigned upon the basis of experimental detection of inversion. The original Walden inversion consisted in a series of reactions by means of which an optically active compound was converted to its enantiomorph. The transformation of dextro-rotatory benzylmethylcarbinol to the levo-rotatory form by the following reactions is illustrative.

(1) $C_6H_5CH_2CH(CH_3)OH + p\text{-}CH_3C_6H_4SO_2Cl$

Rotation +33.02°

$\longrightarrow C_6H_5CH_2CH(CH_3)OSO_2C_6H_4CH_3(p)$

(2) $C_6H_5CH_2CH(CH_3)OSO_2C_6H_4CH_3(p) + CH_3CO_2K$

$\longrightarrow C_6H_5CH_2CH(CH_3)OCOCH_3 + p\text{-}CH_3C_6H_4SO_3K$

(3) $\underset{\displaystyle CH_3}{C_6H_5CH_2\overset{|}{C}HOCOCH_3} + H_2O \xrightarrow{OH^-} \underset{\displaystyle CH_3}{C_6H_5CH_2\overset{|}{C}HOH} + CH_3CO_2H$

Rotation $-32.18°$

It is now known that the change of configuration occurs in step 2, in which the sulfonate group is displaced as an anion by the rearward attack of the acetate ion.

There is evidence that the ionization of an alkyl halide, as the first step in a hydrolysis of the S_N1 type, is not a simple process but occurs in conjunction with solvation. It can be more accurately represented as shown. If the reaction always proceeded in this way the rate should

$$RBr + HOH \longrightarrow RBr(HOH) \longrightarrow R^+ + \bar{B}r(HOH)$$
$$\downarrow H_2O$$
$$R^+(HOH)$$

be dependent on the concentration of the solvent (water in the example); however, the solvent ordinarily is present in such large excess that its concentration does not change significantly during the reaction, and only in special cases can the effect of the solvent be observed. One such reaction is that of triphenylmethyl chloride with methanol in the presence of pyridine. At low concentrations of methanol the rate is proportional to the concentration of the chloride and to the *square* of the concentration of methanol. The latter proportionality indicates that both the chloride anion and the triphenylmethyl carbonium cation may be solvated. The last step in the reaction may be merely the loss of a proton from the solvated carbonium ion.

$$(C_6H_5)_3CCl + 2CH_3OH \longrightarrow (C_6H_5)_3\overset{+}{C}\leftarrow\underset{H}{\underset{|}{O}}CH_3 + \bar{C}lHOCH_3$$
$$\downarrow$$
$$(C_6H_5)_3COCH_3 + H^+$$

Other, similar actions are known to be affected in the same general way by the solvents. Such reactions, instead of being unimolecular, are termolecular, and the driving forces may include both the pulling away of the atom being replaced (by solvation of the resulting anion) and its being pushed away by the entering group which takes its place (hence a *push-pull* mechanism).

It is likely that many reactions now considered to occur by S_N2 mechanisms also may involve solvent participation; for example, in the alkaline hydrolysis of an alkyl halide the halogen atom may associate with water (RBr→HOH) before the rearward attack by the hydroxide ion.

The mechanisms of reaction described provide an explanation of the extraordinary stability of certain halogen compounds. 1-Chloroapocamphane (p. 275) is extremely resistant to alcoholic sodium ethoxide and various other reagents. It is apparent that an S_N1 reaction cannot occur, since the geometry is such that a *planar* carbonium ion cannot form. The face of the carbon atom opposite the chlorine atom is buried within the cyclic structure, and consequently the rearward approach, as in an S_N2 mechanism, is completely blocked. Thus, neither mechanism can operate and the molecule is inert.

Consideration of the two mechanisms also suggests that the order of reactivity within a series of halogen compounds may vary as the diagnostic reagent is changed. Among closely related halides the primary members react most rapidly, and the tertiary members least readily, with sodium iodide in acetone. When silver nitrate is used for testing the same group of halides it is found that the tertiary halides precipitate silver halide most rapidly, and the primary halides least rapidly. Since the first reagent operates by an S_N2 mechanism and the second by an S_N1 process this result is not surprising.

Halogen Interchange

The most common halogen interchanges involve the replacement of chlorine or bromine by iodine, effected by treating the alkyl chloride or bromide with sodium iodide in acetone solution. Sodium chloride and sodium bromide are much less soluble in acetone than the sodium iodide, so the use of acetone tends to force the reversible reaction to completion. An example is the preparation of pentaerythrityl iodide from the bromide in 98 per cent yield.

$$C(CH_2Br)_4 + 4NaI \xrightarrow[\text{solution}]{\text{acetone}} C(CH_2I)_4 + 4NaBr$$

Benzyl iodide and allyl iodide are made similarly from the commercially available chlorides.

Studies of such reactions occurring at the asymmetric carbon atoms of optically active halides have yielded information concerning the nature of replacement reactions in general. When L-2-iodoheptane is treated with sodium iodide in acetone, racemic 2-iodoheptane is formed.

This might, on first thought, seem indicative of an S_N1 mechanism. However, when it is considered that the process is *reversible*, or, in other words, that an L molecule can be changed to a D molecule by the same reaction and at the same rate, then it is obvious that the iodo compound should lose its optical activity even in an S_N2 reaction.

$$I^- + \underset{\text{D}}{\overset{CH_3}{\underset{H\ \ \ C_5H_{11}}{C{-}I}}} \rightleftarrows \underset{\text{L}}{\overset{CH_3}{\underset{H\ \ \ C_5H_{11}}{I{-}C}}} + I^-$$

Confirmation of the proposed rearward attack by the iodide ion was obtained by the use of radioactive sodium iodide. The ratio of the rates of racemization and of entry of radioactive iodine into the organic molecule calculated from this representation of the reaction was identical with that measured experimentally.

The reaction with sodium iodide in acetone provides the basis for a useful test of the reactivity of halogen atoms in alkyl chlorides and bromides of unknown structure. Primary halides are most reactive; under standardized conditions primary bromides give a visible precipitate of sodium bromide within 3 minutes at 25°, whereas secondary and tertiary bromides respond only when the solution is heated to 50°. This order of reactivity is that expected from the mechanism indicated. In a tertiary bromide the bulky alkyl groups largely shield the face of the carbon atom opposite the bromine atom, whereas in a primary bromide the two hydrogen atoms attached to the carbon atom occupy but little space. Accordingly, any process occurring by rearward approach should be slower with a tertiary bromide than with a primary bromide, other factors being equal.

The interchange of fluorine for heavier halogens is a very important method for the synthesis of fluorine compounds. The alkyl halide is treated with hydrogen fluoride in the presence of antimony halides. The catalysts function by exchanging halogen both with the alkyl halide and with the hydrogen fluoride. The important refrigerant Freon (CCl_2F_2) is made from carbon tetrachloride in this way.

$$3CCl_4 + 2SbF_3 \xrightarrow{SbCl_5} 3CCl_2F_2 + 2SbCl_3$$

$$2SbCl_3 + 6HF \longrightarrow 2SbF_3 + 6HCl$$

Hydrogen fluoride reacts with very active halogen compounds without any catalyst. For example, benzotrifluoride can be made from the trichloride and hydrogen fluoride alone.

$$C_6H_5CCl_3 + 3HF \longrightarrow C_6H_5CF_3 + 3HCl$$

The relatively high boiling point of hydrogen fluoride (19.5°) permits these reactions to be forced to completion by removal of hydrogen chloride (b.p. −84.9°) as rapidly as it is formed.

Because of the need for highly inert liquids in connection with the development of atomic energy a great amount of effort has been devoted to the discovery of methods for producing *fluorocarbons*, i.e., compounds containing only carbon and fluorene. The method of direct fluorination with elementary fluorine has been modified so that it affords these compounds in excellent yields. Fluorocarbons from perfluorobutane (C_4F_{10}) to perfluorohexadecane ($C_{18}F_{38}$) are known in the straight-chain series as well as numerous other types of perfluoro compounds. Many such compounds are produced directly from organic compounds and hydrogen fluoride by a one-step electrolytic process carried out at low temperatures.

Hydrolysis

The hydrolysis of halides is employed in the commercial production of various alcohols. An example is the Sharples process for making amyl alcohols from pentanes. The raw material consists chiefly of *n*-pentane and isopentane, and when chlorinated it yields a variety of monochlorides. The hydrolysis is accomplished in a system of vessels through which an emulsion of amyl alcohol, water, and sodium oleate is circulated. A mixture of amyl chlorides and caustic soda is continuously added to this circulating material. A saturated salt solution is continuously withdrawn, and a vapor consisting chiefly of amyl alcohols is constantly given off. The mixture of amyl alcohols is marketed as Pentasol or as the acetate, Pentacetate. The mixture of alcohols is separated by fractional distillation, the chief products being the following.

$CH_3CH_2CH_2CH_2CH_2OH$ $\qquad$ $CH_3CH_2CH_2CH(OH)CH_3$

$CH_3CH_2CH(OH)CH_2CH_3$ $\qquad$ $CH_3CH(CH_3)CH_2CH_2OH$ $\qquad$ $CH_3CH_2CH(CH_3)CH_2OH$

Only primary alcohols are produced satisfactorily from isopentane. Tertiary alkyl halides often undergo dehydrohalogenation to olefins under experimental conditions that are satisfactory for replacement reactions of primary halides; secondary halides also are prone to generate olefins. Olefin formation from a secondary or a tertiary halide may occur through the same carbonium ion that forms in the first stage of an S_N1 hydrolysis; the carbonium ion stabilizes itself by ejection of a proton. Thus the tertiary chloride from isopentane, instead of yielding an alcohol in the Sharples process, generates the olefin trimethylethylene.

$$CH_3\underset{\substack{|\\CH_3}}{\overset{\substack{Cl\\|}}{C}}CH_2CH_3 \xrightarrow{-Cl^-} CH_3\underset{\substack{|\\CH_3}}{\overset{+}{C}}CH_2CH_3 \xrightarrow{-H^+} CH_3\underset{\substack{|\\CH_3}}{C}{=}CHCH_3$$

The same olefin is formed from the isomeric secondary chloride. It is collected and converted to the tertiary alcohol by the hydration process.

$$\left.\begin{array}{c} CH_3\underset{\substack{|\\CH_3}}{\overset{\substack{Cl\\|}}{C}}CH_2CH_3 \\ \\ CH_3\underset{\substack{|\\CH_3}}{CH}\overset{\substack{Cl\\|}}{C}HCH_3 \end{array}\right\} \longrightarrow CH_3\underset{\substack{|\\CH_3}}{C}{=}CHCH_3 \longrightarrow CH_3\underset{\substack{|\\CH_3}}{\overset{\substack{OH\\|}}{C}}CH_2CH_3$$

Benzyl, allyl, and methallyl alcohols are produced on a large scale by hydrolysis of the corresponding chlorides. One method of making ethylene glycol consists in the alkali-catalyzed hydrolysis of ethylene chlorohydrin. The hydrolysis may be effected by heating with sodium bicarbonate under slight pressure. Propylene glycol is made from propylene by a series of reactions similar to those employed in converting ethylene to ethylene glycol.

$$CH_3CH{=}CH_2 \longrightarrow CH_3\overset{\substack{OH\\|}}{C}HCH_2Cl \longrightarrow$$

$$CH_3\overset{\substack{O\\/\ \ \backslash}}{CH{-}CH_2} \longrightarrow CH_3\overset{\substack{OH\\|}}{C}H\overset{\substack{OH\\|}}{C}H_2$$

A method for synthetic glycerol involves the hydrolysis of glycero α,γ-dichlorohydrin, obtained by the action of hypochlorous acid on allyl chloride.

β-Methylglycerol can be produced in a similar way from methallyl chloride.

$$CH_2{=}C(CH_3)CH_2Cl + HOCl \longrightarrow CH_2Cl{-}C(OH)(CH_3){-}CH_2Cl \longrightarrow CH_2OH{-}C(OH)(CH_3){-}CH_2OH$$

Halo Ethers, Halo Esters, and Halo Alcohols. The formation of alcohols by the hydrolysis of alkyl halides results from the fact that the functional carbon atoms in alcohols and halides are in the same oxidation state. Halogen compounds in which a single halogen atom is attached to a carbon atom carrying one singly bound oxygen atom undergo hydrolysis to carbonyl compounds. Such reactions are employed in the preparation of various aldehydes. A convenient method for the synthesis of glyoxal utilizes the hydrolysis of 2,3-dichlorodioxane, made by the chlorination of dioxane (p. 66).

$$\text{2,3-dichlorodioxane } (CH_2{-}O{-}CHCl{-}CHCl{-}O{-}CH_2) + 2H_2O \longrightarrow CH_2OH{-}CH_2OH + CHO{-}CHO + 2HCl$$

2-Bromophthalide, produced by bromination of phthalide, readily undergoes hydrolysis to yield phthalaldehydic acid. The over-all yield is 68 per cent.

$$C_6H_4(CO{-}O{-}CH_2) \longrightarrow C_6H_4(CO{-}O{-}CHBr) \longrightarrow C_6H_4(CO_2H)(CHO)$$

Chloroacetaldehyde is easily available from vinyl acetate, by the addition of chlorine followed by hydrolysis.

$$CH_2{=}CH{-}OCOCH_3 + Cl_2 \longrightarrow ClCH_2CH(Cl)OCOCH_3$$

$$ClCH_2CH(Cl)OCOCH_3 + H_2O \longrightarrow ClCH_2CHO + CH_3CO_2H + HCl$$

In all these compounds the halogen atom on the carbon atom attached to oxygen is very active. α-Halo ethers are almost as reactive as acyl halides (which also have oxygen and halogen attached to the same carbon atom). On the other hand a halogen atom in the β position to an ether oxygen is inert. In the last equation above, it is to be noted that the β-chlorine atom is unaffected during the hydrolysis. Similarly ethyl α,β-dichloroethyl ether undergoes hydrolysis to chloroacetaldehyde.

$$\underset{\displaystyle Cl}{ClCH_2\overset{|}{C}HOCH_2CH_3} + H_2O \longrightarrow ClCH_2C\begin{matrix}\nearrow O \\ \searrow H\end{matrix} + CH_3CH_2OH + HCl$$

α-Halo carbonyl compounds (p. 244) are, in general, more readily hydrolyzed than simple alkyl halides; accordingly, mild conditions are employed in preparations such as that just given to avoid destruction of the halo aldehyde.

The simplest stable halo alcohols are the halohydrins, in which the halogen and hydroxyl groups are located on adjacent carbon atoms. As indicated by the fact that these compounds are common intermediates in the preparation of glycols (p. 60), their hydrolysis is not difficult. The ease of hydrolysis is in sharp contrast to the stability of the halogen in a β-halo ether, which also has a halogen atom and a singly bound oxygen atom on adjacent carbon atoms. The explanation for the rapid alkaline hydrolysis of halohydrins lies in the participation of the hydroxyl group in the reaction, which proceeds by internal displacement of the halogen as follows.

$$R-\underset{Br}{\overset{H}{C}}-\underset{H}{\overset{OH}{C}}-R + OH^- \longrightarrow H_2O + \left[R-\underset{Br}{\overset{H}{C}}-\underset{H}{\overset{O}{C}}-R\right]^- \longrightarrow Br^- + R-\underset{H}{C}\overset{O}{\frown}\underset{H}{C}-R$$

$$R-\underset{H}{C}\overset{O}{\frown}\underset{H}{C}-R + OH^- \longrightarrow R-\underset{H}{\overset{O^-}{C}}-\overset{H}{C}\begin{matrix}R \\ OH\end{matrix} \xrightarrow{H^+} R-\underset{H}{\overset{HO}{C}}-\underset{OH}{\overset{H}{C}}-R$$

It is not uncommon to find that a reaction is altered in some way because of the *participation of a neighboring group*.

The displacement by rearward attack pictured above is not possible if the halogen and hydroxyl groups lie on the same side of a rigid molecule. Thus, of the two cyclohexene chlorohydrins (*a* and *b*), only the *trans* form (*a*) would be expected to react like a simple halohydrin. The *trans* form does indeed react with strong alkali to give the *trans* glycol, but the *cis* form reacts in an entirely different way and is converted to cyclohexanone.

(a) [cyclohexane with H, OH / Cl, H] $\xrightarrow[H_2O]{OH^-}$ [cyclohexane with H, OH / OH, H]

(b) [cyclohexane with H, H / Cl, OH] $\xrightarrow[H_2O]{OH^-}$ [cyclohexanone]

α-Halo Carbonyl Compounds. In the study of the hydrolysis of α-halo ketones a number of unusual transformations have been uncovered. For example, Wallach found that treatment of the dibromo derivative of cyclohexanone yielded 1-hydroxycyclopentanecarboxylic acid.

$$\text{C}_6\text{H}_{10}\text{=O} \longrightarrow \text{dibromo derivative} \longrightarrow \text{C}_5\text{H}_8\langle^{CO_2H}_{OH}$$

Favorsky reported a similar result with 2-chlorocyclohexanone, which is converted by alkali into cyclopentanecarboxylic acid.

$$\text{(2-Cl)C}_6\text{H}_9\text{=O} \longrightarrow \text{C}_5\text{H}_9\text{CO}_2\text{H}$$

A somewhat similar reaction is the transformation of benzyl chloromethyl ketone into methyl hydrocinnamate (80 per cent yield) by the action of sodium methoxide.

$$C_6H_5CH_2COCH_2Cl \xrightarrow{CH_3ONa} C_6H_5CH_2CH_2CO_2CH_3$$

Dihalides. Compounds having two halogen atoms on the same carbon atom may be hydrolyzed to carbonyl compounds, as illustrated by the conversion of benzal chloride to benzaldehyde.

$$C_6H_5CHCl_2 + H_2O \longrightarrow C_6H_5CHO \longrightarrow 2HCl$$

The reaction is of little use in the aliphatic series because the dihalo compounds are hard to prepare and their hydrolysis requires heating with alkali—a treatment which often causes the products to resinify. The method is excellent, however, for the preparation of aromatic aldehydes such as *p*-bromobenzaldehyde.

As aldehydes are sensitive to alkalies, the hydrolysis of benzal halides is carried out with acids or with water in the presence of powdered calcium carbonate. This method has been applied successfully to *o*-xylene, or, better, *o*-methylbenzyl chloride, for the production of phthalaldehyde. A similar hydrolysis of a dichloromethyl group is believed to occur in the Reimer-Tiemann reaction also.

Although benzophenone can be made satisfactorily by this method, the intermediate benzophenone dichloride is not ordinarily obtained from diphenylmethane by chlorination but from benzene and carbon tetrachloride by the Friedel-Crafts procedure.

$$C_6H_5CCl_2C_6H_5 + H_2O \longrightarrow C_6H_5COC_6H_5 + 2HCl$$

It is feasible to convert many suitably constituted ketones and acids to the corresponding α,α-dihalo derivatives, hydrolysis of which yields dicarbonyl compounds. Dichloracetic acid, for example, gives glyoxylic acid.

$$CHCl_2CO_2H \longrightarrow OHCCO_2H$$

Diphenyl triketone is produced by heating the dibromide from dibenzoylmethane with sodium acetate in glacial acetic acid. The addition of water precipitates the hydrate of the triketone. The yield, based on dibenzoylmethane, is 59 per cent.

$$\begin{matrix} C_6H_5CO\diagdown \\ \quad CH_2 \\ C_6H_5CO\diagup \end{matrix} \longrightarrow \begin{matrix} C_6H_5CO\diagdown \\ \quad CBr_2 \\ C_6H_5CO\diagup \end{matrix} \xrightarrow[CH_3CO_2H]{CH_3CO_2Na} \begin{matrix} C_6H_5CO\diagdown \\ \quad CO \\ C_6H_5CO\diagup \end{matrix}$$

Tetramethyl-1,2,3-cyclopentanetrione was made by a similar method.

$$\begin{matrix} (CH_3)_2C-CBr_2 \\ | \quad \rangle CO \\ (CH_3)_2C-CO \end{matrix} \xrightarrow{\text{hot alcoholic sodium acetate}} \begin{matrix} (CH_3)_2C-CO \\ | \quad \rangle CO \\ (CH_3)_2C-CO \end{matrix}$$

This substance was obtained as a colorless hydrate which lost water when distilled, giving a bright blue solid melting at 164°. Analysis indicated that dehydration was about 80 per cent complete.

This process is not suitable for the preparation of glyoxals of the type ArCOCHO, owing to the fact that these substances are more sensitive to alkali than the dihalomethyl ketones. They change in the presence of bases, by an internal Cannizzaro reaction, to salts of α-hydroxy acids. Thus it is possible to prepare mandelic acid as follows.

$$C_6H_5COCH_3 + 2Cl_2 \longrightarrow C_6H_5COCHCl_2 + 2HCl$$

$$C_6H_5COCHCl_2 + 3NaOH \longrightarrow C_6H_5\underset{\displaystyle OH}{\underset{|}{C}}HCO_2Na + 2NaCl + H_2O$$

The over-all yield of mandelic acid,based on acetophenone, is 87 per cent.

Vinal chlorides, which correspond to ketenes, yield acids when hydrolyzed. Di-(p-chlorophenyl)acetic acid, for example, is made from

DDT in this way. The over-all yield of acid, based on the DDT, is 73 per cent.

$$(Cl\text{-}C_6H_4)_2CHCCl_3 \xrightarrow{KOH} (Cl\text{-}C_6H_4)_2C{=}CCl_2 \xrightarrow[H_2O]{KOH}$$

$$(Cl\text{-}C_6H_4)_2CHCO_2K \xrightarrow{H_2SO_4} (Cl\text{-}C_6H_4)_2CHCO_2H$$

Trichlorides. Compounds in which three halogen atoms are held by the same carbon atom can be hydrolyzed to acids. Benzotrichloride, obtained by the chlorination of toluene, is hydrolyzed to benzoic acid on a commercial scale.

$$C_6H_5CCl_3 + 2H_2O \xrightarrow{H^+} C_6H_5CO_2H + 3HCl$$

If, in the Reimer-Tiemann aldehyde synthesis (p. 170), carbon tetrachloride is used instead of chloroform, the product is an acid. Presumably the trichloro derivative is formed as an intermediate. *p*-Hydroxybenzoic acid can be made in this way.

Chloral undergoes an interesting hydrolysis in the presence of sodium cyanide. The product is dichloroacetic acid (see p. 249).

$$Cl_3CCHO + H_2O \xrightarrow{NaCN} Cl_2CHCO_2H + HCl$$

Aromatically bound halogen is activated by electron-withdrawing (*meta*-directing) groups attached to *ortho* or *para* positions in the ring. Thus 2,4-dinitrochlorobenzene is easily hydrolyzed to 2,4-dinitrophenol.

$$C_6H_3Cl(NO_2)_2 + H_2O \longrightarrow C_6H_3(OH)(NO_2)_2 + HCl$$

The hydrolysis of picryl chloride to picric acid occurs even more readily.

Simple aryl halides in general are resistant to hydrolysis under ordinary conditions. In industrial practice, however, it has been found possible to effect hydrolysis of simple aryl chlorides. The Dow process for phenol consists in the treatment of chlorobenzene with sodium hydroxide at 350–400° under a pressure of 5000 lb. per square inch. The chief by-product in this process is phenyl ether, the formation of which is suppressed by adding the ether to the original charge. By-products other than phenyl ether are *o*- and *p*-phenylphenol.

Similar treatment converts the chlorotoluenes to cresols. Since the chlorination of toluene yields almost exclusively the *ortho* and *para* isomers, it would appear that this method would be useful only for producing *o*- and *p*-cresol. This, however, is not the case. Rearrangement occurs by which *o*- and *p*-chlorotoluenes are converted in considerable part to *m*-cresol. Catechol is manufactured by hydrolysis of *o*-dichlorobenzene.

In the Raschig process for phenol, chlorobenzene is an intermediate also. The reaction is carried out in two steps, the first of which is chlorination; the chlorobenzene that is formed is hydrolyzed to phenol. The chlorination is effected in the vapor phase by heating a mixture of benzene, hydrochloric acid, and air. The oxygen of the air reacts with the acid to give chlorine, which then reacts with the benzene.

$$4HCl + O_2 \longrightarrow 2H_2O + 2Cl_2$$

$$C_6H_6 + Cl_2 \longrightarrow C_6H_5Cl + HCl$$

The chlorobenzene is mixed with steam and hydrolyzed to phenol and hydrochloric acid, the latter being used in the first step.

$$C_6H_5Cl + H_2O \longrightarrow C_6H_5OH + HCl$$

The net result is the transformation of benzene and atmospheric oxygen to phenol.

Ammonolysis and Related Reactions

Replacement of halogen atoms by the amino group, i.e., *ammonolysis*, can be effected with many types of halogen compounds. It has been especially useful in the preparation of α-amino acids, the corresponding halogen compounds being readily prepared by halogenation. An example is alanine.

$$CH_3CHBrCO_2H + 2NH_3 \longrightarrow CH_3CH(NH_2)CO_2H + NH_4Br$$

Glycine, leucine, and norleucine are made in a similar way. Other examples are isoleucine, valine, lysine, threonine, taurine, serine and phenylalanine. The α-halo acid is usually allowed to stand for several days with a great excess of ammonia.

Replacement of halogen atoms by substituted amino groups, which may be termed *aminolysis*, is usually feasible and is employed extensively in the synthesis of amines. β-Diethylaminoethyl alcohol, for example, is prepared in 70 per cent yields by condensing diethylamine with ethylene chlorohydrin.

$$(C_2H_5)_2NH + ClCH_2CH_2OH + NaOH \longrightarrow (C_2H_5)_2NCH_2CH_2OH + NaCl + H_2O$$

β-Di-*n*-butylaminoethyl bromide is changed to β-di-*n*-butylaminoethylamine in a similar way, the yield being 55 per cent. Benzylaniline can be prepared in 87 per cent yield by the interaction of benzyl chloride and aniline.

$$C_6H_5CH_2Cl + C_6H_5NH_2 \longrightarrow C_6H_5CH_2NHC_6H_5 + HCl$$

Sodium bicarbonate is used to neutralize the hydrogen chloride as it forms.

Another example of ammonolysis is the synthesis of aminoacetal.

$$BrCH_2CH(OC_2H_5)_2 + 2NH_3 \longrightarrow H_2NCH_2CH(OC_2H_5)_2 + NH_4Br$$

By the use of two moles of chloroacetic acid to one mole of methylamine it is possible to make methylaminodiacetic acid in a 71 per cent yield.

$$CH_3NH_2 + 2ClCH_2CO_2H \xrightarrow{NaOH} CH_3N(CH_2CO_2H)_2 + 2HCl$$

Certain activated aryl halides react readily with ammonia or amines to yield the corresponding aniline derivatives. 2,4-Dinitroaniline is conveniently made from 2,4-dinitrochlorobenzene in this way.

$$C_6H_3Cl(NO_2)_2 + 2NH_3 \longrightarrow C_6H_3NH_2(NO_2)_2 + NH_4Cl$$

At higher temperatures and pressures this type of reaction appears to be general for aryl halides. 4-Bromo-*o*-xylene, for example, is converted to 3,4-dimethylaniline by treatment with ammonia at 195° under a pressure of 700–1000 lb. per square inch, the reaction being catalyzed by cuprous chloride and copper.

$$C_6H_3Br(CH_3)_2 \longrightarrow C_6H_3NH_2(CH_3)_2$$

Iodides are, of course, more reactive than bromides or chlorides; it is not surprising then that iodobenzene reacts with diphenylamine at relatively high temperatures to produce triphenylamine in 85 per cent yield. Nitrobenzene is employed as a solvent with copper powder as a catalyst, potassium carbonate being added to neutralize the acid that is liberated. N-Phenylanthranilic acid is synthesized in a similar way from aniline and *o*-chlorobenzoic acid.

$$o\text{-}ClC_6H_4CO_2H + C_6H_5NH_2 \xrightarrow[K_2CO_3]{CuO} o\text{-}C_6H_5NHC_6H_4CO_2H + HCl$$

Ammonolysis of di- and trihalides appears to be of little value. Chloral reacts with ammonia in the presence of sodium cyanide to give dichloroacetamide.

$$Cl_3CCHO + 2NH_3 \xrightarrow{NaCN} Cl_2CHC(=O)NH_2 + NH_4Cl$$

The reaction resembles that of chloral with water in the presence of sodium cyanide. It has been suggested that the peculiar behavior of chloral is due to the formation of a ketene by dehydrohalogenation.

$$Cl_3C\text{-}CHO \xrightarrow{-HCl} Cl_2C{=}C{=}O$$

Such a ketene would react with ammonia and water to give dichloroacetamide and dichloroacetic acid, respectively.

Chloroform reacts with primary amines in the presence of alkalies to give isonitriles or carbylamines—a reaction that serves as a test for the presence of primary amines.

$$RNH_2 + CHCl_3 + 3NaOH \longrightarrow RN{\equiv}C + 3NaCl + 3H_2O$$

The odor of an isonitrile is so peculiar and so strong that its presence cannot be overlooked.

Williamson's Ether Synthesis

The most general method of forming an ether linkage consists in treatment of an alkyl halide with a metal alkoxide or phenoxide. The preparation of ethyl isobutyl ether from sodium isobutoxide and ethyl iodide is an example.

$$(CH_3)_2CHCH_2ONa + CH_3CH_2I \longrightarrow (CH_3)_2CHCH_2OCH_2CH_3 + NaI$$

The synthesis of ethoxyacetic acid is carried out in a similar manner.

$$C_2H_5ONa + ClCH_2CO_2H \longrightarrow C_2H_5OCH_2CO_2H + NaCl$$

Aryloxyacetic acids, prepared from phenols in a similar way, are useful derivatives for purposes of identification.

This reaction, developed by Williamson, is the usual method for mixed ethers and for ethers of phenols. The synthesis of anisole from phenol, sodium hydroxide, and methyl sulfate is illustrative. Of unusual interest is the formation of α-glyceryl phenyl ether by the interaction of sodium phenoxide and glycerol α-monochlorohydrin.

$$C_6H_5ONa + ClCH_2CHOHCH_2OH \longrightarrow C_6H_5OCH_2CHOHCH_2OH + NaCl$$

The higher phenols can be etherified by heating their salts with alkyl halides under pressure. *p*-Nitrophenyl propyl ether, for example, can be synthesized in nearly quantitative yields by heating potassium *p*-nitrophenoxide with propyl bromide in alcohol at 180° for 3 hours in a sealed tube.

Many natural products contain phenolic hydroxyl groups which must be "protected" during certain of the operations involved in degradation studies. The usual method is to convert them to the corresponding aralkyl ethers. This transformation may be accomplished by treating the phenoxide with an alkylating agent such as methyl iodide or sulfate.

Activated aryl halides (p. 413) may be employed also. Thus *p*-nitrophenyl phenyl ether is made by heating *p*-chloronitrobenzene with phenol and potassium hydroxide. The reaction is carried out without solvent and in the presence of copper as a catalyst.

$$NO_2C_6H_4Cl + C_6H_5OH + KOH \longrightarrow NO_2C_6H_4OC_6H_5 + KCl + H_2O$$

Even bromobenzene can be used in the presence of copper powder. When it is heated with the anhydrous potassium salt of guaiacol, 2-methoxyphenyl phenyl ether is produced in a yield of 60 per cent.

$$o\text{-}CH_3OC_6H_4OK + C_6H_5Br \longrightarrow o\text{-}CH_3OC_6H_4OC_6H_5 + KBr$$

This type of reaction is successful also with 1,1-dihalogen and 1,1,1-trihalogen compounds, affording methods of making acetals and ortho esters, respectively. Thus, ethyl orthoformate is produced in a 45 per cent yield by heating chloroform with sodium ethoxide.

$$CHCl_3 + 3C_2H_5ONa \longrightarrow CH(OC_2H_5)_3 + 3NaCl$$

The Williamson method is of use also in the formation of cyclic ethers. The transformation of chlorohydrins into the corresponding epoxides may be regarded as a special case of this type of reaction. Examples are the synthesis of cyclohexene oxide and of epihalohydrins.

Dehydrochlorination of chlorohydrins may take place between two molecules, producing a cyclic diether. For example, the alkaline hydrolysis of ethylene chlorohydrin yields dioxane as a by-product; the main product, of course, is ethylene glycol.

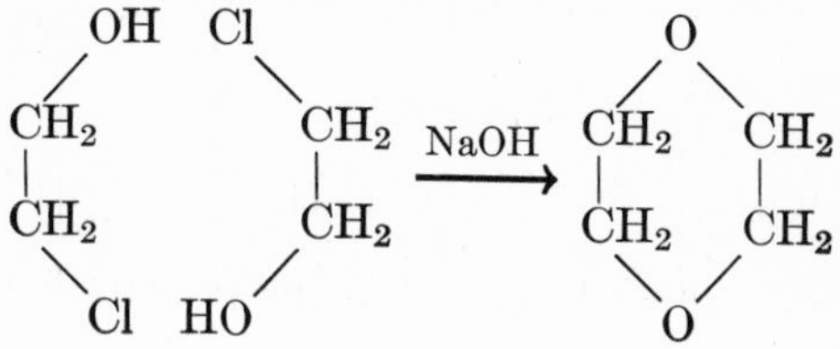

$$\begin{matrix} OH & & Cl \\ CH_2 & & CH_2 \\ | & & | \\ CH_2 & & CH_2 \\ Cl & & HO \end{matrix} \xrightarrow{NaOH} \begin{matrix} & O & \\ CH_2 & & CH_2 \\ | & & | \\ CH_2 & & CH_2 \\ & O & \end{matrix}$$

Esters from Salts

Many esters are difficult to make by direct esterification, and other methods must be sought. Sometimes it is necessary to use a salt of the acid and an alkylating agent such as an alkyl halide or sulfate. For example, methyl 2,4,6-trihydroxybenzoate is made from the silver salt of the acid and methyl iodide.

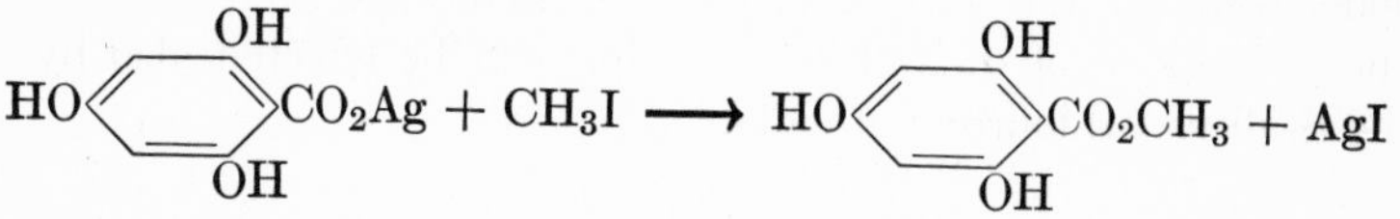

$$HO\text{-}C_6H_2(OH)_2\text{-}CO_2Ag + CH_3I \longrightarrow HO\text{-}C_6H_2(OH)_2\text{-}CO_2CH_3 + AgI$$

Acetonyl formate is produced by the interaction of bromoacetone and potassium formate.

$$CH_3COCH_2Br + HCO_2K \longrightarrow CH_3COCH_2OCHO + KBr$$

The preparation and hydrolysis of this ester constitute a satisfactory preparation of acetol (CH_3COCH_2OH).

Mercaptan Formation

Replacement of halogen by the sulfhydryl group can be accomplished directly by the action of a hydrosulfide.

$$RX + KSH \longrightarrow RSH + KX$$

It is more usual, however, to effect this change indirectly. Thiourea and potassium ethyl xanthate can be alkylated to produce, respectively, S-alkylisothiouronium salts and S-alkyl ethyl xanthates.

$$\mathrm{RX + S{=}C{\begin{smallmatrix}NH_2\\NH_2\end{smallmatrix}} \longrightarrow \left[RS{-}C{\begin{smallmatrix}NH_2\\NH_2\end{smallmatrix}}\right]^+ X^-}$$

$$\mathrm{RX + KS\overset{S}{\overset{\|}{C}}OC_2H_5 \longrightarrow RS\overset{S}{\overset{\|}{C}}OC_2H_5 + KX}$$

Hydrolysis converts these substances to mercaptans.

$$\mathrm{\left[RS{-}C{\begin{smallmatrix}NH_2\\NH_2\end{smallmatrix}}\right]^+ X^- + NaOH \longrightarrow RSH + NaX + H_2O + H_2NCN}$$

$$\mathrm{RS\overset{S}{\overset{\|}{C}}OC_2H_5 + H_2O \longrightarrow RSH + C_2H_5OH + COS}$$

An example of the thiourea method is the preparation of benzyl mercaptan from benzyl chloride.

$$\mathrm{C_6H_5CH_2Cl + S{=}C{\begin{smallmatrix}NH_2\\NH_2\end{smallmatrix}} \longrightarrow \left[C_6H_5CH_2SC{\begin{smallmatrix}NH_2\\NH_2\end{smallmatrix}}\right]^+ Cl^-}$$

$$\mathrm{\left[C_6H_5CH_2SC{\begin{smallmatrix}NH_2\\NH_2\end{smallmatrix}}\right]^+ Cl^- + NaOH}$$

$$\mathrm{\longrightarrow C_6H_5CH_2SH + NaCl + NH_2CN + H_2O}$$

n-Dodecyl mercaptan is produced in a similar way.

The conversion of dihalides to dithiols can be effected also by way of the S-alkylisothiouronium salts.

Formation of Sulfides and Disulfides

Alkyl halides react with mercaptides to form thio ethers.

$$\mathrm{RX + NaSR \longrightarrow R{-}S{-}R + NaX}$$

The reaction is analogous to the Williamson ether synthesis but occurs much more readily. Polyhalogen compounds such as methylene chloride, chloroform, and ethylene bromide react normally, undergoing complete replacement of the halogens.

If the desired sulfide is symmetrical, the synthesis can be effected by treating the halide with sodium or potassium sulfide. An example is encountered in the synthesis of thiodiglycolic acid from chloroacetic acid, the reaction involving the sodium salts.

$$\mathrm{2ClCH_2CO_2Na + Na_2S \longrightarrow S{\begin{smallmatrix}CH_2CO_2Na\\CH_2CO_2Na\end{smallmatrix}} + 2NaCl}$$

The preparation of *n*-propyl sulfide from *n*-propyl bromide is similar. Thiodiglycol is produced in an 86 per cent yield in this way from ethylene chlorohydrin.

$$2HOCH_2CH_2Cl + Na_2S \longrightarrow HOCH_2CH_2SCH_2CH_2OH + 2NaCl$$

Aryl halides such as *p*-chloronitrobenzene and 2,4-dinitrochlorobenzene are sufficiently active to give sulfides by this method. *p*-Nitrophenyl sulfide, for example, can be made by treating *p*-nitrochlorobenzene with sodium sulfide in ethylene glycol. A better method, however, employs potassium ethyl xanthate.

$$2NO_2C_6H_4Cl \xrightarrow{KSC(=S)OC_2H_5} NO_2C_6H_4SC_6H_4NO_2$$

When sodium disulfide is used with reactive halides, symmetrical dialkyl disulfides are produced.

$$2RX + Na_2S_2 \longrightarrow RSSR + 2NaX$$

An example is the synthesis of di-*o*-nitrophenyl disulfide from *o*-chloronitrobenzene.

$$2\,o\text{-}NO_2C_6H_4Cl + Na_2S_2 \longrightarrow o\text{-}NO_2C_6H_4SSC_6H_4NO_2\text{-}o + 2NaCl$$

A similar result may be achieved by the use of sodium thiosulfate.

$$2RX + Na_2S_2O_3 \longrightarrow 2RSSO_3Na \xrightarrow{heat} RSSR + SO_2 + Na_2SO_4$$

Sodium disulfide acts upon acid chlorides to give diacyl disulfides.

$$2RCOCl + Na_2S_2 \longrightarrow RCOSSCOR + 2NaCl$$

Formation of Peroxides

Salts of hydrogen peroxide behave very much like alkali disulfides toward alkyl and acyl halides, yielding alkyl and acyl peroxides, respectively. *p*-Nitrobenzoyl chloride, for example, reacts with sodium peroxide to yield *p*-nitrobenzoyl peroxide in 88 per cent yield.

$$2NO_2C_6H_4COCl + Na_2O_2 \longrightarrow (NO_2C_6H_4C(=O)O)_2 + 2NaCl$$

Nitrile Formation

The displacement of a halogen atom by a cyano group is one of the most useful reactions of halogen compounds. It not only provides a very important method of synthesis of nitriles but at the same time opens a route to the carboxylic acids having one carbon atom more than the original halide. It is thus a method of lengthening carbon chains. Furthermore, it is applicable to a wide variety of halogen compounds.

An example of this type of transformation is the formation of *n*-valeronitrile from *n*-butyl bromide.

$$CH_3CH_2CH_2CH_2Br + NaCN \longrightarrow CH_3CH_2CH_2CH_2CN + NaBr$$

This product is contaminated with about 1 per cent of the corresponding isonitrile, readily detected by its odor.

In practice this reaction affords a way of making the nitriles of the acids having an odd number of carbon atoms from normal alkyl bromides with an even number of carbon atoms, derivable from naturally occurring fatty acids. From *n*-dodecyl bromide, for example, the nitrile of *n*-tridecanoic acid is produced.

$$n\text{-}C_{12}H_{25}Br + KCN \longrightarrow n\text{-}C_{12}H_{25}CN + KBr$$

The reaction is especially valuable for benzyl chloride and similar compounds. Many such halides are obtained conveniently from aromatic hydrocarbons, formaldehyde, hydrochloric acid, and zinc chloride (chloromethylation). Phenylacetonitrile and mesitylacetonitrile are examples of nitriles readily made from such chlorides.

Halogens that are situated near an oxygen-containing functional group react also. Chloroacetic acid and ω-bromoacetophenone yield cyanoacetic acid and benzoylacetonitrile, respectively.

β-Hydroxy and alkoxy groups do not interfere. Ethylene chlorohydrin and the ethyl ether of ethylene bromohydrin yield, respectively, ethylene cyanohydrin and its ethyl ether, β-ethoxypropionitrile.

$$HOCH_2CH_2Cl + NaCN \longrightarrow HOCH_2CH_2CN + NaCl$$

$$C_2H_5OCH_2CH_2Br + NaCN \longrightarrow C_2H_5OCH_2CH_2CN + NaBr$$

Ethylene bromide and trimethylene bromide give succinonitrile and glutaronitrile, respectively. It is noteworthy that trimethylene chlorobromide, because of the difference in reactivity of the two halogen atoms, can be converted to γ-chlorobutyronitrile in a 70 per cent yield.

$$ClCH_2CH_2CH_2Br + KCN \longrightarrow ClCH_2CH_2CH_2CN + KBr$$

Adiponitrile, used in the manufacture of nylon, can be made from tetrahydrofuran by way of 1,4-dichlorobutane.

$$\text{(tetrahydrofuran)} \xrightarrow{HCl} ClCH_2CH_2CH_2CH_2Cl \xrightarrow{NaCN} \begin{array}{l} CH_2CH_2CN \\ | \\ CH_2CH_2CN \end{array}$$

The tetrahydrofuran is obtained from furfural by catalytic elimination of carbon monoxide followed by hydrogenation.

$$\text{(furfural, CHO)} \xrightarrow[400^\circ]{-CO} \text{(furan)} \xrightarrow[Ni]{2H_2} \text{(tetrahydrofuran)}$$

Pimelonitrile likewise may be produced from furfural by way of pentamethylene chloride, derived from pentamethylene glycol.

$$HO(CH_2)_5OH \longrightarrow Cl(CH_2)_5Cl \longrightarrow NC(CH_2)_5CN$$

It is to be emphasized that replacement of halogens by cyano in this way is useful only with primary halides; secondary and tertiary halides usually yield dehydrohalogenation products. Low yields of nitriles have been reported from *sec*-amyl chloride and cyclopentyl bromide.

Many halogen compounds that are too sensitive to be heated with alkali cyanides may be converted to the corresponding nitriles by use of cuprous cyanide. Allyl bromide, for example, gives allyl cyanide in 84 per cent yield with this reagent, whereas with sodium cyanide the product is contaminated with crotononitrile. When the method is applied to crotyl or methylvinylcarbinyl halides, the product in either case consists of 92 per cent of 3-pentenonitrile and 8 per cent of 2-methyl-3-butenonitrile. This is a typical allylic shift (p. 292).

α-Halo ethers can also be used successfully with cuprous cyanide. α-1,3-Dichloroisopropoxypropionitrile, for example, can be made from glycerol α,γ-dichlorohydrin in this way.

$$\begin{array}{l} CH_2Cl \\ | \\ CHOH \\ | \\ CH_2Cl \end{array} \xrightarrow[HCl]{CH_3CHO} \begin{array}{l} CH_2Cl \\ | \\ CHOCH \\ | \\ CH_2Cl \end{array}\!\!\begin{array}{l} \diagup Cl \\ \\ \diagdown CH_3 \end{array} \longrightarrow \begin{array}{l} CH_2Cl \\ | \\ CHOCH \\ | \\ CH_2Cl \end{array}\!\!\begin{array}{l} \diagup CN \\ \\ \diagdown CH_3 \end{array}$$

Acid halides, in like manner, furnish α-ketonitriles. Benzoyl chloride, for example, affords a 65 per cent yield of benzoyl cyanide. It has been reported that in the aliphatic series the acid bromides are superior to the chlorides, good yields being obtained from acetyl, propionyl, isobutyryl, and similar bromides.

The Rosenmund-von Braun Nitrile Synthesis. Aromatic halides can be converted to the corresponding nitriles by treatment with cuprous cyanide. α-Naphthonitrile, for example, is formed in 90 per cent yield from either the chloride or bromide in the presence of pyridine.

$$C_{10}H_7X + CuCN \longrightarrow C_{10}H_7CN + CuX$$

This reaction, discovered long ago, has come to be known as the Rosenmund-von Braun reaction. It proceeds satisfactorily only at relatively high temperatures and is autocatalytic. Another example is the conversion of 9-bromophenanthrene to 9-cyanophenanthrene in 87 per cent yield.

The Rosenmund-von Braun reaction is not limited to simple aryl halides, as is shown by the preparation of *p*-cyanobenzoic acid from *p*-bromobenzoic acid.

$$p\text{-}BrC_6H_4CO_2H \longrightarrow p\text{-}NCC_6H_4CO_2H$$

The Friedel-Crafts Reaction

Alkyl halides often are used in preparing alkyl derivatives of aromatic hydrocarbons by the Friedel-Crafts method. The introduction of methyl, ethyl, or isopropyl groups offers no great difficulty, but the introduction of *n*-propyl or *n*-butyl groups in this way is unsatisfactory. Rearrangement takes place to give chiefly the corresponding branched-chain alkyl derivatives. Thus, benzene and *n*-propyl chloride react in the presence of aluminum chloride to give isopropyl- rather than propylbenzene.

$$C_6H_6 + CH_3CH_2CH_2Cl \xrightarrow{AlCl_3} C_6H_5CH(CH_3)_2 + HCl$$

A remarkable feature of the alkylation of benzene by this method is that the alkyl groups enter the *meta* as well as *ortho-para* positions. Thus, in the presence of large amounts of catalyst, benzene and ethyl bromide react to give 1,3,5-triethylbenzene.

$$C_6H_6 + 3C_2H_5Br \xrightarrow[\text{2 moles}]{AlCl_3} 1,3,5\text{-}C_6H_3(C_2H_5)_3 + 3HBr$$

It has been suggested that the *meta* orientation observed is a result of the reversibility of the Friedel-Crafts process. For example, the 1,3,5-triethylbenzene may be formed as follows.

$$\text{(benzene)} \xrightarrow[AlCl_3]{C_2H_5Br} \text{(ring with } C_2H_5) \xrightarrow[AlCl_3]{C_2H_5Br} \text{(ring with } C_2H_5,\ C_2H_5)$$

$$\xrightarrow[AlCl_3]{C_2H_5Br} \text{(ring with } C_2H_5,\ C_2H_5,\ C_2H_5) \xrightarrow[AlCl_3]{C_2H_5Br} \text{(ring with } C_2H_5,\ C_2H_5,\ C_2H_5,\ C_2H_5) \xrightarrow{AlCl_3} \text{(ring with } C_2H_5,\ C_2H_5,\ C_2H_5)$$

The ethyl group expelled in the last step probably becomes attached to one of the less highly alkylated molecules present.

The Grignard Reaction

One of the most useful reactions of halogen compounds is that with magnesium to form Grignard reagents. Methyl iodide, in spite of its relatively high cost, is commonly used because it is the only methyl halide that is liquid at ordinary temperatures. Methyl bromide and methyl chloride afford high yields, however. Bromides usually are more reactive than the chlorides and give better yields than the iodides. Nevertheless the chlorides often are to be preferred because of their relatively low cost. In some cases they afford more satisfactory results. Examples are the very reactive chlorides such as *t*-butyl, *t*-amyl, and benzyl. Low-molecular-weight secondary chlorides such as *sec*-butyl and cyclohexyl are often used. Cyclohexyl chloride and bromide afford high yields. Satisfactory yields are obtained also with primary chlorides such as *n*-butyl and *n*-amyl. Usually, however, primary bromides have been employed. In the aromatic series the bromides are nearly always preferable.

Allyl and methallyl halides are too reactive to be converted to Grignard reagents by the usual procedure; they yield coupling products instead. Allyl chloride, for example, gives biallyl in a 65 per cent yield.

$$2CH_2{=}CH{-}CH_2Cl + Mg \longrightarrow CH_2{=}CHCH_2CH_2CH{=}CH_2 + MgCl_2$$

Allylmagnesium chloride can be made, however, by the slow addition of an ether solution of allyl chloride to a vigorously stirred mixture of magnesium and ether at ice-bath temperature. Allylmagnesium chloride is insoluble in ether, but a suspension of the reagent in ether can be employed in reactions. Allylmagnesium bromide can be made in 90 per cent yield by the slow addition of a dilute ether solution of allyl bromide to a mixture of ether and a large excess of powdered magnesium. The same technic is successful with certain *p*-alkoxybenzyl halides, which in the ordinary procedure are converted almost entirely to coupling products.

A few halides, on the other hand, are not readily attacked by magnesium. Conspicuous among them are the aryl chlorides, which react so sluggishly that specially activated magnesium and extended reaction periods are required. Phenylmagnesium chloride has been prepared on a commercial scale. For its production high temperature and pressure are employed, chlorobenzene serving as the solvent.

A few aryl bromides likewise require special technic. An example is bromomesitylene, which reacts slowly and often requires a catalyst. An effective catalyst is prepared by heating magnesium, containing 12 per cent copper, with iodine. Pentamethylphenyl bromide has been converted to the corresponding Grignard reagent only by the *entrainment method.* The procedure is to add a very reactive halide such as ethyl bromide to the reaction mixture. The relatively rapid formation of ethylmagnesium bromide serves to promote the reaction of the aryl bromide with the metal, possibly by keeping the surface clean.

Magnesium, like zinc (p. 266), converts 1,2-dihalogen compounds to the corresponding olefins; 1,2-dibromopropane reacts with magnesium to yield propylene. 1,4-Dibromobutane, however, forms a Grignard reagent: $BrMg(CH_2)_4MgBr$. Similar behavior has been reported for several other polymethylene bromides.

The difference in reactivity of chlorine and bromine on the benzene ring is illustrated by the facile formation of *p*-chlorophenylmagnesium bromide. *p*-Dibromobenzene has been converted to the mono- and dibromomagnesium derivatives.

$$p\text{-}BrC_6H_4Br + Mg \longrightarrow p\text{-}BrMgC_6H_4Br \quad + Mg \longrightarrow p\text{-}BrMgC_6H_4MgBr$$

Similar results have been obtained with 3,3′-dibromobiphenyl.

β-Halo ethers react with magnesium, but few of the corresponding Grignard reagents have been detected; the reaction yields instead an olefin and alkoxide or phenoxide (p. 269).

Many organometallic compounds, other than Grignard reagents, are prepared by the action of metals on organic halides. Among the most important of these are the dialkylzincs, which played an extremely important role in organic chemistry before the discovery of the Grignard reagent and which continue to find use. Diisopropylzinc, for example, is made in good yield by the interaction of zinc and a mixture of isopropyl bromide and isopropyl iodide.

$$2C_3H_7Br + 2C_3H_7I + 4Zn = 2(C_3H_7)_2Zn + ZnBr_2 + ZnI_2$$

Diethylzinc is produced in an analogous way. Organozinc compounds are important also as intermediates in the Reformatsky reaction (p. 296).

Another very valuable group of organometallic compounds, prepared from organic halides, is composed of the organolithium derivatives. They may be produced in much the same way as Grignard reagents. Thus *n*-butyllithium is formed in yields as high as 90 per cent by treatment of *n*-butyl bromide with lithium in ethyl ether at about −10°. Many halogen compounds which do not form Grignard reagents satisfactorily afford high yields of lithium derivatives. An example is *p*-dimethylaminobromobenzene.

$$(CH_3)_2N\langle C_6H_4 \rangle Br + 2Li \longrightarrow (CH_3)_2N\langle C_6H_4 \rangle Li + LiBr$$

Perhaps the most valuable aryl lithium compound is phenyllithium, prepared by the action of lithium on bromobenzene.

$$C_6H_5Br + 2Li \longrightarrow C_6H_5Li + LiBr$$

Halogen-Metal Interconversion

When *p*-bromochlorobenzene is treated with *n*-butyllithium, the bromine and lithium atoms exchange places.

$$p\text{-}ClC_6H_4Br + C_4H_9Li \longrightarrow p\text{-}ClC_6H_4Li + C_4H_9Br$$

α-Bromonaphthalene and propyllithium react similarly.

$$C_{10}H_7Br + CH_3CH_2CH_2Li \longrightarrow C_{10}H_7Li + CH_3CH_2CH_2Br$$

This type of interchange is particularly valuable because it occurs with bromo compounds that contain hydroxyl, amino, carboxyl, and other groups which destroy Grignard reagents. Thus, *o*-bromophenol can be converted to salicylic acid in good yield by the following sequence of reactions.

$$o\text{-}C_6H_4(Br)(OH) \xrightarrow{C_4H_9Li} o\text{-}C_6H_4(Li)(OLi) \xrightarrow{CO_2} o\text{-}C_6H_4(CO_2Li)(OLi) \xrightarrow{H^+} o\text{-}C_6H_4(CO_2H)(OH)$$

Interchange has been observed with other halogens and other metals, but its usefulness is due chiefly to the interchange of lithium and bromine atoms.

The Wurtz Reaction

Very reactive metals such as sodium react with alkyl halides in such a way as to effect coupling of two alkyl groups. For example, sodium converts *n*-butyl bromide to *n*-octane.

$$2C_4H_9Br + 2Na \longrightarrow C_4H_9\text{–}C_4H_9 + 2NaBr$$

This type of transformation, known as the Wurtz reaction, is presumed to involve the intermediate formation of an alkyl sodium.

$$RX + 2Na \longrightarrow RNa + NaX$$
$$RNa + RX \longrightarrow R\text{–}R + NaX$$

Support for this mechanism is seen in the observation that isovaleric acid can be obtained by the action of carbon dioxide on a reaction mixture of sodium and isobutyl bromide.

An alternative explanation postulates the formation of free radicals.

$$RX + Na \longrightarrow R\cdot + NaX$$
$$2R\cdot \longrightarrow R\text{–}R$$

This mechanism is known to be correct for the formation of hexaphenylethane from triphenylmethyl chloride and silver.

$$(C_6H_5)_3CCl + Ag \longrightarrow (C_6H_5)_3C\cdot + AgCl$$
$$2(C_6H_5)_3C\cdot \longrightarrow (C_6H_5)_3C\text{–}C(C_6H_5)_3$$

Similarly, it seems certain that free diphenylmethyl radicals are formed as intermediates in the conversion of diphenylbromomethane to tetraphenylethane by treatment with mercury. Evidence for this view is to be found in the following experiment. If the reaction mixture of diphenylbromomethane and mercury contains an equivalent amount of triphenylmethyl, the principal product is pentaphenylethane, the diphenylmethyl radicals being captured by the triphenylmethyl radicals as soon as they are formed.

$$(C_6H_5)_2CHBr + Hg \longrightarrow (C_6H_5)_2CH\cdot + HgBr$$

$$(C_6H_5)_2CH\cdot + (C_6H_5)_3C\cdot \longrightarrow (C_6H_5)_2CHC(C_6H_5)_3$$

The Wurtz reaction can be used for the closure of cycloparaffin rings if the alkyl halide is replaced by a suitably constituted polymethylene halide. Cyclopropane was first made by Freund in 1881 by this method. In 1887 Gustavson discovered that zinc in the presence of a protonic solvent was much more effective.

$$CH_2\begin{matrix}\diagup CH_2Br\\ \diagdown CH_2Br\end{matrix} + Zn \longrightarrow CH_2\begin{matrix}\diagup CH_2\\ |\\ \diagdown CH_2\end{matrix} + ZnBr_2$$

The commercial method involves treatment of trimethylene chloride with zinc in the presence of sodium iodide and sodium carbonate.

In this connection it is noteworthy that a similar treatment converts pentaerythrityl bromide to spiropentane.

$$\begin{matrix}BrCH_2\diagdown & & \diagup CH_2Br\\ & C & \\ BrCH_2\diagup & & \diagdown CH_2Br\end{matrix} + 2Zn \longrightarrow \begin{matrix}CH_2\diagdown & & \diagup CH_2\\ | & C & |\\ CH_2\diagup & & \diagdown CH_2\end{matrix} + 2ZnBr_2$$

1,1-Dimethylcyclopropane, 1,1-diethylcyclopropane, and 1-ethyl-1-*n*-butylcyclopropane have been made in a similar way.

A method of synthesis of alkyl cyclopropyl ethers likewise involves this type of closure.

$$ROCH\begin{matrix}\diagup CH_2Br\\ \diagdown CH_2Br\end{matrix} + Mg \longrightarrow ROCH\begin{matrix}\diagup CH_2\\ |\\ \diagdown CH_2\end{matrix} + MgBr_2$$

An especially interesting procedure for preparing the ethers of glycerol α,γ-dibromohydrin consists in the synthesis of a chloromethyl ether, which is then subjected to differential alkylation by the Grignard reagent.

$$\begin{matrix}CH_2Br\\ |\\ CHOH\\ |\\ CH_2Br\end{matrix} \xrightarrow[HCl]{CH_2O} \begin{matrix}CH_2Br\\ |\\ CHOCH_2Cl\\ |\\ CH_2Br\end{matrix} \xrightarrow{RMgX} \begin{matrix}CH_2Br\\ |\\ CHOCH_2R\\ |\\ CH_2Br\end{matrix}$$

One of the most remarkable closures of the cyclopropane ring occurs when neoalkyl halides are treated with sodium or an alkyl sodium. An explanation of this unusual dehydrohalogenation has been advanced which assumes that the free radical formed initially undergoes disproportionation to yield a 1,3-biradical; intramolecular coupling produces the cyclopropane derivative.

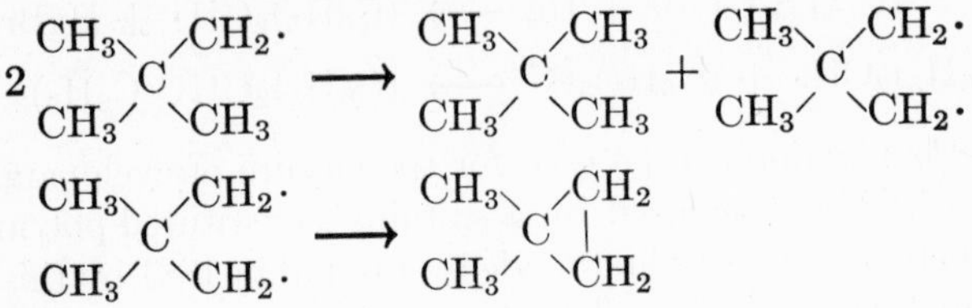

$$2\,(CH_3)_2C(CH_3)CH_2\cdot \longrightarrow (CH_3)_2C(CH_3)_2 + (CH_3)_2C(CH_2\cdot)_2$$

$$(CH_3)_2C(CH_2\cdot)_2 \longrightarrow (CH_3)_2C\begin{matrix}CH_2\\ |\\ CH_2\end{matrix}$$

A similar result has been obtained with isobutyl chloride, which yields methylcyclopropane.

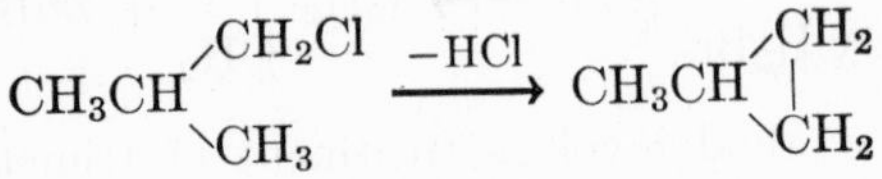

$$CH_3CH\begin{matrix}CH_2Cl\\ CH_3\end{matrix} \xrightarrow{-HCl} CH_3CH\begin{matrix}CH_2\\ |\\ CH_2\end{matrix}$$

The Fittig Reaction

The Wurtz reaction was used by Fittig to couple two aromatic radicals, but the yields were always low. For example, the amount of biphenyl obtained from bromobenzene was only 5 per cent of the theoretical. Although of extremely limited synthetic value, this reaction has aroused much interest because of the nature of the by-products that are isolated.

A very careful study of the products obtained by the action of sodium on chlorobenzene revealed the presence of benzene, biphenyl, *o*-terphenyl, *p*-terphenyl, triphenylene, and 2,2′-diphenylbiphenyl. It has been assumed that free radicals form, subsequently undergoing association to biphenyl and disproportionation to benzene and phenylene radicals. Combination of the radicals accounts for the formation of the observed products.

It is extremely interesting that, when the reaction was carried out in toluene, the formation of biphenyl was entirely suppressed, a large amount of benzene being formed along with 4-methylbiphenyl and diphenylmethane. These results can be interpreted on the assumption that the phenyl radicals attack the solvent, removing nuclear as well as lateral hydrogen atoms, thus creating free tolyl or benzyl radicals.

The Wurtz-Fittig Reaction

Although the Fittig method is not satisfactory for coupling two aromatic radicals, it is useful in joining an aromatic radical to an alkyl radical. For example, when a mixture of equimolecular amounts of *n*-butyl bromide and bromobenzene is treated with sodium, *n*-butylbenzene is formed in 70 per cent yield. This transformation, known as the Wurtz-Fittig reaction, affords satisfactory yields only when bromides are involved.

The Ullmann Method

Many biphenyl derivatives are most conveniently made by means of Ullmann's method, which involves the treatment of halobenzenes with copper powder. The synthesis of *o*-bitolyl is an example. It can be produced in 63 per cent yield from *o*-iodotoluene.

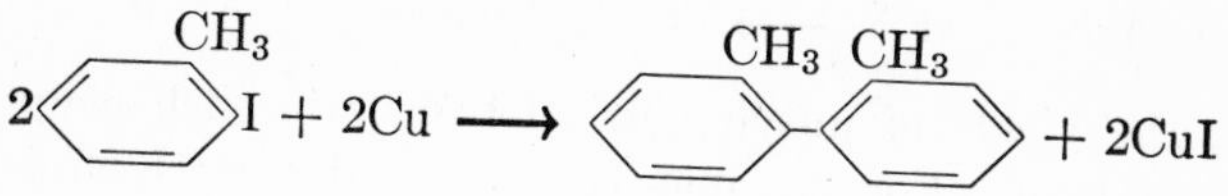

CH_3 CH_3 CH_3
2 ⟨ ⟩I + 2Cu ⟶ ⟨ ⟩—⟨ ⟩ + 2CuI

The halogen atom must be active, which is the reason iodo compounds are commonly employed. Good results can be obtained also with activated chloro derivatives such as *o*-chloronitrobenzene, which affords a 61 per cent yield of 2,2′-dinitrobiphenyl.

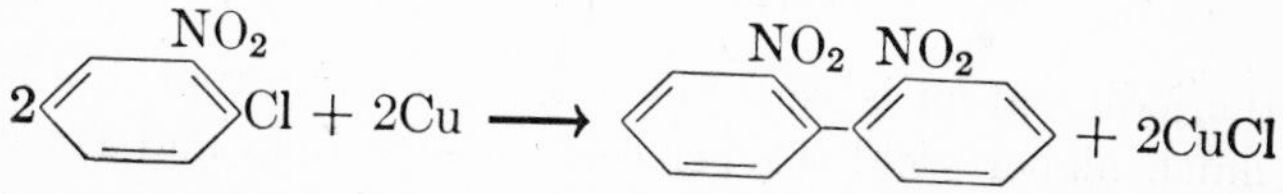

NO_2 NO_2 NO_2
2 ⟨ ⟩Cl + 2Cu ⟶ ⟨ ⟩—⟨ ⟩ + 2CuCl

p-Quaterphenyl has been synthesized by applying Ullmann's procedure to 4-iodobiphenyl.

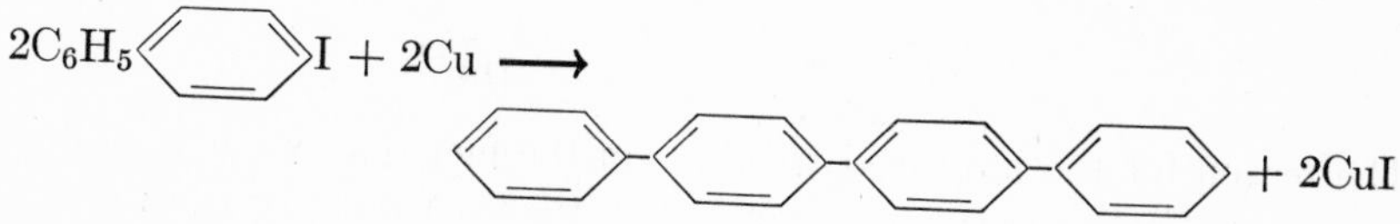

$2C_6H_5$⟨ ⟩I + 2Cu ⟶
⟨ ⟩—⟨ ⟩—⟨ ⟩—⟨ ⟩ + 2CuI

Treatment of ethyl 4-iodo-3-nitrobenzoate with copper bronze in nitrobenzene affords a 69 per cent yield of ethyl 2,2′-dinitro-4,4′-biphenyldicarboxylate.

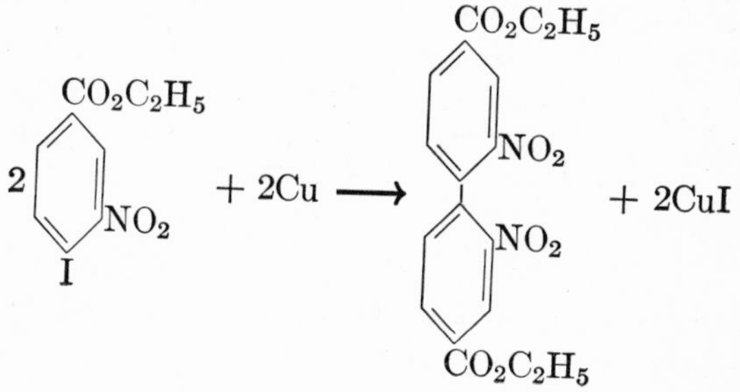

$CO_2C_2H_5$ $CO_2C_2H_5$
2 ⟨ ⟩NO_2 (I) + 2Cu ⟶ ⟨ ⟩NO_2—⟨ ⟩NO_2 + 2CuI
$CO_2C_2H_5$

The Ullmann method has been used also in the synthesis of 2,2′,4,4′,6,6′-hexachloro-3,3′-dimethylbiphenyl.

Cl (ring) 2Cl, I, H_3C, Cl $+ 2Cu \longrightarrow$ Cl Cl (biphenyl) Cl, Cl, H_3C, Cl, Cl, CH_3 $+ 2CuI$

Unsymmetrical biaryls have been made also by the Ullmann procedure. When a mixture of equal amounts of two different aryl halides is treated with copper, it is to be expected that the desired unsymmetrical biaryl will be accompanied by two symmetrical biaryls.

$$ArX + Ar'X \longrightarrow Ar–Ar– + ArAr' + Ar'Ar'$$

In fact, the yields of unsymmetrical biaryls in such couplings are generally not high. For example, compounds I and II afford only a 20 per cent yield of III.

CO_2CH_3, Br — I; NO_2, I — II; CO_2CH_3 NO_2 — III

Since the iodine atom is very much more reactive than the bromine atom, a much higher yield (68 per cent) results if I*a* and II*a* are employed.

CO_2CH_3, I — I*a*; NO_2, Br — II*a*

The reason for the improved yield lies in the fact that the nitro group is a more effective activating group than the carbomethoxyl group, offsetting the fact that an iodide is more reactive than a bromide. Compounds I*a* and II*a* evidently react at nearly the same rate.

Cases are known in which the unsymmetrical biaryl is the only product obtained. Picryl chloride and iodobenzene yield only 2,4,6-trinitrobiphenyl.

NO_2, O_2N, Cl, NO_2 + I(ring) $+ 2Cu \longrightarrow$

NO_2, O_2N, NO_2 (biphenyl) $+ CuI + CuCl$

The Ullmann method has been extended to the polyphenyls. When a mixture of 4-iodobiphenyl and 4,4′-diiodobiphenyl was treated with copper powder at 250–275°, *p*-sexiphenyl was formed in a yield of 25 per cent.

$$C_6H_5C_6H_4I + IC_6H_4C_6H_4I + IC_6H_4C_6H_5 + 4Cu \longrightarrow C_6H_5(C_6H_4)_4C_6H_5 + 4CuI$$

The same result has been obtained by treating *p*-iodoterphenyl with copper bronze.

Intramolecular condensations have been effected also. 1,8-Diiodonaphthalene, for example, yields perylene.

$$2\ C_{10}H_6I_2 \longrightarrow C_{20}H_{12}$$

Similarly 2,2′-diiodo-5,5′-dimethoxybibenzyl can be converted to the corresponding dimethoxydihydrophenanthrene.

$$CH_3OC_6H_3(I)CH_2\text{–}CH_2C_6H_3(I)OCH_3 \longrightarrow CH_3OC_6H_3(CH_2\text{—}CH_2)C_6H_3OCH_3$$

Dehalogenation

Dehalogenation may be accomplished by the use of metals or such reducing agents as hydrogen iodide, zinc and acids, stannous chloride, and sodium arsenite. For example, cetyl iodide is converted to *n*-hexadecane in an 85 per cent yield by the action of zinc and hydrochloric acid.

$$CH_3(CH_2)_{14}CH_2I \longrightarrow CH_3(CH_2)_{14}CH_3$$

The nearly quantitative conversion of benzilic acid to diphenylacetic acid by the action of phosphorus and iodine presumably involves intermediate formation of the iodo derivative.

$$(C_6H_5)_2C(OH)CO_2H \longrightarrow (C_6H_5)_2C(I)CO_2H \longrightarrow (C_6H_5)_2CHCO_2H$$

Bromoform and iodoform are reduced to methylene bromide and methylene iodide, respectively, by the use of sodium arsenite.

$$CHBr_3 + Na_3AsO_3 + NaOH \longrightarrow CH_2Br_2 + Na_3AsO_4 + NaBr$$

$$CHI_3 + Na_3AsO_3 + NaOH \longrightarrow CH_2I_2 + Na_3AsO_4 + NaI$$

Tin and hydrobromic acid serve to convert 1,6-dibromo-2-naphthol to 6-bromo-2-naphthol.

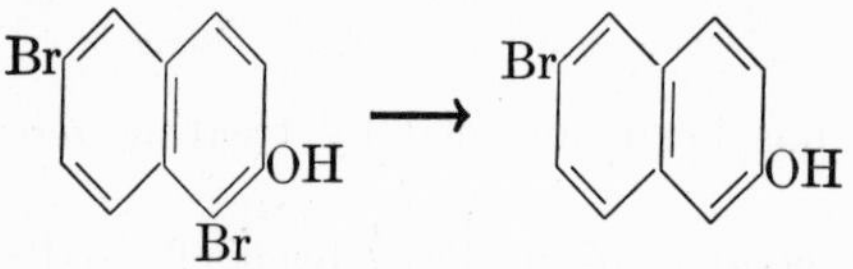

Br OH Br ⟶ Br OH

Compounds that contain halogen atoms on adjacent carbon atoms can be dehalogenated by the action of certain metals to yield the corresponding olefinic compounds. Zinc, for example, converts ethylene bromide to ethylene. Similarly, from 1,1,1,2-tetrachloroethane, vinylidene chloride can be made.

$$CH_2ClCCl_3 + Zn \longrightarrow CH_2{=}CCl_2 + ZnCl_2$$

Hexachloroethane is converted to tetrachloroethylene, an anthelmintic used in place of carbon tetrachloride for hookworms and other parasites.

$$CCl_3CCl_3 \longrightarrow CCl_2{=}CCl_2$$

This reaction is useful in syntheses in which it is necessary to "protect" an olefinic linkage during certain operations. An example is the synthesis of vinylacetic acid from allyl cyanide. Contact with alkalies causes the cyanide to rearrange to crotononitrile (p. 255).

$$CH_2{=}CHCH_2CN \longrightarrow CH_3CH{=}CHCN$$

The dibromide, however, can be hydrolyzed with alkaline reagents, and, from the dibromo acid, vinylacetic acid can be obtained.

$$\underset{\displaystyle Br}{CH_2}\underset{\displaystyle Br}{CH}CH_2CN \longrightarrow \underset{\displaystyle Br}{CH_2}\underset{\displaystyle Br}{CH}CH_2CO_2H \longrightarrow CH_2{=}CHCH_2CO_2H$$

It should be pointed out, however, that the foregoing method has lost much of its practical value in view of the discovery that allyl cyanide can be hydrolyzed satisfactorily by use of concentrated hydrochloric acid.

In the separation of 1-butene from 2-butene it has been found expedient to prepare the dibromides, which can be separated by fractional distillation. The pure hydrocarbons are then obtained by the action of zinc on the bromides.

$$CH_3CH_2\underset{Br}{\underset{|}{C}}H\underset{Br}{\underset{|}{C}}H_2 + Zn \longrightarrow CH_3CH_2CH{=}CH_2 + ZnBr_2$$

$$CH_3\underset{Br}{\underset{|}{C}}H\underset{Br}{\underset{|}{C}}HCH_3 + Zn \longrightarrow CH_3CH{=}CHCH_3 + ZnBr_2$$

The binary mixture, magnesium-magnesium iodide, has been used successfully to prepare dioxene and dioxadiene from the appropriate chlorine derivatives of dioxane.

$$\text{O(CH}_2\text{CHCl)(CH}_2\text{CHCl)O ring} \longrightarrow \text{O(CH}_2\text{CH)(CH}_2\text{CH)O ring, CH=CH} \quad \text{Dioxene}$$

$$\text{O(ClCH–CHCl)(ClCH–CHCl)O ring} \longrightarrow \text{O(CH=CH)(CH=CH)O ring} \quad \text{Dioxadiene}$$

Debromination of 1,2-dibromo compounds may be accomplished by treatment with sodium iodide or potassium iodide. Presumably, the corresponding diiodo compound is formed as an intermediate. It is a general rule that 1,2-diiodo compounds are unstable and dissociate into iodine and the corresponding unsaturated compound. For example, ethylene iodide reverts to ethylene and iodine when heated.

$$\begin{matrix} CH_2I \\ | \\ CH_2I \end{matrix} \longrightarrow \begin{matrix} CH_2 \\ \| \\ CH_2 \end{matrix} + I_2$$

The synthesis of allyl iodide from glycerol by the action of phosphorus and iodine must be due to a similar reaction. The 1,2,3-triiodopropane to be expected is unstable and dissociates into iodine and allyl iodide.

$$\underset{\substack{|\\OH}}{CH_2}–\underset{\substack{|\\OH}}{CH}–\underset{\substack{|\\OH}}{CH_2} \xrightarrow{P + I_2} [CH_2(I)CH(I)CH_2(I)] \xrightarrow{-I_2} CH_2{=}CHCH_2I$$

This procedure is in effect a device for converting a 1,2-glycol into the corresponding olefin. It has been found to be convenient to employ phosphorus diiodide (P_2I_4) for this purpose. In the hands of Kuhn and his coworkers this method gave remarkable results in the synthesis of diphenylpolyenes. Hydrocinnamoin, for example, yielded 1,6-diphenyl-1,3,5-hexatriene.

$$\underset{\text{OH}\ \ \text{OH}}{C_6H_5CH{=}CHCH{-}CHCH{=}CHC_6H_5} \longrightarrow C_6H_5(CH{=}CH)_3C_6H_5$$

The procedure proved to be effective with 1,4- and 1,6-glycols also, the tetraene being made as follows.

$$\underset{\text{OH}\qquad\quad \text{OH}}{C_6H_5CH{=}CHCHCH{=}CHCHCH{=}CHC_6H_5} \longrightarrow C_6H_5(CH{=}CH)_4C_6H_5$$

The purification of α,β-unsaturated ketones frequently gives trouble. Kohler discovered that conversion to a solid dibromide was often helpful, since this derivative could be purified by recrystallization and from it the unsaturated ketone could be made in nearly pure condition.

$$RCH{=}CHCOR \xrightarrow{Br_2} \underset{\text{Br}\ \text{Br}}{RCHCHCOR} \xrightarrow{KI}$$

$$\underset{\text{I}\ \ \text{I}}{[RCHCHCOR]} \xrightarrow{-I_2} RCH{=}CHCOR$$

It has been shown that the rate at which bromine is removed by this method varies with the nature of the compound. The following examples show some of the variations.

Compound	Quantitative removal in
$\underset{\text{Br}\ \text{Br}}{C_6H_5CHCHCO_2H}$	15 minutes
$\underset{\text{Br}\ \text{Br}}{C_6H_5CHCHCHO}$	1 hour
$CHBrCO_2H{-}CHBrCO_2H$	15 minutes
$\underset{\text{Br}\ \text{Br}}{CH_3CHCHCO_2H}$	30 minutes
$\underset{\text{Br}\ \text{Br}}{C_6H_5CHCHCH_3}$	10 hours
$BrCH_2CHBr(CH_2)_8CO_2H$	20 hours

A synthesis of olefins from α,β-dibromo ethers, which is very similar to dehalogenation of 1,2-dihalogen compounds, consists in the removal of the elements of an alkyl hypobromite. The action of a Grignard reagent on an α,β-dibromo ether gives the bromo ether from which the olefin can be derived. The elimination is effected by the use of zinc. If allylmagnesium bromide (p. 258) is used, the final product is a diene.

$$\overset{\text{Br}}{\underset{|}{\ }}\!\!\!\!CH_2\overset{\text{Br}}{\underset{|}{\ }}\!\!\!\!CHOR + R'MgX \longrightarrow \overset{\text{Br}}{\underset{|}{\ }}\!\!\!\!CH_2\overset{\text{R}'}{\underset{|}{\ }}\!\!\!\!CHOR + MgXBr$$

$$\overset{\text{Br}}{\underset{|}{\ }}\!\!\!\!CH_2\overset{\text{R}'}{\underset{|}{\ }}\!\!\!\!CHOR + Zn \longrightarrow CH_2{=}CHR' + Zn(OR)Br$$

β-Halo ethers in general react with metals to yield olefins and alcohols or phenols according to this equation (p. 258). An example is the conversion of β-bromophenetole to ethylene and phenol by treatment with magnesium.

$$2C_6H_5OCH_2CH_2Br + 2Mg \longrightarrow (C_6H_5O)_2Mg + MgBr_2 + 2C_2H_4$$

The formation of ethyl vinyl ether from β-chloroethyl acetal by the action of sodium is another example.

$$ClCH_2CH(OC_2H_5)_2 + 2Na \longrightarrow CH_2{=}CHOC_2H_5 + C_2H_5ONa + NaCl$$

Applied to ortho esters of α-halogen acids, this procedure yields ketene acetals.

$$R\underset{\underset{\text{Br}}{|}}{C}HC(OC_2H_5)_3 + 2Na \longrightarrow RCH{=}C(OC_2H_5)_2 + NaBr + C_2H_5ONa$$

Tetrahydrofurfuryl bromide reacts with magnesium to give a 62 per cent yield of 4-penten-1-ol. This unsaturated alcohol is made in an 83 per cent yield by treating tetrahydrofurfuryl chloride with sodium.

$$\text{(tetrahydrofurfuryl chloride: ring with O, } CH_2Cl) + 2Na \longrightarrow CH_2{=}CHCH_2CH_2CH_2ONa + NaCl$$

$$CH_2{=}CHCH_2CH_2CH_2ONa \xrightarrow{H_2O} CH_2{=}CHCH_2CH_2CH_2OH$$

Certain halo vinyl ethers yield acetylenic derivatives. Thus, β-bromovinyl phenyl ether is converted to the corresponding phenoxide and acetylene.

$$C_6H_5OCH{=}CHBr + 2Na \longrightarrow C_6H_5ONa + NaBr + C_2H_2$$

As was pointed out earlier (p. 258), β-halo ethers cannot be used satisfactorily for the preparation of Grignard reagents.

Dehydrohalogenation

Many halogen compounds may be caused to lose the elements of a hydrogen halide, i.e., undergo dehydrohalogenation, to yield the corresponding unsaturated compounds. Removal of one molecule of hydrogen halide generates an olefinic compound; of two, a diene or an acetylenic compound. Dehydrohalogenation proceeds most readily with tertiary alkyl halides, less so with secondary, and least readily with primary. When two or more different olefins are possible, the rule, formulated by Zaytzeff, is that the most highly alkylated ethylene will predominate among the products. This generalization recalls the fact that a tertiary hydrogen atom is more reactive than a primary (p. 34). Thus an alkyl halide of the type $RCH_2\underset{\displaystyle Cl}{\underset{|}{C}}HCH_3$ would yield the olefin $RCH{=}CHCH_3$ rather than $RCH_2CH{=}CH_2$. This result accords with the prediction based on the concept of hyperconjugation, since the monoalkyl olefin possesses at least one less α-hydrogen atom than the dialkyl olefin.

An important example of dehydrochlorination is the conversion of ethylene chloride to vinyl chloride. The reaction is carried out industrially by dropping the dichloride on hot alkali.

$$CH_2ClCH_2Cl \longrightarrow CH_2{=}CHCl + HCl$$

Vinylidene chloride is produced by the salt-bath chlorination of ethylene chloride followed by a dehydrochlorination.

Pentachloroethane readily loses a molecule of hydrogen chloride and can serve in an interesting way as a hydrochlorinating agent.

$$CCl_3CHCl_2 + RNH_2 \longrightarrow CCl_2{=}CCl_2 + RNH_2 \cdot HCl$$

For example, it converts ephedrin to ephedrin hydrochloride, tetrachloroethylene being the other product.

2,3-Dibromopropene is made from 1,2,3-tribromopropane by heating with a very concentrated sodium hydroxide solution.

$$\overset{\displaystyle Br}{\overset{|}{C}}H_2\overset{\displaystyle Br}{\overset{|}{C}}H\overset{\displaystyle Br}{\overset{|}{C}}H_2 \xrightarrow{NaOH} CH_2{=}CBrCH_2Br$$

This example is interesting because it illustrates the general rule that a vinyl bromide is relatively unreactive. The difference in reactivity of the two bromine atoms in the propene is predictable as an extension of Schmidt's rule, which states that a double bond strengthens the adjacent single bond and weakens the next following. The bromine atom in position 2 is not easily removed by dehydrohalogenating agents. The halogen atom in position 3 is not eliminated because the adjacent carbon atom carries no hydrogen atom.

The synthesis of muconic acid from ethyl α,α'-dibromoadipate illustrates a very general reaction of α-halo carbonyl compounds.

$$\begin{array}{c} CO_2C_2H_5 \\ | \\ CHBr \\ | \\ CH_2 \\ | \\ CH_2 \\ | \\ CHBr \\ | \\ CO_2C_2H_5 \end{array} \longrightarrow \begin{array}{c} CO_2H \\ | \\ CH \\ \| \\ CH \\ | \\ CH \\ \| \\ CH \\ | \\ CO_2H \end{array}$$

Pyridine, quinoline, and similar tertiary amines are very good dehydrohalogenating agents for many compounds. An example is the use of pyridine to prepare 3,5,7-decatriene.

$$C_3H_7CHClCH{=}CHCHClC_3H_7 \xrightarrow{\text{pyridine}} C_2H_5CH{=}CHCH{=}CHCH{=}CHC_2H_5$$

Triple bonds are produced when vinyl halides are treated with very strong dehydrohalogenating agents such as sodium amide and molten alkali. Phenylacetylene is made in 67 per cent yield by dropping β-bromostyrene on molten potassium hydroxide at a temperature of 200–230°. Since phenylacetylene boils at 143°, it distils from the unchanged bromostyrene.

$$C_6H_5CH{=}CHBr + KOH \longrightarrow C_6H_5C{\equiv}CH + KBr + H_2O$$

Phenylacetylene can be obtained also by dehydrohalogenation of α-chlorostyrene, prepared by the action of phosphorus pentachloride on acetophenone (p. 317). 1-Decyne and 3-cyclohexylpropyne are formed in similar ways.

$$CH_3(CH_2)_7CBr{=}CH_2 + NaNH_2 \longrightarrow CH_3(CH_2)_7C{\equiv}CH + NaBr + NH_3$$

$$\begin{array}{c} CHCH_2CBr{=}CH_2 \\ \diagup \quad \diagdown \\ CH_2 \quad CH_2 \\ | \qquad | \\ CH_2 \quad CH_2 \\ \diagdown \quad \diagup \\ CH_2 \end{array} + NaNH_2 \longrightarrow \begin{array}{c} CHCH_2C{\equiv}CH \\ \diagup \quad \diagdown \\ CH_2 \quad CH_2 \\ | \qquad | \\ CH_2 \quad CH_2 \\ \diagdown \quad \diagup \\ CH_2 \end{array} + NaBr + NH_3$$

In these reactions the dehydrohalogenating agent is powdered sodium amide suspended in mineral oil.

Many acetylenic acids can be made in satisfactory yields from dibromo acids by eliminating two molecules of hydrogen halide. A salt of acetylenedicarboxylic acid is produced from α,β-dibromosuccinic acid by heating with methanolic potassium hydroxide. An 88 per cent yield of acetylenedicarboxylic acid may be obtained after acidification of the reaction mixture.

$$\begin{matrix} CO_2H \\ | \\ CHBr \\ | \\ CHBr \\ | \\ CO_2H \end{matrix} + 4KOH \longrightarrow \begin{matrix} CO_2K \\ | \\ C \\ \vert\vert\vert \\ C \\ | \\ CO_2K \end{matrix} + 2KBr + 4H_2O$$

Phenylpropiolic acid may be derived in a similar way from ethyl cinnamate.

$$C_6H_5CH{=}CHCO_2C_2H_5 \longrightarrow C_6H_5\underset{Br}{\underset{|}{C}}H\underset{Br}{\underset{|}{C}}HCO_2H \longrightarrow C_6H_5C{\equiv}CCO_2H$$

In a like fashion methyl oleate furnishes stearolic acid.

$$CH_3(CH_2)_7CH{=}CH(CH_2)_7CO_2CH_3 \longrightarrow$$

$$CH_3(CH_2)_7\underset{Br}{\underset{|}{C}}H\underset{Br}{\underset{|}{C}}H(CH_2)_7CO_2H \longrightarrow CH_3(CH_2)_7C{\equiv}C(CH_2)_7CO_2H$$

Propargyl alcohol is formed in yields as high as 69 per cent by treating 3-chloro-2-propen-1-ol with sodium hydroxide solution. The chloropropenol is readily obtained by hydrolysis of 1,3-dichloropropene, a by-product in the preparation of allyl chloride from propylene.

$$ClCH{=}CHCH_2Cl \xrightarrow[H_2O]{NaOH} ClCH{=}CHCH_2OH$$

$$ClCH{=}CHCH_2OH \xrightarrow{-HCl} HC{\equiv}CCH_2OH$$

The hydrolysis of 1,3-dichloropropene to 3-chloro-2-propen-1-ol is instructive because it illustrates the great difference in the reactivity of allyl and vinyl chlorides.

Tolane is made in 84 per cent yields from stilbene bromide by dehydrobromination with ethanolic potassium hydroxide.

$$C_6H_5\underset{Br}{\underset{|}{C}}H\underset{Br}{\underset{|}{C}}HC_6H_5 \xrightarrow{-2HBr} C_6H_5C{\equiv}CC_6H_5$$

DDT readily loses one molecule of hydrogen chloride (p. 246).

$$(ClC_6H_4)_2CHCCl_3 \xrightarrow{-HCl} (ClC_6H_4)_2C{=}CCl_2$$

Dehydrochlorination of 1,1-dichloro-2,2-di(*p*-chlorophenyl)ethane under the influence of ferric chloride produces not only 1-chloro-2,2-di(*p*-chlorophenyl)ethylene but also a rearrangement product, 4,4′-dichlorostilbene chloride.

$$(ClC_6H_4)_2CHCHCl_2 \longrightarrow (ClC_6H_4)_2C{=}CHCl \quad \text{and} \quad ClC_6H_4\underset{\substack{|\\Cl}}{C}H\underset{\substack{|\\Cl}}{C}HC_6H_4Cl$$

A synthesis of difluoromalonic acid involves dehydrochlorination followed by oxidation of the resulting diene. The raw material is diethyl ketone, and the steps are as follows.

$$CH_3CH_2COCH_2CH_3 \longrightarrow CH_3CH_2CF_2CH_2CH_3 \longrightarrow ClCH_2CH_2CF_2CH_2CH_2Cl \longrightarrow CH_2{=}CHCF_2CH{=}CH_2 \longrightarrow CF_2(CO_2H)_2$$

In α,β-dihalogen derivatives the β-halogen atom is more readily removed than the α. When, for example, benzalacetone dibromide is treated with sodium acetate in ethanol, α-bromobenzalacetone is produced in a 73 per cent yield.

$$C_6H_5CHBrCHBrCOCH_3 + CH_3CO_2Na \longrightarrow C_6H_5CH{=}CBrCOCH_3 + CH_3CO_2H + NaBr$$

Ketene diethylacetal is made in a 75 per cent yield by treatment of the acetal of bromoacetaldehyde with potassium *t*-butoxide in *t*-butyl alcohol solution.

$$BrCH_2CH\begin{matrix}\diagup OC_2H_5\\ \diagdown OC_2H_5\end{matrix} \xrightarrow{-HBr} CH_2{=}C\begin{matrix}\diagup OC_2H_5\\ \diagdown OC_2H_5\end{matrix}$$

Dehydrohalogenation of coumarin dibromide is accompanied by rearrangement and the development of a carboxyl group, the final product being coumarilic acid. It would appear that ring opening is followed by a ring closure, which is an intramolecular alkylation; dehydrobromination then takes place. The yield of coumarilic acid is 88 per cent.

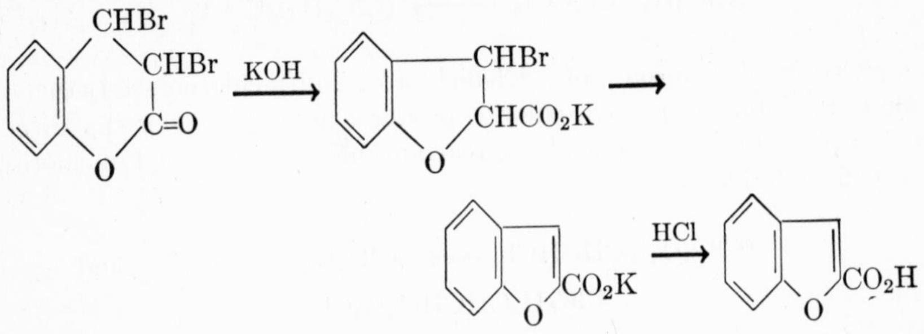

$$\text{(3,4-dibromo-dihydrocoumarin)} \xrightarrow{KOH} \text{(2-carboxy-3-bromo-dihydrobenzofuran, K salt: CHBr–CHCO}_2\text{K)} \longrightarrow \text{(benzofuran-2-CO}_2\text{K)} \xrightarrow{HCl} \text{(benzofuran-2-CO}_2\text{H)}$$

α-Bromocinnamaldehyde is formed in 85 per cent yield by the action of potassium carbonate on the dibromide of cinnamaldehyde.

$$C_6H_5CHBrCHBrCHO \xrightarrow{K_2CO_3} C_6H_5CH{=}CBrCHO$$

Dehydrohalogenation, although a very general reaction, sometimes fails. It has been observed that attempts to introduce a double bond at the bridgehead in compounds of the camphane and pinane series are unsuccessful. In fact, no compound is known of type I or II which has a double bond at A or B. This generalization, known as Bredt's rule,

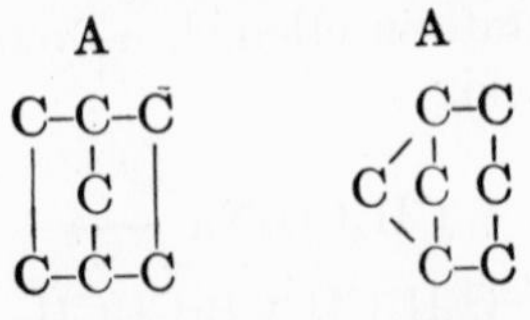

(Structures I and II: bicyclic carbon skeletons with bridgehead positions A and B)

finds support in attempts to dehydrohalogenate certain bicyclic compounds having a halogen atom at or near a bridgehead.

It is impossible, for example, to convert bromocamphor (III) to the corresponding unsaturated camphor derivative (IV).

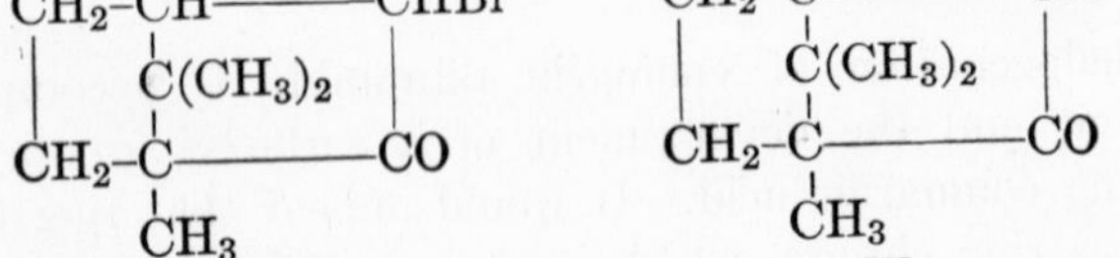

(III: bromocamphor, CHBr adjacent to CO; IV: corresponding bridgehead-unsaturated camphor, C=CH adjacent to CO)

Similarly, hydrogen bromide cannot be eliminated from the anhydride of bromocamphoric acid (V); dehydrobromination will occur, however, with the esters (VI), yielding the corresponding unsaturated acid (VII).

```
       Br                           Br
       |                            |
CH2-C———————CO              CH2-C-CO2R              CH=C-CO2H
|   |         \             |   |                   |  |
|   C(CH3)2    O            |   C(CH3)2             |  C(CH3)2
|   |         /             |   |                   |  |
CH2-C———————CO              CH2-C-CO2R              CH2-C-CO2H
    |                           |                      |
    CH3                         CH3                    CH3
     V                          VI                     VII
```

This acid, however, does not form a normal anhydride. Under drastic treatment it yields the anhydride (VIII) of the isomeric acid.

```
CH-CH———————CO
||  |         \
||  C(CH3)2    O
||  |         /
CH-C————————CO
    |
    CH3
   VIII
```

It has been mentioned above (p. 238) that 1-chloroapocamphane (IX) is resistant to the action of sodium ethoxide.

```
      CH2——CH2
     /   CH3   \
    /     |     \
CH————————C——————C-Cl
    \     |     /
     \   CH3   /
      CH2——CH2

         IX
```

CHAPTER 20

Organometallic Compounds

HISTORICAL

The term organometallic is used to denote those substances in which a metal is joined directly to carbon. The first of these to be made was diethylzinc, prepared by Frankland in 1849 from ethyl iodide and the metal.

$$2C_2H_5I + 2Zn \longrightarrow (C_2H_5)_2Zn + ZnI_2$$

The alkylzinc compounds, although inflammable and difficult to handle, proved invaluable. They were volatile and their molecular weights could be determined. This was of great assistance in assigning the proper valence to the metal. Moreover, these compounds were useful in synthesis, serving many of the purposes for which we now use the Grignard reagent.

As time went on, organometallic derivatives containing other metals were synthesized. Among these are compounds of magnesium, lithium, mercury, lead, and aluminum. Nearly all the metals are capable of forming such derivatives.

It will be convenient to discuss the magnesium compounds first since they have been carefully studied and illustrate most of the types of reactions found in the entire group of organometallic compounds.

THE GRIGNARD REAGENT

The Grignard reaction was first effected by Barbier in 1899. By treating a methylheptenone with methyl iodide and magnesium he prepared the corresponding dimethylheptenol.

$$(CH_3)_2C{=}CHCH_2CH_2COCH_3 \xrightarrow[CH_3I]{Mg}$$

$$\xrightarrow{H_2O} (CH_3)_2C{=}CHCH_2CH_2\underset{\displaystyle OH}{\underset{|}{C}}(CH_3)_2$$

In 1900 Grignard divided the synthesis into two steps, the first of which is that known by his name.

$$RX + Mg \longrightarrow RMgX$$

Structure. The role played by ethers in the preparation and use of the Grignard reagent is probably to form coordination complexes with the magnesium compounds. In view of the tendency of magnesium to form hydrated (solvated) inorganic salts it would not be surprising to find that RMgX in ether solution exists as solvated forms such as those shown. Actually there is evidence that RMgX forms both a

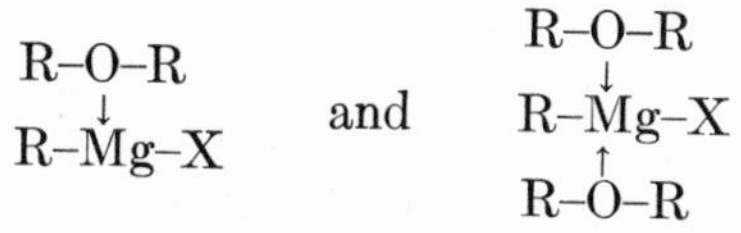

$$\begin{array}{c} \text{R–O–R} \\ \downarrow \\ \text{R–Mg–X} \end{array} \quad \text{and} \quad \begin{array}{c} \text{R–O–R} \\ \downarrow \\ \text{R–Mg–X} \\ \uparrow \\ \text{R–O–R} \end{array}$$

mono- and a dietherate, which probably have just these structures. Such combination of RMgX with other electron donors which cannot react further is possible also. Pyridine (p. 496) is an example, and it has been used as the solvent in place of ether.

It has been shown that in a Grignard solution disproportionation of RMgX occurs in accordance with the following equilibrium.

$$2\text{RMgX} \rightleftarrows \text{R}_2\text{Mg} + \text{MgX}_2$$

All the molecules concerned in this equilibrium presumably exist as etherates in the usual ether solutions, but in the interest of brevity solvation ordinarily is not indicated in formulas and equations. It is of interest that solutions of R_2Mg can be prepared from ordinary Grignard solutions by the careful addition of dioxane. This ether evidently forms polymeric solvates with the magnesium halides; these are of very low solubility and hence separate as precipitates.

Similar polymeric solvates form from RMgX and R_2Mg. The most soluble solvate is that of R_2Mg; hence cautious addition of dioxane to Grignard solutions precipitates all the halogen compounds. The resulting solutions containing only R_2Mg have properties very similar to those of the ordinary Grignard reagent. The use of a solution of R_2Mg seldom offers any advantage in synthesis.

Ether solutions of Grignard reagents conduct the electric current. Accordingly, at least some of the molecules discussed above must be capable of ionizing in the ether medium. Analogy with inorganic magnesium compounds would suggest the ionization $\text{RMgX} \rightleftharpoons \text{RMg}^+ + \text{X}^-$, and this equilibrium undoubtedly exists. A similar ionization of R_2Mg would give rise to the ions RMg^+ and R^-, and further ionization of RMg^+ might also give the carbanion R^- along with Mg^{++}. However, it is hardly to be expected that the *free* carbanion will exist in the system; it is highly nucleophilic, and if it were formed in the solution it would be expected to displace ether from some of the complexes noted above, yielding anionic complexes. For example, it might react as follows.

$$RMgX + R^- \longrightarrow \left[\begin{matrix} & R & \\ & | & \\ R- & Mg & -X \end{matrix}\right]^-$$

Similar combinations with R_2Mg and MgX_2 may be written. The evidence for the existence of such complex anions lies in the electrolysis; magnesium is present in *both the cation and the anion.*

Some reactions of the Grignard reagent are most readily understood if it is assumed that the reagent can provide free radicals. These may arise through the following equilibrium.

$$RMgX \rightleftharpoons R\cdot + \cdot MgX$$

From the above discussion it is seen that the Grignard reagent actually is quite complex. As a consequence of this complexity it is often difficult to choose between alternative mechanisms for its reactions. However, most of the reactions can be correlated by the view that the magnesium compound furnishes a carbanion to an electrophilic reagent. The carbanion may be released directly from the reagent RMgX or from one of the complex anions mentioned above, or it may form after a preliminary coordination of the reacting molecules. As an example of the last possibility, the first step in the reaction of a ketone and a Grignard reagent probably is the displacement of one of the ether molecules from the solvated form, as follows.

$$\begin{matrix} C_2H_5 \quad C_2H_5 \\ \diagdown \; \diagup \\ O \\ \downarrow \\ R\text{–}Mg\text{–}X \\ \uparrow \\ O \\ \diagup \; \diagdown \\ C_2H_5 \quad C_2H_5 \end{matrix} + \begin{matrix} O \\ \| \\ C \\ \diagup \; \diagdown \\ R' \quad R' \end{matrix} \longrightarrow \begin{matrix} C_2H_5 \quad C_2H_5 \\ \diagdown \; \diagup \\ O \\ \downarrow \\ R\text{–}Mg\text{–}X \\ \uparrow \\ O \\ \| \\ C \\ \diagup \; \diagdown \\ R' \quad R' \end{matrix} + (C_2H_5)_2O$$

The next step may be the migration of R, as a carbanion, to the carbon atom of the ketone.

Analysis. A qualitative test for the Grignard reagent consists in mixing the solution with Michler's ketone in benzene, adding water and finally iodine.

$$(CH_3)_2N-C_6H_4-CO-C_6H_4-N(CH_3)_2 \xrightarrow{RMgX} \xrightarrow{H_2O}$$

$$(CH_3)_2N-C_6H_4-C(OH)(R)-C_6H_4-N(CH_3)_2 \xrightarrow[CH_3CO_2H]{I_2}$$

$$\left[(CH_3)_2N{=}C_6H_4{=}C(R)-C_6H_4-N(CH_3)_2\right]^+ X^-$$

If RMgX is present a green-blue color is observed.

Methylmagnesium halides react with water to give methane, and advantage is taken of this to determine the amount of reagent present. All that is necessary is to collect the gas and measure its volume. This method is applicable to a few other Grignard reagents—those which yield gaseous hydrocarbons.

A general method of quantitative estimation consists in decomposing the reagent with water and titrating the basic magnesium salt with standard acid.

$$RMgX + H_2O \longrightarrow RH + Mg(OH)X$$

$$Mg(OH)X + HX \longrightarrow MgX_2 + H_2O$$

A disadvantage of this method is that it gives high results on solutions which have been attacked by atmospheric oxygen (p. 282); the oxidation product (ROMgX) neutralizes one equivalent of acid in the final titration.

Reactions of the Grignard Reagent

The reactions of the Grignard reagent are very numerous and lead to a wide variety of products. The types of reactions, however, are few in number. It will be helpful to consider each type separately.

1. Compounds Containing Active Hydrogen Atoms. Water, alcohols, primary and secondary amines, many amides, and sulfhydryl compounds decompose the Grignard reagent.

$$\begin{aligned} RMgX + H_2O &\longrightarrow RH + Mg(OH)X \\ + R'OH &\longrightarrow RH + Mg(OR')X \\ + R'NH_2 &\longrightarrow RH + Mg(NHR')X \\ + R'SH &\longrightarrow RH + Mg(SR')X \end{aligned}$$

All such reactions may be regarded as neutralizations ($R^- + H^+ \longrightarrow RH$). The decomposition of a Grignard reagent with heavy water produces a deuterium compound; phenylmagnesium bromide yields monodeuterobenzene.

$$C_6H_5MgBr + D_2O \longrightarrow C_6H_5D + Mg(OD)Br$$

In general, a hydrogen atom attached to any element other than carbon will react in this manner. Such hydrogen atoms are said to be *active.* Many carbonyl compounds give this reaction also because they react in the enol modification; e.g., ethyl acetoacetate reacts with methylmagnesium iodide to give 1 mole of methane.

$$CH_3\overset{\overset{\large OH}{|}}{C}{=}CHCO_2C_2H_5 + CH_3MgI \longrightarrow CH_4 + CH_3\overset{\overset{\large OMgI}{|}}{C}{=}CHCO_2C_2H_5$$

There are some instances in which hydrogen on carbon is sufficiently reactive to decompose the reagent. Acetylene is an example.

$$2RMgX + HC{\equiv}CH \longrightarrow 2RH + XMgC{\equiv}CMgX$$

The activation of methylene groups by adjacent unsaturation (p. 339) may be sufficient to enable them to react with Grignard reagents. For example, cyclopentadiene decomposes methylmagnesium iodide.

$$\begin{array}{l}CH{=}CH\\ |\\ CH{=}CH\end{array}\!\!\!>CH_2 + CH_3MgI \longrightarrow \begin{array}{l}CH{=}CH\\ |\\ CH{=}CH\end{array}\!\!\!>CHMgI + CH_4$$

The carbanion $\begin{array}{l}CH{=}CH\\ |\\ CH{=}CH\end{array}\!\!\!>HC{:}$, being stabilized by resonance, is displaced because it is much less basic than the methyl carbanion. Other examples are 2,4-pentadiene, indene, and fluorene, and a similar reaction occurs with certain heterocyclic compounds; pyrrole and indole react with Grignard reagents to give magnesium derivatives which are useful in synthesis.

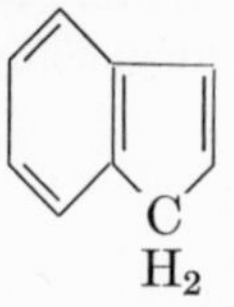

Indene

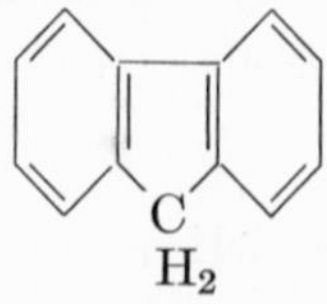

Fluorene

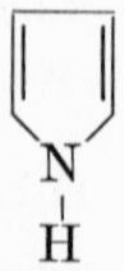

Pyrrole

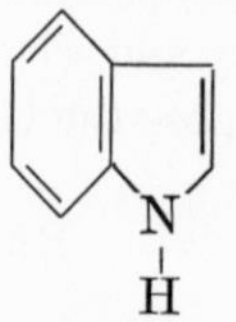

Indole

The reaction with active hydrogen compounds like these is of especial interest as a method of preparing Grignard reagents directly from hydrocarbons and heterocyclic substances.

The hydrolysis of the Grignard reagent provides an indirect method for the reduction of certain halogen compounds to hydrocarbons, and it is occasionally used for this purpose. For example, pure *n*-pentane is obtained from 2-bromopentane by conversion to the Grignard reagent and hydrolysis.

$$CH_3CH_2CH_2\underset{\displaystyle Br}{\underset{|}{C}}HCH_3 \xrightarrow{Mg} CH_3CH_2CH_2\underset{\displaystyle MgBr}{\underset{|}{C}}HCH_3$$

$$\xrightarrow{H_2O} CH_3CH_2CH_2CH_2CH_3$$

The most general use of the reaction of Grignard reagents with active hydrogen compounds is in analytical work. This reaction is the basis of the Tschugaeff-Zerewitinoff determination of active hydrogen atoms. The method consists in treating a weighed amount of the compound to be tested with an excess of a methylmagnesium halide and measuring the methane evolved. One mole of resorcinol, for example, gives 2 moles of methane.

$$C_6H_4(OH)_2 + 2CH_3MgI \longrightarrow 2CH_4 + C_6H_4(OMgI)_2$$

A modification of this method is due to Kohler. He devised a means of preparing and storing *a standard solution* of methylmagnesium iodide. An excess of the reagent is used, and after the reaction is complete the unused reagent is determined by addition of water and measurement of the methane evolved. If 1 mole of benzoin is treated with 3 moles of reagent it will be found that 1 mole of methane is evolved at once and that a total of 2 moles of reagent is used. This leads to the conclusion that the molecule contains a carbonyl group in addition to one active hydrogen atom.

$$\begin{array}{l} C_6H_5CO \\ \quad\;| \\ C_6H_5CHOH \end{array} + 2CH_3MgX \longrightarrow \begin{array}{l} C_6H_5C(OMgX)(CH_3) \\ \quad\;| \\ C_6H_5CHOMgX \end{array} + CH_4$$

It is most important to avoid reactions of this type in synthetic work. Thus the ether and reactants should be free from water, alcohols, and all other compounds that have active hydrogen atoms. It is to be emphasized that this type of reaction is faster than those generally sought in synthetic work. When salicylaldehyde, for instance, is treated with a

Grignard reagent the hydroxyl group decomposes the reagent before the aldehyde group is attacked.

$$o\text{-}HOC_6H_4CHO + RMgX \longrightarrow o\text{-}XMgOC_6H_4CHO + RH$$

2. Oxygen, Sulfur, and Halogens. Chemiluminescence is observed when a Grignard reagent is exposed to air or oxygen; $BrMgC_6H_4MgBr$ gives a particularly intense glow. The reaction is a complex one and seems to consist of the following steps.

$$RMgX + O_2 \longrightarrow \underset{\text{Peroxide}}{RO_2MgX}$$

$$RO_2MgX + RMgX \longrightarrow 2ROMgX$$

From the alcoholate so formed the alcohol is obtained by treatment with dilute acids.

$$ROMgX + HX \longrightarrow ROH + MgX_2$$

The absorption of oxygen is very rapid, and care must be taken to exclude it from the apparatus containing the reagent. This is generally done by using a volatile ether as solvent. Ethyl ether vapors, for example, flow out of the apparatus so rapidly as to prevent the oxygen from entering.

As indicated above (p. 279), the quantitative analysis of the Grignard reagent by hydrolysis and titration with acid is subject to serious error when applied to solutions that have undergone oxidation.

The oxidation of aliphatic reagents leads to the corresponding alcohols in high yields but has little or no synthetic value since the halides used in preparing reagents in the first place are generally made from the alcohols. In the aromatic series where the reaction might be useful it is much more complex. Only unsatisfactory yields of phenols can be had in this way.

Sulfur reacts similarly, giving rise to mercaptans and thiophenols. Rubber stoppers normally contain uncombined sulfur, and if the reagent is allowed to come into contact with them the product will be contaminated with unpleasant-smelling sulfur derivatives.

Halogens cleave RMgX compounds as follows.

$$RMgX + X_2 \longrightarrow RX + MgX_2$$

This reaction gives excellent yields of iodo compounds and provides a method for getting these from the corresponding chloro or bromo compounds. Propyl bromide, isoamyl chloride, bromobenzene, and *p*-bromotoluene give the corresponding iodo derivatives in yields of 80 per cent.

3. Addition Reactions. Compounds containing double or triple bonds generally react additively with the reagent. The common types of linkages are C=O, C=S, C=N, C≡N, N=O, and N=N. Only a few ethylenic and no acetylenic linkages react in this manner.

The initial stage in all these reactions can be formulated as the addition of the carbanion, R^-, to the positive end of the double bond.

$$R^- + \overset{|}{\underset{|}{C}}{=}O \longrightarrow R{-}\overset{|}{\underset{|}{C}}{-}O^-$$

In the interest of brevity the ionization of the reagent and product is usually not shown in equations.

Aldehydes, the most reactive of the carbonyl compounds, combine readily with Grignard reagents to give alcoholates from which secondary alcohols are obtained by hydrolysis.

$$RC\overset{\displaystyle /\!\!/ O}{-}H + R'MgX \longrightarrow R\overset{\displaystyle OMgX}{\overset{|}{C}}HR' \xrightarrow{HX} R\overset{\displaystyle OH}{\overset{|}{C}}HR'$$

Formaldehyde, as already noted (p. 85), leads to the formation of primary alcohols.

$$RMgX + CH_2O \longrightarrow RCH_2OMgX \xrightarrow{HX} RCH_2OH$$

The reaction is useful in building up a carbon chain (p. 85), e.g., octyl and undecyl alcohols are made from their next lower homologs in this way. Cyclohexylcarbinol is obtained from cyclohexyl chloride in 65 to 70 per cent yields by this method.

$$C_6H_{11}Cl \longrightarrow C_6H_{11}MgCl \longrightarrow C_6H_{11}CH_2OH$$

(cyclohexyl ring: CHCl / CH₂ CH₂ / CH₂ CH₂ / CH₂ → CHMgCl / CH₂ CH₂ / CH₂ CH₂ / CH₂ → CHCH₂OH / CH₂ CH₂ / CH₂ CH₂ / CH₂)

If excess aldehyde is present the carbinolates may undergo oxidation. Under these conditions, for example, benzaldehyde and ethylmagnesium bromide give propiophenone.

$$C_6H_5CHO + C_2H_5MgBr \longrightarrow C_6H_5\overset{\displaystyle OMgBr}{\overset{|}{C}}HC_2H_5$$

$$\xrightarrow{C_6H_5CHO} C_6H_5CH_2OMgBr + C_6H_5COC_2H_5$$

The halomagnesium alcoholates also catalyze condensation reactions of the aldol type. In most cases, therefore, an excess of Grignard reagent must be present if good yields are to be obtained; it is customary to use an excess of this reagent and to add the other reactant to it gradually.

Ketones are converted to tertiary alcohols by the Grignard method (p. 86).

$$RCOR + R'MgX \longrightarrow \begin{matrix} R \\ R{-}COMgX \\ R' \end{matrix} \xrightarrow{H_2O} \begin{matrix} R \\ R{-}COH \\ R' \end{matrix}$$

In practice this method is limited to those tertiary alcohols in which the three radicals are different. An example is the synthesis of ethylmethylphenylcarbinol from acetophenone and ethylmagnesium bromide.

$$C_6H_5COCH_3 \xrightarrow{C_2H_5MgBr} C_6H_5\overset{\displaystyle OMgBr}{\underset{\displaystyle C_2H_5}{C}}{-}CH_3 \xrightarrow{H_2O} \begin{matrix} C_6H_5 \\ CH_3{-}COH \\ C_2H_5 \end{matrix}$$

Ketones that have large and complex radicals often react very slowly, and reduction is then frequently observed.

$$\begin{matrix} R \\ R' \end{matrix}{>}C{=}O + RCH_2CH_2MgX \longrightarrow \begin{matrix} R \\ R' \end{matrix}{>}CHOMgX + RCH{=}CH_2$$

Acids contain one active hydrogen atom and react with RMgX to give the salt and 1 mole of hydrocarbon. The salt will react with any excess reagent; in this way ketones form, but they are attacked by the reagent and converted to carbinols.

$$RC\begin{matrix} {=}O \\ {-}OH \end{matrix} + R'MgX \longrightarrow R'H + RC\begin{matrix} {=}O \\ {-}OMgX \end{matrix}$$

$$RC\begin{matrix} {=}O \\ {-}OMgX \end{matrix} + R'MgX \longrightarrow \left[\begin{matrix} R & & OMgX \\ & C & \\ R' & & OMgX \end{matrix}\right] \longrightarrow \left[\begin{matrix} R \\ R' \end{matrix}{>}C{=}O\right]$$

$$\left[\begin{matrix} R \\ R' \end{matrix}{>}C{=}O\right] + R'MgX \longrightarrow \begin{matrix} R \\ R'{-}COMgX \\ R' \end{matrix} \xrightarrow{H_2O} \begin{matrix} R \\ R'{-}COH \\ R' \end{matrix}$$

This method is not often used because it is wasteful of the reagent.

Esters, as indicated earlier (p. 110), generally lead to the formation of tertiary alcohols.

Formates give secondary alcohols, through the formation and reaction of aldehydes.

$$R'MgX + HC\begin{matrix} \nearrow O \\ \searrow OR \end{matrix} \longrightarrow \left[H\text{-}C\begin{matrix} \nearrow OMgX \\ \swarrow R' \quad \searrow OR \end{matrix} \right] \longrightarrow [R'CHO]$$

$$[R'CHO] + R'MgX \longrightarrow \begin{matrix} R' \\ R' \end{matrix} \!\!> CHOMgX \xrightarrow{H_2O} \begin{matrix} R' \\ R' \end{matrix} \!\!> CHOH$$

Ethyl carbonate is used to prepare tertiary alcohols in which all three radicals are alike.

$$C{=}O\begin{matrix} \nearrow OC_2H_5 \\ \searrow OC_2H_5 \end{matrix} \xrightarrow{RMgX} \xrightarrow{H_2O} R_3COH$$

Acid chlorides react very rapidly with Grignard reagents. Advantage may be taken of this in the synthesis of ketones.

$$RC\begin{matrix} \nearrow O \\ \searrow Cl \end{matrix} + R'MgX \longrightarrow \left[\begin{matrix} R \\ R' \end{matrix} \!\!> C < \!\! \begin{matrix} OMgX \\ Cl \end{matrix} \right] \longrightarrow \begin{matrix} R \\ R' \end{matrix} \!\!> C{=}O + MgXCl$$

$$\begin{matrix} R \\ R' \end{matrix} \!\!> C{=}O + R'MgX \longrightarrow \begin{matrix} R \\ R' \\ R' \end{matrix} \!\!> COMgX \longrightarrow \begin{matrix} R \\ R' \\ R' \end{matrix} \!\!> COH$$

If the process is properly conducted the ketone can be isolated. Similar results are obtained with acid anhydrides.

$$\begin{matrix} RC(=O) \\ RC(=O) \end{matrix} \!\!> O + R'MgX \longrightarrow \left[\begin{matrix} R \\ R' \end{matrix} \!\!> C < \!\! \begin{matrix} OMgX \\ O\text{-}C(=O)\text{-}R \end{matrix} \right] \longrightarrow \begin{matrix} R \\ R' \end{matrix} \!\!> C{=}O$$

The use of an excess of reagent converts both acid chlorides and anhydrides to the corresponding tertiary alcohols.

Amides of the types $RC(=O)\text{-}NH_2$ and $RC(=O)\text{-}NHR$ have active hydrogen atoms and decompose the reagent. Ketones may be obtained from them in satisfactory yields, however, by the use of three or four equivalents of reagent and long periods of heating. Useful synthetic methods employing amides of the type $RC(=O)-NR_2$ have been developed. The reagent reacts with amides to give fairly stable intermediates which can be isolated and decomposed to give ketones.

$$RC(=O)NR_2 + R'MgX \longrightarrow RR'C(OMgX)NR_2$$

$$RR'C(OMgX)NR_2 \xrightarrow{H_2O} RR'C{=}O + MgXOH + RNH_2$$

Formamides lead to the production of aldehydes (Bouveault's method).

$$HC(=O)N(C_2H_5)_2 \xrightarrow{RMgX} RC(=O)H$$

Carbon dioxide is useful in the synthesis of acids from the Grignard reagent.

$$RMgX + O{=}C{=}O \longrightarrow RC(=O)OMgX \xrightarrow{HX} RC(=O)OH$$

This reaction is run at low temperatures to prevent transformation of the salt into the carbinol.

$$RC(=O)OMgX + RMgX \longrightarrow \left[R_2C(OMgX)_2\right] \longrightarrow R_2C{=}O$$

$$R_2C{=}O + RMgX \longrightarrow R_3COMgX$$

Dry Ice can be used advantageously since it not only furnishes the carbon dioxide but acts as a refrigerant as well. Moreover, the reagent can be poured on the Dry Ice, thus obtaining a more favorable concentration of the reactants. The synthesis finds use in the preparation of acids from secondary and tertiary halides, which do not react with alkali cyanide to give nitriles.

TABLE XXVIII

1,2 AND 1,4 ADDITION

	Per Cent of 1,4 Addition	
	C_2H_5MgBr	C_6H_5MgBr
$CH_2{=}CHCHO$	0	0
$CH_3CH{=}CHCOCH_3$	75	40
$(CH_3)_2C{=}CHCOCH_3$	0	0
$C_6H_5CH{=}CHCOCH_3$	60	12
$C_6H_5CH{=}CHCOCH_2CH_3$	71	40
$C_6H_5CH{=}CHCOCH(CH_3)_2$	100	88
$C_6H_5CH{=}CHCOC(CH_3)_3$	100	100
$C_6H_5CH{=}CHCOC_6H_5$	99	94
$C_6H_5C{\equiv}CCOC_6H_5$	...	0

Ketones and esters containing conjugated systems of the type C=C–C=O may react with the Grignard reagent either in the 1,2 or the 1,4 manner.

$$RCH{=}CHC(=O)R' + R''MgX \xrightarrow{1,2} RCH{=}CHC(OMgX)(R')R''$$

$$RCH{=}CHC(=O)R' + R''MgX \xrightarrow{1,4} (R)(R'')CHCH{=}C(OMgX)R'$$

The mode of the addition depends on the nature of R,R′, and R″. If R is large, 1,2 addition is favored. If R′ is large, 1,4 addition is favored. Aliphatic reagents (R″ equals alkyl) favor 1,4 addition whereas aromatic reagents (R″ equals aryl) favor 1,2 addition. Frequently both 1,2 and 1,4 addition occur simultaneously. The examples given in Table XXVIII illustrate these generalizations.

1,4 Addition is also known to occur in lateral-nuclear systems such as are found in benzalquinaldine and α,β-diphenylbenzalacetophenone.

$$\text{(2-quinolyl)CH=CHC}_6\text{H}_5 \xrightarrow{\text{C}_6\text{H}_5\text{MgBr}} \xrightarrow{\text{H}_2\text{O}} \text{(2-quinolyl)CH}_2\text{CH(C}_6\text{H}_5)_2$$

$$(\text{C}_6\text{H}_5)_2\text{C=C(C}_6\text{H}_5)\text{—C(=O)C}_6\text{H}_5 \xrightarrow{\text{C}_6\text{H}_5\text{MgBr}} (\text{C}_6\text{H}_5)_2\text{C=C(C}_6\text{H}_5)\text{—C(OMgBr)=C}\langle\text{CH=CH—CH=CH—CH(C}_6\text{H}_5)\rangle$$

The latter reaction does not take place under ordinary conditions; to bring it about most of the ether is replaced by benzene and the higher-boiling solution is allowed to reflux. This procedure is called "forcing."

Among the most reactive carbonyl compounds are the ketenes and the isocyanates. They react rapidly with the Grignard reagent and yield, respectively, ketones and amides.

$$\text{CH}_2\text{=C=O} + \text{RMgX} \longrightarrow \text{CH}_2\text{=C}\begin{matrix}\text{OMgX}\\\text{R}\end{matrix} \xrightarrow{\text{H}_2\text{O}} \left[\text{CH}_2\text{=C}\begin{matrix}\text{OH}\\\text{R}\end{matrix}\right] \longrightarrow \text{CH}_3\text{C(=O)—R}$$

$$\text{RN=C=O} + \text{R'MgX} \longrightarrow \text{RN=C}\begin{matrix}\text{OMgX}\\\text{R'}\end{matrix} \xrightarrow{\text{H}_2\text{O}} \left[\text{RN=C}\begin{matrix}\text{OH}\\\text{R'}\end{matrix}\right] \longrightarrow \text{RNHC}\begin{matrix}\text{O}\\\text{R'}\end{matrix}$$

The Grignard reagent reacts with nitriles to give imine derivatives from which ketones are formed by hydrolysis.

$$\text{RC}\equiv\text{N} + \text{R'MgX} \longrightarrow \begin{matrix}\text{R}\\\text{R'}\end{matrix}\text{C=NMgX} \xrightarrow{\text{H}_2\text{O}} \begin{matrix}\text{R}\\\text{R'}\end{matrix}\text{C=NH} \xrightarrow{\text{H}_2\text{O}} \begin{matrix}\text{R}\\\text{R'}\end{matrix}\text{C=O}$$

The method is applicable to aliphatic nitriles in which R is primary and larger than methyl. Aromatic nitriles also undergo the reaction.

The electronic formula of sulfur dioxide indicates that at least one oxygen atom is linked to the sulfur atom by a double bond.

$$\text{O=S=O} \quad \text{or} \quad \text{O}\leftarrow\text{S=O}$$

The addition reaction with the Grignard reagent is that which would be predicted. The products are sulfinic acids (p. 446).

$$RMgX + SO_2 \longrightarrow RS\begin{matrix}\diagup OMgX \\ \diagdown O\end{matrix} \xrightarrow{H_2O} RSO_2H$$

The use of the Grignard reagent with polyfunctional molecules brings up the question of relative reactivities of the groups. Enteman and Johnson, using phenylmagnesium bromide, have established the following order.

$$-CHO > -COCH_3 > -NCO > -COF > -COC_6H_5 > -COCl > -COBr > -CO_2C_2H_5 > -C{\equiv}N$$

The fact that $-COF$ stands ahead of $-COCl$ appears to show that the reaction is additive and not metathetical.

4. Cyclic Ethers. Ethers in general are unaffected by the Grignard reagent, but three- and four-membered cyclic ethers undergo reaction with accompanying opening of the ring. Ethylene oxide is used to lengthen the carbon chain.

$$\overset{\diagup O \diagdown}{CH_2{-}CH_2} + RMgX \longrightarrow RCH_2CH_2OMgX \xrightarrow{H_2O} RCH_2CH_2OH$$

Propylene oxide reacts similarly but yields secondary alcohols.

$$\underset{\diagdown O \diagup}{CH_3CH{-}CH_2} + RMgX \longrightarrow \underset{OMgX}{CH_3CHCH_2R} \xrightarrow{H_2O} \underset{OH}{CH_3CHCH_2R}$$

Although trimethylene oxide reacts to form primary alcohols, it has not found general application in the lengthening of carbon chains; the yields are not high and the oxide has been a relatively rare reagent.

$$\underset{\diagdown O \diagup}{CH_2CH_2CH_2} + RMgX \longrightarrow RCH_2CH_2CH_2OMgX \xrightarrow{H_2O} RCH_2CH_2CH_2OH$$

5. Ortho Esters. Orthoformic esters react with Grignard reagents to give acetals of aldehydes.

$$HC\begin{matrix}\diagup OR \\ -OR \\ \diagdown OR\end{matrix} + R'MgX \longrightarrow R'{-}\underset{H}{C}\begin{matrix}\diagup OR \\ -OR\end{matrix} + Mg\begin{matrix}\diagup OR \\ \diagdown X\end{matrix}$$

This has been used in the preparation of aldehydes.

Orthocarbonic esters, similarly, lead to acetals of ketones.

$$\mathrm{RO{-}C(OR)_2{-}OR} + 2\mathrm{R'MgX} \longrightarrow \mathrm{R'_2C(OR)_2} + 2\mathrm{Mg(OR)X}$$

This reaction has found little application in synthesis.

6. Alkylation by Means of the Grignard Reagent. Compounds such as allyl bromide and benzyl chloride which contain very reactive halogen atoms are alkylated by interaction with RMgX.

$$\mathrm{CH_2{=}CHCH_2Br + RMgX \longrightarrow RCH_2CH{=}CH_2 + MgXBr}$$

$$\mathrm{C_6H_5CH_2Cl + RMgX \longrightarrow C_6H_5CH_2R + MgXCl}$$

The important method of Lespieau and Bourguel is based on this reaction. Bromoallyl bromide reacts with butylmagnesium bromide, for example, to give a bromoheptene which is converted to 1-heptyne by the action of alkali.

$$\mathrm{C_4H_9MgX + BrCH_2C(Br){=}CH_2 \longrightarrow C_4H_9CH_2C(Br){=}CH_2 \longrightarrow C_5H_{11}C{\equiv}CH}$$

α-Halogen ethers are alkylated readily.

$$\mathrm{RCH(Cl)OCH_2R + R'MgX \longrightarrow RCH(R')OCH_2R + MgXCl}$$

Esters of sulfonic acids resemble alkyl halides in this respect.

$$\mathrm{RSO_3R' + R''MgX \longrightarrow R'{-}R'' + RSO_3MgX}$$

Alkyl sulfates behave similarly. n-Propylbenzene is made in yields of 70 to 75 per cent by the interaction of benzylmagnesium chloride and ethyl sulfate.

$$\mathrm{C_6H_5CH_2MgCl + 2(C_2H_5)_2SO_4 \longrightarrow C_6H_5CH_2CH_2CH_3 + C_2H_5Cl + (C_2H_5SO_4)_2Mg}$$

Similarly, isodurene is formed by treating mesitylmagnesium bromide with methyl sulfate.

$$\mathrm{(CH_3)_3C_6H_2MgBr + 2(CH_3)_2SO_4 \longrightarrow (CH_3)_3C_6H_2CH_3 + CH_3Br + (CH_3SO_4)_2Mg}$$

A useful application of this method is found in alkylation by means of γ-chloropropyl sulfonates.

$$RSO_3{-}CH_2CH_2CH_2Cl + C_6H_5CH_2MgCl \longrightarrow C_6H_5CH_2CH_2CH_2CH_2Cl + RSO_3MgCl$$

Many inorganic halides are alkylated by treatment with RMgX.

$$AsCl_3 + 3RMgX \longrightarrow R_3As + 3MgXCl$$
$$HgCl_2 + 2RMgX \longrightarrow R_2Hg + 2MgXCl$$
$$SbCl_3 + 3RMgX \longrightarrow R_3Sb + 3MgXCl$$
$$BiCl_3 + 3RMgX \longrightarrow R_3Bi + 3MgXCl$$
$$SnCl_4 + 4RMgX \longrightarrow R_4Sn + 4MgXCl$$
$$2PbCl_2 + 4C_2H_5MgBr \longrightarrow (C_2H_5)_4Pb + Pb + 4MgClBr$$

7. Coupling of the Grignard Reagent. Certain inorganic halides react in such a way as to couple the alkyl groups of the reagent. Thus cupric chloride converts benzylmagnesium chloride largely to bibenzyl.

$$2C_6H_5CH_2MgCl + 2CuCl_2 \longrightarrow C_6H_5CH_2CH_2C_6H_5 + 2CuCl + 2MgCl_2$$

Silver bromide is particularly effective; by its use high yields have been obtained of coupling products such as biphenyl, bianisyl, *n*-octane, and bicyclohexyl. Other metal salts also have been used. In all such reactions the salt acts as an oxidizing agent.

Organic halides also may bring about coupling. For example, benzyl chloride reacts with methylmagnesium iodide to give bibenzyl in yields of about 75 per cent.

$$2C_6H_5CH_2Cl + 2CH_3MgI \longrightarrow C_6H_5CH_2CH_2C_6H_5 + C_2H_6 + 2MgICl$$

A certain amount of alkylation also is observed.

$$C_6H_5CH_2Cl + CH_3MgI \longrightarrow C_6H_5C_2H_5 + MgICl$$

Most of the coupling reactions of the latter type involve benzyl halides or their derivatives. Benzal chloride and benzotrichloride are interesting examples. With methylmagnesium iodide they yield, respectively, stilbene chloride and tolane tetrachloride.

$$2C_6H_5CHCl_2 + 2CH_3MgI \longrightarrow C_6H_5CHClCHClC_6H_5 + CH_3CH_3 + 2MgICl$$

$$2C_6H_5CCl_3 + 2CH_3MgI \longrightarrow C_6H_5CCl_2CCl_2C_6H_5 + CH_3CH_3 + 2MgICl$$

It is remarkable that hindered benzoyl chlorides undergo coupling of this type also. From mesitoyl chloride and methylmagnesium iodide mesitil is obtained.

$$2\,CH_3\text{-}C_6H_2(CH_3)_2\text{-}COCl + 2CH_3MgI \longrightarrow CH_3\text{-}C_6H_2(CH_3)_2\text{-}COCO\text{-}C_6H_2(CH_3)_2\text{-}CH_3 + CH_3CH_3 + 2MgICl$$

Mesitoyl chloride — Mesitil

Azo compounds react with the Grignard reagent in a peculiar manner. Each nitrogen atom takes up MgX, and the alkyl groups couple or undergo disproportionation.

$$C_6H_5N{=}NC_6H_5 + 2RMgX \longrightarrow C_6H_5N(MgX)\text{—}N(MgX)C_6H_5 + 2R\cdot$$

$$2R\cdot \longrightarrow R\text{–}R \quad \text{(coupling)}$$

$$2R'CH_2CH_2\cdot \longrightarrow R'CH_2CH_3 + R'CH{=}CH_2 \quad \text{(disproportionation)}$$

Like the coupling with metal salts, the over-all process is one of oxidation-reduction. In the equations just given the free radical R· is assumed to be the first product of the oxidation of the Grignard reagent.

8. Rearrangements. Grignard reagents prepared from allyl halides furnish carbanions which are resonance hybrids. The resonance structures from an unsubstituted allyl halide are, of course, identical.

$$CH_2{=}CH\text{–}CH_2Br \longrightarrow CH_2{=}CH\text{–}CH_2MgBr$$

$$\rightleftharpoons MgBr^+ + CH_2{=}CH\text{–}\bar{C}H_2 \longleftrightarrow \bar{C}H_2\text{–}CH{=}CH_2$$

Similarly, for the ion from a 2-substituted allyl halide identical resonance structures may be written. However, a 1- or 3-substituted allyl halide leads to a carbanion in which the charge may be located on either of two carbon atoms of unlike substitution.

$$RCH{=}CH\text{–}CH_2Br \longrightarrow RCH{=}CHCH_2MgBr$$

$$\rightleftharpoons MgBr^+ + RCH{=}CH\bar{C}H_2 \longleftrightarrow R\bar{C}H\text{–}CH{=}CH_2$$

It thus happens that reactions of certain allylic Grignard reagents lead to mixtures of two products; for example, when the Grignard reagent from cinnamyl chloride is carbonated two acids are formed.

$$C_6H_5CH{=}CHCH_2Cl \xrightarrow{Mg} \text{Grignard reagent}$$

$$\xrightarrow{CO_2} \xrightarrow{H_2O} C_6H_5CH{=}CHCH_2CO_2H + C_6H_5\underset{\underset{CO_2H}{|}}{CH}{-}CH{=}CH_2$$

The principal product from this reaction is the second one.

The reaction of benzylmagnesium chloride with formaldehyde produces *o*-tolylcarbinol instead of *β*-phenethyl alcohol.

$$C_6H_5CH_2MgCl + CH_2O \longrightarrow \begin{cases} \rightarrow C_6H_5CH_2CH_2OH \\ \rightarrow o\text{-}CH_3C_6H_4CH_2OH \end{cases}$$

Certain other reagents, such as benzaldehyde, acetyl chloride, and ethyl chloroformate, also lead to products containing the *o*-tolyl group. Still others, such as ketones, ethyl orthoformate, and carbon dioxide, yield only products containing the benzyl group. The rearrangement in these reactions, like that in the simpler allylic systems, can be explained by the theory of resonance; on this basis the rearrangement involves two steps, addition of the carbanion and a 1,3-shift of a hydrogen atom, as follows.

$$C_6H_5CH_2^- \longleftrightarrow (\text{ring}{=}CH_2,\ \text{ortho } ^-\text{, H}) \xrightarrow{CH_2O} (\text{ring}{=}CH_2,\ \text{ortho } CH_2O^-\text{, H}) \longrightarrow o\text{-}CH_3C_6H_4{-}CH_2O^-$$

In an alternative explanation it is assumed that the reaction is initiated by the coordination of the carbonyl oxygen atom with the magnesium atom of the Grignard reagent in the covalent state.

$$C_6H_5CH_2{-}Mg{-}Cl + \overset{O}{\overset{\|}{CH_2}} \longrightarrow C_6H_5CH_2{-}\underset{Cl}{Mg} \leftarrow O{=}CH_2$$

The 1,3-shift of the benzyl group with its electron pair from the magnesium atom to the electrophilic carbon atom of the formaldehyde would result in the normal product, *β*-phenylethyl alcohol. The attraction of the formaldehyde carbon atom for electrons from the neighboring benzene ring might account for the rearrangement product.

$$C_6H_5CH_2MgCl \cdot O{=}CH_2 \longrightarrow C_6H_5CH_2CH_2OMgCl$$

$$C_6H_5CH_2MgCl \cdot O{=}CH_2 \longrightarrow CH_2{=}C_6H_5(H)(CH_2OMgCl) \longrightarrow o\text{-}CH_3C_6H_4CH_2OMgCl$$

9. Other Reactions of the Grignard Reagent. Ketones and esters whose carbonyl groups are relatively unreactive toward the reagent often give rise to reactions other than addition. Three types of these so-called abnormal reactions have been observed: reduction, enolization, and condensation. Which of the four reactions will take place depends largely on the nature of the radicals adjoining the carbonyl group and in the Grignard reagent.

TABLE XXIX

Reactions of the Grignard Reagent

	CH_3MgI	n-C_3H_7MgBr	$(CH_3)_2CHMgBr$	$(CH_3)_3CMgCl$
CH_3CHO	AA		A	AA
$(CH_3)_2CHCHO$	A		AA	AR
$(CH_3)_3CCHO$		AA	AR	RR
$CH_3COC(CH_3)_3$	AA		EC	EC
$(CH_3)_2CHCOCH(CH_3)_2$	AA		RR	RR
$C_6H_5CH_2CO_2C_2H_5$			EECC	
$(CH_3)_3CCO_2C_2H_5$				no reaction

When primary alkyl groups are present the addition or normal reaction always predominates. Complications arise, however, when branched radicals are involved. Table XXIX shows some of these effects. A, R, E, and C denote, respectively, addition, reduction, enolization, and condensation; if the yield is 50 per cent or better the letter is doubled. An equation illustrating reduction has been given earlier (p. 284). The enolization is well illustrated by the behavior of acetomesitylene; the product is the enolate.

$$CH_3C_6H_2(CH_3)_2COCH_3 + RMgX \longrightarrow CH_3C_6H_2(CH_3)_2C(OMgX){=}CH_2 + RH$$

The condensations observed are of the acetoacetic ester type.

$$2C_6H_5CH_2CO_2C_2H_5 \xrightarrow{RMgX} C_6H_5\underset{\displaystyle COCH_2C_6H_5}{\underset{|}{C}}HCO_2C_2H_5 + C_2H_5OH$$

It is necessary to use lithium alkyls rather than Grignard reagents to prepare alcohols containing more than two secondary or tertiary alkyl groups.

Other Organometallic Compounds

All the alkali metals form organometallic compounds. These are usually made by the action of the metal on the R_2Hg or R_2Zn compound.

$$(CH_3)_2Zn + 2Na \rightleftharpoons 2CH_3Na + Zn$$

They react in much the same way as Grignard reagents. Carbon dioxide, for example, converts them to the sodium salts of acids.

$$CH_3Na + CO_2 \longrightarrow CH_3CO_2Na$$

They are thought to be intermediates in the Wurtz-Fittig reaction (p. 262), which is useful for the formation of ArR compounds.

$$ArX + 2Na \longrightarrow ArNa + NaX \quad \text{(fast)}$$
$$RX + 2Na \longrightarrow RNa + NaX \quad \text{(slow)}$$
$$ArNa + RX \longrightarrow ArR + NaX \quad \text{(fast)}$$
$$ArNa + ArX \longrightarrow ArAr + NaX \quad \text{(slow)}$$

The use of arylsodiums is often convenient. In preparing triphenylcarbinol from ethyl benzoate and chlorobenzene, magnesium is nearly useless whereas sodium gives a very good yield. Presumably phenylsodium is the reagent involved in this condensation.

The lithium compounds may be prepared by the action of the metal on RX.

$$p\text{-}(CH_3)_2NC_6H_4Br + 2Li \longrightarrow p\text{-}(CH_3)_2NC_6H_4Li + LiBr$$

Ether solutions of aryl- and alkyllithiums can be prepared in almost the same manner as the corresponding Grignard solutions. The use of lithium instead of magnesium often increases the value of the organometallic reagent, the lithium compound being more reactive or reacting in a different way. The use of alkyllithiums in the synthesis of secondary and tertiary carbinols having branched groups has been mentioned (p. 295); another example of the utility of the lithium compounds is seen in the reaction of benzalacetophenone with phenyllithium, which proceeds chiefly in the 1,2 manner.

The halogen-metal interchange, described above (p. 259), is often useful for the preparation of lithium compounds that cannot be made directly.

Organozinc compounds are less reactive than the corresponding magnesium compounds. This is well illustrated by the fact that dialkylzincs can be handled in an atmosphere of carbon dioxide. The zinc derivatives generally have been superseded in synthetic work by magnesium compounds. However, they appear to offer definite advantages in some types of preparations.

The synthesis of hydrocarbons of the type R_4C can be accomplished in yields of 25 to 50 per cent by treating a tertiary alkyl halide with a dialkylzinc. An example is dimethyldiethylmethane.

$$2\ \begin{matrix} CH_3\diagdown \\ CH_3-CCl \\ C_2H_5\diagup \end{matrix} + (C_2H_5)_2Zn \longrightarrow 2(CH_3)_2C(C_2H_5)_2 + ZnCl_2$$

The Blaise method for making ketones consists in the interaction of an acid chloride and an alkylzinc iodide.

$$RCOCl + CH_3ZnI \longrightarrow RCOCH_3 + ZnICl$$

The Reformatsky Reaction. Closely allied to certain of the Grignard condensations is the Reformatsky reaction. It involves the condensation of an α-halo ester with an aldehyde or ketone by use of metallic zinc. An example is the formation of ethyl β-hydroxy-α,α-dimethylbutyrate from acetaldehyde and ethyl α-bromoisobutyrate. The reaction creates a new carbon-to-carbon linkage and appears to take place in three steps. An organozinc halide is formulated as the initial product.

$$Br\overset{\displaystyle CH_3}{\underset{\displaystyle CH_3}{\overset{|}{\underset{|}{C}}}}-CO_2C_2H_5 + Zn \longrightarrow BrZn\overset{\displaystyle CH_3}{\underset{\displaystyle CH_3}{\overset{|}{\underset{|}{C}}}}-CO_2C_2H_5$$

Addition of this compound to the carbonyl group of the aldehyde occurs next.

$$CH_3CHO + BrZn\overset{\displaystyle CH_3}{\underset{\displaystyle CH_3}{C}}\!-CO_2C_2H_5 \longrightarrow CH_3\overset{\displaystyle BrZnO}{C}H\overset{\displaystyle CH_3}{\underset{\displaystyle CH_3}{C}}\!-CO_2C_2H_5$$

The final step involves decomposition with dilute acid.

$$CH_3\overset{\displaystyle BrZnO}{C}H\overset{\displaystyle CH_3}{\underset{\displaystyle CH_3}{C}}\!-CO_2C_2H_5 + HX \longrightarrow CH_3\overset{\displaystyle OH}{C}H\overset{\displaystyle CH_3}{\underset{\displaystyle CH_3}{C}}\!-CO_2C_2H_5 + ZnXBr$$

Ethyl β-hydroxy-α,
α-dimethylbutyrate

Frequently the hydroxy ester is not isolated. Instead, the product is the corresponding unsaturated ester formed, presumably, by dehydration of the hydroxy ester. An illustration is the formation of ethyl sorbate from zinc, crotonaldehyde, and ethyl bromoacetate.

$$CH_3CH{=}CHCHO + BrCH_2CO_2C_2H_5$$

$$\longrightarrow CH_3CH{=}CH{-}CH{=}CHCO_2C_2H_5$$

Ethyl sorbate

Application of the Reformatsky method to ketones is illustrated by the preparation of ethyl β-hydroxy-β-phenylbutyrate from zinc, acetophenone, and ethyl bromoacetate.

$$C_6H_5COCH_3 + BrCH_2CO_2C_2H_5 \longrightarrow C_6H_5\overset{\displaystyle OZnBr}{\underset{\displaystyle CH_3}{C}}\!-CH_2CO_2C_2H_5$$

$$\xrightarrow{H_2O} C_6H_5\overset{\displaystyle OH}{\underset{\displaystyle CH_3}{C}}\!-CH_2CO_2C_2H_5$$

Ethyl β-hydroxy-β-phenylbutyrate

The use of zinc instead of magnesium in the Reformatsky method has the advantage that the organozinc intermediate has little tendency to attack ordinary esters. It is this fact which makes the method possible; otherwise, the organozinc compound would be unstable since it contains groups which would interact. It is true that a few esters can be used instead of aldehydes or ketones but these are formates, oxalates, or α-alkoxy esters—compounds in which the ester carbonyl group possesses unusually high activity. An extremely interesting example is the condensation of ethyl bromoacetate with ethyl formate.

$$C_2H_5OCHO + BrCH_2CO_2C_2H_5 \xrightarrow{Zn} C_2H_5O\overset{OZnBr}{\overset{|}{C}}HCH_2CO_2C_2H_5$$

$$\downarrow HX$$

$$C_6H_3(CO_2C_2H_5)_3 \longleftarrow O{=}CHCH_2CO_2C_2H_5$$

Ethyl trimesate

The expected aldehyde ester is not obtained. Under the conditions of the experiment it trimerizes to give ethyl trimesate.

Organocadmium compounds are still less reactive than organozinc compounds and have proved to be more useful than the zinc compounds for transforming acid chlorides into ketones.

Attempts to make organoiron compounds from Grignard reagents and iron halides were unsuccessful until cyclopentadienylmagnesium bromide was caused to react with ferric chloride. The usual reaction between a Grignard reagent and ferric chloride is a coupling, similar to the reaction with cupric chloride. The product obtained from cyclopentadienylmagnesium bromide proved to contain iron, having the composition $(C_5H_5)_2Fe$. It is an extraordinarily stable solid. It resists the action of water; in fact, it can be steam-distilled. It is similarly stable to alkali and strong acid. Oxidizing agents convert it to a blue salt, containing the cation $(C_5H_5)_2Fe^+$, from which the original substance can be regenerated by reduction.

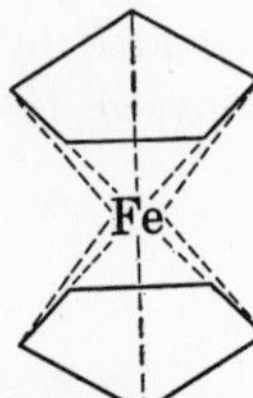

Ferrocene

FIG. 17.

These and other unexpected properties of the substance have led to the suggestion that it represents a new aromatic system of the structure shown in Fig. 17, and the name *ferrocene* has been proposed.

The most important technical use of organometallic compounds is that of tetraethyllead as an antiknock compound. It is made from ethyl chloride and sodium-lead alloy (p. 64).

$$4C_2H_5Cl \xrightarrow{Na(Pb)} (C_2H_5)_4Pb$$

Organomercury compounds have been made in numerous ways. A Grignard reagent acts on mercury bichloride to give the corresponding dialkylmercury.

$$2RMgX + HgCl_2 \longrightarrow R_2Hg + 2MgXCl$$

Diphenylmercury is made by treating bromobenzene with sodium amalgam.

$$2C_6H_5Br \xrightarrow{Na(Hg)} (C_6H_5)_2Hg$$

Many aromatic compounds may be mercurated by treatment with mercury salts (p. 471).

PROBLEMS

1. Outline useful synthetic methods for obtaining the following substances from readily available materials.

a. *p*-Iodotoluene.
b. *p*-Chlorobenzophenone.
c. Ethylmethylphenylacetic acid.
d. 1-Heptyne.
e. *n*-Propylbenzene.
f. Triphenylstibine.
g. 1,1-Diphenylethylene.
h. α-Naphthoic acid.
i. α-Bromocaproic acid.
j. 1-Bromo-2-phenylethane.

2. For each of the following compounds indicate a method of synthesis which involves a Grignard reagent.

a. $(C_4H_9)_3COH$

b. $CH_3\diagdown$ C_2H_5–COH $C_6H_5\diagup$

c. $(C_2H_5)_3CCO_2H$

d. $C_6H_5C(OH)(H)$—C_2H_5

e. $CH_3(CH_2)_6CH_2OH$

f. $C_6H_5CH_2SO_2H$

g. $CH_2\langle^{CH_2CH_2}_{CH_2CH_2}\rangle CHCH_2OH$

3. Write an equation for the reactions between methylmagnesium iodide and (*a*) aniline, (*b*) oxygen, (*c*) benzoin.

4. A sample of 0.098 g. of a compound whose formula is $C_{10}H_{12}O_4$ reacts with methylmagnesium iodide to give 22.3 ml. of methane under standard conditions. How many of the oxygen atoms are present as hydroxyl groups?

SUGGESTED READINGS

M. T. Goebel and C. S. Marvel, "The Oxidation of Grignard Reagents," *J. Am. Chem. Soc.*, *55*, 1693 (1933).

C. E. Enteman, Jr. and J. R. Johnson, "The Relative Reactivity of Various Functional Groups toward a Grignard Reagent," *J. Am. Chem. Soc.*, *55*, 2900 (1933).

J. B. Conant and A. H. Blatt, "The Action of the Grignard Reagent on Highly Branched Carbonyl Compounds," *J. Am. Chem. Soc.*, *51*, 1227 (1929).

M. S. Kharasch and S. Weinhouse, "Grignard Reagents—Their Reducing Action and Rates of Addition," *J. Org. Chem.*, *1*, 209 (1936).

H. Gilman, "Organometallic Compounds," Gilman's *Organic Chemistry*, Chapter 4, John Wiley & Sons, New York, 1943.

G. E. Coates, "Organometallic Compounds of the First Three Periodic Groups," *Quart. Revs. London*, *4*, 217 (1950).

H. Gilman and G. E. Dunn, "Relationships between Organic Compounds of Silicon and Carbon," *Chem. Revs.*, *52*, 77 (1953).

N. G. Gaylord and E. I. Becker, "The Reaction between Grignard Reagents and the Oxirane Ring," *Chem. Revs.*, *49*, 413 (1951).

R. L. Shriner, "The Reformatsky Reaction," *Org. Reactions*, *1*, 1 (1942).

CHAPTER 21

Reactions of the Carbonyl Group

The characteristic reactions of the carbonyl compounds are attributable to the polarization of the carbonyl function.

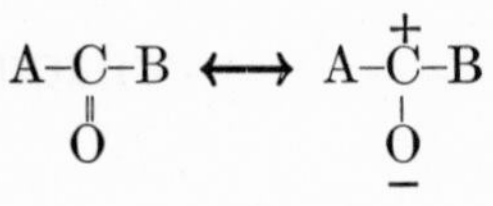

$$\underset{\overset{\|}{O}}{A{-}C{-}B} \longleftrightarrow \underset{\underset{-}{\overset{|}{O}}}{A{-}\overset{+}{C}{-}B}$$

The positively charged carbon atom in the polarized structure is highly electrophilic, and the reactions of simple carbonyl compounds with such reagents as water, alcohols, cyanide ion, and bisulfite ion may be regarded as, initially, processes of neutralization. The formation of hemiacetal is shown as an example.

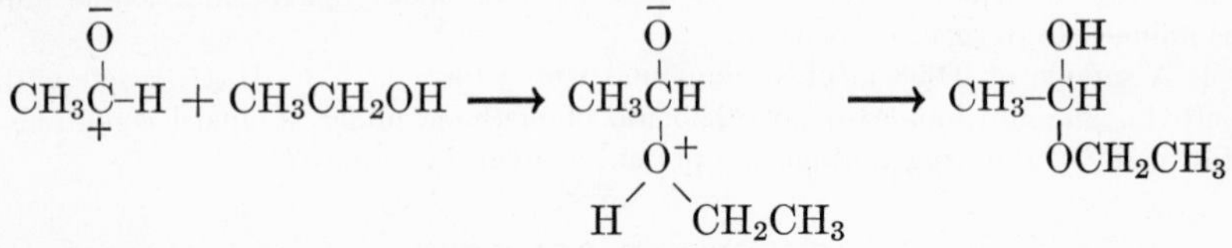

$$CH_3\overset{\overset{\bar{O}}{|}}{\underset{+}{C}}{-}H + CH_3CH_2OH \longrightarrow CH_3\overset{\overset{\bar{O}}{|}}{C}H{-}\overset{+}{O}(H)CH_2CH_3 \longrightarrow CH_3{-}\overset{\overset{OH}{|}}{C}H{-}OCH_2CH_3$$

Obviously, the reactivity of a given carbonyl group will depend in large measure upon the nature of the groups to which it is joined directly. If a strongly electron-donating group, such as amino or hydroxyl, is attached it will almost completely neutralize the carbonyl carbon atom. The result is that amides and acids are much less reactive as carbonyl compounds than are the aldehydes and ketones. The simple carbonyl compounds can be arranged in the following order of decreasing carbonyl reactivity: aldehydes > ketones > esters > acids > amides.

Electron-withdrawing atoms and groups often enhance the reactivity of carbonyl compounds. The following, for example, possess unusually reactive carbonyl groups.

$$CCl_3CHO \qquad RCOCHO \qquad CO(CO_2H)_2$$

Since the initial attack of the carbonyl function in reactions similar to the hemiacetal formation shown above is by a bulky molecule or anion it is not surprising to find that the reactivity of a given carbonyl group is strongly influenced by the steric as well as by the electronic nature of the two attached groups. Thus the following is the decreasing order of activity among aldehydes and ketones.

$$\begin{matrix}H\diagdown \\ \quad C{=}O \\ H\diagup\end{matrix} > \begin{matrix}R\diagdown \\ \quad C{=}O \\ H\diagup\end{matrix} > \begin{matrix}R\diagdown \\ \quad C{=}O \\ R\diagup\end{matrix}$$

Methyl ketones are more reactive than their higher homologs.

$$\begin{matrix}CH_3\diagdown \\ \quad CO \\ CH_3\diagup\end{matrix} > \begin{matrix}C_2H_5\diagdown \\ \quad CO \\ CH_3\diagup\end{matrix} > \begin{matrix}C_2H_5\diagdown \\ \quad CO \\ C_2H_5\diagup\end{matrix}$$

Also, cyclic ketones are more reactive than their open-chain analogs.

$$\begin{matrix}CH_2{-}CH_2\diagdown \\ | \qquad\qquad CO \\ CH_2{-}CH_2\diagup\end{matrix} > CH_3CH_2COCH_2CH_3$$

When the radicals are very large and complex the carbonyl group may become almost entirely inert. Dimesityl ketone is an example.

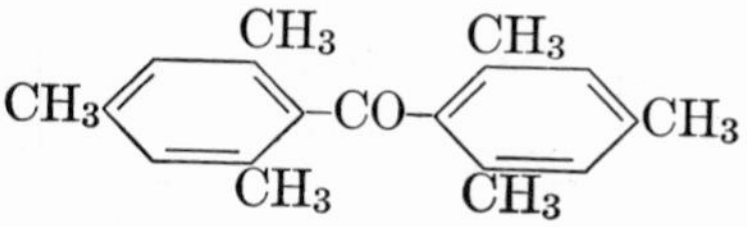

$$(CH_3)_3C_6H_2{-}CO{-}C_6H_2(CH_3)_3$$

Transformations of the Carbonyl Group

Water. Only extremely reactive carbonyl compounds form hydrates that can be isolated, but it is probable that the tendency is characteristic of all aldehydes and perhaps of ketones also.

$$\underset{\displaystyle H}{\overset{}{RC}}{=}O + H_2O \rightleftharpoons \underset{\displaystyle H}{RC}(OH)_2$$

Chloral forms a hydrate whose structure is known to be $Cl_3CCH(OH)_2$. Glyoxals react similarly: $RCOCHO + H_2O \longrightarrow RCOCH(OH)_2$. There is good reason to believe that formaldehyde is hydrated in water solution. The partial pressure of the aldehyde over its aqueous solution is far less than one would expect.

Alcohols. As was stated earlier (p. 82), aldehydes react with alcohols to form hemiacetals, and these in turn are converted to acetals (p. 82).

$$RCHO + R'OH \rightleftharpoons RCH\begin{matrix} \diagup OH \\ \diagdown OR' \end{matrix}$$

Hemiacetal

$$RCH\begin{matrix} \diagup OH \\ \diagdown OR' \end{matrix} + R'OH \rightleftharpoons RCH\begin{matrix} \diagup OR' \\ \diagdown OR' \end{matrix} + H_2O$$

Acetal

The rate of acetalization depends on the nature of the aldehyde as well as on that of the alcohol. Aromatic aldehydes react rapidly but give low yields on account of an unfavorable equilibrium. Many aliphatic aldehydes afford excellent yields, but the reaction is slower. The examples given in Table XXX illustrate these points.

TABLE XXX

ACETALS

Acetal	Amount of Acetal at Equilibrium	Reaction Rate Constant
Methyl butyral	96.4%	0.83×10^{-3}
Methyl acetal	93.8	1.02
Ethyl acetal	90.7	2.37
Ethyl isobutyral	83.5	1.56
t-Butyl acetal	31.2	11.34
Ethyl benzal	36.3	Ca. 100
Ethyl *m*-nitrobenzal	41.8	Ca. 200

Calcium chloride is a better catalyst for acetal formation than zinc or ferric chloride. Boron trifluoride and ammonium chloride are also useful catalysts.

Cyclic acetals or dioxolanes are formed by glycols.

$$CH_3CHO + \begin{matrix} HOCH_2 \\ | \\ HOCH_2 \end{matrix} \rightleftharpoons CH_3CH\begin{matrix} \diagup OCH_2 \\ | \\ \diagdown OCH_2 \end{matrix} + H_2O$$

α-Hydroxy acids are 1,2-dihydroxy compounds and, like 1,2-glycols, are capable of forming cyclic acetone derivatives. Mandelic acid, for example, combines with acetone under the influence of sulfuric acid to yield a dioxolone.

$$\underset{\text{OH}\ \ \text{OH}}{C_6H_5CH\text{-}C{=}O} + CH_3COCH_3 \longrightarrow C_6H_5CH\text{-}CO\ (\text{O},\ \text{O} \text{ bridged by } C(CH_3)_2) + H_2O$$

The dioxolone is closely related to esters and acetals. When treated with liquid ammonia it yields mandelamide.

Hydroxy aldehydes and ketones in which the two groups are not too far apart show a tendency to form cyclic hemiacetals. Glycolaldehyde and acetol are examples.

$$\underset{\text{OH}}{CH_2CHO} \rightleftharpoons CH_2\text{-}\underset{\text{OH}}{CH}\ (\text{ring through O})$$

Glycolaldehyde

$$CH_3COCH_2OH \rightleftharpoons CH_3\underset{\text{OH}}{C}\text{—}CH_2\ (\text{ring through O})$$

Acetol

This behavior is more marked in γ- and δ-hydroxy aldehydes and ketones which give rings of five and six members, respectively.

These reactions are especially important in sugar chemistry. The ring forms written for glucose and methylglucosides represent, respectively, a hemiacetal and an acetal.

Glucose (open)		Glucose (ring)		Methyl glucoside
HC=O		HC(OH)—		HC(OCH₃)—
HCOH		HCOH		HCOH
HOCH	$\rightleftharpoons$	HOCH O		HOCH O
HCOH		HCOH		HCOH
HCOH		HC—		HC—
CH_2OH		CH_2OH		CH_2OH

Glucose — Methyl glucoside

Of use also in sugar chemistry is the formation of cyclic acetals and ketals with benzaldehyde and acetone.

$$\begin{matrix}\text{HCOH}\\ |\\ \text{HCOH}\end{matrix} + C_6H_5CHO \rightleftharpoons \begin{matrix}\text{HC—O}\\ |\\ \text{HC—O}\end{matrix}\!\!>\!CHC_6H_5 + H_2O$$

$$\begin{matrix}\text{HCOH}\\ |\\ \text{HCOH}\end{matrix} + OC\!\begin{matrix}CH_3\\ CH_3\end{matrix} \rightleftharpoons \begin{matrix}\text{HC—O}\\ |\\ \text{HC—O}\end{matrix}\!\!>\!C\!\begin{matrix}CH_3\\ CH_3\end{matrix} + H_2O$$

Acetals are sensitive to acids but are unattacked by alkalies. Advantage is taken of the latter property to protect aldehyde groups. Aldehydes cannot be handled in contact with alkalies or oxidizing agents. The problem can be solved by converting them to acetals, from which they can be regained at a later point in the synthesis. The preparation of glyceraldehyde from acrolein illustrates this device.

$$CH_2{=}CHCHO + 2C_2H_5OH + HCl \longrightarrow ClCH_2CH_2CH(OC_2H_5)_2 + H_2O$$

$$ClCH_2CH_2CH(OC_2H_5)_2 + KOH \longrightarrow CH_2{=}CHCH(OC_2H_5)_2 + KCl + H_2O$$

$$CH_2{=}CHCH(OC_2H_5)_2 + H_2O + [O]\ (KMnO_4) \longrightarrow \underset{OH}{CH_2}{-}\underset{OH}{CH}CH(OC_2H_5)_2$$

$$\underset{OH}{CH_2}\underset{OH}{CH}CH(OC_2H_5)_2 + H_2O \xrightarrow{H_2SO_4} \underset{OH}{CH_2}\underset{OH}{CH}CHO + 2C_2H_5OH$$

Ketones form acetals but react less readily than aldehydes. The cyclic ketals, like the sugar derivative mentioned above, are the most readily obtained. In one procedure a solution of a ketone in ethylene glycol and benzene containing a trace of *p*-toluenesulfonic acid is refluxed in an apparatus connected to a water separator. The benzene serves to carry the water out of the reaction mixture, and its removal in the separator causes the reaction to go toward completion. Methyl γ-ketopimelate gives the ethylenedioxy derivative in about 60 per cent yield by this method.

$$CH_3O\overset{O}{\overset{\|}{C}}CH_2CH_2\overset{O}{\overset{\|}{C}}CH_2CH_2\overset{O}{\overset{\|}{C}}OCH_3 + HOCH_2CH_2OH$$

$$\xrightarrow{H^+} CH_3O\overset{O}{\overset{\|}{C}}CH_2CH_2{-}\overset{O{-}CH_2{-}CH_2{-}O}{C}{-}CH_2CH_2\overset{O}{\overset{\|}{C}}OCH_3 + H_2O$$

A remarkable feature of this preparation is that the ketal formation is accompanied by little or no transesterification (p. 108).

Monofunctional alcohols, as well as diols other than α-glycols, react less readily with ketones. For this reason, simple ketals are generally made by treating the ketones with an orthoformic ester.

$$\begin{matrix} CH_3 \\ CH_3 \end{matrix} \!\!> C{=}O + HC(OC_2H_5)_3 \longrightarrow \begin{matrix} CH_3 \\ CH_3 \end{matrix} \!\!> C <\!\! \begin{matrix} OC_2H_5 \\ OC_2H_5 \end{matrix} + HC \begin{matrix} \nearrow O \\ \searrow OC_2H_5 \end{matrix}$$

Mercaptans. Thiols are much more reactive toward carbonyl compounds than alcohols. Aldehydes react with mercaptans without catalyst to give hemimercaptals, which may react spontaneously, or, in the presence of added acidic catalyst, with a second molecule of mercaptan to form mercaptals. Although phenols do not yield acetals with aldehydes, thiophenol reacts readily even with ketones. The reaction with acetone occurs in the cold in the presence of hydrogen chloride.

$$\begin{matrix} CH_3 \\ CH_3 \end{matrix} \!\!> C{=}O + 2C_6H_5SH \xrightarrow{H^+} \begin{matrix} CH_3 \\ CH_3 \end{matrix} \!\!> C <\!\! \begin{matrix} SC_6H_5 \\ SC_6H_5 \end{matrix} + H_2O$$

Amino Compounds. Like water and alcohols, amino compounds react with aldehydes to give addition compounds. Ammonia gives rise to the aldehyde ammonias (p. 79).

$$RCHO + NH_3 \rightleftharpoons RCH <\!\! \begin{matrix} OH \\ NH_2 \end{matrix}$$

Like the corresponding hydrates and alcoholates the aldehyde-ammonias are unstable, being readily broken down to ammonia and the aldehydes. They are useful in the purification of aldehydes.

Primary and secondary amines add to formaldehyde to produce methylol derivatives which are stable.

$$RNH_2 + CH_2O \longrightarrow RNHCH_2OH$$

Carbonyl compounds which have a marked tendency to enolize react with ammonia and amines to yield nitrogen derivatives which may be formulated as imines or amines.

$$RCOCH_2CO_2R + RNH_2 \longrightarrow \underset{}{R\overset{\overset{NR}{\parallel}}{C}{-}CH_2CO_2R} \quad \text{or} \quad R\overset{\overset{NHR}{|}}{C}{=}CHCO_2R$$

Evidence favors the latter structure.

The exceptional behavior of formaldehyde with ammonia has already been mentioned (p. 79).

Benzaldehyde does not give a simple addition compound with ammonia but a complex molecule, hydrobenzamide, formed from three molecules of aldehyde and two of ammonia.

$$3C_6H_5CHO + 2NH_3 \longrightarrow \underset{\text{Hydrobenzamide}}{C_6H_5CH <\!\! \begin{matrix} N{=}CHC_6H_5 \\ N{=}CHC_6H_5 \end{matrix}} + 3H_2O$$

Hydrobenzamide is related to Schiff bases, substances formed by the interaction of aldehydes and primary amines. Benzalaniline is an example.

$$C_6H_5CHO + C_6H_5NH_2 \rightleftharpoons \underset{\text{Benzalaniline}}{C_6H_5CH{=}NC_6H_5} + H_2O$$

Benzalaniline is easily reduced to benzylaniline.

$$C_6H_5CH{=}NC_6H_5 + H_2 \xrightarrow{Ni} C_6H_5CH_2NHC_6H_5$$

Amines are often obtained in good yields when solutions of carbonyl compounds and ammonia are subjected to reduction. For example, α-phenethylamine is prepared in this way. The occurrence of the reaction suggests that ammonia adds to the carbonyl group of acetophenone and other ketones, even though the addition products cannot be isolated. The fact that tertiary amines can be made from carbonyl compounds and secondary amines by reduction, as shown in the second example below, indicates that the addition products can undergo reduction directly.

$$C_6H_5C(=O)CH_3 + NH_3 \rightleftharpoons C_6H_5C(OH)(CH_3)NH_2 \rightleftharpoons C_6H_5C(CH_3){=}NH + H_2O$$

$$C_6H_5C(OH)(CH_3)NH_2 \xrightarrow[Ni]{H_2} C_6H_5CH(CH_3)NH_2 \xleftarrow[Ni]{H_2} C_6H_5C(CH_3){=}NH$$

$$(CH_3CH_2)_2NH + CH_3CHO \xrightarrow[Ni]{H_2} (CH_3CH_2)_3N + H_2O$$

Both these reactions are carried out with hydrogen and nickel catalyst. The process, known as reductive alkylation, is of value for the synthesis of amines of many types.

Hydroxylamine probably reacts in the same way as ammonia, but water is eliminated and oximes result (p. 80).

$$R_2C{=}O + NH_2OH \rightleftharpoons \left[R_2C(OH){-}NHOH\right] \rightleftharpoons R_2C{=}NOH + H_2O$$

This reaction is reversible. It is general for aldehydes and ketones.

The oximes of aldehydes and unsymmetrical ketones exist in *syn* and *anti* forms which correspond to *cis-trans* isomers. In most instances the configurations of oximes of ketones have been assigned on the basis of the products obtained by subjecting them to the action of certain acidic reagents such as phosphorus pentachloride in ether. An isomerization known as the Beckmann rearrangement occurs. The products are amides, and the reaction of a symmetrical ketoxime can be represented as follows.

$$\begin{matrix} R \diagdown & & \\ & C{=}N & \longrightarrow \text{RCONHR} \\ R' \diagup & \;\; | & \\ & \;\; OH & \end{matrix}$$

If the ketoxime is unsymmetrical, two products, R′CONHR and RCONHR′, might be expected. Actually one of these is obtained from the *syn* oxime and the other from the *anti* oxime. The course of this rearrangement has been studied with great care, and it is now known that the shift of groups is *anti* rather than *syn*. The following scheme has been used to represent the sequence of changes.

$$\begin{matrix} R{-}\underset{\underset{NOH}{\|}}{C}{-}R' & \longrightarrow & R'{-}\underset{\underset{RN}{\|}}{C}{-}OH & \longrightarrow & R'{-}\underset{\underset{NHR}{|}}{C}{=}O \end{matrix}$$

$$\begin{matrix} R{-}\underset{\underset{HON}{\|}}{C}{-}R' & \longrightarrow & HO{-}\underset{\underset{NR'}{\|}}{C}{-}R & \longrightarrow & R{-}\underset{\underset{NHR'}{|}}{C}{=}O \end{matrix}$$

Many of the reagents that bring about the Beckmann transformation are capable of forming intermediate products resembling esters by reaction with the oxime hydroxyl group; such reagents are sulfuric acid, polyphosphoric acid, and thionyl chloride. It has been suggested that the rearrangement is caused by the tendency of such intermediates to ionize. As a positive charge develops on the nitrogen atom one of the organic residues shifts *with its electron pair* to neutralize it. If the ionization and the migration are simultaneous, it is understandable that the migrating group becomes attached to the nitrogen atom at the face opposite that which originally held the hydroxyl group. The Beckmann rearrangement thus seems related to the Walden inversion (p. 224).

$$\begin{matrix} R{-}\underset{\underset{N{-}O{-}SO_3H}{\|}}{C}{-}R & \longrightarrow & \underset{\underset{R{-}N}{\|}}{\overset{+}{C}}{-}R \;\; + \bar{O}SO_3H & \longrightarrow & HO_3SO{-}\underset{\underset{R{-}N}{\|}}{C}{-}R \end{matrix}$$

$$\xrightarrow{H_2O} H_2SO_4 + \underset{\underset{RN}{\|}}{HOCR} \longrightarrow \underset{\underset{RNH}{|}}{OCR}$$

The Beckmann rearrangement is useful in determining the structure of ketones. Hydrolysis of the amide gives an acid and an amine; from these the structure of the original ketone is deduced.

This rearrangement is of value in synthetic work. An industrial example is the synthesis of ε-caprolactam from the oxime of cyclohexanone.

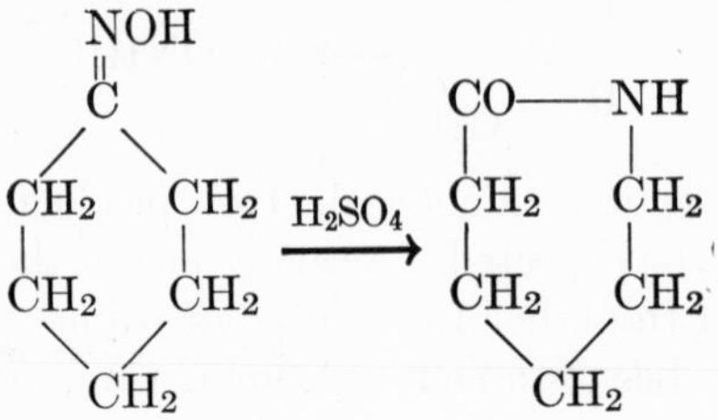

$$\begin{array}{c} NOH \\ \| \\ C \\ \diagup \quad \diagdown \\ CH_2 \quad CH_2 \\ | \qquad | \\ CH_2 \quad CH_2 \\ \diagdown \quad \diagup \\ CH_2 \end{array} \xrightarrow{H_2SO_4} \begin{array}{c} CO\text{——}NH \\ | \qquad | \\ CH_2 \quad CH_2 \\ | \qquad | \\ CH_2 \quad CH_2 \\ \diagdown \quad \diagup \\ CH_2 \end{array}$$

Oxime of cyclohexanone ε-Caprolactam

Hydrazine reacts with aldehydes and ketones to give hydrazones, which in turn may react with a second molecule of the carbonyl compound to yield azines.

$$R_2CO + H_2NNH_2 \longrightarrow \underset{\text{Hydrazone}}{R_2C{=}N{-}NH_2} + H_2O$$

$$R_2C{=}N{-}NH_2 + OCR_2 \longrightarrow \underset{\text{Azine}}{R_2C{=}N{-}N{=}CR_2} + H_2O$$

Aliphatic aldehydes react so rapidly that the intermediate hydrazones cannot be isolated; even by use of an excess of hydrazine the azine is practically the only product. Hydrazones of ketones tend to change to the azine and free hydrazine.

Phenylhydrazine reacts to give phenylhydrazones (p. 81).

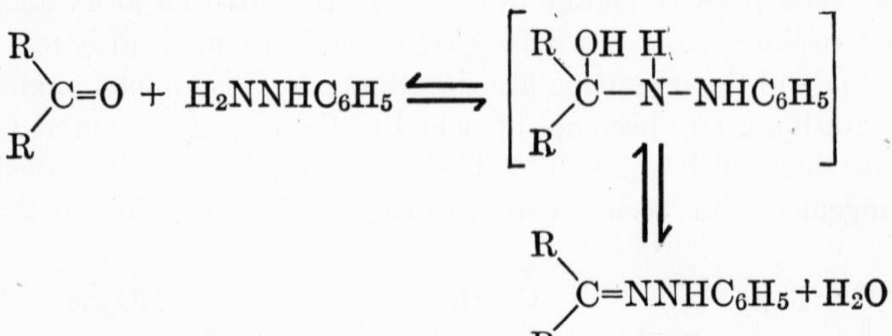

$$\begin{array}{l} R \\ \;\diagdown \\ \;\; C{=}O \\ \;\diagup \\ R \end{array} + H_2NNHC_6H_5 \rightleftharpoons \left[\begin{array}{l} R\;\; OH\;\; H \\ \;\diagdown\;\; | \quad\;\; | \\ \quad\; C{-}N{-}NHC_6H_5 \\ \;\diagup \\ R \end{array}\right]$$

$$\Big\downarrow\!\!\uparrow$$

$$\begin{array}{l} R \\ \;\diagdown \\ \;\; C{=}NNHC_6H_5 + H_2O \\ \;\diagup \\ R \end{array}$$

The reversibility is illustrated by one of the methods of recovering the carbonyl compounds from the hydrazone. This consists in heating the phenylhydrazone with a carbonyl compound such as a glyoxal which is highly reactive.

$$R_2C{=}NNHC_6H_5 + H_2O \rightleftharpoons R_2CO + H_2NNHC_6H_5$$

$$RCOCHO + H_2NNHC_6H_5 \longrightarrow RCOCH{=}NNHC_6H_5 + H_2O$$

α-Hydroxy aldehydes and ketones react with phenylhydrazine to give phenylosazones.

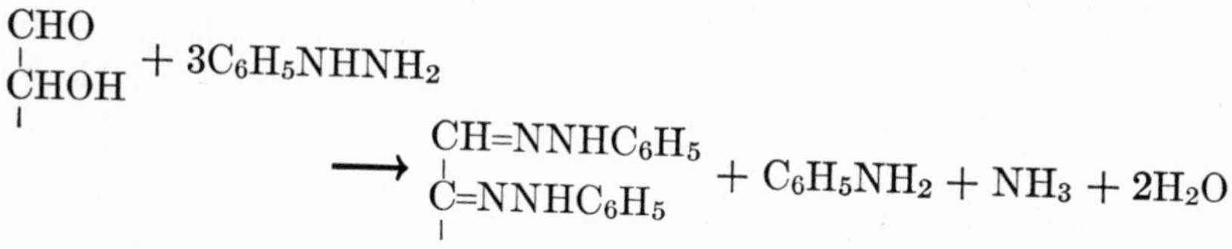

$$\begin{array}{l} CHO \\ | \\ CHOH \\ | \end{array} + 3C_6H_5NHNH_2 \longrightarrow \begin{array}{l} CH{=}NNHC_6H_5 \\ | \\ C{=}NNHC_6H_5 \\ | \end{array} + C_6H_5NH_2 + NH_3 + 2H_2O$$

These are yellow solids which crystallize well and are of great value in the purification and characterization of sugars.

2,4-Dinitrophenylhydrazine is much used in identification work because the 2,4-dinitrophenylhydrazones are generally solid.

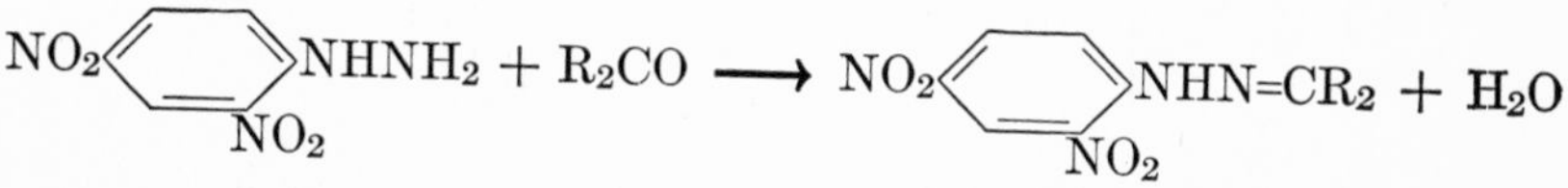

$$NO_2C_6H_3(NO_2)NHNH_2 + R_2CO \longrightarrow NO_2C_6H_3(NO_2)NHN{=}CR_2 + H_2O$$

β-Diketones and β-keto esters yield phenylhydrazones, but the reaction goes farther and gives cyclic products. Acetylacetone, for example, yields 1-phenyl-3,5-dimethylpyrazole.

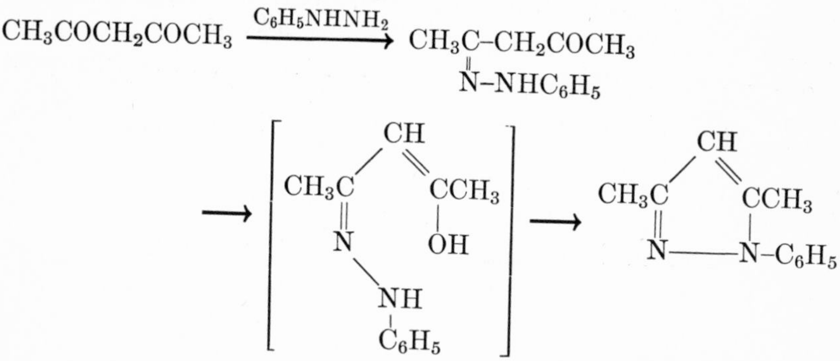

$$CH_3COCH_2COCH_3 \xrightarrow{C_6H_5NHNH_2} \begin{array}{l} CH_3C{-}CH_2COCH_3 \\ \;\;\;\;\| \\ \;\;\;\;N{-}NHC_6H_5 \end{array}$$

$$\longrightarrow \left[\begin{array}{ccc} & CH & \\ CH_3C & & CCH_3 \\ \| & & | \\ N & & OH \\ & NH & \\ & | & \\ & C_6H_5 & \end{array} \right] \longrightarrow \begin{array}{ccc} & CH & \\ CH_3C & & CCH_3 \\ \| & & | \\ N & \text{———} & N{-}C_6H_5 \end{array}$$

Ethyl acetoacetate reacts similarly to give 1-phenyl-3-methylpyrazolone.

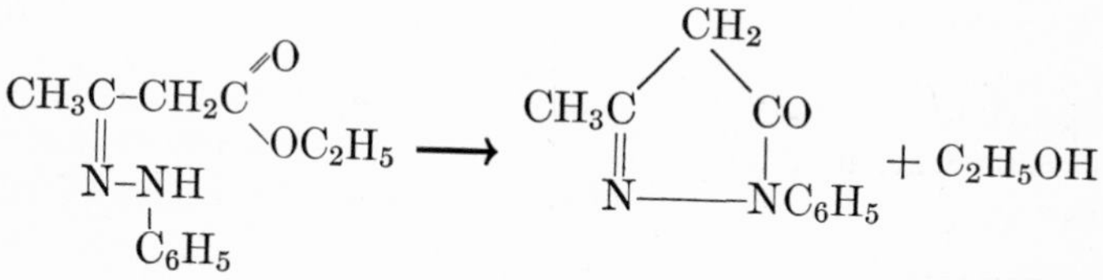

$$\begin{array}{l} CH_3C{-}CH_2C{\overset{\displaystyle O}{\underset{\displaystyle OC_2H_5}{}}} \\ \;\;\;\| \\ \;\;\;N{-}NH \\ \;\;\;\;\;\;\;\;| \\ \;\;\;\;\;\;\;\;C_6H_5 \end{array} \longrightarrow \begin{array}{ccc} & CH_2 & \\ CH_3C & & CO \\ \| & & | \\ N & \text{———} & NC_6H_5 \end{array} + C_2H_5OH$$

Similarly semicarbazide gives rise to semicarbazones (p. 81).

$$R_2C{=}O + H_2NNHCONH_2 \longrightarrow R_2C{=}NNHCONH_2 + H_2O$$

Girard's reagent, now much used in the isolation of ketonic compounds, is similar to the foregoing and has the advantage of being highly polar and, therefore, yields derivatives that are extremely soluble in water.

$$(CH_3)_3N + ClCH_2CO_2C_2H_5 + NH_2NH_2 \longrightarrow \underset{\text{Girard's reagent}}{[(CH_3)_3NCH_2CONHNH_2]Cl} + C_2H_5OH$$

With a ketone it reacts to give

$$\left[(CH_3)_3NCH_2CONHN{=}C\begin{matrix}R\\R\end{matrix}\right]Cl$$

Sodium Bisulfite. Aldehydes, aliphatic (but not aryl) methyl ketones, and cyclic ketones up to cycloöctanone yield sodium bisulfite addition compounds (p. 83).

$$RCHO + NaHSO_3 \longrightarrow RCH\begin{matrix}OH\\SO_3Na\end{matrix}$$

Table XXXI shows the amounts of bisulfite addition compounds formed at the end of 20 and 70 minutes. The bisulfite addition com-

TABLE XXXI

BISULFITE ADDITION COMPOUNDS

	Per Cent Bisulfite Compound	
	20 min.	70 min.
Acetaldehyde	86.6	88.7
Acetone	39.7	58.9
Methyl ethyl ketone	22.5	38.4
Methyl propyl ketone	11.0	25.5
Methyl isopropyl ketone	5.4	13.0
Pinacolone	5.6	5.6

pounds of formaldehyde and of acetaldehyde have been proved to be the hydroxy sulfonates; i.e., the sulfur atom is joined directly to carbon as indicated in the general formula $RCH\begin{smallmatrix}\diagup OH\\ \diagdown SO_3Na\end{smallmatrix}$. Bisulfite addition compounds are reconverted to the aldehydes or ketones by either acids or bases.

Hydrogen Cyanide. Hydrogen cyanide reacts additively with aldehydes and many ketones to give cyanohydrins (p. 84). The reaction is general for aldehydes but is limited in the ketone series. Cyanohydrins are formed by acetone, diethyl ketone, and pinacolone, but not by diisopropyl ketone. The rate of addition is often greatly increased by the presence of a trace of a base such as ammonia, piperidine, or quinoline.

The Strecker synthesis of amino acids involves a combination of this reaction with another in which the hydroxyl group is replaced by an amino group (p. 191).

$$RCHO + HCN \longrightarrow RCH\begin{smallmatrix}\diagup OH\\ \diagdown CN\end{smallmatrix} \xrightarrow{NH_3} \underset{\displaystyle NH_2}{RCHCN} \xrightarrow{H_2O} \underset{\displaystyle NH_2}{RCHCO_2H}$$

The condensation is carried out by treating an aldehyde with ammonium chloride and sodium cyanide.

The Grignard Reagent. The addition of the Grignard reagent to carbonyl compounds has already been discussed. The Reformatsky reaction mentioned earlier is very similar.

Oxidizing Agents. Aldehydes are readily oxidized. The Fehling, Tollens, and Benedict tests for aldehydes are based on this property (p. 77). One industrial synthesis of acetic acid involves air oxidation of acetaldehyde in the presence of manganous oxide (p. 60).

Many aldehydes undergo oxidation merely by standing in contact with the air. This is called autoxidation. It is prevented by the presence of certain substances known an antioxidants. Hydroquinone is commonly used for this purpose. There is evidence also that autoxidation is catalytic; pure benzaldehyde, for instance, does not undergo autoxidation. Autoxidation is often accompanied by chemiluminescence.

Reducing Agents. Aldehydes, ketones, and esters are all capable of being reduced but differ widely in the conditions necessary to bring about the reaction. Certain methods of reduction deserve special mention.

Under suitable conditions aldehydes and ketones may be hydrogenated to give the corresponding alcohols. The usual catalysts are platinum and nickel. Bimolecular reduction is also possible; the products are glycols. This type of reduction is characteristic of ketones and yields pinacols.

$$2\,\begin{matrix}R\diagdown \\ \quad CO \\ R\diagup\end{matrix} + 2H \longrightarrow \begin{matrix} R\diagdown \quad \diagup R \\ C{-}C \\ R\diagup | \quad | \diagdown R \\ OH\;OH \end{matrix}$$

It is of theoretical interest that bimolecular reduction of aldehydes is also possible. Saturated aldehydes give only traces of glycols, but α,β-unsaturated aldehydes and aromatic aldehydes undergo this type of reduction more readily. Acetaldehyde, acrolein, and benzaldehyde give, respectively, 2,3-butanediol, 1,5-hexadiene-3,4-diol, and hydrobenzoin.

$$2CH_3CHO + H_2 \longrightarrow CH_3\overset{OH}{\overset{|}{C}}H\overset{OH}{\overset{|}{C}}HCH_3$$

2,3-Butanediol

$$2CH_2{=}CHCHO + H_2 \longrightarrow \begin{matrix} CH_2{=}CHCHOH \\ | \\ CH_2{=}CHCHOH \end{matrix}$$

1,5-Hexadiene-3,4-diol

$$2C_6H_5CHO + H_2 \longrightarrow C_6H_5\overset{OH}{\overset{|}{C}}H\overset{OH}{\overset{|}{C}}HC_6H_5$$

Hydrobenzoin

Amalgamated magnesium is used frequently to produce pinacols.

$$2\,\begin{matrix}R\diagdown \\ \quad CO \\ R\diagup\end{matrix} + Mg \longrightarrow \begin{matrix} R\diagdown \qquad \diagup R \\ C{-\!-\!-}C \\ R\diagup | \qquad | \diagdown R \\ O{-}Mg{-}O \end{matrix} \xrightarrow{H_2O} \begin{matrix} R\diagdown \qquad \diagup R \\ C{-\!-\!-}C \\ R\diagup | \qquad | \diagdown R \\ OH \quad OH \end{matrix}$$

Benzopinacol can be made conveniently by photochemical reduction. Benzophenone is dissolved in isopropyl alcohol and the solution exposed to sunlight. Benzopinacol and acetone are formed.

$$2C_6H_5COC_6H_5 + (CH_3)_2CHOH \longrightarrow \begin{matrix}(C_6H_5)_2COH \\ | \\ (C_6H_5)_2COH\end{matrix} + CH_3COCH_3$$

Benzopinacol

The most convenient general method for reducing benzophenones to pinacols is by the use of the binary mixture $Mg + MgI_2$. The latter behaves as though it were magnesious iodide.

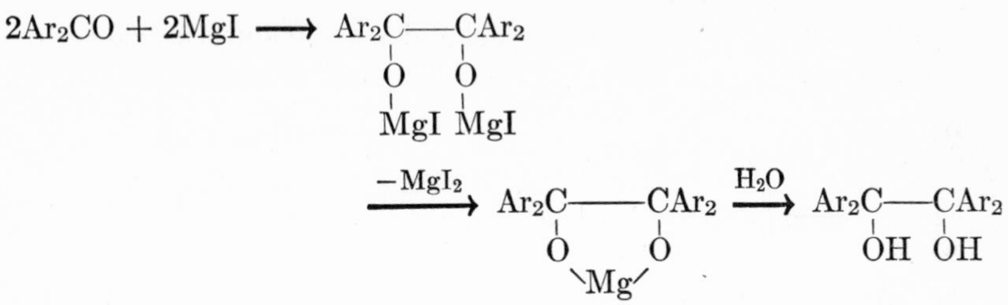

$$2Ar_2CO + 2MgI \longrightarrow \underset{\substack{| \\ O \\ | \\ MgI}}{Ar_2C}\!-\!\!-\!\!\underset{\substack{| \\ O \\ | \\ MgI}}{CAr_2}$$

$$\xrightarrow{-MgI_2} \underset{\substack{| \\ O}}{Ar_2C}\!-\!\!-\!\!\!-\!\!\underset{\substack{| \\ O}}{CAr_2} \;(\text{O's bridged by Mg}) \xrightarrow{H_2O} \underset{\substack{| \\ OH}}{Ar_2C}\!-\!\!-\!\!\underset{\substack{| \\ OH}}{CAr_2}$$

The most interesting reaction of the pinacols is the rearrangement they undergo when treated with acids. The process, known as the pinacol-pinacolone rearrangement, leads to ketones, as shown in the accompanying illustrations. It is believed that the rearrangement results from the fact that a carbonium ion is produced by removal of a hydroxyl group as an anion under the influence of the acidic reagent. One of the groups moves to the deficient carbon atom, with its electron pair, forming a new ion which is the protonated form of the ketone.

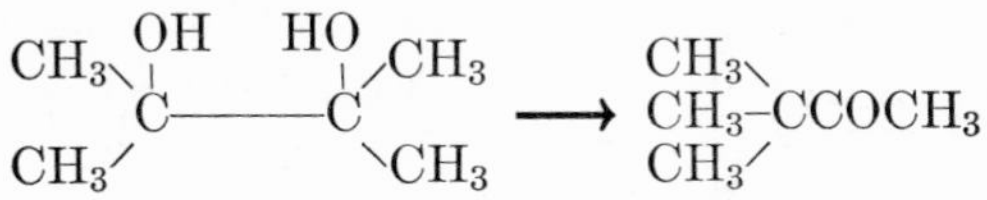

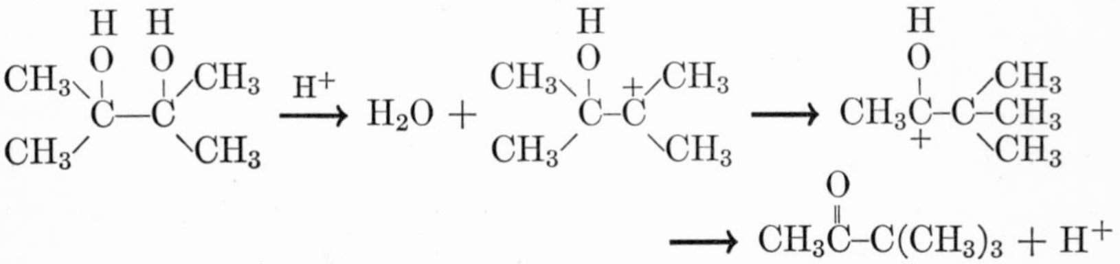

$$(CH_3)_2C(OH)\!-\!C(OH)(CH_3)_2 \longrightarrow (CH_3)_3C\!-\!COCH_3$$

Pinacol → Pinacolone

$$(C_6H_5)_2C(OH)\!-\!C(OH)(C_6H_5)_2 \longrightarrow (C_6H_5)_3CCOC_6H_5$$

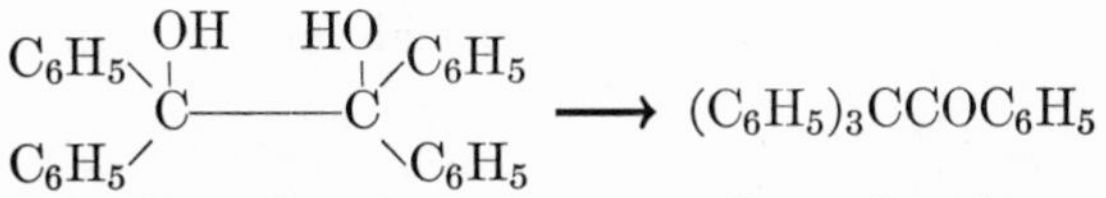

Benzopinacol → Benzopinacolone

$$(CH_3)_2C(OH)\!-\!C(OH)(CH_3)_2 \xrightarrow{H^+} H_2O + (CH_3)_2C(OH)\!-\!\overset{+}{C}(CH_3)_2 \longrightarrow CH_3\overset{+}{C}(OH)\!-\!C(CH_3)_3$$

$$\longrightarrow CH_3\overset{\overset{O}{\|}}{C}\!-\!C(CH_3)_3 + H^+$$

Zinc and hydrochloric acid reduce a carbonyl group to a methylene group. This is the Clemmensen method.

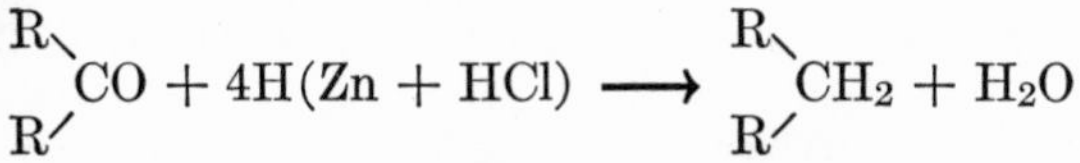

$$\begin{matrix} R \\ R' \end{matrix}\!\!>\!CO + 4H(Zn + HCl) \longrightarrow \begin{matrix} R \\ R' \end{matrix}\!\!>\!CH_2 + H_2O$$

It is especially useful in the introduction of saturated side chains into aromatic compounds. Hexylresorcinol and γ-phenylbutyric acid are examples. The ketones are readily available by the Friedel-Crafts method.

$$\text{HO-C}_6\text{H}_3(\text{OH})\text{-COC}_5\text{H}_{11} \longrightarrow \text{HO-C}_6\text{H}_3(\text{OH})\text{-C}_6\text{H}_{13}$$

Hexylresorcinol

$$C_6H_5CO(CH_2)_2CO_2H \longrightarrow C_6H_5(CH_2)_3CO_2H$$

γ-Phenylbutyric acid

Aldehydes and ketones may also be reduced to the corresponding hydrocarbons by the Wolff-Kishner method. The hydrazone is first formed and then decomposed catalytically by heating in a closed tube with potassium ethoxide or hydroxide. The sequence of reactions is as follows.

$$\begin{matrix} R \\ R' \end{matrix}\!\!>CO \xrightarrow{N_2H_4} \begin{matrix} R \\ R' \end{matrix}\!\!>C{=}NNH_2 \xrightarrow{KOH} \begin{matrix} R \\ R' \end{matrix}\!\!>CH_2 + N_2$$

The reaction is of wide application; it usually gives good results with aldehydes, ketones, cyclic ketones, keto acids, and unsaturated carbonyl compounds.

Zinc in the presence of aqueous sodium hydroxide is useful in reducing ketones to secondary alcohols. Thus benzophenone yields benzohydrol.

$$\begin{matrix} C_6H_5 \\ C_6H_5 \end{matrix}\!\!>CO + H_2(Zn + NaOH) \longrightarrow \begin{matrix} C_6H_5 \\ C_6H_5 \end{matrix}\!\!>CHOH$$

Esters may be reduced to primary alcohols either by sodium and alcohol or by catalytic hydrogenation.

$$RCO_2R' + 2H_2 \longrightarrow RCH_2OH + R'OH$$

Aluminum isopropoxide is a good reducing agent and seems to be specific for the carbonyl group. Ethylenic linkages, nitro groups, and other unsaturated groupings are unaffected. The reduction of cinnamaldehyde and *p*-nitrobenzaldehyde may be cited by way of illustration.

$$3C_6H_5CH{=}CHCHO + Al\left(OCH\begin{matrix} CH_3 \\ CH_3 \end{matrix}\right)_3 \longrightarrow (C_6H_5CH{=}CHCH_2O)_3Al + 3CH_3COCH_3$$

$$(C_6H_5CH{=}CHCH_2O)_3\,Al \xrightarrow{H_2O} C_6H_5CH{=}CHCH_2OH$$

$$NO_2\text{-}C_6H_4\text{-}CHO \xrightarrow{Al(OCH(CH_3)_2)_3} NO_2\text{-}C_6H_4\text{-}CH_2OH$$

The Cannizzaro Reaction. The Cannizzaro reaction (p. 89) involves both reduction and oxidation. When an aromatic aldehyde or formaldehyde is heated with alkali the corresponding alcohol and acid (as salt) are formed in equal amounts.

$$2HCHO + NaOH \longrightarrow CH_3OH + HCO_2Na$$

$$2ArCHO + NaOH \longrightarrow ArCH_2OH + ArCO_2Na$$

Advantage is taken of this in preparing certain benzyl alcohols by using formaldehyde and an aromatic aldehyde together. This is called a "crossed" Cannizzaro reaction.

$$CH_3C_6H_4CHO + CH_2O + KOH \longrightarrow CH_3C_6H_4CH_2OH + HCO_2K$$

The Cannizzaro reaction also occurs with other aliphatic aldehydes, though much less generally. *n*-Butyraldehyde and *n*-valeraldehyde, for example, undergo this reaction completely when heated with aqueous barium hydroxide for 14 hours at 150°.

Exceptional behavior is encountered with benzaldehyde derivatives in which the two *ortho* positions are occupied by chlorine, bromine, iodine, or fluorine. In these cases the aldehyde group is eliminated as formic acid. Nitro groups produce the same effect.

$$2,6\text{-}Cl_2C_6H_3CHO + KOH \longrightarrow m\text{-}C_6H_4Cl_2 + HCO_2K$$

Similarly 50 per cent potassium hydroxide solution cleaves 2,6-dichloroacetophenone to potassium acetate and *m*-dichlorobenzene.

$$2,6\text{-}Cl_2C_6H_3COCH_3 + KOH \longrightarrow m\text{-}C_6H_4Cl_2 + CH_3CO_2K$$

α-Keto aldehydes when treated with alkali undergo a reaction which is essentially an *intramolecular* Cannizzaro reaction. The product is the salt of a hydroxy acid.

$$RCOCHO + NaOH \longrightarrow RCH(OH)\text{-}CO_2Na$$

Glyoxylic acid likewise undergoes the Cannizzaro reaction. The products are sodium oxalate and sodium glycolate.

$$2\ \begin{array}{l} C\overset{\nearrow O}{-}H \\ | \\ C\overset{\nearrow O}{-}OH \end{array} + 3NaOH \longrightarrow \begin{array}{l} CH_2OH \\ | \\ CO_2Na \end{array} + \begin{array}{l} CO_2Na \\ | \\ CO_2Na \end{array} + 2H_2O$$

Glyoxylic acid

Glyoxylic acid is the simplest aldehyde acid. It can be made by the hydrolysis of dichloroacetic acid. It is of especial interest because it exists as the hydrate. This is true of the free acid and of its salts as well.

$$CHCl_2CO_2H + 2H_2O \longrightarrow (HO)_2CHCO_2H + 2HCl$$

Acyloin Formation. In ether solution esters react with sodium to give acyloins. The mechanism seems to involve the formation of a free radical which dimerizes; the dimer loses sodium alkoxide to give the α-diketone, which is reduced by metallic sodium to the enediolate. The free enediol (p. 203) rearranges to the acyloin. By this method butyroin, for example, may be made in 80 per cent yields.

$$C_3H_7C\begin{array}{l}\nearrow O \\ \searrow OC_2H_5\end{array} \xrightarrow{Na} \left[C_3H_7\overset{ONa}{\overset{|}{C}}OC_2H_5 \right] \longrightarrow \begin{array}{c} ONa \\ | \\ C_3H_7C{-}OC_2H_5 \\ | \\ C_3H_7C{-}OC_2H_5 \\ | \\ ONa \end{array} \xrightarrow{-2C_2H_5ONa}$$

$$\begin{array}{l} C_3H_7CO \\ | \\ C_3H_7CO \end{array} \xrightarrow{2Na} \begin{array}{l} C_3H_7CONa \\ \| \\ C_3H_7CONa \end{array} \longrightarrow \begin{array}{l} C_3H_7COH \\ \| \\ C_3H_7COH \end{array} \longrightarrow \begin{array}{l} C_3H_7CHOH \\ | \\ C_3H_7CO \end{array}$$

The method is general for esters; propionoin, isobutyroin, and pivaloin can be made in yields of 55, 75, and 60 per cent, respectively.

By using xylene or toluene as solvent to obtain higher reaction temperatures and consequent greater solubility of the sodium derivatives the method has been extended successfully to the synthesis of acyloins from twelve to thirty-six carbon atoms. The yields of all are high.

Glycolaldehyde or formoin is the simplest acyloin. Acetoin is available commercially, being made by a special fermentation process.

The Tishchenko Reaction. It was suggested by Tishchenko that the Cannizzaro reaction involves intermediate formation of an ester.

$$2C_6H_5CHO \longrightarrow C_6H_5C\overset{\nearrow O}{-}OCH_2C_6H_5$$

In the presence of alkali the ester would, of course, be saponified. If sodium benzoxide is used the ester is the chief product.

$$2C_6H_5CHO \xrightarrow{C_6H_5CH_2ONa} C_6H_5C(=O)OCH_2C_6H_5$$

In general, aldehydes may be converted to esters under the influence of metal alkoxides. For example, acetaldehyde in the presence of aluminum ethoxide yields ethyl acetate.

$$2CH_3CHO \xrightarrow{Al(OC_2H_5)_3} CH_3C(=O)OCH_2CH_3$$

This is known as Tishchenko's method and is general. However, it has found little use because the catalyst soon becomes "poisoned" and loses its activity.

Catalytic hydrogenation is widely used in reducing carbonyl compounds to alcohols. Other useful procedures involve tin and hydrochloric acid, sodium amalgam, iron and acetic acid, aluminum amalgam, and electrolytic methods.

Potassium Cyanide: The Benzoin Condensation. Aromatic aldehydes dimerize under the influence of an alkali cyanide to give benzoins.

$$2ArCHO \longrightarrow ArCOC(OH)(H)Ar$$

This is a general reaction of great importance. It is not limited to aromatic aldehydes but takes place with certain aliphatic aldehydes such as phenylglyoxal.

$$2C_6H_5COCHO \xrightarrow{KCN} C_6H_5COCOC(OH)(H)COC_6H_5$$

Phosphorus Pentachloride. This reagent converts aldehydes and ketones to the corresponding dichloro derivatives.

$$\begin{matrix} R \\ R' \end{matrix}\!\!>C{=}O + PCl_5 \longrightarrow \begin{matrix} R \\ R' \end{matrix}\!\!>CCl_2 + POCl_3$$

This reaction is general but finds little use. Its application in the synthesis of acetylenic compounds already has been noted.

Polymerization. Polymerization is characteristic of aldehydes. Formaldehyde, for example, forms paraformaldehyde or polyoxymethylene.

$$nCH_2O \longrightarrow (CH_2O)_n$$

The formula of the polymer is represented as follows.

$$---OCH_2OCH_2OCH_2OCH_2OCH_2OCH_2OCH_2---$$

Ring formation often halts polymerization. Acetaldehyde gives a liquid trimer, paraldehyde (p. 91). Metaldehyde, a solid tetramer of acetaldehyde, is apparently also a ring compound. Neither the trimer nor the tetramer reduces Fehling's solution. Both revert to acetaldehyde when heated.

The Willgerodt Reaction. Willgerodt found that alkyl aryl ketones could be converted to the amides of the corresponding ω-aryl fatty acids by treatment with yellow ammonium sulfide. For example, β-acetonaphthone yields the amide of β-naphthylacetic acid, and β-propionaphthone yields the amide of β-(β-naphthyl)-propionic acid.

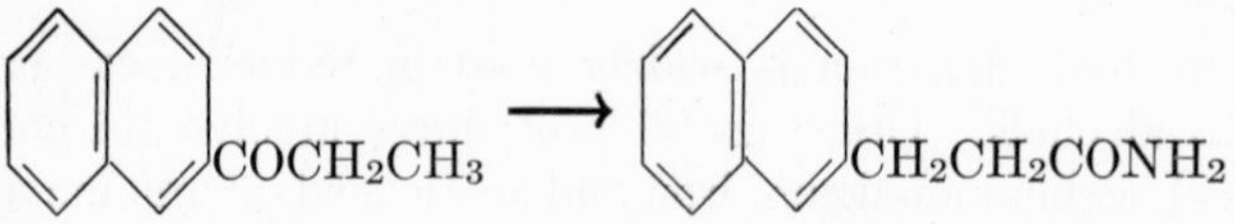

$$C_{10}H_7COCH_2CH_3 \longrightarrow C_{10}H_7CH_2CH_2CONH_2$$

It has been established that the reaction is not peculiar to ketones but occurs also with aldehydes, alcohols, olefins, and acetylenes.

PROBLEMS

1. By means of an equation indicate the reaction that takes place between

a. $(CH_3)_2CO$ and $NaHSO_3$

b. C_6H_5CHO and H_2NOH

c. $(C_6H_5)_2CO$ and sodium in ethyl alcohol

d. $CH_2\langle{}^{CH_2CH_2}_{CH_2CH_2}\rangle CO$ and $C_6H_5NHNH_2$

e. CH_3CH_2CHO and NH_4CN

2. Outline a method for making

a. $CH_3COCH_2CH_3$

b. $\begin{matrix}CH_2{-}CH_2\\ | \\ CH_2{-}CH_2\end{matrix}\rangle C(OCH_3)_2$

c. $CH_3CH(OC_2H_5)_2$

d. 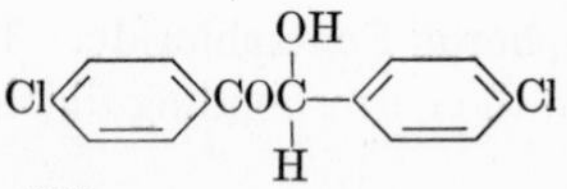 $Cl{-}C_6H_4{-}CO{-}CH(OH){-}C_6H_4{-}Cl$

e. 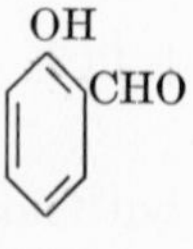 o-HOC_6H_4CHO

SUGGESTED READINGS

M. L. Moore, "The Leuckart Reaction," *Org. Reactions*, *5*, 301, 1949.

W. S. Emerson, "The Preparation of Amines by Reductive Alkylation," *Org. Reactions*, *4*, 174.

E. L. Martin, "The Clemmensen Reduction," *Org. Reactions*, *1*, 155, 1942.

CHAPTER 22

Substitution and Condensation Reactions of Carbonyl Compounds

Halogenation

Compounds that contain the group $-\overset{|}{\underset{\underset{\textstyle H}{|}}{C}}-C\overset{\diagup\!\!\!\diagup O}{\diagdown}$ can generally be halogenated easily to give monohalogen derivatives. This includes aldehydes and ketones, as well as acids and their derivatives. This type of halogenation is extremely useful in synthesis. The ease with which the reaction proceeds varies considerably and depends on the nature of the other groups in the molecule.

The bromination of acetone has been studied extensively and will serve as an illustration of this type of halogenation.

$$CH_3\overset{O}{\overset{\|}{C}}-CH_3 + Br_2 \longrightarrow CH_3\overset{O}{\overset{\|}{C}}-CH_2Br + HBr$$

The remarkable ease with which this type of compound undergoes bromination is due to the activating effect of the carbonyl group and is more or less proportional to the reactivity of this group. This is in keeping with the fact that the halogen atom always replaces a hydrogen atom on the α-carbon atom. If there is no α-hydrogen atom halogenation takes place no more readily than it does with saturated aliphatic hydrocarbons.

The only carbonyl compounds in which halogenation proceeds with difficulty are the acids. Even though an acid may contain one or more α-hydrogen atoms it will react only slowly with chlorine or bromine and not at all with iodine. This accords with the earlier observation that the carboxylic acids exist as chelated dimers and, thus, have no true carbonyl group.

In many acid derivatives such as acid chlorides and anhydrides resonance effects are less pronounced, and these substances can be halogenated with comparative ease. Methods for halogenating acids generally involve catalysts which produce the acid chlorides or anhydrides as intermediates. The classical procedure for doing this is to treat the acid with red phosphorus and chlorine or bromine and then water. In the bromination of acetic acid, for example, the reactions involved are the following.

$$3\mathrm{CH_3CO_2H} + \tfrac{9}{2}\,\mathrm{Br_2} + \mathrm{P} \longrightarrow 3\underset{\mathrm{Br}}{\underset{|}{\mathrm{CH_2}}}\mathrm{COBr} + \mathrm{H_3PO_3} + 3\mathrm{HBr}$$

$$\underset{\mathrm{Br}}{\underset{|}{\mathrm{CH_2}}}\mathrm{COBr} + \mathrm{H_2O} \longrightarrow \underset{\mathrm{Br}}{\underset{|}{\mathrm{CH_2}}}\mathrm{CO_2H} + \mathrm{HBr}$$

This is known as the Hell-Volhard-Zelinsky method.

It has since been recognized that the same result may be attained by use of a trace of a phosphorus trihalide as a catalyst. This produces some acid halide which is then halogenated and in turn reacts with unchanged acid to give more acid halide. The reactions involved in the bromination of an acid in the presence of a trace of phosphorus trichloride are as follows.

$$3\mathrm{RCH_2CO_2H} + \mathrm{PCl_3} \longrightarrow 3\mathrm{RCH_2COCl} + \mathrm{H_3PO_3}$$

$$\mathrm{RCH_2COCl} + \mathrm{Br_2} \longrightarrow \mathrm{R}\underset{\mathrm{Br}}{\underset{|}{\mathrm{C}}}\mathrm{HCOCl} + \mathrm{HBr}$$

$$\mathrm{R}\underset{\mathrm{Br}}{\underset{|}{\mathrm{C}}}\mathrm{HCOCl} + \mathrm{RCH_2CO_2H} \rightleftharpoons \mathrm{R}\underset{\mathrm{Br}}{\underset{|}{\mathrm{C}}}\mathrm{HCO_2H} + \mathrm{RCH_2COCl}$$

From these equations it is clear that only catalytic amounts of phosphorus trichloride are needed. This mechanism is supported by the fact that acid chlorides are known to form equilibrium mixtures with acids.

$$\mathrm{RCOCl} + \mathrm{R'CO_2H} \rightleftharpoons \mathrm{RCO_2H} + \mathrm{R'COCl}$$

It seems altogether probable then that in the Hell-Volhard-Zelinsky and other methods for halogenating acids operation is really on acid chlorides or anhydrides.*

Compounds which have a methylene ($\mathrm{CH_2}$) or methinyl (CH) group between two carbonyl groups have a great tendency to enolize and consequently are very easily halogenated. Dibenzoylmethane, for example, absorbs bromine very rapidly to give a dibromide.

* It should be pointed out that acid chlorides are themselves really acid anhydrides. Acetyl chloride, for example, is a mixed anhydride of acetic and hydrochloric acids. This explains the observation that acid chlorides and acid anhydrides have very similar chemical properties.

$$C_6H_5COCH_2COC_6H_5 + 2Br_2 \longrightarrow C_6H_5COCBr_2COC_6H_5 + 2HBr$$

Similarly ethyl acetoacetate yields the α-bromo derivative. It is particularly interesting that dry hydrogen bromide converts this ester to the corresponding γ-bromo derivative. Presumably the α-isomer reacts with hydrogen bromide to give bromine which replaces a γ-hydrogen atom.

$$CH_3COCH_2CO_2C_2H_5 + Br_2 \underset{\text{slow}}{\overset{\text{fast}}{\rightleftharpoons}} CH_3COCHBrCO_2C_2H_5$$

$$CH_3COCHBrCO_2C_2H_5 \xrightarrow{HBr} \underset{\displaystyle Br}{CH_2}COCH_2CO_2C_2H_5$$

Iodination of enolic compounds can be effected by treatment with iodine, hydrogen peroxide being used to remove the hydrogen iodide. Ethyl α-iodoacetoacetate is obtained in 90 per cent yields from ethyl acetoacetate.

It is possible to convert an aldehyde into the corresponding acid chloride by direct chlorination. *o*-Chlorobenzoyl chloride is made in this way.

$$o\text{-}ClC_6H_4CHO + Cl_2 \xrightarrow{140\text{–}160°} o\text{-}ClC_6H_4COCl + HCl$$

If the process is interrupted when half the theoretical amount of chlorine has been added and the reaction mixture is allowed to cool, a solid is formed which is an addition compound of the aldehyde with the acid chloride.

$$ClC_6H_4C(=O)H + ClC_6H_4C(=O){-}Cl \longrightarrow ClC_6H_4C(=O){-}OCH(Cl)C_6H_4Cl$$

This reaction between an aldehyde and an acid chloride to give a chloro ester is general.

The Haloform Reaction. A reaction which is characteristic of methyl ketones is that brought about by the action of hypohalities. It converts methyl ketones to the salts of the corresponding acids (p. 89).

$$RCOCH_3 + 3NaOX \longrightarrow RCO_2Na + HCX_3 + 2NaOH$$

Alcohols whose oxidation products are methyl ketones give this reaction also. Ethyl alcohol and acetaldehyde give it, but methanol does not.

β-Diketones may also yield haloforms. The process probably involves cleavage of the dihalogen derivative. An interesting example is the degradation of methone to β,β-dimethylglutaric acid.

$$(CH_3)_2C\begin{matrix} \diagup CH_2CO \\ \\ \diagdown CH_2CO \end{matrix}\!\!\!\!\!> CH_2 \longrightarrow \left[(CH_3)_2C\begin{matrix} \diagup CH_2CO \\ \\ \diagdown CH_2CO \end{matrix}\!\!\!\!\!> CX_2 \right]$$

Methone

$$\longrightarrow (CH_3)_2C\begin{matrix} \diagup CH_2CO_2Na \\ \\ \diagdown CH_2COCHX_2 \end{matrix} \longrightarrow (CH_3)_2C\begin{matrix} \diagup CH_2CO_2H \\ \\ \diagdown CH_2CO_2H \end{matrix}$$

β,β-Dimethylglutaric acid

Perhaps the most elegant use of the haloform degradation is the conversion of unsaturated ketones to the corresponding acids. Ordinary oxidizing agents would attack the ethylenic bond. Cinnamic acid can be made from benzalacetone by this method.

$$C_6H_5CH{=}CHCOCH_3 \longrightarrow C_6H_5CH{=}CHCO_2H$$

Oxidation

Aldehydes and ketones which have a methylene group next to the carbonyl group are oxidized to dicarbonyl compounds by selenium dioxide.

$$RCOCH_3 + SeO_2 \longrightarrow RCOCHO + Se + H_2O$$

The same transformation may be brought about by the use of nitrous acid. A ketoxime is formed and yields a dicarbonyl compound when hydrolyzed. The synthesis of methyl phenyl diketone is an example.

$$C_6H_5COCH_2CH_3 + HONO \longrightarrow C_6H_5CO\underset{\underset{NOH}{\|}}{C}CH_3 + H_2O$$

$$C_6H_5CO\underset{\underset{NOH}{\|}}{C}CH_3 + H_2O \longrightarrow C_6H_5COCOCH_3 + H_2NOH$$

Enolization

Enolization is characteristic of compounds which contain methylene, or methinyl groups situated between two carbonyl or similar unsaturated groups. Such groups exhibit unusual chemical reactivity, and are said to be "active." Malonic esters, acetoacetic esters, cyanoacetic esters, and 1,3-diketones such as acetylacetone and dibenzoylmethane are among the important examples.

$CH_3COCH_2CO_2C_2H_5$

Acetoacetic ester

$CH_2\langle^{CO_2C_2H_5}_{CN}$

Cyanoacetic ester

$CH_2(CO_2C_2H_5)_2$
Malonic ester

$CH_3COCH_2COCH_3$
Acetylacetone

$C_6H_5COCH_2COC_6H_5$
Dibenzoylmethane

The most important of these are ethyl acetoacetate and ethyl malonate, which have been considered earlier (p. 158). The properties of these substances will be set forth by reference to examples.

Condensation Reactions

Aldehydes, ketones, esters, anhydrides, and similar compounds containing active hydrogen atoms undergo many reactions involving the formation of carbon-carbon linkages. Various types have been studied; among these are the aldol, Perkin, Knoevenagel, acetoacetic ester, Michael, Claisen, Claisen-Schmidt, Dieckmann, Tollens, and Mannich reactions. Actually many of these types of reactions are so similar that differentiation is often difficult.

The most satisfactory classification which has been made separates these reactions into four categories: alkylation, the Claisen condensation, the aldol condensation, and the Michael condensation. The first three of these will be considered here; the Michael condensation will be discussed later (p. 347).

Alkylation

In the alkylation reaction (p. 159) the reactants are generally a reactive methylene compound, such as ethyl acetoacetate, and an alkyl halide. The reaction is usually effected by a base which presumably converts the active methylene compound into an enolate ion capable of acting as an electron donor. The alkylation of ethyl acetoacetate with *n*-butyl bromide may be used as an example.

$$CH_3COCH_2CO_2C_2H_5 \xrightarrow{\text{base}} CH_3\overset{\overset{\Large O}{\|}}{C}-\overset{\cdot\cdot}{\bar{C}}HCO_2C_2H_5 \quad (a)$$

$$\updownarrow$$

$$CH_3\overset{:\ddot{O}:^-}{\overset{|}{C}}=CHCO_2C_2H_5 \quad (b)$$

The enolate ion is a resonance hybrid of the structures *a* and *b*. It is alkylated by the alkyl halide, the reaction being most easily represented as involving structure *a*.

$$[CH_3CO\bar{C}HCO_2C_2H_5]Na^+ + RX \longrightarrow \underset{\displaystyle |\atop \displaystyle R}{CH_3COCHCO_2C_2H_5} + NaX$$

A second radical may be introduced if desired.

$$\left[\underset{\displaystyle |\atop \displaystyle R}{CH_3CO\bar{C}CO_2C_2H_5}\right]Na^+ + RX \longrightarrow CH_3CO\overset{\displaystyle R\atop \displaystyle |}{\underset{\displaystyle |\atop \displaystyle R}{C}}CO_2C_2H_5 + NaX$$

The two R groups so introduced may be alike or different. The introduction of the first alkyl radical greatly reduces the enolization tendency; this accounts for the fact that the second alkyl group tends to go in more slowly than the first.

With *n*-butyl bromide the following alkylation products are obtained.

$$CH_3CO\underset{\displaystyle |\atop \displaystyle C_4H_9}{C}HCO_2C_2H_5 \qquad CH_3CO\overset{\displaystyle C_4H_9\atop \displaystyle |}{\underset{\displaystyle |\atop \displaystyle C_4H_9}{C}}CO_2C_2H_5$$

The enol form of the monoalkyl derivative is less acidic than that of the original ester. This is very fortunate because it permits the alkylation of the latter in the presence of the former, thus making possible monoalkylation with very little dialkylation. The explanation is to be sought in the ability of the more strongly acidic enol to displace the weaker one from its salt.

$$CH_3\overset{\displaystyle OH\atop \displaystyle |}{C}{=}CHCO_2C_2H_5 + \left[CH_3\overset{\displaystyle O\atop \displaystyle |}{C}{=}\underset{\displaystyle |\atop \displaystyle R}{C}CO_2C_2H_5\right]Na$$

$$\longrightarrow CH_3CO\underset{\displaystyle |\atop \displaystyle R}{C}HCO_2C_2H_5 + \left[CH_3\overset{\displaystyle O\atop \displaystyle |}{C}{=}CHCO_2C_2H_5\right]Na$$

Primary and secondary alkyl halides give this reaction. Allyl and benzyl halides react very readily. Vinyl and aryl halides, however, do not react. Many other types of compounds react in the same way as do the alkyl halides. Acid chlorides and anhydrides give acylation products. Like other very reactive substances—such as α-halogen ethers, for example—acid halides and anhydrides cannot be used in alcohol solution.

Ethylene oxide or ethylene chlorohydrin reacts to give a lactone. The latter can be transformed into acetopropyl alcohol.

$$[CH_3COCHCO_2C_2H_5]Na + \underset{\diagdown O \diagup}{CH_2{-}CH_2} \longrightarrow \begin{array}{l} CH_3COCH{-}CO \\ \quad\;\; | \qquad \rangle O \\ \quad CH_2{-}CH_2 \end{array} + C_2H_5ONa$$

$$\begin{array}{l} CH_3COCH{-}CO \\ \quad\;\; | \qquad \rangle O \\ \quad CH_2{-}CH_2 \end{array} + H_2O \longrightarrow CH_3COCH_2CH_2CH_2OH + CO_2$$

Ethyl acetosuccinate is made by condensing the sodium derivative of ethyl acetoacetate with ethyl chloroacetate.

$$[CH_3COCHCO_2C_2H_5]Na + ClCH_2CO_2C_2H_5 \longrightarrow \underset{\text{Ethyl acetosuccinate}}{\begin{array}{l} CH_3COCHCH_2CO_2C_2H_5 \\ \qquad\quad | \\ \qquad CO_2C_2H_5 \end{array}} + NaCl$$

A reaction of especial interest takes place when the salt of ethyl acetoacetate or ethyl malonate is treated with iodine. Two molecules of ethyl acetoacetate are coupled together in the following manner.

$$2[CH_3COCHCO_2C_2H_5]Na \longrightarrow \begin{array}{l} CH_3COCHCO_2C_2H_5 \\ \qquad\quad | \\ CH_3COCHCO_2C_2H_5 \end{array} + 2NaI$$

This is probably an alkylation involving the intermediate formation of an iodo ester which acts as the alkylating agent. Ethyl malonate may be used as an example.

$$[CH(CO_2C_2H_5)_2]Na + I_2 \longrightarrow ICH(CO_2C_2H_5)_2 + NaI$$

$$[CH(CO_2C_2H_5)_2]Na + ICH(CO_2C_2H_5)_2 \longrightarrow \begin{array}{l} CH(CO_2C_2H_5)_2 \\ | \\ CH(CO_2C_2H_5)_2 \end{array} + NaI$$

This reaction has been used to form rings.

$$\left[\begin{array}{l} CH_2C(CO_2C_2H_5)_2 \\ | \\ CH_2 \\ | \\ CH_2C(CO_2C_2H_5)_2 \end{array}\right] Na_2 + I_2 \longrightarrow CH_2 \begin{array}{l} \diagup CH_2{-}C(CO_2C_2H_5)_2 \\ \qquad\qquad | \\ \diagdown CH_2{-}C(CO_2C_2H_5)_2 \end{array} + 2NaI$$

Ketones also may be alkylated. Sodium amide generally is used to form the enolate. From acetone methyl ethyl ketone may be made.

$$CH_3COCH_3 + NaNH_2 \longrightarrow [CH_3COCH_2]Na + NH_3$$

$$\Big\downarrow CH_3I$$

$$CH_3COCH_2CH_3$$

This process may be continued until six methyl groups have been introduced, forming hexamethylacetone, $(CH_3)_3CCOC(CH_3)_3$.

Chloromethyl ether is a very unusual alkylating agent, giving O-alkyl derivatives under ordinary conditions.

$$[CH_3COCHCO_2C_2H_5]Na + ClCH_2OCH_3 \longrightarrow \underset{\displaystyle OCH_2OCH_3}{CH_3\overset{}{C}}{=}CHCO_2C_2H_5 + NaCl$$

The Claisen Condensation

The Claisen type of condensation may be formulated as follows.

$$RC\begin{matrix}{\nearrow O}\\{\searrow Y}\end{matrix} + {>}CHCO \longrightarrow RC\overset{O}{\diagup}{-}C{-}CO + HY$$

The electron-donating component is usually an ester or ketone and $RC\begin{matrix}{\nearrow O}\\{\searrow Y}\end{matrix}$ is generally an ester, anhydride, or acid chloride. The acetoacetic ester and Dieckmann condensations are to be regarded as special cases of the Claisen condensation.

$$RC\begin{matrix}{\nearrow O}\\{\searrow OR}\end{matrix} + RCH_2C\begin{matrix}{\nearrow O}\\{\searrow OR}\end{matrix} \longrightarrow RC(=O){-}\underset{\displaystyle R}{CH}C(=O){-}OR + ROH$$

Whereas the Claisen condensation is usually effected by bases, an analogous reaction has been carried out between acetic anhydride and acetophenone with boron trifluoride as the catalyst.

$$\begin{matrix}CH_3C{=}O\\ {>}O\\ CH_3C{=}O\end{matrix} + CH_3COC_6H_5 \xrightarrow{BF_3} CH_3COCH_2COC_6H_5 + CH_3CO_2H$$

With active methylene compounds acid chlorides normally give C-acyl products but under certain special conditions O-acyl derivatives or enol esters may be produced. An example is the action of acetyl chloride on the sodium derivative of ethyl acetoacetate in the presence of pyridine.

$$[CH_3COCHCO_2C_2H_5]Na + CH_3COCl \xrightarrow{\text{pyridine}} CH_3\overset{\displaystyle OCOCH_3}{C}{=}CHCO_2C_2H_5 + NaCl$$

Benzoylation of ethyl acetoacetate leads to a diketo ester.

$$[CH_3COCHCO_2C_2H_5]Na + C_6H_5COCl \longrightarrow \begin{matrix} CH_3CO \\ C_6H_5CO \end{matrix}\!\!>\!CHCO_2C_2H_5 + NaCl$$

Hydrolysis with a very dilute solution of ammonia removes the acetyl group and serves as a preparative method for ethyl benzoylacetate.

$$\begin{matrix} CH_3CO \\ C_6H_5CO \end{matrix}\!\!>\!CHCO_2C_2H_5 + H_2O + NH_3 \longrightarrow C_6H_5COCH_2CO_2C_2H_5 + CH_3CO_2NH_4$$

Acetoacetic Ester Condensation. The essential feature of the acetoacetic ester condensation is the elimination of the OR radical from one molecule of an ester along with an α-hydrogen atom from another ester molecule. Mixtures of esters generally give mixtures of products. Thus ethyl acetate and ethyl propionate yield about equal amounts of the four possible products.

$$CH_3CH_2CO_2C_2H_5 + CH_3CO_2C_2H_5 \longrightarrow \begin{cases} CH_3CH_2COCH_2CO_2C_2H_5 \\ CH_3COCH_2CO_2C_2H_5 \\ CH_3CO\underset{\displaystyle CH_3}{\underset{|}{C}}HCO_2C_2H_5 \\ CH_3CH_2CO\underset{\displaystyle CH_3}{\underset{|}{C}}HCO_2C_2H_5 \end{cases}$$

Exceptional in this respect is ethyl oxalate, which, having no α-hydrogen atoms, cannot condense with itself in the Claisen manner.

The acetoacetic ester reaction is very general but ordinarily does not occur unless the ester in question has two α-hydrogen atoms. Condensation in the presence of sodium ethoxide is successful with ethyl propionate but fails with ethyl isobutyrate.

$$2CH_3CH_2CO_2C_2H_5 \xrightarrow{NaOC_2H_5} CH_3\underset{\displaystyle COCH_2CH_3}{\underset{|}{C}}HCO_2C_2H_5 + C_2H_5OH$$

However, ethyl isobutyrate will condense in the presence of mesitylmagnesium bromide or sodium triphenylmethyl.

$$2\,\begin{matrix} CH_3 \\ CH_3 \end{matrix}\!\!>\!CHCO_2C_2H_5 \xrightarrow{C_9H_{11}MgBr} \begin{matrix} CH_3 \\ CH_3 \end{matrix}\!\!>\!C\!\!<\!\begin{matrix} CO_2C_2H_5 \\ COCH(CH_3)_2 \end{matrix} + C_2H_5OMgBr + C_9H_{12}$$

The reversibility of the ester condensation is one of its distinguishing features. In the condensation of a simple ester like ethyl acetate the first step appears to be the formation of an anion by displacement of one of the α-hydrogen atoms. Only a minute concentration of the anion could be expected to result from the action of sodium ethoxide on ethyl acetate, since ethanol is a strong acid in comparison to the ester.

$$CH_3CO_2C_2H_5 + CH_3CH_2O^- \rightleftharpoons \bar{C}H_2CO_2C_2H_5 + C_2H_5OH$$

However, the carbanion formed immediately adds to another molecule of the ester. The addition product loses a molecule of ethanol to give the anion of acetoacetic ester.

$$CH_3\overset{\overset{O}{\|}}{C}{-}OC_2H_5 + \bar{C}H_2CO_2C_2H_5 \rightleftharpoons CH_3\underset{\underset{OC_2H_5}{|}}{\overset{\overset{O^-}{|}}{C}}{-}CH_2CO_2C_2H_5$$

$$\rightleftharpoons CH_3\overset{\overset{O^-}{|}}{C}{=}CHCO_2C_2H_5 + C_2H_5OH$$

In this last step there is formed the anion of an acid, acetoacetic ester, which is a much stronger acid than ethanol, the salt of which was used as the condensing agent. This fact determines the over-all equilibrium among the various reversible reactions. It is favorable to the formation of acetoacetic ester.

Another reaction that might be expected to accompany the formation of acetoacetic ester is further acylation to the diketo ester.

$$CH_3CO_2C_2H_5 + CH_3\overset{\overset{O}{\|}}{C}\bar{C}HCO_2C_2H_5$$

$$\rightleftharpoons \begin{matrix} CH_3CO \diagdown \\ \quad \bar{C}CO_2C_2H_5 \\ CH_3CO \diagup \end{matrix} + C_2H_5OH$$

The equilibrium here, however, favors the reverse reaction; the diketo ester is cleaved by alcohol in the presence of base. Thus little or none of it forms during the ordinary acetoacetic ester condensation. When it is necessary to introduce a second acyl group into a β-keto ester the acylating agent chosen is usually the acid chloride and the reaction is carried out in an inert solvent like benzene (p. 324).

It was indicated above that the acetoacetic ester condensation of an α,α-disubstituted ester like isobutyric ester cannot be accomplished with sodium ethoxide as the condensing agent. The explanation is that the product of the condensation, ethyl isobutyrylisobutyrate, having no hydrogen atom on the methylene carbon atom, is not a stronger acid than ethanol; accordingly the formation of the sodium salt of the condensation product, the process that furnishes the driving force in the condensation of ethyl acetate, cannot occur. The success of the reaction in the presence of a very strong base like sodium triphenylmethyl or mesitylmagnesium bromide results from the fact that the first step, the formation of the anion of isobutyric ester, is *irreversible* when such a very strong base is used.

$$(CH_3)_2CHCO_2C_2H_5 + \bar{C}(C_6H_5)_3 \longrightarrow (CH_3)_2\bar{C}CO_2C_2H_5 + (C_6H_5)_3CH$$

The condensation of ethyl oxalate with esters leads to the formation of α-keto esters.

$$RCH_2CO_2R + (CO_2R)_2 \longrightarrow \underset{\displaystyle COCO_2R}{RCHCO_2R} + ROH$$

These have the remarkable property of decomposing thermally to give carbon monoxide and the corresponding substituted malonic ester. This reaction is used, for example, to make ethyl phenylmalonate.

$$C_6H_5CH_2CO_2C_2H_5 + (CO_2C_2H_5)_2 \longrightarrow \underset{\displaystyle COCO_2C_2H_5}{C_6H_5CHCO_2C_2H_5} \xrightarrow[-CO]{heat} C_6H_5CH(CO_2C_2H_5)_2$$

This type of transformation is also involved in the synthesis of pimelic acid from cyclohexanone. It consists in the hydrolysis of the keto ester obtained by pyrolysis of the ethoxalyl derivative.

$$\text{(cyclic keto ester: } \overset{O}{\overset{\|}{C}} \text{ bonded to } CH_2 \text{ and } CHCOCO_2C_2H_5\text{; ring } CH_2-CH_2-CH_2\text{)} \xrightarrow{-CO} \text{(cyclic: } \overset{O}{\overset{\|}{C}} \text{ bonded to } CH_2 \text{ and } CHCO_2C_2H_5\text{; ring } CH_2-CH_2-CH_2\text{)} \xrightarrow{H_2O} (CH_2)_5\begin{matrix} CO_2H \\ CO_2H \end{matrix}$$

Pimelic acid

When heated alone ethyl acetoacetate yields dehydroacetic acid.

$$\left.\begin{matrix} CH_3-\underset{OH}{C}=CH-\underset{OC_2H_5}{C}=O \\ \\ C_2H_5O-\underset{O}{\overset{\|}{C}}-\overset{H}{\underset{H}{C}}-COCH_3 \end{matrix}\right] \longrightarrow \begin{matrix} CH_3C=CH-CO \\ O-CO-CHCOCH_3 \end{matrix} + 2C_2H_5OH$$

Dehydroacetic acid

Dieckmann Method. When the Claisen condensation takes place intramolecularly it is generally spoken of as Dieckmann's method. For example, ethyl adipate reacts with sodium ethoxide to give 2-carbethoxy-cyclopentanone.

$$\begin{matrix} CH_2C(=O)-OC_2H_5 \\ CH_2 \\ CH_2 \\ CH_2C(=O)-OC_2H_5 \end{matrix} \xrightarrow{NaOC_2H_5} \begin{matrix} CH_2 \\ CH_2 \quad CO \\ CH_2-CHCO_2C_2H_5 \end{matrix} + C_2H_5OH$$

The conversion of dibasic acids to cyclic ketones by heating in the presence of metal salts (p. 144) is formally similar to the Dieckmann reaction. Monofunctional acids give acyclic aldehydes or ketones in this process. Acetic acid yields acetone when passed through a hot tube containing manganous oxide.

$$2CH_3CO_2H \xrightarrow{MnO} CH_3COCH_3 + CO_2 + H_2O$$

Similarly, adipic acid may be converted to cyclopentanone by heating with barium hydroxide (p. 144). The mechanism in this case appears to be the following:

$$(CH_2)_4\begin{array}{l}\diagup CO_2H\\ \diagdown CO_2H\end{array} + Ba(OH)_2 \longrightarrow \left[(CH_2)_4\begin{array}{l}\diagup CO_2\\ \diagdown CO_2\end{array}\right]^{=} Ba^{++} + 2H_2O$$

$$2\left[(CH_2)_4\begin{array}{l}\diagup CO_2\\ \diagdown CO_2\end{array}\right]^{=} Ba^{++} \longrightarrow Ba(OH)_2 + 2\left[(CH_2)_3\begin{array}{l}\diagup CO\\ \;|\\ \diagdown CHCO_2\end{array}\right]^{-} Ba^{++}$$

$$2\left[(CH_2)_3\begin{array}{l}\diagup CO\\ \;|\\ \diagdown CHCO_2\end{array}\right]^{-} Ba^{++} + (CH_2)_4\begin{array}{l}\diagup CO_2H\\ \diagdown CO_2H\end{array}$$

$$\longrightarrow 2(CH_2)_3\begin{array}{l}\diagup CO\\ \;|\\ \diagdown CHCO_2H\end{array} + \left[(CH_2)_4\begin{array}{l}\diagup CO_2\\ \diagdown CO_2\end{array}\right]^{=} Ba^{++}$$

$$(CH_2)_3\begin{array}{l}\diagup CO\\ \;|\\ \diagdown CHCO_2H\end{array} \longrightarrow (CH_2)_3\begin{array}{l}\diagup CO\\ \;|\\ \diagdown CH_2\end{array} + CO_2$$

From this it will be seen that only catalytic amounts of barium hydroxide are needed. Actually, 1 mole of adipic acid is converted to cyclopentanone in yields of 80 per cent by use of about $\frac{1}{20}$ mole of barium hydroxide. Lead salts of acids have been found to give yields as high as 80 to 90 per cent of the corresponding ketones.

This method has been used in the synthesis of large rings (p. 365). The effect of chain length on the tendency of dibasic acids to form cyclic anhydrides or cyclic ketones is expressed by the Blanc rule. It states that when adipic and pimelic acids are heated with acetic anhydride and then distilled (at about 300°) cycloalkanones are formed, whereas succinic and glutaric acids under similar conditions yield cyclic anhydrides.

Aldehydes may be made by decomposing a mixture of acids one of which is formic acid.

$$RCO_2H + HCO_2H \xrightarrow{MnO} RCHO + H_2O + CO_2$$

Mixed ketones are also obtained in this way.

$$RCO_2H + R'CO_2H \longrightarrow R'COR + H_2O + CO_2$$

This method has the disadvantage of producing the two symmetrical ketones, RCOR and R'COR', as well as the mixed ketone.

Thorpe discovered that nitriles undergo self-condensation in the presence of strong bases, yielding imino nitriles that are converted to ketones by hydrolysis and decarboxylation. One of the most successful methods of making cyclic ketones of many members is due to Ziegler, who used the Thorpe reaction to close rings. He found that certain dinitriles could be caused to condense intramolecularly to give imino nitriles which by hydrolysis and decarboxylation yield cyclic ketones. The catalyst is an alkali metal derivative of a secondary amine.

$$(CH_2)_n\begin{array}{l} \diagup CH_2CN \\ \diagdown CH_2CN \end{array} \xrightarrow{LiNR_2} (CH_2)_n\begin{array}{c} \diagup CHCN \diagdown \\ \diagdown CH_2 \diagup \end{array} C{=}NH$$

$$\downarrow H_2O$$

$$(CH_2)_n\begin{array}{c} \diagup CH_2 \diagdown \\ \diagdown CH_2 \diagup \end{array} CO \xleftarrow{-CO_2} (CH_2)_n\begin{array}{c} \diagup CHCO_2H \diagdown \\ \diagdown CH_2 \diagup \end{array} C{=}O$$

Yields as high as 50 per cent are obtained in the synthesis of cyclopentadecanone—a compound which is an important artificial musk.

Pimelic esters undergo the Dieckmann reaction to yield cyclohexanone derivatives after hydrolysis and decarboxylation of the cyclization product.

$$(CH_2)_3\begin{array}{l} \diagup CH_2CO_2R \\ \diagdown CH_2CO_2R \end{array} \xrightarrow[-ROH]{NaOR} \begin{array}{ccc} & CO & \\ \diagup & & \diagdown \\ CH_2 & & CHCO_2R \\ | & & | \\ CH_2 & & CH_2 \\ \diagdown & & \diagup \\ & CH_2 & \end{array}$$

Many variations of this method have been discovered. Ethyl succinate, for example, gives succinosuccinic ester.

$$\begin{array}{l} \quad\; O \\ \quad\; \| \\ \quad\; C{-}OC_2H_5 \\ \;\diagup \\ CH_2 \\ | \\ HCH \\ | \\ CO_2C_2H_5 \end{array} \quad \begin{array}{l} HCHCO_2C_2H_5 \\ \quad\;\, | \\ \quad\;\, | \\ C_2H_5OOCCH_2 \end{array} \longrightarrow \begin{array}{ccc} & CO & \\ \diagup & & \diagdown \\ CH_2 & & CHCO_2C_2H_5 \\ | & & | \\ CH & & CH_2 \\ \diagup \quad \diagdown & & \diagup \\ C_2H_5O_2C \quad & CO & \end{array} + 2C_2H_5OH$$

Ethyl oxalate can be condensed with ethyl glutarate to yield a diketonic ester.

$$\begin{array}{l} CO_2C_2H_5 \\ | \\ CO_2C_2H_5 \end{array} + \begin{array}{c} CO_2C_2H_5 \\ | \\ H\text{-}C\text{-}H \\ \quad \rangle CH_2 \\ H\text{-}C\text{-}H \\ | \\ CO_2C_2H_5 \end{array} \longrightarrow \begin{array}{c} CHCO_2C_2H_5 \\ CO \diagup \quad \diagdown \\ | \qquad CH_2 \\ CO \diagdown \quad \diagup \\ CHCO_2C_2H_5 \end{array} + 2C_2H_5OH$$

The Aldol Condensation

The aldol condensation embraces a group of reactions among which are the aldol, Perkin, Knoevenagel, Tollens, and Mannich condensations. The electron-accepting reactant is generally an aldehyde (but may be a ketone), and the electron-donating component may be an anhydride, ester, β-keto ester, or other active methylene compound. The reactions have the following generalized form.

$$RC\begin{array}{l} {}^{\nearrow O} \\ {}_{\searrow H} \end{array} + \underset{|\quad\;\;|}{CH_2CO} \longrightarrow R\overset{OH}{\overset{|}{C}}H\underset{|\quad\;\;|}{CHCO}$$

Usually the β-hydroxy or aldol compound loses water.

$$R\overset{OH}{\overset{|}{C}}H\underset{|\quad\;\;|}{CHCO} \longrightarrow RCH{=}\underset{|\quad\;\;|}{C\text{-}CO} + H_2O$$

An example is the formation of benzalacetone from benzaldehyde and acetone.

$$C_6H_5CHO + CH_3COCH_3 \longrightarrow C_6H_5CH{=}CHCOCH_3 + H_2O$$

In the older classifications the term aldol condensation was reserved for the reaction between two molecules of a simple aldehyde or ketone. Less reactive substances require more drastic conditions, and, by reference to these, various names have been given to the aldol type of reaction.

Aldehydes dimerize in the presence of alkalies to give aldols (p. 87).

$$RCH_2CHO + RCH_2CHO \underset{NaOH}{\rightleftharpoons} RCH_2\overset{OH}{\overset{|}{C}}H\underset{\underset{R}{|}}{C}HCHO$$

This type of reaction is very general. Usually the initial reaction product loses water, giving an α,β-unsaturated carbonyl compound. Aldol itself, for example, is easily converted to crotonaldehyde (p. 87).

$$\underset{\text{Aldol}}{CH_3\overset{OH}{\overset{|}{C}}HCH_2CHO} \xrightarrow{-H_2O} \underset{\text{Crotonaldehyde}}{CH_3CH{=}CHCHO}$$

Aldol can be hydrogenated to give the corresponding glycol, which when dehydrated yields 1,3-butadiene, a raw material for synthetic rubbers.

Acetophenone undergoes an analogous transformation under the influence of hydrogen chloride. The product is dypnone.

$$2C_6H_5COCH_3 \longrightarrow C_6H_5\overset{CH_3}{\overset{|}{C}}{=}CHCOC_6H_5 + H_2O$$

This condensation is best carried out with aluminum *t*-butoxide as the catalyst.

α,β-Unsaturated compounds in general tend to undergo chain cleavage under the influence of alkalies. This probably involves hydration to the aldol, which then breaks down.

$$RCH{=}CHCOR \overset{H_2O}{\rightleftharpoons} R\underset{OH}{\underset{|}{C}}HCH_2COR \rightleftharpoons RCHO + CH_3COR$$

Methyl ethyl ketone is of exceptional interest because it can undergo aldol condensations involving either the methyl or the methylene group. It has been found experimentally that when the catalyst is hydrogen chloride the methylene group is attacked chiefly. Sodium ethoxide leads to condensations primarily affecting the methyl group. The condensation of methyl ethyl ketone with benzaldehyde illustrates this.

$$CH_3COCH_2CH_3 + C_6H_5CHO \xrightarrow{\text{alkali}} C_6H_5CH{=}CHCOCH_2CH_3$$

$$CH_3COCH_2CH_3 + C_6H_5CHO \xrightarrow{\text{acid}} CH_3CO\underset{CHC_6H_5}{\underset{\|}{C}}CH_3$$

Perkin Condensation. Anhydrides are relatively unreactive and even with aldehydes require long treatment at elevated temperatures. These are the conditions that characterize the Perkin reaction. Thus benzaldehyde, when heated with a mixture of sodium acetate and acetic anhydride, gives rise to cinnamic acid.

$$C_6H_5CHO + (CH_3CO)_2O \longrightarrow C_6H_5CH{=}CHCO_2H + CH_3CO_2H$$

This probably proceeds through the intermediate acetoxy acid.

$$\underset{\displaystyle |\atop OCOCH_3}{C_6H_5CHCH_2CO_2H} \longrightarrow C_6H_5CH{=}CHCO_2H + CH_3CO_2H$$

The reaction is general for aromatic aldehydes. Condensation always takes place on the α-carbon atom of the reagent. Thus, from propionic anhydride and sodium propionate α-methylcinnamic acid is produced.

$$C_6H_5CHO + (CH_3CH_2CO)_2O \longrightarrow C_6H_5CH{=}\underset{\displaystyle |\atop CH_3}{C}CO_2H + CH_3CH_2CO_2H$$

It is generally accepted that the condensation takes place between the aldehyde and the anhydride, the salt merely acting as a catalyst.

An interesting example of the Perkin reaction is the condensation between benzaldehyde, succinic anhydride, and sodium acetate.

$$C_6H_5CHO + \begin{matrix} CH_2{-}CO \\ | \quad\quad O \\ CH_2{-}CO \end{matrix} \longrightarrow \begin{matrix} C_6H_5CH{-}CH{-}CO \\ | \quad\quad | \quad\quad O \\ OH \quad CH_2{-}CO \end{matrix}$$

$$\longrightarrow \begin{matrix} C_6H_5CH{-}CHCO_2H \\ | \quad\quad | \\ O \quad\quad CH_2 \\ \diagdown \;\; \diagup \\ CO \end{matrix}$$

Phenylparaconic acid

Apparently the aldol rearranges, for the final product is the lactonic acid, phenylparaconic acid. This acid is of particular interest because heat converts it to α-naphthol.

$$C_6H_4\text{-lactone (CH–CH–COOH, O, CH}_2\text{, CO)} \longrightarrow C_6H_5\text{–CH=CH–CH}_2\text{–C(=O)OH} \longrightarrow \text{CH=CH–CH}_2\text{–C(=O) ring} \longrightarrow \alpha\text{-naphthol (OH)}$$

Applied to salicylaldehyde, the Perkin synthesis yields the salt of *o*-hydroxycinnamic acid. The free acid, however, is unstable and immediately forms the lactone, coumarin.

$$o\text{-}C_6H_4(OH)CHO + (CH_3CO)_2O \xrightarrow{CH_3CO_2Na} o\text{-}C_6H_4(OH)CH{=}CHCO_2H$$

$$\xrightarrow{-H_2O} \text{Coumarin (}C_6H_4\text{ fused ring: }CH{=}CH{-}CO{-}O\text{)}$$

Coumarin

The Perkin condensation is also involved in the synthesis of amino acids through the azlactones. The method is illustrated by the preparation of DL-phenylalanine from benzaldehyde and acetylaminoacetic acid. The product of the condensation, known as an azlactone, is converted to the amino acid by a series of transformations involving hydrolysis, hydrogenation, and a second hydrolysis.

$$C_6H_5CHO + \underset{NHCOCH_3}{CH_2CO_2H} \xrightarrow[CH_3CO_2Na]{(CH_3CO)_2O} C_6H_5CH{=}C{-}CO \text{ (azlactone ring: } N{=}C(CH_3){-}O\text{)}$$

$$\xrightarrow{H_2O} \underset{NHCOCH_3}{C_6H_5CH{=}CCO_2H} \xrightarrow[Pt]{H_2} \underset{NHCOCH_3}{C_6H_5CH_2CHCO_2H} \xrightarrow[(HCl)]{H_2O} \underset{NH_2}{C_6H_5CH_2CHCO_2H}$$

Claisen-Schmidt Method. Schmidt introduced the use of a 10 per cent aqueous sodium hydroxide solution as catalyst. By this method, for example, benzaldehyde is caused to react with acetophenone to give benzalacetophenone.

$$C_6H_5CHO + CH_3COC_6H_5 \xrightarrow{NaOH} C_6H_5CH{=}CHCOC_6H_5 + H_2O$$

Similarly from benzaldehyde and acetone are obtained benzalacetone and dibenzalacetone.

$$C_6H_5CHO + CH_3COCH_3 \xrightarrow[-H_2O]{NaOH} C_6H_5CH{=}CHCOCH_3$$

Benzalacetone

$$\xrightarrow{C_6H_5CHO} C_6H_5CH{=}CHCOCH{=}CHC_6H_5$$

Dibenzalacetone

Knoevenagel Method. Knoevenagel found that condensations between carbonyl compounds and active methylene compounds often could be effected by using ammonia or an amine as the catalyst. Piperidine and diethylamine are probably used more frequently than other amines. An example is the condensation of formaldehyde with ethyl malonate.

$$CH_2O + 2CH_2(CO_2C_2H_5)_2 \xrightarrow{(C_2H_5)_2NH} CH_2\begin{matrix} \diagup CH(CO_2C_2H_5)_2 \\ \diagdown CH(CO_2C_2H_5)_2 \end{matrix} + H_2O$$

Similarly benzaldehyde condenses with malonic acid in the presence of piperidine.

$$C_6H_5CHO + CH_2(CO_2H)_2 \longrightarrow C_6H_5CH{=}C(CO_2H)_2 + H_2O$$

It has been shown that the catalyst in the Knoevenagel reaction is really the ammonium (piperidinium, diethylammonium) ion formed by traces of acid present in the aldehyde. If the aldehyde is freed from acid the reaction does not take place. Unless one of the reactants is an acid, it is best to use piperidine acetate.

Tollens' Condensation. Tollens developed a method of condensing formaldehyde with aldehydes and ketones which depends on the use of calcium hydroxide as catalyst. It requires long treatment and tends to give polymethylol derivatives. An interesting example is the synthesis of pentaerythritol from acetaldehyde.

$$CH_3CHO \xrightarrow{CH_2O} HOCH_2CH_2CHO \xrightarrow{2CH_2O} (HOCH_2)_3CCHO$$

$$\xrightarrow{CH_2O} (HOCH_2)_4C + HCO_2H$$

It will be noted that the process involves a threefold aldol condensation followed by a "crossed" Cannizzaro reaction.

Pentaerythritol is converted by nitric acid into pentaerythritol tetranitrate, $C(CH_2ONO_2)_4$. The tetranitrate is similar to nitroglycerine and is an extremely important explosive. It is called PETN.

The synthesis of pantothenic acid involves an interesting example of the Tollens condensation. Pantothenic acid, a member of the vitamin B group, has been found in a great variety of foods. It has growth-promoting properties and a curative action against dermatitis developing in chicks fed on a heated diet. Pantothenic acid consists of $(+)\alpha,\gamma$-dihydroxy-β,β-dimethylbutyric acid joined with β-aminopropionic acid (β-alanine) by means of an amide linkage.

$$HOCH_2\underset{\displaystyle CH_3}{\overset{\displaystyle CH_3}{\underset{|}{\overset{|}{C}}}}{-}\overset{\displaystyle OH}{\overset{|}{C}}HC\overset{\displaystyle \diagup\!\!\diagup O}{}{-}NHCH_2CH_2CO_2H$$

Pantothenic acid

The acid was synthesized from isobutyraldehyde. The aldehyde was first converted into α,α-dimethyl-β-hydroxypropionaldehyde by treatment with formaldehyde in the presence of potassium carbonate.

$$\begin{array}{l} CH_3 \\ | \\ CHCHO \\ | \\ CH_3 \end{array} + CH_2O \xrightarrow{K_2CO_3} HOCH_2\begin{array}{c} CH_3 \\ | \\ C \\ | \\ CH_3 \end{array}CHO$$

The hydroxy aldehyde was then transformed into the corresponding cyanohydrin through its bisulfite addition compound.

$$HOCH_2\begin{array}{c} CH_3 \\ | \\ C \\ | \\ CH_3 \end{array}CHO + NaHSO_3 \longrightarrow HOCH_2\begin{array}{c} CH_3 \\ | \\ C \\ | \\ CH_3 \end{array}\!\!-\!\!\begin{array}{c} \\ \\ CHSO_3Na \\ | \\ OH \end{array}$$

$$HOCH_2\begin{array}{c} CH_3 \\ | \\ C \\ | \\ CH_3 \end{array}\!\!-\!\!\begin{array}{c} \\ \\ CHSO_3Na \\ | \\ OH \end{array} + KCN \longrightarrow HOCH_2\begin{array}{c} CH_3 \\ | \\ C \\ | \\ CH_3 \end{array}\!\!-\!\!\begin{array}{c} \\ \\ CHCN \\ | \\ OH \end{array} + NaKSO_3$$

Treatment with hydrochloric acid changed the nitrile to the lactone of the dihydroxy acid.

$$HOCH_2\begin{array}{c} CH_3 \\ | \\ C \\ | \\ CH_3 \end{array}\!\!-\!\!\begin{array}{c} \\ \\ CHCN \\ | \\ OH \end{array} + H_2O + HCl \longrightarrow CH_3\text{-}\begin{array}{c} CH_3 \;\; OH \\ | \quad\;\; | \\ C\text{—}CH\text{-}CO \\ | \qquad\quad | \\ CH_2\text{———}O \end{array} + NH_4Cl$$

The dihydroxy acid was resolved by means of its quinine salt, and the active lactones were condensed with β-alanine ester to give the two ethyl pantothenates. Hydrolysis of these yielded (+) rotatory and (−) rotatory pantothenic acids.

$$CH_3\begin{array}{c} CH_3 \;\; OH \\ | \quad\;\; | \\ C\text{—}CH\text{-}CO \\ | \qquad\quad | \\ CH_2\text{———}O \end{array} + NH_2CH_2CH_2CO_2C_2H_5$$

$$\longrightarrow HOCH_2\begin{array}{c} CH_3 \\ | \\ C \\ | \\ CH_3 \end{array}\!\!-\!\!\begin{array}{c} \\ \\ CHCONHCH_2CH_2CO_2C_2H_5 \\ | \qquad\qquad\qquad \\ OH \qquad\qquad\qquad \end{array}$$

$$\xrightarrow{H_2O} HOCH_2\begin{array}{c} CH_3 \\ | \\ C \\ | \\ CH_3 \end{array}\!\!-\!\!\begin{array}{c} \\ \\ CHCONHCH_2CH_2CO_2H \\ | \qquad\qquad\qquad \\ OH \qquad\qquad\qquad \end{array}$$

Pantothenic acid

The synthetic (+) pantothenic acid showed the expected biological activity when assayed on chicks and rats.

Mannich Reaction. If aldol condensations are carried out in the presence of amines, amino ketones frequently result. The interaction of formaldehyde, acetophenone, and dimethylamine is an example. In practice the base is isolated as the hydrochloride.

$$C_6H_5COCH_3 + CH_2O + (CH_3)_2NH \cdot HCl \longrightarrow C_6H_5COCH_2CH_2N(CH_3)_2 \cdot HCl + H_2O$$

This is known as the Mannich reaction.

Reactions of Hydrocarbons Which Contain Active Methylene Groups. Special mention must be made of certain active methylene compounds which bear no formal resemblance to carbonyl compounds. These are cyclopentadiene and its benzologs, indene and fluorene. They enter into condensation reactions with aldehydes and ketones to give fulvenes. Cyclopentadiene reacts with benzaldehyde and acetone to give phenyl- and dimethylfulvene, respectively.

```
              /CH=CH                         /CH=CH
C6H5CHO + CH2   |      ---> C6H5CH=C           |     + H2O
              \CH=CH                         \CH=CH
                                  Phenylfulvene

CH3\          /CH=CH        CH3\     /CH=CH
    C=O + CH2   |      --->     C=C    |     + H2O
CH3/          \CH=CH        CH3/     \CH=CH
                                Dimethylfulvene
```

It is interesting to note that dimethylfulvene possesses active hydrogen —a fact which is in harmony with its vinylogous relationship to cyclopentadiene (see Chapter **23**). Biphenylenemethylethylene has been condensed with anisaldehyde.

$$(C_6H_4)_2C{=}CHCH_3 + OHC\text{-}C_6H_4\text{-}OCH_3 \longrightarrow (C_6H_4)_2C{=}CHCH{=}CH\text{-}C_6H_4\text{-}OCH_3 + H_2O$$

PROBLEMS

1. Outline satisfactory methods for making the following compounds from readily available raw materials. Indicate the catalysts used and classify the condensation reactions which are involved.

a. $m\text{-}NO_2C_6H_4CH{=}CHCO_2H$

b. $C_6H_5CH{=}CHNO_2$

c. $CH_3COCH_2COCO_2C_2H_5$

d. $CO(CH_2CO_2H)_2$

e. $C_6H_5COCH_2CO_2C_2H_5$

f. $CH_3COCH(C_6H_5)CO_2C_2H_5$

g. $C_2H_5COCH_2C_6H_5$

h. $CH_2{-}CO{-}CHCO_2C_2H_5$ (ring closed by $CH_2{-}CH_2$)

```
h. CH2–CO–CHCO2C2H5
   |        |
   CH2——————CH2
```

i. $CH(CO_2C_2H_5)_3$

j. $CH_3CH(CO_2C_2H_5)COCO_2C_2H_5$

```
j. CH3CHCO2C2H5
        |
        COCO2C2H5
```

k. $C_6H_5CH(CO_2C_2H_5)_2$

l. $CH_3COCH{=}CH{-}C_4H_3O$ (2-furyl)

```
                       CH——CH
                       ||    ||
l. CH3COCH=CH–C       CH
                 \    /
                   O
```

m. $CH_3COCH(CO_2C_2H_5)CH_2CO_2C_2H_5$

```
m. CH3COCHCO2C2H5
          |
          CH2CO2C2H5
```

n. $C_6H_5CH{=}CHCOCH{=}CHC_6H_5$

o. $p\text{-}CH_3C_6H_4CH{=}CHCN$

p. $(C_2H_5O_2C)_2C{=}C(CO_2C_2H_5)_2$

q. $HO_2C(CH_2)_5CO_2H$

r. $C_6H_5CH(CN)CH_2COC_6H_5$

s. $CH_3COCH(CH_3){-}CH(CH_3)COCH_3$

```
s. CH3COCH–CHCOCH3
          |   |
          CH3 CH3
```

t. $CH_3COCH_2CH_2CO_2H$

2. For each of the following compounds outline a useful method of synthesis from readily available materials. Indicate the catalysts which would be used.

a. $C_6H_5CH{=}CHCOCH_3$

b. $(CH_3)(C_2H_5)CHCO_2H$

```
   CH3\
b.      CHCO2H
   C2H5/
```

c. $CH_3COCH(C_2H_5)(C_4H_9)$

```
          /C2H5
c. CH3COCH
          \C4H9
```

d. $C_6H_5CH{=}C(C_2H_5)CO_2H$

```
d. C6H5CH=CCO2H
          |
          C2H5
```

e. Cyclopentanone

```
e.     CO
      /  \
   CH2    CH2
    |      |
   CH2————CH2
```

f. $CH_3(CH_2)_5CO(CH_2)_5CH_3$

g. $C_6H_5COCH_2COCO_2C_2H_5$

h. CH_3CHCO_2H / CH_3CHCO_2H

```
h. CH3CHCO2H
   CH3CHCO2H
```

i. $(C_2H_5)(CH_3)C{=}CHCO_2C_2H_5$

```
i. C2H5\
        C=CHCO2C2H5
   CH3/
```

j.

```
j. CH3\
       CHCO2H
   CH2<
       CHCO2H
   CH3/
```

SUGGESTED READINGS

N. Rabjohn, "Selenium Dioxide Oxidation," *Org. Reactions*, *5*, 331, 1949.

W. S. Ide and J. S. Buck, "The Synthesis of Benzoins," *Org. Reactions*, *4*, 269, 1948.

S. M. McElvain, "The Acyloins," *Org. Reactions*, *4*, 256, 1948.

D. Todd, "The Wolff-Kishner Reduction," *Org. Reactions*, *4*, 423, 1948.

M. Carmack, M. A. Spielman, "Willgerodt Reaction," *Org. Reactions*, *3*, 83, 1946.

A. L. Wilds, "Reduction with Aluminum Alkoxides," *Org. Reactions*, *2*, 178, 1944.

J. R. Johnson, "The Perkin and Related Reactions," *Org. Reactions*, *1*, 210, 1942.

C. R. Hauser and B. E. Hudson, Jr., "The Acetoacetic Ester Condensation and Certain Related Reactions," *Org. Reactions*, *1*, 266, 1942.

F. F. Blicke, "The Mannich Reaction," *Org. Reactions*, *1*, 303, 1942.

CHAPTER 23

Unsaturated Carbonyl Compounds

Unsaturated carbonyl compounds result from many of the condensations considered in the preceding chapter and are known in large numbers and in great variety. In general they possess the properties of olefins as well as those of saturated carbonyl compounds. However, if the ethylenic bond is in the α,β position with respect to the carbonyl group, i.e., if the two form a conjugated system, certain peculiarities are encountered. These result from the fact that the positive charge on the carbonyl carbon atom of the polarized structure of the carbonyl group may be assigned to the more remote carbon atom of the olefinic system, as shown in the formulas.

$$\overset{4}{\gt C}=\overset{3}{C}-\overset{2}{C}=\overset{1}{O} \longleftrightarrow \gt C=C-\overset{+}{C}-\bar{O} \longleftrightarrow \gt\overset{+}{C}-C=C-\bar{O}$$

Thus, when the molecule is attacked by a nucleophilic reagent (A^- or A:), addition may occur at either position 2 or position 4. In many such reactions the process appears to consist in the addition of a reagent HA in two steps, the addition of the anion A followed by the addition of the proton. If A attaches at position 2 it would seem that there is only one course for the second stage of the reaction, that is, the addition of the proton to the oxygen atom.

$$\gt C=C-\overset{+}{C}-\bar{O} + A^- \longrightarrow \gt C=C-\underset{A}{C}-O^- \xrightarrow{H^+} \gt C=C-\underset{A}{\overset{OH}{C}}-$$

However, if A links at position 4 the resulting anion is capable of resonance, the negative charge appearing at both positions 1 and 3. The addition then may be completed in two different ways, depending upon whether the proton combines with the oxygen atom or the carbon atom at position 3. Most such reactions lead to products of type II, and since

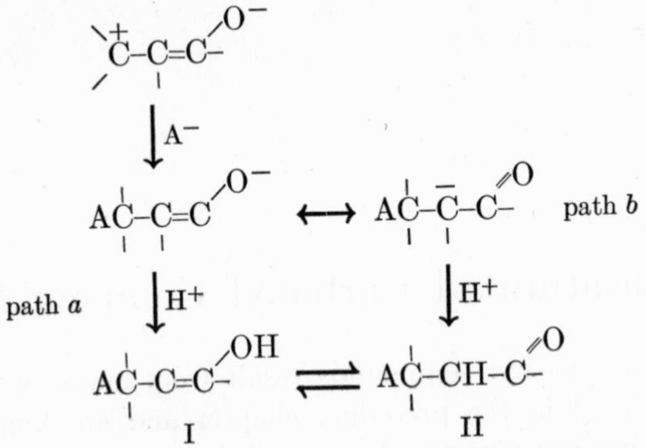

$$\overset{+}{\text{C}}\text{—C=C}\overset{\text{O}^-}{\diagup} \xrightarrow{A^-} \text{AC—C=C—O}^- \longleftrightarrow \text{AC—}\bar{\text{C}}\text{—C=O} \text{ (path } b\text{)}$$

$$\text{path } a: \xrightarrow{H^+} \underset{\text{I}}{\text{AC—C=C—OH}} \rightleftharpoons \underset{\text{II}}{\text{AC—CH—C=O}}$$

these are usually more stable than the corresponding enols (represented by formula I) it is not always possible to say whether the addition was of the 1,4 type followed by ketonization or whether it was of the 3,4 type. For this reason it seems preferable to designate the process as *conjugate addition.*

Bimolecular Reduction. α,β-Unsaturated ketones and esters often undergo bimolecular reduction in which the two simple molecules are joined not at position 2 but at position 4. This may be thought of as conjugate addition as contrasted to pinacol formation which is to be regarded as 1,2 addition.

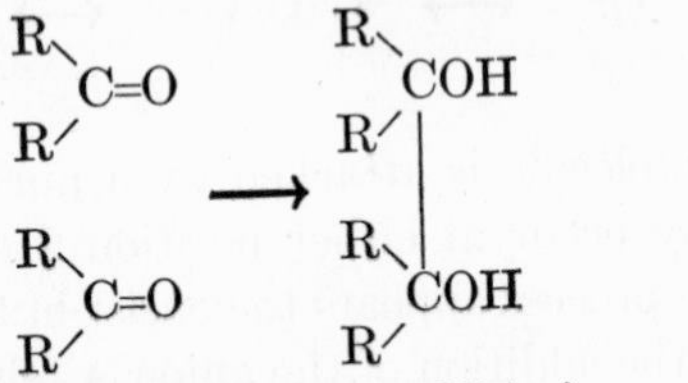

$$2\ \text{RR'C=O} \longrightarrow \text{RR'C(OH)—C(OH)RR'}$$

Pinacol formation (1,2 addition)

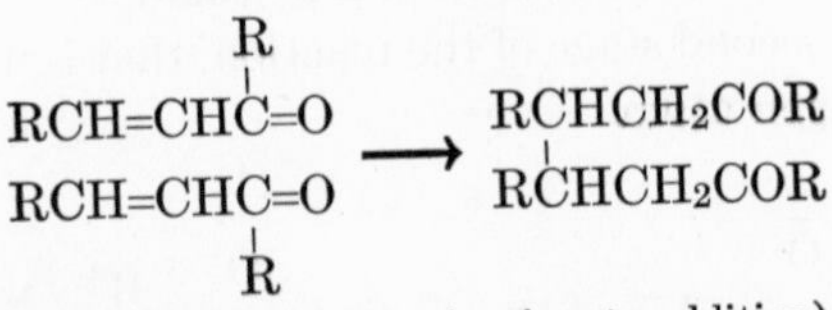

$$\begin{array}{l}\text{RCH=CHC(R)=O}\\ \text{RCH=CHC(R)=O}\end{array} \longrightarrow \begin{array}{l}\text{RCHCH}_2\text{COR}\\ \text{|}\\ \text{RCHCH}_2\text{COR}\end{array}$$

Bimolecular reduction (conjugate addition)

An example of bimolecular reduction of this type is the conversion of methyl cinnamate to methyl β,β'-diphenyladipate.

$$2C_6H_5CH{=}CHCO_2CH_3 \xrightarrow{Al(Hg)} \begin{array}{l}C_6H_5CHCH_2CO_2CH_3\\ |\\ C_6H_5CHCH_2CO_2CH_3\end{array}$$

Ammonia and Amines. α,β-Unsaturated ketones and esters react with ammonia and primary and secondary amines to give β-amino compounds. Mesityl oxide, for example, combines with ammonia and with methylamine as follows.

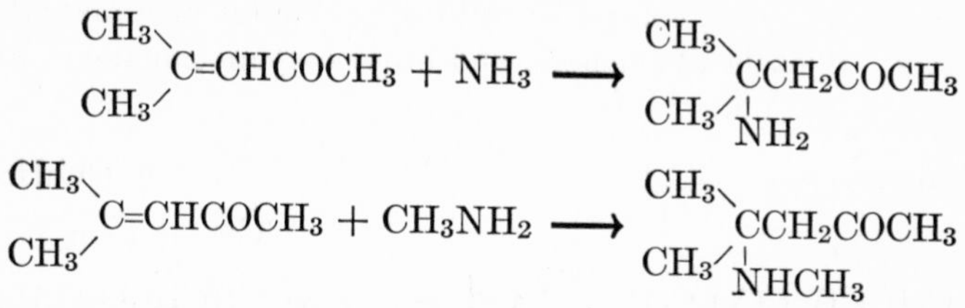

$$(CH_3)_2C{=}CHCOCH_3 + NH_3 \longrightarrow (CH_3)_2C(NH_2)CH_2COCH_3$$

$$(CH_3)_2C{=}CHCOCH_3 + CH_3NH_2 \longrightarrow (CH_3)_2C(NHCH_3)CH_2COCH_3$$

Phorone condenses with ammonia to form triacetoneamine. The mechanism appears to involve two steps each of which may be looked upon as being of the conjugate type.

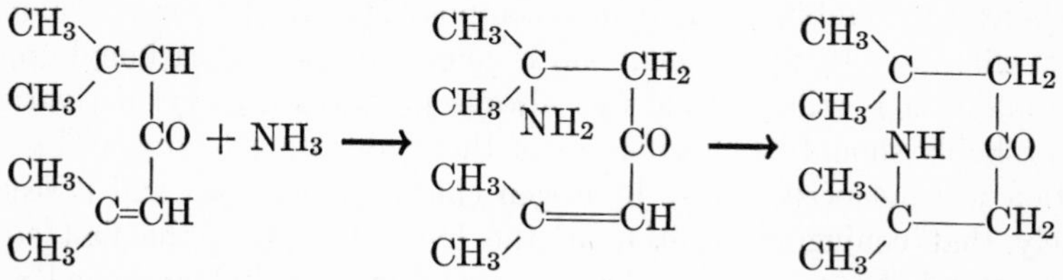

$$[(CH_3)_2C{=}CH]_2CO + NH_3 \longrightarrow (CH_3)_2C(NH_2)CH_2COCH{=}C(CH_3)_2 \longrightarrow \underset{\text{Triacetoneamine}}{(CH_3)_2C{-}CH_2{-}CO{-}CH_2{-}C(CH_3)_2{-}NH \text{ (ring)}}$$

Ethyl crotonate combines with diethylamine to give the corresponding β-amino propionate. The reaction can be reversed by heat.

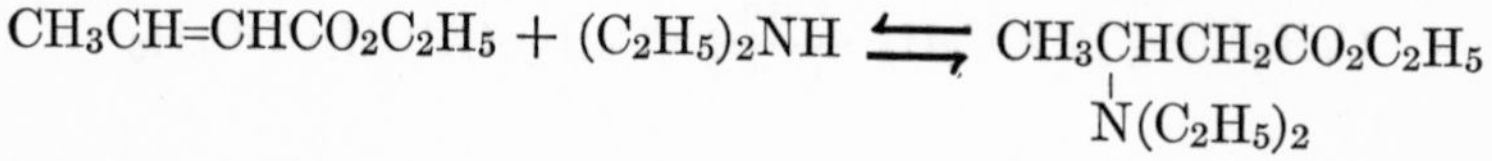

$$CH_3CH{=}CHCO_2C_2H_5 + (C_2H_5)_2NH \rightleftharpoons CH_3CH(N(C_2H_5)_2)CH_2CO_2C_2H_5$$

Hydrazine. The reaction between aldehydes and hydrazine normally leads to the formation of azines. However, unsaturated aldehydes tend to undergo ring closure to give pyrazolines. Cinnamaldehyde reacts in this manner when treated with an excess of hydrazine; the product is 5-phenylpyrazoline.

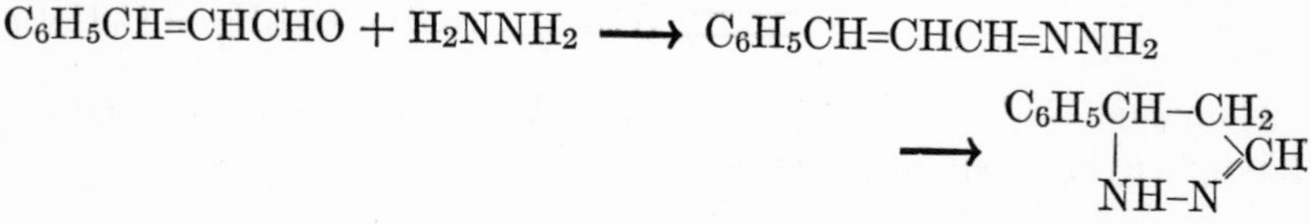

$$C_6H_5CH{=}CHCHO + H_2NNH_2 \longrightarrow C_6H_5CH{=}CHCH{=}NNH_2 \longrightarrow \begin{array}{l} C_6H_5CH{-}CH_2 \\ \quad | \qquad \rangle CH \\ \;\; NH{-}N \end{array}$$

Phenylhydrazine reacts similarly to give 1,5-diphenylpyrazoline.

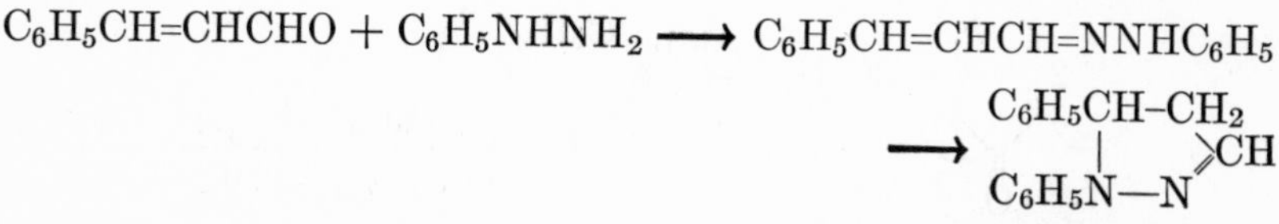

$$C_6H_5CH{=}CHCHO + C_6H_5NHNH_2 \longrightarrow C_6H_5CH{=}CHCH{=}NNHC_6H_5 \longrightarrow \begin{array}{l} C_6H_5CH{-}CH_2 \\ \qquad | \qquad \rangle CH \\ C_6H_5N{-}N \end{array}$$

The ring closure in these examples is due to an internal conjugate addition.

Hydrogen Cyanide. Whereas the formation of cyanohydrins by the addition of hydrogen cyanide is limited to aldehydes and a few of the more reactive ketones, conjugate addition will occur with many ketones and esters. Benzalacetophenone and ethyl α-cyanocinnamate undergo this type of reaction.

$$C_6H_5CH{=}CHCOC_6H_5 + HCN \longrightarrow C_6H_5\underset{\textstyle CN}{\underset{|}{C}}HCH_2COC_6H_5$$

$$C_6H_5CH{=}\underset{\textstyle CN}{\underset{|}{C}}CO_2C_2H_5 + HCN \longrightarrow C_6H_5\underset{\textstyle CN}{\underset{|}{C}}H\underset{\textstyle CN}{\underset{|}{C}}HCO_2C_2H_5$$

Aromatic Hydrocarbons. It has been pointed out that aromatic hydrocarbons may combine with olefinic compounds in the presence of aluminum chloride. If the olefinic bond is conjugated with a carbonyl group the addition is still possible but always produces a β-aryl derivative. It probably should be classified as of the conjugate category. This reaction will not occur unless hydrogen chloride is present, and it seems likely that conjugate addition of the hydrogen ion is the first step. The second step would then be a normal alkylation. Many condensations of this type are known. An interesting example is the addition of benzene to benzalacetophenone.

$$C_6H_5CH{=}CHCOC_6H_5 \xrightarrow[AlCl_3]{C_6H_6} (C_6H_5)_2CHCH_2COC_6H_5$$

This reaction appears to take place reversibly, for, in benzene solution, *p*-bromobenzalacetophenone gives the same product; bromobenzene is also formed.

$$BrC_6H_4CH{=}CHCOC_6H_5 + 2C_6H_6 \xrightleftharpoons{AlCl_3} (C_6H_5)_2CHCH_2COC_6H_5 + C_6H_5Br$$

Cinnamic acid and *p*-benzoquinone also react. From the latter, 2,5-diphenylhydroquinone is formed.

$$2\,(p\text{-benzoquinone}) + 2C_6H_6 \xrightarrow{AlCl_3} \text{2,5-}(C_6H_5)_2C_6H_2(OH)_2 + C_6H_4(OH)_2$$

However, a method is known by which α,β-unsaturated carbonyl compounds can be arylated in the α-position. This consists in treating the unsaturated compound with an aryldiazonium chloride or bromide in a buffered solution and in the presence of a copper salt. α-(p-Chlorophenyl)-cinnamaldehyde can be made in this way.

$$C_6H_5CH{=}CHCHO + ClC_6H_4N_2Cl \xrightarrow[\text{alcohol}]{Cu^{++},\ CH_3CO_2Na} C_6H_5CH{=}\underset{\displaystyle C_6H_4Cl}{\underset{|}{C}}CHO + N_2 + HCl$$

The Principle of Vinylogy

This principle is an empirical rule formulated so as to include as many as possible of the peculiar effects ordinarily ascribed to conjugation. With reference to a conjugated system of the type $R{-}(\overset{|}{C}{=}\overset{|}{C})_n{-}\underset{2}{\overset{|}{C}}{=}\underset{1}{O}$, the principle states that the function of the oxygen atom does not change with n, and that the function of carbon atom 2 may be usurped by the carbon atom joined to R.

An interesting example of the operation of this principle is furnished by the vinylogous series ethyl acetate, ethyl crotonate, and ethyl sorbate.

$$CH_3\overset{\displaystyle O}{\overset{/\!/}{C}}{-}OC_2H_5 \qquad \text{Ethyl acetate}$$

$$CH_3 \vdots {-}CH{=}CH \vdots \overset{\displaystyle O}{\overset{/\!/}{C}}{-}OC_2H_5 \qquad \text{Ethyl crotonate}$$

$$CH_3 \vdots {-}CH{=}CH{-}CH{=}CH \vdots \overset{\displaystyle O}{\overset{/\!/}{C}}{-}OC_2H_5 \qquad \text{Ethyl sorbate}$$

In each the terminal methyl group is reactive. With ethyl oxalate in the presence of potassium ethoxide they give the corresponding ethoxalyl derivatives.

$$\begin{array}{l} CH_2CO_2C_2H_5 \\ | \\ COCO_2C_2H_5 \end{array}$$

$$\begin{array}{l} CH_2CH{=}CHCO_2C_2H_5 \\ | \\ COCO_2C_2H_5 \end{array}$$

$$\begin{array}{l} CH_2CH{=}CH{-}CH{=}CHCO_2C_2H_5 \\ | \\ COCO_2C_2H_5 \end{array}$$

Glutaconic Esters

Another conspicuous example of the vinylogy principle is found in a comparison of malonic ester with its next higher vinylog, glutaconic ester. Glutaconic acid is made from citric acid by the following series of transformations.

$$\begin{array}{c}CH_2CO_2H\\ | \\ HO\text{-}CCO_2H\\ | \\ CH_2CO_2H\end{array} \xrightarrow{H_2SO_4} \begin{array}{c}CH_2CO_2H\\ | \\ CO\\ | \\ CH_2CO_2H\end{array} \xrightarrow{H_2} \begin{array}{c}CH_2CO_2H\\ | \\ CHOH\\ | \\ CH_2CO_2H\end{array} \xrightarrow{-H_2O} \begin{array}{c}CHCO_2H\\ \| \\ CH\\ | \\ CH_2CO_2H\end{array}$$

It can also be made from malonic ester and chloroform.

$$2CH_2(CO_2C_2H_5)_2 + CHCl_3 + \xrightarrow{NaOC_2H_5} \begin{array}{c}C\text{-}(CO_2C_2H_5)_2\\ \| \\ CH\\ | \\ CH(CO_2C_2H_5)_2\end{array} \longrightarrow \begin{array}{c}CHCO_2H\\ \| \\ CH\\ | \\ CH_2CO_2H\end{array}$$

The methylene group exhibits an activity similar to that in malonic esters. Glutaconic esters can be alkylated, for example.

$$\begin{array}{c}CH_2CO_2R\\ | \\ CH\\ \| \\ CHCO_2R\end{array} \xrightarrow{NaOR} \xrightarrow{CH_3I} \underset{(a)}{\begin{array}{c}CH_3CHCO_2R\\ | \\ CH\\ \| \\ CHCO_2R\end{array}} \longrightarrow \underset{(b)}{\begin{array}{c}CH_3CCO_2R\\ \| \\ CH\\ | \\ CH_2CO_2R\end{array}}$$

The monomethyl compound (*a*) rearranges to an isomeric form (*b*) by a shift of a hydrogen atom, and the second methyl group goes on the new methylene group to give the α,α'-dimethyl derivative.

The ready rearrangement of glutaconic acid and its derivatives is due to the mobile three-carbon system.

$$\text{-}CH_2CH{=}CH\text{-} \rightleftharpoons \text{-}CH{=}CHCH_2\text{-}$$

Of especial interest is the anhydride, which exists as an enol.

$$\begin{array}{ccc} & CH{=}C\diagup OH & \\ \diagup & & \diagdown \\ CH & & O \\ \diagdown\!\diagdown & & \diagup \\ & CH\text{-}CO & \end{array}$$

Unsaturated Aldehydes

An interesting example of conjugate addition is observed when cinnamaldehyde is treated with sodium bisulfite. Addition takes place reversibly in the 1,2 manner, and irreversibly and much more slowly in the conjugate manner. The primary addition product (I) if allowed to stand in solution gradually changes to the di-bisulfite addition product (II) with the liberation of an equivalent amount of free aldehyde.

$$\underset{\text{I}}{C_6H_5CH{=}CHCH\begin{matrix}\diagup OH\\ \diagdown SO_3Na\end{matrix}} \rightleftharpoons C_6H_5CH{=}CHC\begin{matrix}\diagup\!\!\!\diagup O\\ \diagdown H\end{matrix} + NaHSO_3$$

$$C_6H_5CH{=}CHCHO \xrightarrow{NaHSO_3} \underset{SO_3Na}{C_6H_5\overset{|}{C}HCH_2CHO}$$

$$\underset{\text{II}}{\underset{SO_3Na}{C_6H_5\overset{|}{C}HCH_2CH}\begin{matrix}\diagup OH\\ \diagdown SO_3Na\end{matrix}} \underset{}{\overset{NaHSO_3}{\rightleftharpoons}} \underset{SO_3Na}{C_6H_5\overset{|}{C}HCH_2CHO}$$

Michael Condensation

Active methylene compounds have been found to react in the conjugate manner with many α,β-unsaturated ketones and esters. This is known as the Michael condensation. The condensation of malonic ester with mesityl oxide is an example. Here we might expect 1,2 (aldol) condensation or conjugate (Michael) condensation.

$$(CH_3)_2C{=}CH\underset{CH_3}{\overset{|}{C}}{=}O \xrightarrow[NaOC_2H_5]{1,2} (CH_3)_2C{=}CH{-}\underset{CH_3}{\overset{OH}{C}}{-}CH(CO_2C_2H_5)_2$$

$$(CH_3)_2C{=}CH\underset{CH_3}{\overset{|}{C}}{=}O \xrightarrow[NaOC_2H_5]{1,4} (CH_3)_2\underset{CH(CO_2C_2H_5)_2}{\overset{}{C}}{-}CH_2COCH_3$$

It is to be emphasized that, like the aldol condensation, the Michael condensation is reversible. In the above case the Michael is the one actually observed. Subsequent transformations of the product yield methone.

$$
\begin{array}{l}
CH_3 \qquad\qquad\qquad O \\
\quad \diagdown \qquad\qquad\quad /\!/ \\
\quad C\text{——}CH_2C\text{–}CH_2 \\
\quad \diagup \;|\qquad\qquad\quad | \\
CH_3 \;|\quad O \qquad\; H \\
\quad\;\; | \;\; /\!/ \\
\quad CHC \\
\quad\;\; | \quad \diagdown \\
\quad\;\; | \qquad OC_2H_5 \\
\quad CO_2C_2H_5
\end{array}
\longrightarrow
\begin{array}{l}
CH_3 \quad CH_2 \\
\quad \diagdown \diagup \quad \diagdown \\
\qquad C \qquad\quad CO \\
\quad \diagup \;| \qquad\quad | \\
CH_3 \;\; | \qquad\quad | \\
\qquad\;\; CH \quad\; CH_2 \\
CO_2C_2H_5 \diagup \;\diagdown\; CO \diagup
\end{array}
\longrightarrow
\begin{array}{l}
CH_3 \quad CH_2 \\
\quad \diagdown \diagup \quad \diagdown \\
\qquad C \qquad\quad CO \\
\quad \diagup \;| \qquad\quad | \\
CH_3 \;\; | \qquad\quad | \\
\quad CH_2 \quad CH_2 \\
\qquad\; \diagdown \;\; \diagup \\
\qquad\quad CO
\end{array}
$$

Methone

Another example of the use of the Michael reaction is the synthesis of tricarballylic acid from ethyl fumarate and malonic ester.

$$CH_2(CO_2C_2H_5)_2 + C_2H_5O_2CCH{=}CHCO_2C_2H_5$$

$$\xrightarrow{NaOC_2H_5} \begin{array}{l} CH(CO_2C_2H_5)_2 \\ | \\ CHCO_2C_2H_5 \\ | \\ CH_2CO_2C_2H_5 \end{array} \longrightarrow \begin{array}{l} CH_2CO_2H \\ | \\ CHCO_2H \\ | \\ CH_2CO_2H \end{array}$$

Tricarballylic acid

The Michael condensation is widely applicable. Nitromethane, for example, reacts with methyl cinnamate in the conjugate manner.

$$C_6H_5CH{=}CH\underset{\displaystyle OCH_3}{\underset{|}{C}}{=}O + CH_3NO_2 \longrightarrow C_6H_5\underset{\displaystyle CH_2NO_2}{\underset{|}{C}}HCH_2CO_2CH_3$$

The condensation of two molecules of ethyl malonate with one of formaldehyde (p. 337) appears to involve 1,2 or aldol addition followed by conjugate or Michael addition.

$$H_2C{=}O + CH_2\begin{array}{l} \diagup CO_2C_2H_5 \\ \diagdown CO_2C_2H_5 \end{array} \longrightarrow \left[\begin{array}{l} \quad OH \\ \quad\; | \\ H_2C\text{–}CH \begin{array}{l} \diagup CO_2C_2H_5 \\ \diagdown CO_2C_2H_5 \end{array} \end{array} \right]$$

$$\xrightarrow{-H_2O} CH_2{=}C\begin{array}{l} \diagup CO_2C_2H_5 \\ \diagdown CO_2C_2H_5 \end{array} \xrightarrow{CH_2(CO_2C_2H_5)_2} CH_2\begin{array}{l} \diagup CH(CO_2C_2H_5)_2 \\ \diagdown CH(CO_2C_2H_5)_2 \end{array}$$

Hydrolysis of the complex ester and decarboxylation of the corresponding acid yield glutaric acid.

$$CH_2\begin{array}{l} \diagup CH(CO_2C_2H_5)_2 \\ \diagdown CH(CO_2C_2H_5)_2 \end{array} \longrightarrow CH_2\begin{array}{l} \diagup CH(CO_2H)_2 \\ \diagdown CH(CO_2H)_2 \end{array} \longrightarrow CH_2\begin{array}{l} \diagup CH_2CO_2H \\ \diagdown CH_2CO_2H \end{array}$$

The same sequence of condensation reactions is encountered in the reaction of benzaldehyde with acetophenone. At temperatures below 30°, benzalacetophenone—the result of 1,2 addition—is the principal product. At higher temperatures conjugate addition of acetophenone to benzalacetophenone occurs.

$$C_6H_5CH{=}CHCOC_6H_5 + C_6H_5COCH_3 \longrightarrow \begin{matrix} C_6H_5COCH_2\diagdown \\ \qquad\qquad CHC_6H_5 \\ C_6H_5COCH_2\diagup \end{matrix}$$

From this example it is seen that saturated ketones are sufficiently reactive to enter into Michael condensations.

The synthesis of DL-glutamic acid from ethyl bromomalonate, phthalimide, and ethyl acrylate illustrates the use of the Michael condensation in conjunction with Gabriel's amine synthesis (p. 422).

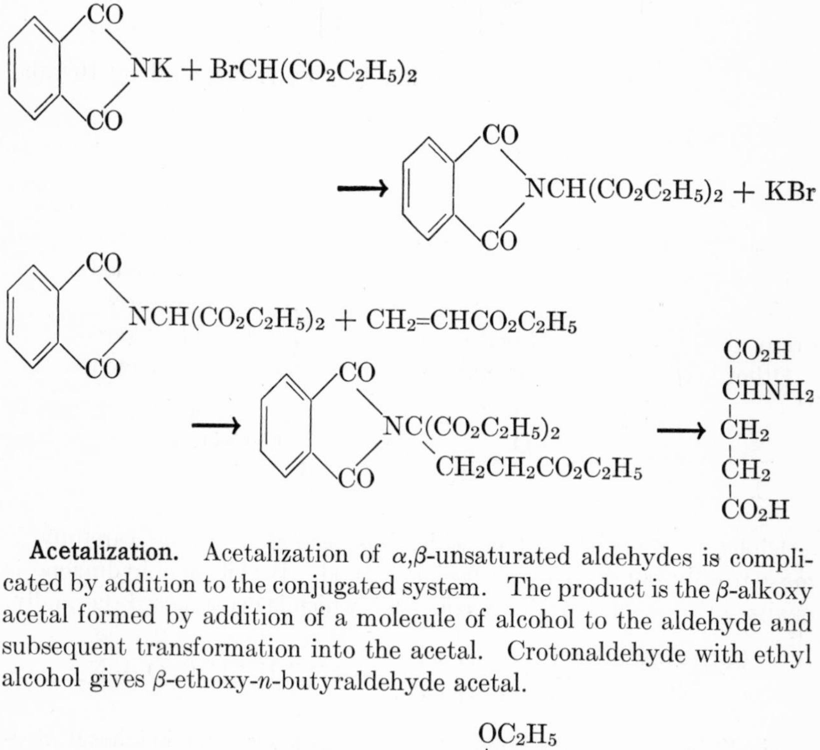

$$C_6H_4\begin{matrix}\diagup CO \diagdown \\ \diagdown CO \diagup\end{matrix}NK + BrCH(CO_2C_2H_5)_2 \longrightarrow C_6H_4\begin{matrix}\diagup CO \diagdown \\ \diagdown CO \diagup\end{matrix}NCH(CO_2C_2H_5)_2 + KBr$$

$$C_6H_4\begin{matrix}\diagup CO \diagdown \\ \diagdown CO \diagup\end{matrix}NCH(CO_2C_2H_5)_2 + CH_2{=}CHCO_2C_2H_5 \longrightarrow C_6H_4\begin{matrix}\diagup CO \diagdown \\ \diagdown CO \diagup\end{matrix}NC\begin{matrix}(CO_2C_2H_5)_2 \\ \diagdown CH_2CH_2CO_2C_2H_5\end{matrix} \longrightarrow \begin{matrix} CO_2H \\ | \\ CHNH_2 \\ | \\ CH_2 \\ | \\ CH_2 \\ | \\ CO_2H \end{matrix}$$

Acetalization. Acetalization of α,β-unsaturated aldehydes is complicated by addition to the conjugated system. The product is the β-alkoxy acetal formed by addition of a molecule of alcohol to the aldehyde and subsequent transformation into the acetal. Crotonaldehyde with ethyl alcohol gives β-ethoxy-n-butyraldehyde acetal.

$$CH_3CH{=}CHCHO + 3C_2H_5OH \longrightarrow CH_3\overset{\overset{\textstyle OC_2H_5}{|}}{C}HCH_2CH(OC_2H_5)_2 + H_2O$$

A way around the difficulty is illustrated in the synthesis of glyceraldehyde given on p. 304.

Ketenes. Ketenes are unsaturated ketones in which an olefinic double bond is twinned with the carbonyl double bond. They may be looked upon as intramolecular anhydrides. Actually their reactions are generally those of acid anhydrides. It is believed that a ketene reacts as a typical carbonyl compound; in most instances the initial addition compound is unstable and rearranges. The reactions with water, ammonia, and alcohols are illustrative.

$$R_2C{=}C{=}O + H_2O \longrightarrow \left[R_2C{=}C\begin{matrix}\diagup OH\\ \diagdown OH\end{matrix}\right] \longrightarrow R_2CHCO_2H$$

$$+ NH_3 \longrightarrow \left[R_2C{=}C\begin{matrix}\diagup OH\\ \diagdown NH_2\end{matrix}\right] \longrightarrow R_2CHCONH_2$$

$$+ ROH \longrightarrow \left[R_2C{=}C\begin{matrix}\diagup OH\\ \diagdown OR\end{matrix}\right] \longrightarrow R_2CHCO_2R$$

The simplest member of the series, ketene, is prepared by thermal decomposition of acetone.

$$CH_3COCH_3 \longrightarrow CH_2{=}C{=}O + CH_4$$

In the laboratory excellent yields are obtained by passing acetone vapors over an electrically heated metal filament at 700–750°.

Pyrolysis of acetic acid to produce ketene and water is carried out on a commercial scale in connection with the production of acetic anhydride, the latter being formed by addition of acetic acid to ketene.

Other ketenes fall into two classes, aldoketenes and ketoketenes.

$$\begin{matrix}R\diagdown\\ \quad C{=}C{=}O\\ H\diagup\end{matrix} \qquad\qquad \begin{matrix}R\diagdown\\ \quad C{=}C{=}O\\ R\diagup\end{matrix}$$

Aldoketene — Ketoketene

Diphenylketene, the ketene which has been studied most carefully, is most readily obtained by a special method. Benzil monohydrazone is oxidized by mercuric oxide to azibenzyl, which is decomposed thermally.

$$\begin{matrix}C_6H_5C{=}NNH_2\\ |\\ C_6H_5CO\end{matrix} \longrightarrow \begin{matrix}C_6H_5CN_2\\ |\\ C_6H_5CO\end{matrix} \longrightarrow (C_6H_5)_2C{=}C{=}O + N_2$$

The "twinned" double bond structure characteristic of ketenes is present also in carbon suboxide, a dehydration product of malonic acid.

$$\begin{matrix}O{=}C{-}CH_2{-}C{=}O\\ |\qquad\qquad |\\ OH\qquad\quad OH\end{matrix} \xrightarrow{P_2O_5} O{=}C{=}C{=}C{=}O + 2H_2O$$

Carbon suboxide

Carbon suboxide reacts with water and alcohol to give, respectively, malonic acid and ethyl malonate.

Ketene dimerizes to diketene, which is used in the synthesis of acetoacetic esters and acetoacetanilide. The dimer is an unsaturated lactone, which may be formed as indicated in the accompanying equation.

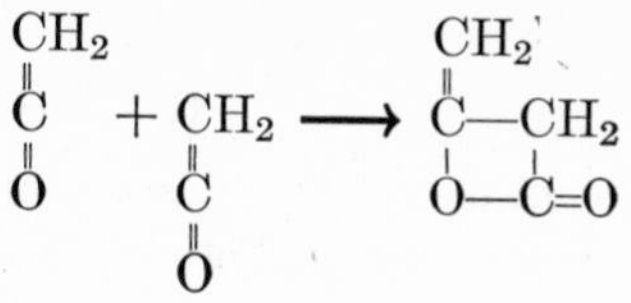

$$\begin{matrix} CH_2 \\ \| \\ C \\ \| \\ O \end{matrix} + \begin{matrix} CH_2 \\ \| \\ C \\ \| \\ O \end{matrix} \longrightarrow \begin{matrix} CH_2 & \\ \| & \\ C - & CH_2 \\ | & | \\ O - & C{=}O \end{matrix}$$

In reactions with water, alcohols, and amines the lactone ring is opened, as shown in the equations.

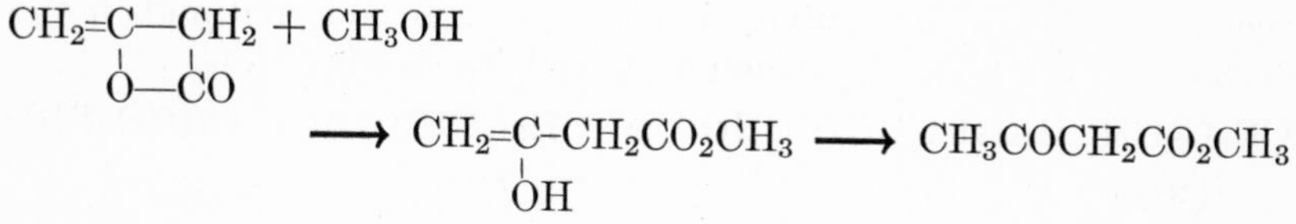

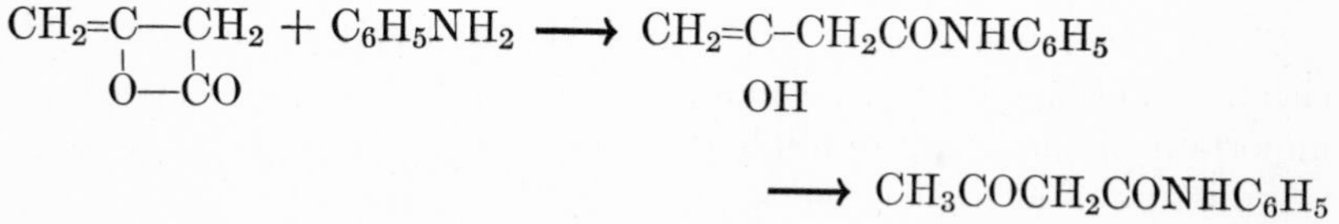

$$\begin{matrix} CH_2{=}C - & CH_2 \\ | & | \\ O - & CO \end{matrix} + CH_3OH \longrightarrow \begin{matrix} CH_2{=}C{-}CH_2CO_2CH_3 \\ | \\ OH \end{matrix} \longrightarrow CH_3COCH_2CO_2CH_3$$

$$\begin{matrix} CH_2{=}C - & CH_2 \\ | & | \\ O - & CO \end{matrix} + C_6H_5NH_2 \longrightarrow \begin{matrix} CH_2{=}C{-}CH_2CONHC_6H_5 \\ OH \end{matrix} \longrightarrow CH_3COCH_2CONHC_6H_5$$

The higher aldoketenes yield dimers of the same type. Ketoketenes, however, dimerize to tetraalkylcyclobutanediones. The dimer of dimethylketene is illustrative.

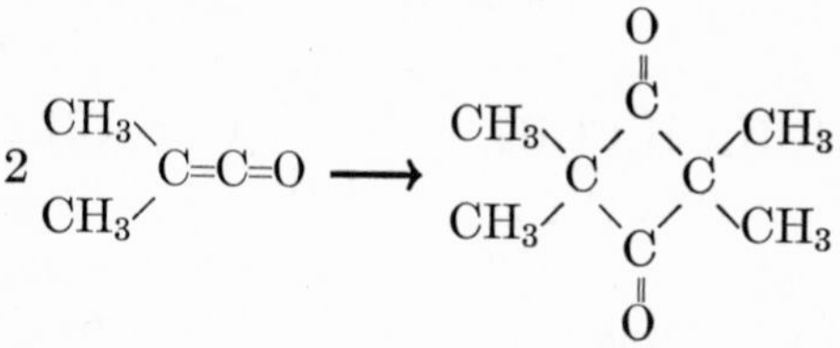

$$2 \begin{matrix} CH_3 \diagdown \\ \quad C{=}C{=}O \\ CH_3 \diagup \end{matrix} \longrightarrow \begin{matrix} & & O & & \\ & & \| & & \\ & & C & & \\ CH_3 \diagdown & \diagup & & \diagdown & \diagup CH_3 \\ & C & & C & \\ CH_3 \diagup & \diagdown & & \diagup & \diagdown CH_3 \\ & & C & & \\ & & \| & & \\ & & O & & \end{matrix}$$

An important reaction of ketene is that with formaldehyde; the product is β-propiolactone.

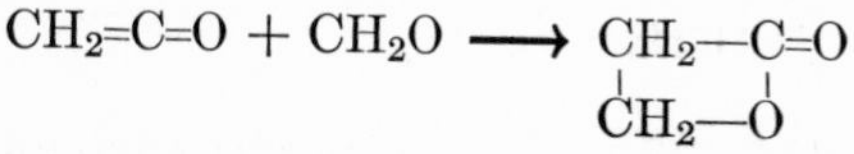

$$CH_2{=}C{=}O + CH_2O \longrightarrow \begin{matrix} CH_2 - & C{=}O \\ | & | \\ CH_2 - & O \end{matrix}$$

The lactone is very reactive because of the strain associated with the small ring. In the presence of basic catalysts it reacts with alcohols to give hydroxy esters; however, in the absence of catalysts or with an acidic catalyst alkoxy acids are formed.

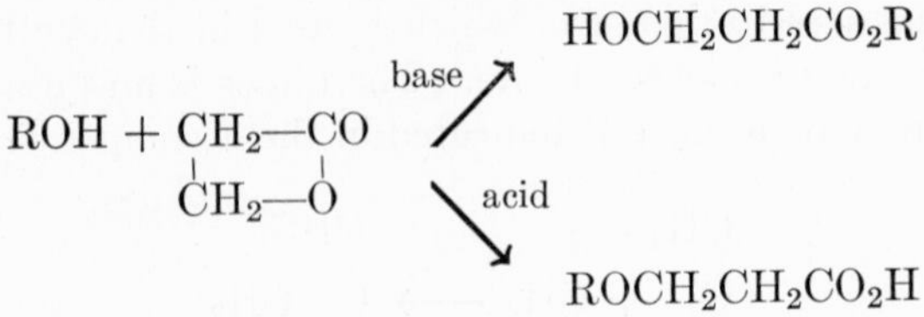

$$\text{ROH} + \begin{array}{l}\text{CH}_2\text{—CO}\\ |\qquad\ |\\ \text{CH}_2\text{—O}\end{array} \begin{array}{l}\xrightarrow{\text{base}} \text{HOCH}_2\text{CH}_2\text{CO}_2\text{R}\\ \xrightarrow{\text{acid}} \text{ROCH}_2\text{CH}_2\text{CO}_2\text{H}\end{array}$$

Although amines may react in both ways, ammonia gives the amino acid almost exclusively; β-alanine is manufactured in this way.

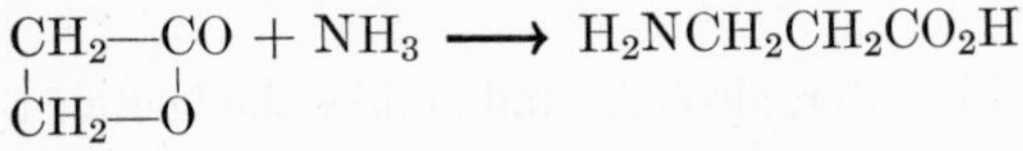

$$\begin{array}{l}\text{CH}_2\text{—CO}\\ |\qquad\ |\\ \text{CH}_2\text{—O}\end{array} + \text{NH}_3 \longrightarrow \text{H}_2\text{NCH}_2\text{CH}_2\text{CO}_2\text{H}$$

Citronellal. Citronellal is an unsaturated aldehyde occurring in citronellol and oil of eucalyptus. It has a pleasant odor and finds use in perfumes. The following structures have been ascribed to it.

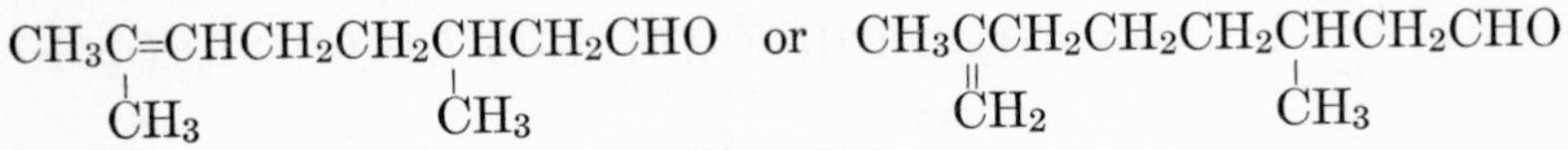

$$\text{CH}_3\underset{\text{CH}_3}{\underset{|}{\text{C}}}\text{=CHCH}_2\text{CH}_2\underset{\text{CH}_3}{\underset{|}{\text{C}}}\text{HCH}_2\text{CHO} \quad\text{or}\quad \text{CH}_3\underset{\text{CH}_2}{\underset{\|}{\text{C}}}\text{CH}_2\text{CH}_2\text{CH}_2\underset{\text{CH}_3}{\underset{|}{\text{C}}}\text{HCH}_2\text{CHO}$$

Citronellal

Citral. Of much greater importance is the closely related aldehyde citral. It occurs in a large number of essential oils and is the most important of the group of aliphatic terpenes. As it occurs in nature it is a mixture of at least two and probably four forms.

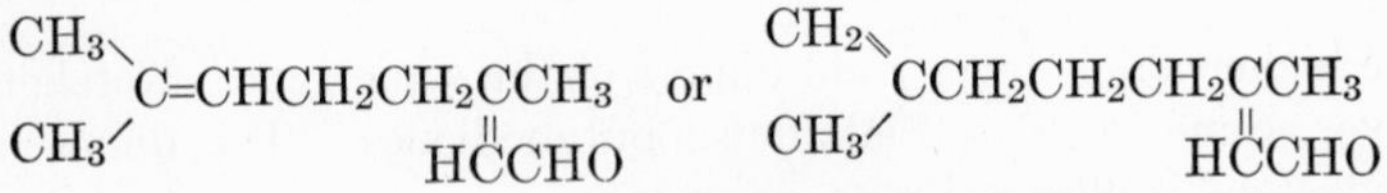

$$\begin{array}{l}\text{CH}_3\diagdown\\ \qquad\text{C=CHCH}_2\text{CH}_2\text{CCH}_3\\ \text{CH}_3\diagup\qquad\qquad\quad\ \|\\ \qquad\qquad\qquad\ \text{HCCHO}\end{array} \quad\text{or}\quad \begin{array}{l}\text{CH}_2\diagdown\\ \qquad\text{CCH}_2\text{CH}_2\text{CH}_2\text{CCH}_3\\ \text{CH}_3\diagup\qquad\qquad\qquad\ \|\\ \qquad\qquad\qquad\quad\ \text{HCCHO}\end{array}$$

Citral *a* (Geranial)

$$\begin{array}{l}\text{CH}_3\diagdown\\ \qquad\text{C=CHCH}_2\text{CH}_2\text{CCH}_3\\ \text{CH}_3\diagup\qquad\qquad\quad\ \|\\ \qquad\qquad\quad\ \text{OHCCH}\end{array} \quad\text{or}\quad \begin{array}{l}\text{CH}_2\diagdown\\ \qquad\text{CCH}_2\text{CH}_2\text{CH}_2\text{CCH}_3\\ \text{CH}_3\diagup\qquad\qquad\qquad\ \|\\ \qquad\qquad\qquad\ \text{OHCCH}\end{array}$$

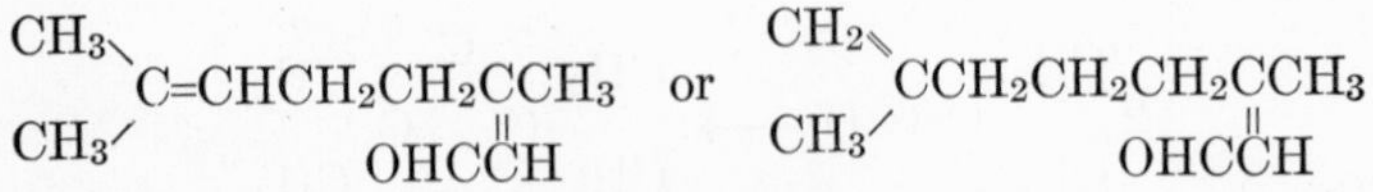

Citral *b* (Neral)

The structure of citral was proved by cleavage with alkali to acetaldehyde and a methylheptenone which in turn gave acetone and levulinic acid when oxidized.

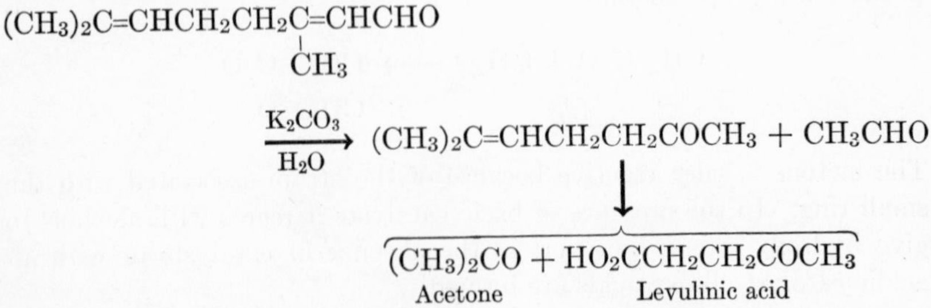

$$(\text{CH}_3)_2\text{C=CHCH}_2\text{CH}_2\underset{\text{CH}_3}{\underset{|}{\text{C}}}\text{=CHCHO}$$

$$\xrightarrow[\text{H}_2\text{O}]{\text{K}_2\text{CO}_3} (\text{CH}_3)_2\text{C=CHCH}_2\text{CH}_2\text{COCH}_3 + \text{CH}_3\text{CHO}$$

$$\downarrow$$

$$\underset{\text{Acetone}}{(\text{CH}_3)_2\text{CO}} + \underset{\text{Levulinic acid}}{\text{HO}_2\text{CCH}_2\text{CH}_2\text{COCH}_3}$$

It should be noted in passing that both citronellal and citral obey the isoprene rule (p. 371). This is a characteristic of terpene hydrocarbons and their derivatives.

The alkaline cleavage of citral illustrates a general reaction of α,β-unsaturated carbonyl compounds. Another example from the terpene series is the scission of pulegone to acetone and a cyclohexanone derivative by prolonged treatment with alkali or acid. Presumably the process involves hydration followed by a reverse aldol condensation.

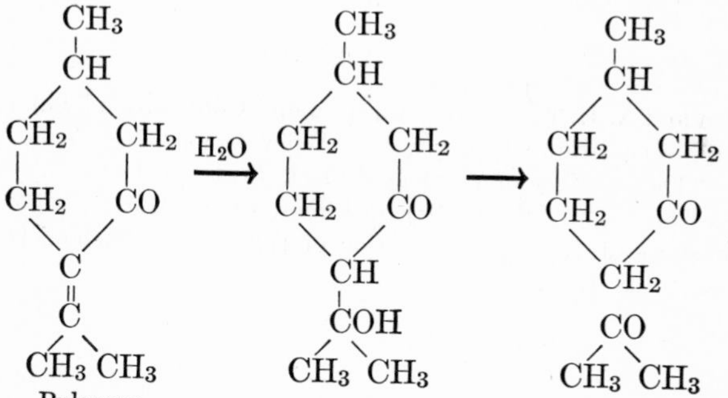

$$CH_3CH\langle CH_2CH_2C(=C(CH_3)_2)COCH_2\rangle \xrightarrow{H_2O} CH_3CH\langle CH_2CH_2CH(C(OH)(CH_3)_2)COCH_2\rangle \longrightarrow CH_3CH\langle CH_2CH_2CH_2COCH_2\rangle + CO(CH_3)_2$$

Pulegone

1,3,5-Trisubstituted Benzenes. The processes leading to the formation of mesitylene and 1,3,5-triphenylbenzene from acetone and acetophenone, respectively, can be formulated as follows. It will be noted that the last step in each case is a condensation involving an active methyl group joined to a carbonyl group by a system of two vinylene linkages.

$$CH_3C(CH_3){=}O + CH_3C(CH_3){=}O \longrightarrow CH_3C(CH_3){=}CHC(CH_3){=}O$$

$$\downarrow (CH_3)_2CO$$

$$CH_3C(HCH_2)=CH{-}C(CH_3)=CH{-}C(=O)CH_3 \longrightarrow \text{1,3,5-}(CH_3)_3C_6H_3$$

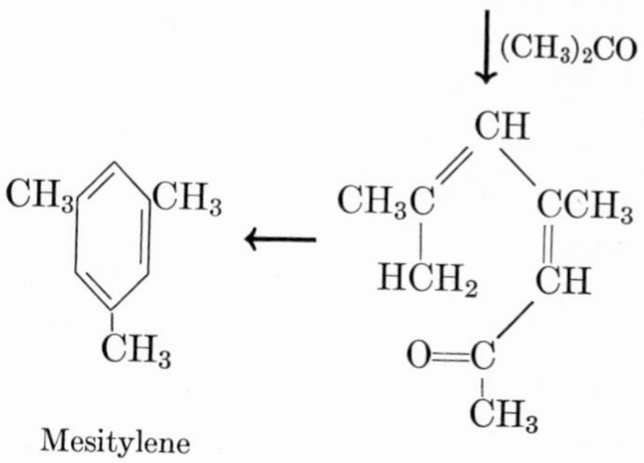

Mesitylene

$$C_6H_5C(CH_3)O + CH_3COC_6H_5 \longrightarrow C_6H_5C(CH_3){=}CHCOC_6H_5$$

$$\downarrow C_6H_5COCH_3$$

C_6H_5 C_6H_5 C_6H_5 ← $C_6H_5C(=CH-)CH_2$ ... $CC_6H_5=CH-C(=O)C_6H_5$

1,3,5-Triphenylbenzene

SUGGESTED READINGS

C. F. H. Allen and A. H. Blatt, "Unsaturation and Conjugation," Gilman's *Organic Chemistry*, Second Ed., Chapter 6, John Wiley & Sons, New York, 1943.

R. C. Fuson, "The Principle of Vinylogy," *Chem. Revs.*, *16*, 1 (1935).

H. A. Bruson, "Cyanoethylation," *Org. Reactions*, *5*, 79, 1949.

W. E. Hanford and J. Sauer, "Preparation of Ketenes and Ketene Dimers," *Org. Reactions*, *3*, 108, 1946.

CHAPTER 24

Compounds Which Contain Two or More Carbonyl Groups

Dialdehydes

Glyoxal, the simplest dialdehyde, is made industrially by the dehydrogenation of ethylene glycol. Monomeric glyoxal is the simplest colored organic molecule; even in the vapor state it is green. Like other glyoxals it is transformed by alkalies into the salt of the corresponding hydroxy acid.

$$\text{CHOCHO} + \text{NaOH} \longrightarrow \underset{\displaystyle |\atop \text{OH}}{\text{CH}_2}\text{CO}_2\text{Na}$$

It reacts with *o*-phenylenediamine to give quinoxaline.

$$\begin{array}{c}\text{CHO}\\|\\\text{CHO}\end{array} + \begin{array}{c}\text{H}_2\text{N}\\ \\ \text{H}_2\text{N}\end{array}\!\!\text{C}_6\text{H}_4 \longrightarrow \text{C}_8\text{H}_6\text{N}_2 + 2\text{H}_2\text{O}$$

Quinoxaline

This reaction is characteristic of compounds which contain "twinned" carbonyl groups, –COCO–.

Ketoaldehydes

Glyoxals have the general formula RCOCHO and are α-ketoaldehydes. They resemble glyoxal itself but are generally more stable. However, all show a great tendency to polymerize.

The action of aqueous alkali converts glyoxals to salts of α-hydroxy acids, as shown in the accompanying equation for the transformation of phenylglyoxal into mandelic acid. Much information concerning the

$$C_6H_5COCHO \xrightarrow{OH^-} \underset{\displaystyle OH}{C_6H_5CH}\text{–}CO_2^- \xrightarrow{H^+} \underset{\displaystyle OH}{C_6H_5CH}CO_2H$$

mechanism of this reaction has been gained from tracer studies employing carbon and hydrogen isotopes. The first step is believed to be the attack of the aldehyde carbon atom by the hydroxide ion, forming the intermediate *a*, followed by the shift of a *hydride ion* (hydrogen with the electron pair) to give the anion *b*, which then undergoes neutralization yielding the mandelate ion.

$$C_6H_5\overset{\displaystyle O}{\overset{\|}{C}}{}^*\text{–}\overset{\displaystyle O}{\overset{\|}{C}}\text{–}H \xrightarrow{OH^-} C_6H_5\overset{\displaystyle O}{\overset{\|}{C}}{}^*\text{–}\underset{\displaystyle H}{\overset{\displaystyle O^-}{C}}\text{–}OH$$

a

$$\longrightarrow C_6H_5\underset{\displaystyle H}{\overset{\displaystyle \bar{O}}{C}}{}^*\text{–}\overset{\displaystyle O}{C}\text{–}OH \longrightarrow C_6H_5\underset{\displaystyle H}{\overset{\displaystyle OH}{C}}{}^*\text{–}\overset{\displaystyle O}{C}\text{–}O^-$$

b

That the hydrogen atom which appears on the α-carbon atom of the mandelic acid is the one originally part of the aldehyde function is shown by the fact that, when the reaction is carried out with barium deuteroxide in deuterium oxide (heavy water), the mandelic acid formed does not contain any carbon-deuterium link. An alternative mechanism in which the migration of the phenyl group, rather than of the hydride ion, is proposed is shown to be incorrect by the use of mandelic acid containing the carbon isotope of atomic weight 14 in the ketone carbonyl function (indicated by the asterisk in the equation). The mandelic acid obtained was oxidized by chromic acid to benzoic acid and carbon dioxide. The radioactive carbon atom was found in the benzoic acid, showing that the phenyl group had not migrated.

β-Ketoaldehydes

β-Ketoaldehydes are interesting because they exist only in the enolic modification. They can be made by the Claisen condensation between ketones and ethyl formate.

$$RCOCH_3 + HCO_2C_2H_5 \xrightarrow{NaOC_2H_5} RCOCH_2CHO + C_2H_5OH$$

Evidently the aldehydic form changes to the enol form.

$$RCOCH_2CHO \longrightarrow RCOCH{=}CHOH$$

For this reason the substances are called "hydroxymethylene" compounds. These compounds are among the few which violate Erlenmeyer's rule that the grouping $\overset{|}{\underset{|}{C}}=\underset{|}{C}-OH$ is incapable of existence.

Diketones

α-Diketones such as biacetyl are distinguished from other types of diketones by their ability to form quinoxalines and by the fact that they are cleaved by hydrogen peroxide.

$$RCOCOR + H_2O_2 \longrightarrow 2RCO_2H$$

In the aromatic series benzils are made by oxidation of benzoins formed by condensation of aldehydes.

$$2ArCHO \longrightarrow ArCO\underset{\underset{OH}{|}}{C}HAr \longrightarrow ArCOCOAr$$

Benzils rearrange to salts of benzilic acids when heated with alkalies.

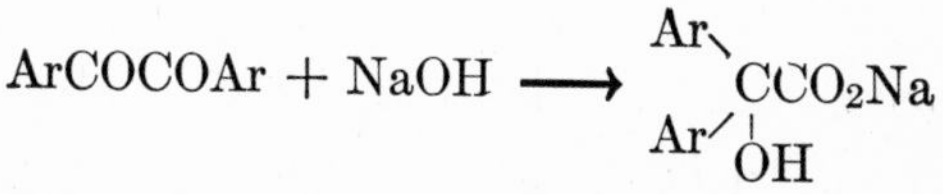

$$ArCOCOAr + NaOH \longrightarrow \begin{matrix} Ar \diagdown \\ Ar \diagup \end{matrix} \underset{\underset{OH}{|}}{C}CO_2Na$$

β-Diketones such as acetylacetone have an active methylene group and show properties typical of active methylene compounds. β-Diketones react with phenylhydrazine to give phenylhydrazones, which, however, are unstable and form cyclic compounds by loss of water. These heterocyclic derivatives are known as pyrazoles. Acetylacetone yields 1-phenyl-3,5-dimethylpyrazole.

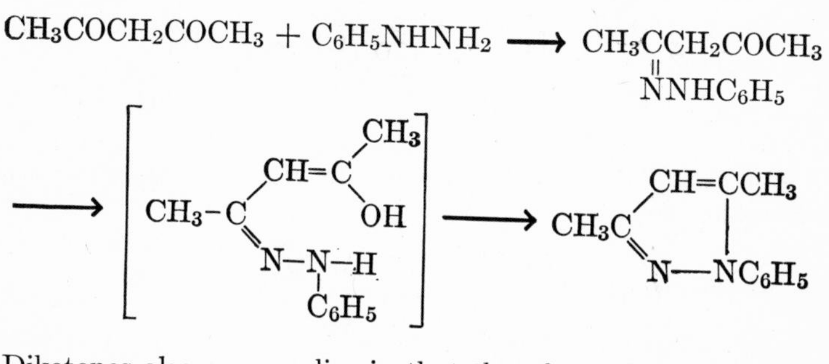

$$CH_3COCH_2COCH_3 + C_6H_5NHNH_2 \longrightarrow CH_3\underset{\underset{NNHC_6H_5}{\|}}{C}CH_2COCH_3$$

$$\longrightarrow \left[CH_3-C \begin{matrix} \diagup CH=C \begin{matrix} \diagup CH_3 \\ \diagdown OH \end{matrix} \\ \diagdown\!\!\diagdown N-\underset{\underset{C_6H_5}{|}}{N}-H \end{matrix} \right] \longrightarrow CH_3C \begin{matrix} \diagup CH=CCH_3 \\ \diagdown\!\!\diagdown N—NC_6H_5 \end{matrix}$$

β-Diketones also are peculiar in that they form chelated metal salts. The copper salt of acetylacetone, for example, has the following structure.

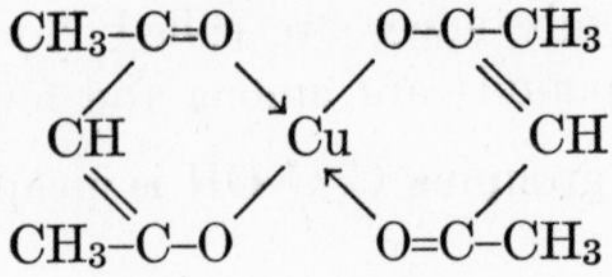

$$\begin{array}{ccccc} CH_3\text{-}C{=}O & & & O\text{-}C\text{-}CH_3 \\ CH & & Cu & & CH \\ CH_3\text{-}C\text{-}O & & & O{=}C\text{-}CH_3 \end{array}$$

γ-Diketones show a great tendency to yield furans. If acetonylacetone is treated with a dehydrating agent α,α'-dimethylfuran is formed. Presumably the enol form is an intermediate.

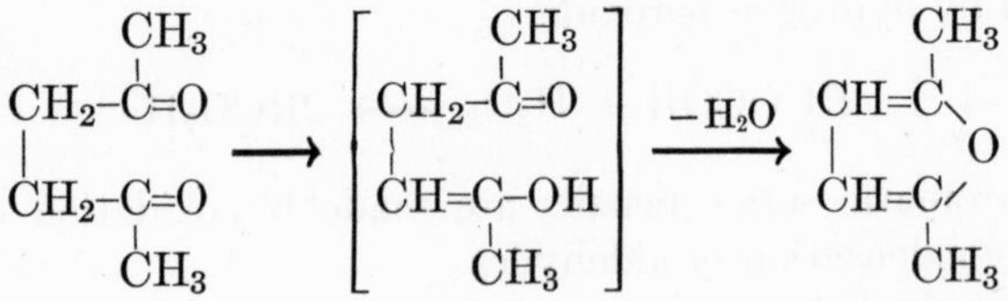

$$\begin{array}{l} \quad CH_3 \\ CH_2\text{-}C{=}O \\ | \\ CH_2\text{-}C{=}O \\ \quad CH_3 \end{array} \longrightarrow \left[\begin{array}{l} \quad CH_3 \\ CH_2\text{-}C{=}O \\ | \\ CH{=}C\text{-}OH \\ \quad CH_3 \end{array}\right] \xrightarrow{-H_2O} \begin{array}{l} \quad CH_3 \\ CH{=}C\diagdown \\ | \qquad O \\ CH{=}C\diagup \\ \quad CH_3 \end{array}$$

α,α'-Dimethylfuran

δ-Diketones undergo cyclization so readily that they cannot be isolated; cyclohexenones are obtained instead.

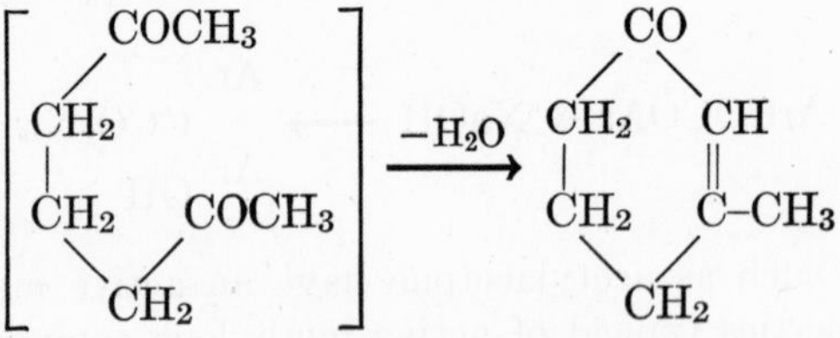

$$\left[\begin{array}{ccc} & COCH_3 & \\ CH_2 & & \\ | & & \\ CH_2 & & COCH_3 \\ & CH_2 & \end{array}\right] \xrightarrow{-H_2O} \begin{array}{ccc} & CO & \\ CH_2 & & CH \\ | & & \| \\ CH_2 & & C\text{-}CH_3 \\ & CH_2 & \end{array}$$

ϵ-Diketones cyclize readily but can be obtained as such. The ring closure gives a cyclopentene derivative.

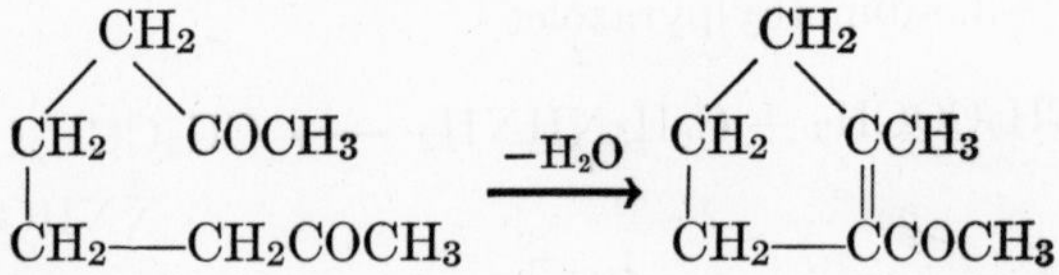

$$\begin{array}{cc} & CH_2 \\ CH_2 & COCH_3 \\ | & \\ CH_2 & \text{—}CH_2COCH_3 \end{array} \xrightarrow{-H_2O} \begin{array}{cc} & CH_2 \\ CH_2 & CCH_3 \\ | & \| \\ CH_2 & \text{—}CCOCH_3 \end{array}$$

Aromatic δ- and ϵ-diketones are made by the Friedel-Crafts reaction and are stable.

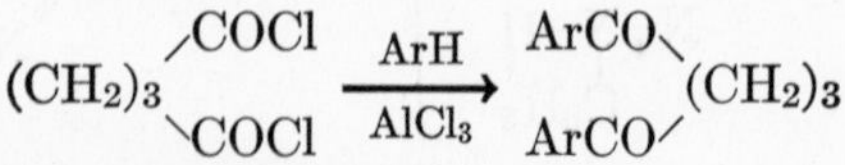

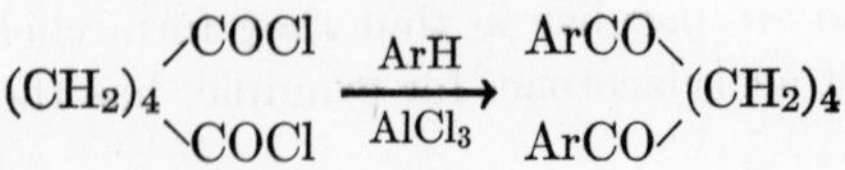

$$(CH_2)_3\begin{array}{l}\diagup COCl \\ \diagdown COCl\end{array} \xrightarrow[AlCl_3]{ArH} \begin{array}{r} ArCO\diagdown \\ ArCO\diagup \end{array}(CH_2)_3$$

$$(CH_2)_4\begin{array}{l}\diagup COCl \\ \diagdown COCl\end{array} \xrightarrow[AlCl_3]{ArH} \begin{array}{r} ArCO\diagdown \\ ArCO\diagup \end{array}(CH_2)_4$$

Polycarbonyl Compounds

Triketones and tetraketones are also known. Diphenyl triketone, for example, is a yellow solid resulting from the hydrolysis of dibromodibenzoylmethane.

$$C_6H_5COCBr_2COC_6H_5 \longrightarrow \underset{\text{Diphenyl triketone}}{C_6H_5COCOCOC_6H_5}$$

The corresponding tetraketone can be made by oxidation of the formoin obtained from phenylglyoxal.

$$2C_6H_5COCHO \xrightarrow{KCN} C_6H_5COCO\overset{OH}{\overset{|}{C}}HCOC_6H_5 \xrightarrow{-H_2} \underset{\text{Diphenyl tetraketone}}{C_6H_5COCOCOCOC_6H_5}$$

Both the tri- and tetraketones tend to lose carbon monoxide to form the next lower member of the series.

$$C_6H_5COCOCOCOC_6H_5 \xrightarrow{-CO} C_6H_5COCOCOC_6H_5 \xrightarrow{-CO} C_6H_5COCOC_6H_5$$

Tracer studies have shown that in the presence of alkali and cupric salts the triketone loses its central carbonyl group as carbon dioxide.

PROBLEMS

1. What is the action of hot aqueous alkali on

a. C_6H_5CHO? *b.* C_6H_5COCHO? *c.* $C_6H_5COCH_3$?

2. Suggest ways of distinguishing between

a. $C_6H_5COCOC_6H_5$ and $C_6H_5COCH_2COC_6H_5$.
b. $CH_3COCOCH_3$ and CH_3CH_2COCHO.
c. $CH_3COCH_2CH_2COCH_3$ and $CH_3CH_2COCH_2COCH_3$.

3. Indicate a method of synthesis for

a.
```
     CH——CH
     ‖    ‖
 C6H5C    CC6H5
      \  /
       O
```

b. $CH_3C_6H_4CO(CH_2)_2COC_6H_4CH_3$

CHAPTER 25

Ring Formation

Historical

A molecule containing two functional groups capable of reacting with each other may undergo *internal* reaction to give a *cyclic* compound, or many such molecules may react to form a *polymer*. Which course obtains appears to depend chiefly on the size of the ring to be formed. It was early observed that six-membered rings formed easily, whereas rings of other sizes were unknown in nature and had not been synthesized. Indeed, until about the year 1880 it was generally supposed that rings smaller or larger than this could not exist. Moreover, there were theoretical grounds for this opinion, for it was evident that the three- and four-membered rings, at least, could not be made from carbon atoms having the rigid tetrahedral form which had been used so successfully in solving structural problems. If the four bonds of a carbon atom are directed towards the vertices of a regular tetrahedron, each forms an angle of 109 degrees and 28 minutes with the others. As a matter of fact, it is impossible by use of such atoms to construct any ring of fewer

TABLE XXXII

VALENCE ANGLES AND DEVIATIONS

Hydrocarbon	Formula	Angle	Deviation
Ethylene (cycloethane)	$CH_2{=}CH_2$	0°	54° 44′
Cyclopropane	$CH_2{-}CH_2$ ╲ ╱ CH_2	60°	24° 44′
Cyclobutane	$CH_2{-}CH_2$ │ │ $CH_2{-}CH_2$	90°	9° 44′
Cyclopentane	$CH_2{-}CH_2$╲ │ CH_2 $CH_2{-}CH_2$╱	108°	0° 44′

than six members. Table XXXII shows the angles that are required for the formation of the smaller rings, together with the deviation in each of the valence bonds in such rings from the normal position in the regular tetrahedron.

Between 1880 and 1885, however, came a rapid succession of events which revolutionized chemist's ideas of cyclic compounds and laid the foundations of modern alicyclic chemistry. The first of these was the discovery that β-chloropropionic acid when heated with dry sodium ethoxide was converted to a compound containing a ring of four carbon atoms—1,3-cyclobutanedicarboxylic acid.

$$\begin{array}{l} CH_2CH_2CO_2H \\ | \\ Cl \quad\quad Cl \\ \quad\quad\quad | \\ HO_2CCH_2\text{–}CH_2 \end{array} \longrightarrow \begin{array}{l} \quad\quad CH_2\text{–}CHCO_2H \\ \quad\quad | \quad\quad\quad | \\ HO_2CCH\text{—}CH_2 \end{array}$$

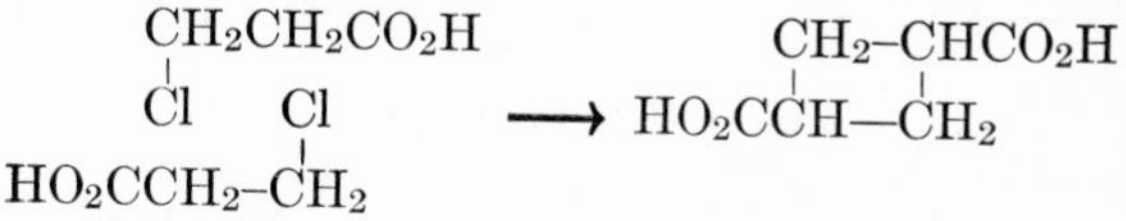

β-Chloropropionic acid — 1,3-Cyclobutanedicarboxylic acid

Almost immediately after this discovery, Freund succeeded in making cyclopropane—a hydrocarbon containing a three-membered ring—by the action of sodium on trimethylene bromide. A little later, Perkin found that ethyl malonate condenses with trimethylene bromide in the presence of sodium ethoxide to give ethyl 1,1-cyclobutanedicarboxylate.

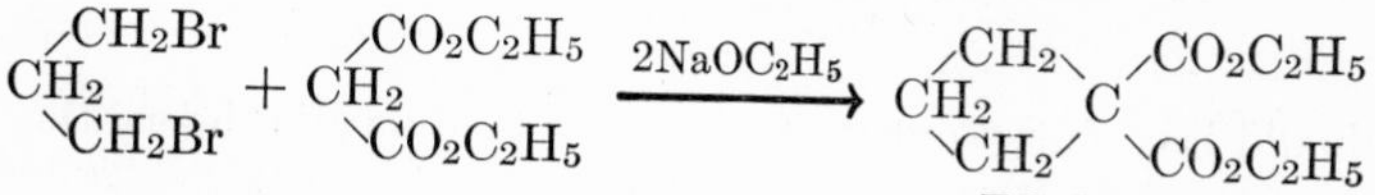

$$CH_2\begin{array}{l}\diagup CH_2Br \\ \diagdown CH_2Br\end{array} + CH_2\begin{array}{l}\diagup CO_2C_2H_5 \\ \diagdown CO_2C_2H_5\end{array} \xrightarrow{2NaOC_2H_5} CH_2\begin{array}{l}\diagup CH_2 \diagdown \\ \diagdown CH_2 \diagup\end{array}C\begin{array}{l}\diagup CO_2C_2H_5 \\ \diagdown CO_2C_2H_5\end{array}$$

Ethyl 1,1-cyclobutanedicarboxylate

These results established the existence of three- and four-membered carbon rings and demanded drastic revision of the current opinions regarding the stereochemical nature of the carbon atom.

The Baeyer Strain Theory

An ingenious and very plausible explanation for the existence of small rings was advanced by Baeyer, who assumed that the normal angle between the valence bonds of carbon was 109 degrees and 28 minutes, but *that it was possible for this angle to be altered.* However, any deviation from this angle was supposed to bring about a condition of *strain* which was, according to the theory, attended by a corresponding decrease in stability. The greater the strain involved, the less would be the stability of the compound.

Striking confirmation of this theory was obtained almost at once by Perkin, who succeeded in preparing a compound containing the *cyclo-*

pentane ring. By condensation of two molecules of malonic ester with one of trimethylene bromide, he obtained a tetracarbethoxypentane whose sodium derivative, when treated with iodine, gave ethyl 1,1,2,2-cyclopentanetetracarboxylate.

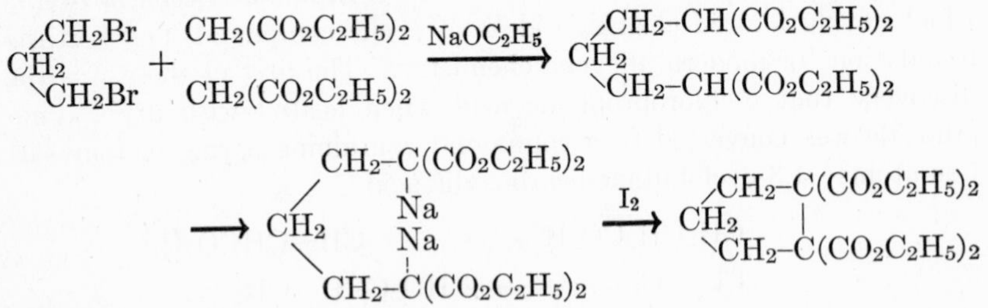

$$CH_2\begin{matrix}\diagup CH_2Br \\ \diagdown CH_2Br\end{matrix} + \begin{matrix}CH_2(CO_2C_2H_5)_2 \\ CH_2(CO_2C_2H_5)_2\end{matrix} \xrightarrow{NaOC_2H_5} CH_2\begin{matrix}\diagup CH_2\text{–}CH(CO_2C_2H_5)_2 \\ \diagdown CH_2\text{–}CH(CO_2C_2H_5)_2\end{matrix}$$

$$\longrightarrow CH_2\begin{matrix}\diagup CH_2\text{–}C(CO_2C_2H_5)_2 \\ \quad\quad | \\ \quad\quad Na \\ \quad\quad Na \\ \quad\quad | \\ \diagdown CH_2\text{–}C(CO_2C_2H_5)_2\end{matrix} \xrightarrow{I_2} CH_2\begin{matrix}\diagup CH_2\text{–}C(CO_2C_2H_5)_2 \\ \quad\quad | \\ \diagdown CH_2\text{–}C(CO_2C_2H_5)_2\end{matrix}$$

Hydrolysis of the ester gave an acid which when heated lost carbon dioxide and yielded 1,2-cyclopentanedicarboxylic acid.

$$CH_2\begin{matrix}\diagup CH_2\text{–}C\begin{matrix}\diagup CO_2H \\ \diagdown CO_2H\end{matrix} \\ \quad\quad | \\ \diagdown CH_2\text{–}C\begin{matrix}\diagup CO_2H \\ \diagdown CO_2H\end{matrix}\end{matrix} \xrightarrow{-2CO_2} CH_2\begin{matrix}\diagup CH_2\text{–}CHCO_2H \\ \quad\quad | \\ \diagdown CH_2\text{–}CHCO_2H\end{matrix}$$

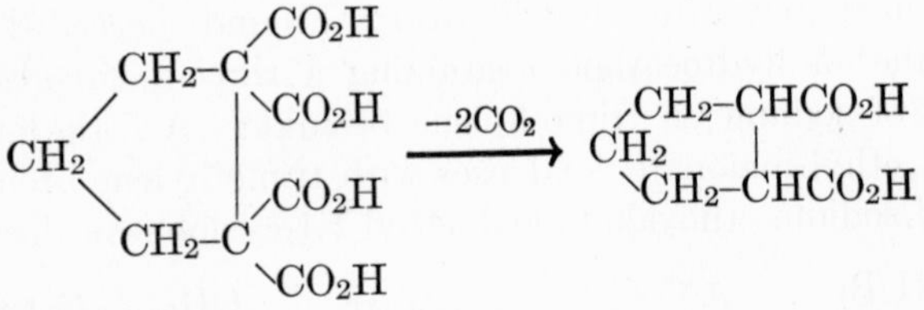

It should be pointed out that according to Baeyer's theory the cyclopropane ring, since it possessed greater strain, should be less stable than the cyclobutane ring, and that, in turn, should be less stable than the cyclopentane ring. The 1,2-cyclopentanedicarboxylic acid was indeed found to be extremely stable, completely fulfilling the predictions of the theory.

It may be said at once that for hydrocarbons having rings smaller than the cyclohexane nucleus the theory of Baeyer is in fairly satisfactory agreement with the facts known at the present time, although the physical nature of the strain is not yet fully understood.

Strainless Rings

An integral part of Baeyer's strain theory was that the carbon atoms of the ring must lie in a plane, and on this basis he predicted that the formation of large rings would involve *negative* strain. From an inspection of the following figures it is evident that in cyclohexane and compounds containing larger rings the planar configuration requires that the angle formed by the valence bonds be somewhat greater than normal and that the amount of this stretching increase proportionately to the size of the ring.

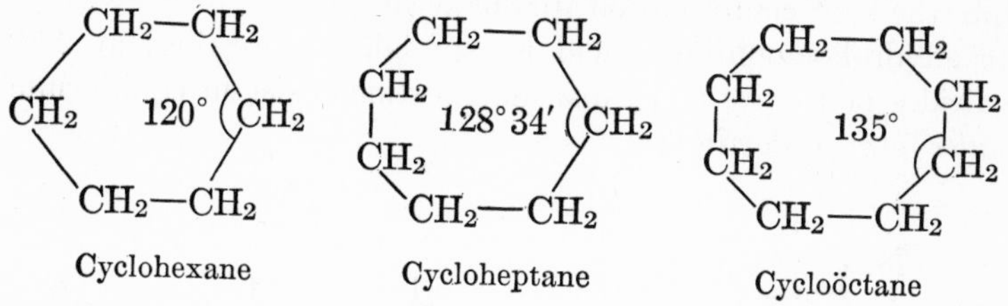

120° Cyclohexane | 128°34′ Cycloheptane | 135° Cycloöctane

This postulate was supposed to account for the fact that rings of more than six members had not been made or discovered in nature and were presumably very unstable. Moreover, it implied that very large rings would be incapable of existence.

This part of Baeyer's theory has proved to be misleading if not entirely erroneous. Sachse was the first to perceive that the so-called negative strain need not exist and that the large rings might be, in fact, strainless. This idea was disregarded by chemists for nearly thirty years but was eventually revived and elaborated by Mohr, and has now been fully confirmed by experiment. The idea of Sachse may be illustrated by reference to models. When, by the use of tetrahedral atoms, models are constructed for rings containing more than five members it is found that the atoms forming the ring do not lie in a plane. For example, six tetrahedral atoms may be united as shown in Fig. 18, *a* or *c*. These

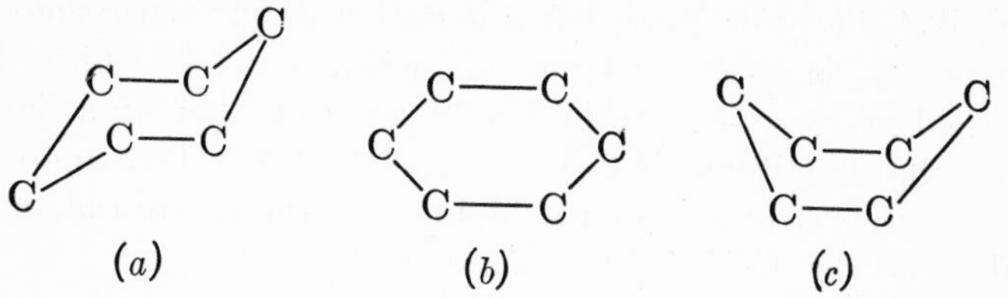

(*a*) (*b*) (*c*)

Fig. 18.

models differ from the planar one shown in *b* in that they can be constructed without distortion of the tetrahedral form of the atoms involved. For the atoms to be in a plane as in *b*, it is necessary, as noted earlier, to introduce negative strain, i.e., to increase the angle between the annular bonds to values greater than the normal. Since stable rings are now known which contain more than thirty members there is no necessity for assuming a planar form for any ring of more than five members. Rings of the nonplanar type are known as *strainless rings*.

The strainless models for cyclohexane shown in *a* and *c* are called, respectively, the "chair" (or Z) and "boat" (or C) forms; they are said to differ in *conformation*. In the simple cyclohexane systems the chair conformation is the preferred one. However, bridged systems often require the boat conformation (p. 365).

Hexahydrohomophthalic acid is especially interesting; at 220° the anhydrides of the *cis* and *trans* modifications exist in equilibrium and *the latter form predominates.*

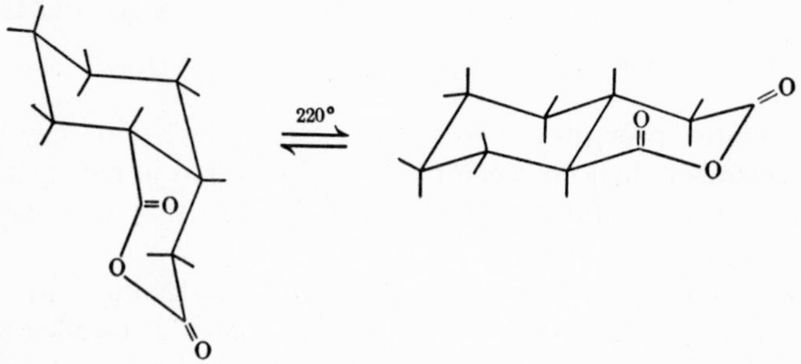

Fig. 19.

Examination of the three-dimensional formulas of the two hexahydrohomophthalic anhydrides in Fig. 19 reveals that the more stable *trans* form is more nearly planar than the less stable *cis* form. Of the bonds available for linkage at each apex of even the simple cyclohexane ring, one, called the *equatorial* bond, has a direction in or near the plane which most nearly approximates the six carbon atoms of the ring, while the other, called the *polar* bond, has a direction which is perpendicular to this plane. It is generally true that a compound in which the substituent is held by an equatorial bond is more stable than a similar one in which the substituent is held by a polar bond. Thus methylcyclohexane has the structure shown in Fig. 20; the equatorial bonds are labeled *e*, and the unlabeled bonds are polar.

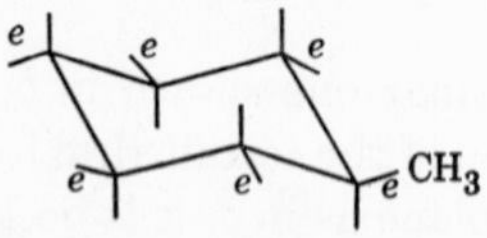

Fig. 20.

Bridged systems like the *trans* endocyclic derivative of hexahydrophthalic acid, the structure of which is shown below, are necessarily rigid. Each of the three cyclohexane systems that compose the structure is held in the boat conformation. Because of the rigidity of the system the *trans* acid cannot form an anhydride.

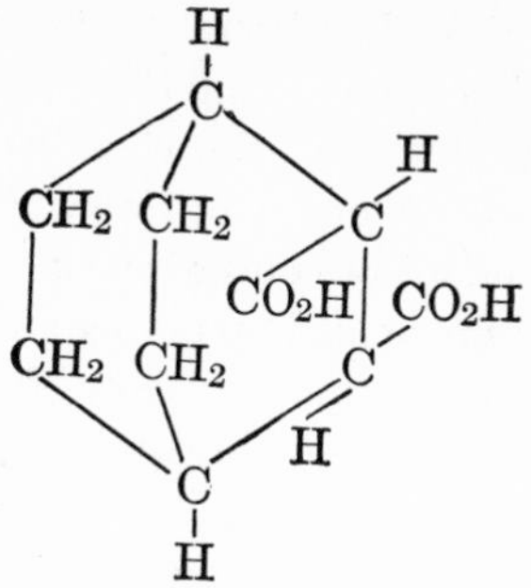

Compounds containing very large carbon rings have been found to possess stabilities comparable with those of the corresponding open-chain compounds. It should be mentioned, however, that even in these substances there is evidence that some strain persists because of repulsive forces between peripheral hydrogen atoms. It is believed, in fact, that because of this effect the cyclopentane ring is not quite planar.

The peculiar properties of the benzene ring are attributed to resonance stabilization, which can be at the maximum only when all the atoms concerned are in the same plane. Examination of models shows that cycloöctatetraene cannot be planar and leads to the prediction that this hydrocarbon should be highly unsaturated, rather than aromatic. This prediction has been verified; the hydrocarbon is very reactive, readily undergoing oxidation, reduction, polymerization, etc. It can be made in good yield by the polymerization of acetylene in the presence of nickel cyanide or the chelate nickel derivatives of active methylene compounds.

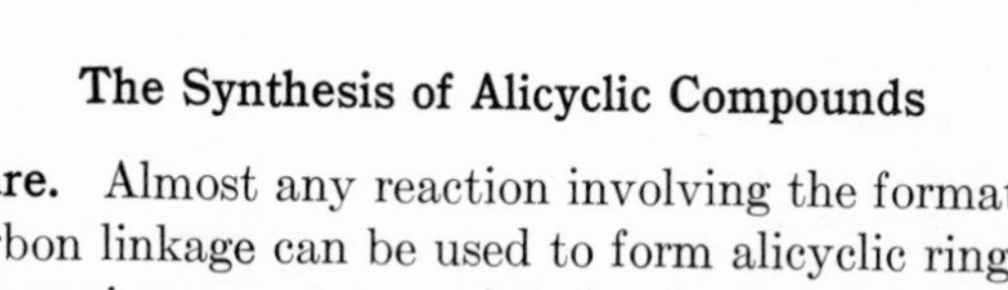

$$4HC\equiv CH \xrightarrow{\text{cat.}}$$

Cycloöctatraene
("chair" conformation)

The Synthesis of Alicyclic Compounds

Ring Closure. Almost any reaction involving the formation of a new carbon-to-carbon linkage can be used to form alicyclic rings from linear molecules. Some important examples already considered are the Dieckmann adaptation of the Claisen condensation, the Perkin method, the method of Ziegler, and the thermal decomposition of suitable dibasic acids or their salts.

The closure of large rings has been effected by use of the so-called dilution principle, which requires that the reactions be carried out in very dilute solutions. Obviously, the chances of *inter*molecular reaction are decreased by lowered concentration whereas those of *intra*molecular reaction are independent of concentration.

Large rings have been made also by taking advantage of the volatility of the products. Polyesters form reversibly, for example, and some of the cyclic forms are always present in equilibrium with the linear polymers. Slow distillation causes the equilibrium to shift as the ring compound distils. Thus the polyester from ethylene glycol and succinic acid yields a sixteen-membered cyclic ester when distilled *in vacuo* at 300°.

$$--(COCH_2CH_2CO_2CH_2CH_2OCOCH_2CH_2CO_2CH_2CH_2O)_x--$$

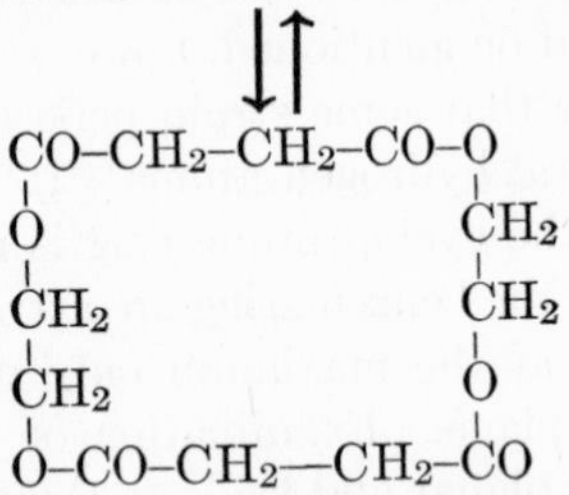

$$\downarrow\uparrow$$

```
CO–CH2–CH2–CO–O
|             |
O             CH2
|             |
CH2           CH2
|             |
CH2           O
|             |
O–CO–CH2—CH2–CO
```

The Diene or Diels-Alder Condensation. Perhaps the most useful method for forming carbocyclic rings is the diene or Diels-Alder condensation. It may be illustrated by the condensation of maleic anhydride with 1,3-butadiene.

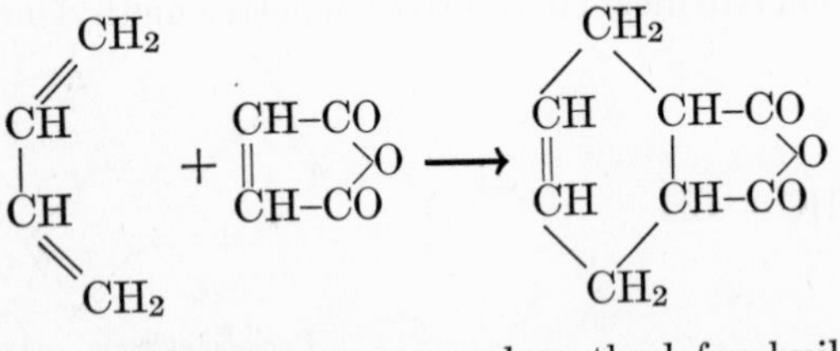

```
  CH2                               CH2
 //                                /   \
CH          CH–CO                CH    CH–CO
|       +   ||    >O    ⟶       ||    |     >O
CH          CH–CO                CH    CH–CO
 \\                                \   /
  CH2                               CH2
```

This synthesis provides a very general method for building six-membered rings. In place of maleic anhydride may be used many α,β-unsaturated carbonyl compounds such as acrolein and benzoquinone. The reaction is so general for 1,3-butadienes that it is used as a test for the system of linkages –C=C–C=C–.

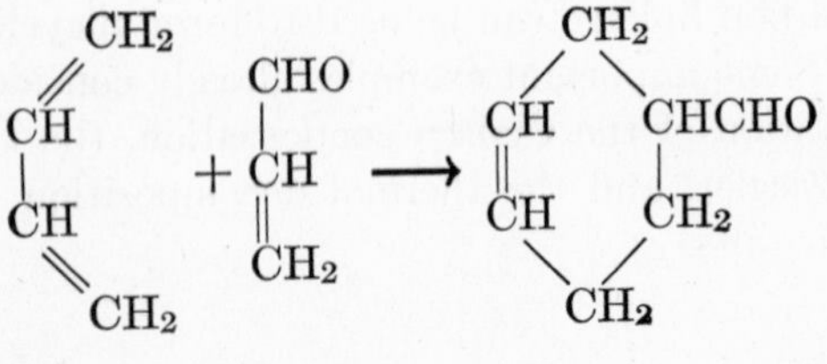

```
  CH2                        CH2
 //        CHO              /   \
CH          |             CH    CHCHO
|       +  CH      ⟶      ||    |
CH          ||            CH    CH2
 \\        CH2              \   /
  CH2                        CH2
```

```
    CH                                    CH
  //  \                                 / |  \
CH     CH2     CH–CO                 CH CH2  CH–CO
|      |    +  ||    >O   ⟶         ||  |    |     >O
CH     CH2     CH–CO                 CH CH2  CH–CO
  \\  /                                 \ |  /
    CH                                    CH
```

```
                      O                              O
                      ||                             ||
        CH2           C                     CH2      C
       //           /   \                  /   \   /   \
  CH3C            CH     CH          CH3C       CH       CH
   |         +    ||     ||    ⟶      ||        |        ||
   CH             CH     CH           CH        CH       CH
     \\             \   /               \     /    \    /
       CH2            C                   CH2        C
                      ||                             ||
                      O                              O
```

It will be noted that in these examples a 1,3-diene condenses with an olefinic compound in which the double bond is conjugated with a carbonyl group. To these compounds, known as *dienophiles*, may be added derivatives of cyanoacetic and acetoacetic esters of the following types.

```
        CN                        COCH3
       /                         /
RCH=C                     RCH=C
       \                         \
        CO2C2H5                   CO2C2H5
```

However, the synthesis is possible for many unsaturated compounds which do not belong to this category. Among these are styrene, vinyl chloride, vinyl acetate, and allyl chloride. Even ethylene and acetylene can function as dienophiles.

The condensation of vinyl acetate with cyclopentadiene affords an entry into the norcamphor series.

```
   CH                                         CH
  //  \                                     / |  \
CH      \          CH2                    CH  |   CH2
|        CH2  +    ||     O     ⟶        ||  CH2|       O
CH      /          CHOC–CH3               CH  |   CHOC–CH3
  \\  /                                     \ |  /
   CH                                         CH
```

```
        CH                      CH                      CH
      / |  \                  / |  \                  / |  \
H2  CH2 |   CH2        H2O  CH2 |   CH2        (O)  CH2 |   CH2
⟶   |  CH2|      O     ⟶    |  CH2|            ⟶    |  CH2|
    CH2 |   CHOC–CH3        CH2 |   CHOH            CH2 |   CO
      \ |  /                  \ |  /                  \ |  /
        CH                      CH                      CH
                                                   Norcamphor
```

The Closure of Non-Benzenoid Heterocyclic Rings

The various types of reaction possible in the case of bifunctional molecules are illustrated by the hydroxy acids, which, as has been stated, react differently depending on the distance between the functional groups.

$$CH_2(CH_2)_nC(=O)OH \text{ (with } CH_2\text{ bearing } OH) \longrightarrow \begin{cases} CH_2(CH_2)_n{-}CO \text{ (ring closed through } {-}O{-}) & (1) \\ CH_2{=}CH(CH_2)_{n-1}C(=O)OH & (2) \\ \text{cyclic double ester: } O{-}CH_2(CH_2)_n{-}CO{-}O{-}CH_2(CH_2)_n{-}CO \text{ (ring)} & (3) \\ HOCH_2(CH_2)_n{-}\left[C(=O){-}OCH_2(CH_2)_n\right]_xC(=O)OH & (4) \end{cases}$$

Reaction 1 or 3 is to be expected when a five- or six-membered ring would be formed. Otherwise reaction 4 is the normal one. Lactone formation as in reaction 1 occurs when $n = 2$ or 3. The formation of a double bond (reaction 2) takes place when $n = 1$. When $n = 0$ the double lactone (lactide) forms. In all other cases ($n > 3$) reaction 4 predominates.

In addition to lactones there are many other non-aromatic heterocyclic types that are familiar. Among them are acid anhydrides, lactams, cyclic acetals, cyclic ketals, and imides.

An interesting example is dimethylmaleic anhydride. Dimethylmaleic acid is so unstable that it has never been isolated. The anhydride is formed spontaneously.

$$\begin{matrix} CH_3C{-}CO_2H \\ \| \\ CH_3C{-}CO_2H \end{matrix} \xrightarrow{-H_2O} \begin{matrix} CH_3C{-}CO \\ \| \quad\;\; \rangle O \\ CH_3C{-}CO \end{matrix}$$

This anhydride also can be used in the Diels-Alder condensation. The synthesis of dimethylmaleic anhydride is carried out in the following way.

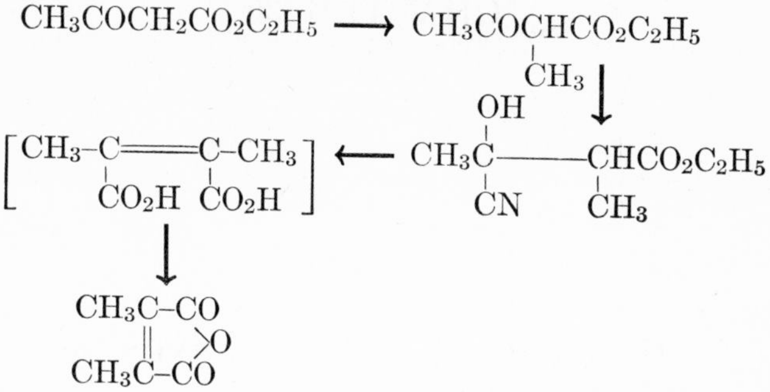

$$CH_3COCH_2CO_2C_2H_5 \longrightarrow CH_3CO\underset{\displaystyle CH_3}{\underset{|}{C}}HCO_2C_2H_5$$

$$\downarrow$$

$$\left[\begin{array}{c} CH_3\text{–}C{=\!=\!=}C\text{–}CH_3 \\ \quad | \qquad\quad | \\ \quad CO_2H \ CO_2H \end{array}\right] \longleftarrow CH_3\overset{\displaystyle OH}{\underset{\displaystyle CN}{C}}\text{———}\underset{\displaystyle CH_3}{C}HCO_2C_2H_5$$

$$\downarrow$$

$$\begin{array}{l} CH_3C\text{–}CO \\ \quad \| \quad \rangle O \\ CH_3C\text{–}CO \end{array}$$

Dimethylmaleic anhydride

PROBLEMS

1. Show by examples how the following types of reaction can be used to close alicyclic rings:

a. Diene synthesis.
b. Malonic ester method.
c. Dieckmann reaction.
d. Ziegler method.

2. What structural characteristics must a molecule possess in order to undergo cyclization?

3. Outline methods for making the following substances from open-chain compounds.

a. $CH_2\langle{}^{CH_2CH_2}_{CH_2CH_2}\rangle CHCO_2H$

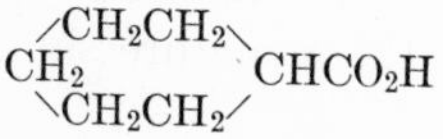

b. Ring: CH_2 — $CHCO_2CH_3$ — $CHCO_2CH_3$ — CH_2 — CH_2 — CH_2

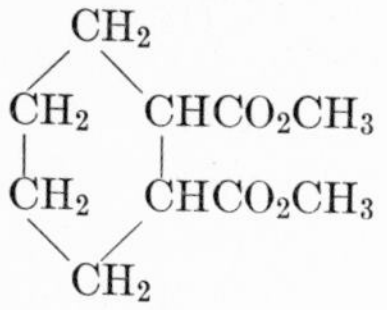

c. $\begin{array}{l} CH_2\text{–}CHCO_2H \\ | \qquad\quad \rangle CH_2 \\ CH_2\text{–}CHCO_2H \end{array}$

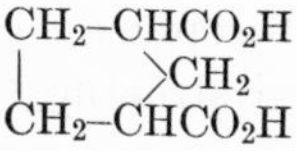

d. Ring: CH_2–$CHCO_2CH_3$ — CO — CH_2–CH_2 — CH_2

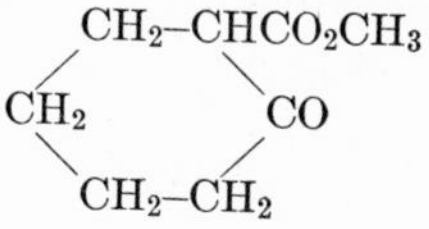

e. $\begin{array}{l} CH_2\text{–}CO \\ | \qquad | \\ CH_2\text{–}CH_2 \end{array}$

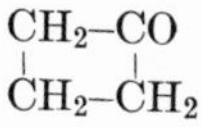

f. $(CH_2)_{14}\langle{}^{CH_2}_{CH_2}\rangle CO$

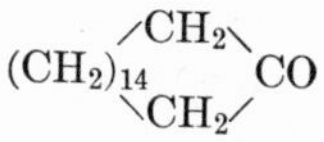

SUGGESTED READINGS

W. H. Perkin, "Early History of the Synthesis of Closed Carbon Chains," *J. Chem. Soc.*, 1347 (1929).

R. C. Fuson, "Alicyclic Compounds and the Theory of Strain," Gilman's *Organic Chemistry*, Second Ed., Chapter 1, John Wiley & Sons, New York, 1943.

CHAPTER 26

Polymerization and Polymers

NATURAL POLYMERS

There are many natural polymers or giant molecules. Nature turns to these for the building of strong or rigid structures. Among the most important natural polymers are caoutchouc or unvulcanized rubber, proteins, and cellulose.

The natural rubber molecule is a polymer in which isoprene units are arranged linearly. It has a molecular weight of about 400,000; i.e., the average molecule contains almost 10,000 isoprene units. The configuration of the carbon chains about the olefinic double bond in rubber is *cis*. A related natural polymer, balata, has the *trans* configuration; balata lacks many of the desirable properties of rubber. The caoutchouc (natural rubber) molecule can be represented by the structure shown.

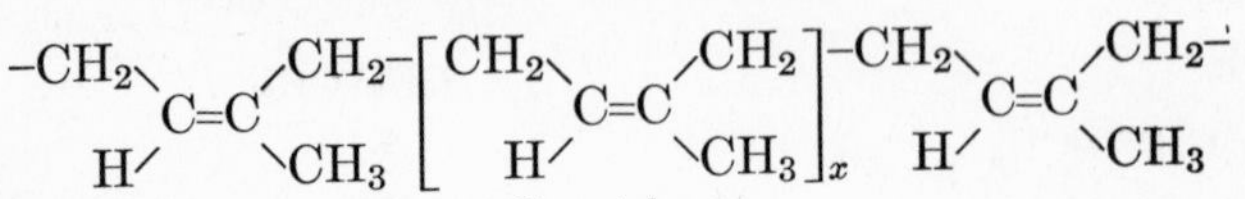

$$-CH_2(H)C{=}C(CH_3)CH_2-\left[CH_2(H)C{=}C(CH_3)CH_2\right]_x-CH_2(H)C{=}C(CH_3)CH_2-$$

Caoutchouc

It is of great interest that the *terpenes* and related groups of naturally occurring substances may be thought of as constructed of isoprene units. This structural feature may be observed in the skeletal structures of camphor, carane, and vitamin A.

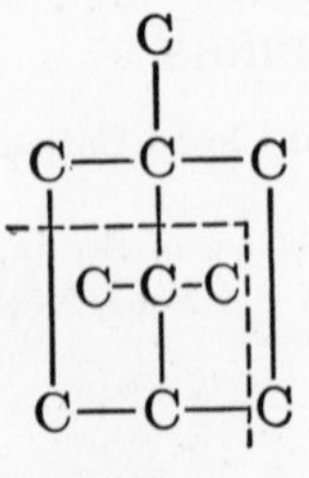

Camphor

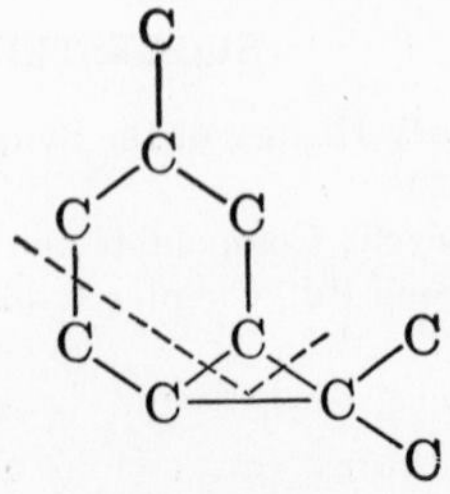

Carane

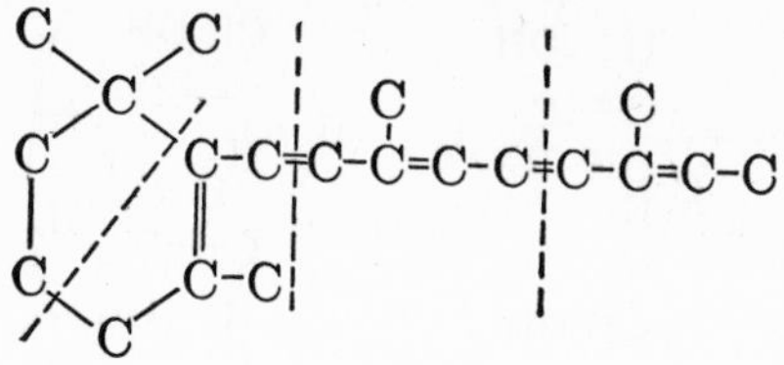

Vitamin A

The occurrence of isoprene units is so general that investigators of the structures of natural products generally consider the most probable formula of an unknown compound to be that which contains the maximum number of isoprene units. This generalization, called the "isoprene rule," has been very useful in the determination of the structure of natural products. Its use can be illustrated by the sesquiterpene bisabolene, which has the formula $C_{15}H_{24}$ and contains one ring and three olefinic linkages. Ozonization converts it into succinic acid, acetone, and levulinic acid. These data do not permit a decision to be made between formulas *a* and *b*. The isoprene rule, however, eliminates formula *b* as a probability.

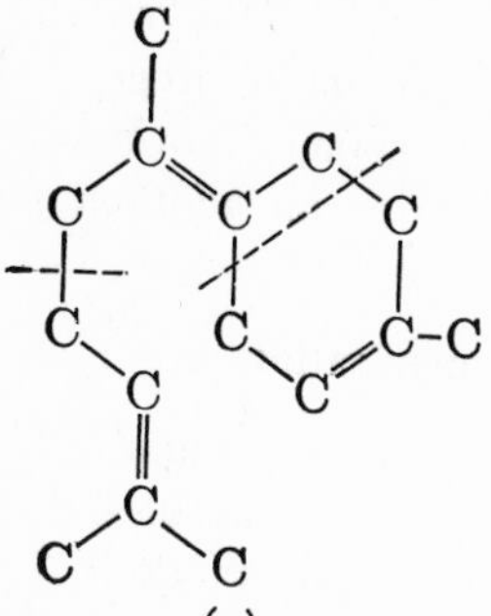

(*a*) 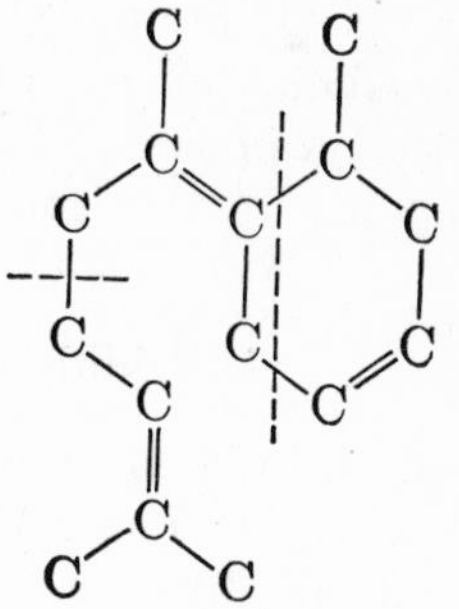 (*b*)

Proteins are natural polymers but differ from others in that they contain a variety of different structural units. However, all are of the same type—α-amino acids—and the polymers may be represented as follows.

$$\text{H--NH}\overset{\text{R}}{\overset{|}{\text{C}}}\text{HCO}\left[\text{NH}\overset{\text{R}}{\overset{|}{\text{C}}}\text{HCO}\right]_x\text{--OH}$$

Their molecular weights vary from 34,000 for egg albumen to about 50 million for the filterable virus from tobacco mosaic.

Cellulose can be hydrolyzed to glucose and is believed to consist of anhydroglucopyranose units (p. 209). The polymer is thought to be a polyacetal of the following type.

SYNTHETIC POLYMERS

Although none of the natural polymers has been synthesized as yet, chemists have been able to imitate them and usually to improve upon them by synthesis. Indeed, the thousands of known synthetic polymers offer a vast array of types affording almost any desired combination of properties. Some of these polymers will now be described.

The modern concept of polymerization is best expressed in the definition given by Carothers: *a polymerization process is one which is functionally capable of continuing indefinitely*. Such reactions lead, theoretically, to molecules of infinite size. Polymerization thus includes not only the self-addition of unsaturated molecules to give giant molecules (macromolecules) but also intermolecular combinations which can proceed indefinitely by elimination of water, ammonia, hydrogen halide, or other small molecules. A process of the latter type is known as a *condensation polymerization;* one of the former type as an *addition polymerization.*

Addition Polymerization

Unsaturated substances of many types are capable of undergoing self-addition with the formation of macromolecules. The polymers formed from olefinic hydrocarbons and many of their derivatives and from diolefins are the most useful addition polymers.

The preparation of polymers from *mixtures* of unsaturated substances is of fundamental importance in the production of commercial materials. A substance obtained *by polymerizing a mixture of two compounds either of which will polymerize alone is known as a copolymer*. If one of the compounds is incapable of polymerizing alone but does polymerize in conjunction with the second component, then the product is known as a *heteropolymer*.

Effects of Substituents in Olefins and Olefin Derivatives. The study of a great variety of ethylene derivatives has revealed that the tendency toward polymerization is profoundly affected by the substituents attached to the unsaturated carbon atoms. Although ethylene is susceptible to free-radical polymerization (p. 383), compounds of the formula $RCH{=}CH_2$ fail to polymerize under the influence of peroxides and yield only dimers, trimers, and very low polymers in the presence of an acidic catalyst. The only unsymmetrically substituted dialkylethylene ($R_2C{=}CH_2$) that has been subjected to intensive study is isobutylene [$(CH_3)_2C{=}CH_2$]; it yields high polymers readily, but only under the influence of acidic catalyst. On the other hand, it has not yet been possible to prepare macromolecules from dialkylethylenes of the type $RCH{=}CHR$, nor from tri- or tetraalkylethylenes.

An olefin derivative of the type $YCH{=}CH_2$, in which Y increases the polarizability of the ethylenic link, polymerizes much more readily. In this category may be included the dienes, styrene, vinyl halides, acrylonitrile (vinyl cyanide), vinyl acetate, vinyl ketones and ethers, and acrylic acid and its esters. Generally, substitution of an alkyl group on the β-carbon atom retards polymerization more effectively than the introduction of the same alkyl group on the α-carbon atom. For example, crotonic esters ($CH_3CH{=}CHCO_2R$) show little tendency toward polymerization, whereas α-methylacrylic esters ($CH_2{=}\underset{\displaystyle CH_3}{\underset{|}{C}}CO_2R$) polymerize as readily as the acrylic esters ($CH_2{=}CHCO_2R$).

Polymerization Initiators. Addition polymerization has been induced by physical means, such as heating, irradiation with ultraviolet light, exposure to α-particles, and the action of an electric discharge. Chemical catalysts capable of initiating polymerization include various oxidizing agents (oxygen, hydrogen peroxide, benzoyl peroxide and other organic peroxides, ozonides, persulfates, perborates, percarbonates, etc.), metal and metalloid halides (halides of aluminum, tin, boron, etc.), and alkali metals.

The Polymerization of Styrene and the Mechanism of Polymerization. The investigations of the factors that influence the polymerization of styrene have been much more extensive than those in connection with other olefins and olefin derivatives. The reaction may be represented by the following equation.

$$x\,C_6H_5CH{=}CH_2 \longrightarrow \left(\begin{array}{l}-CH-CH_2-\\ \;\;\;|\\ \;\;C_6H_5\end{array}\right)_x$$

It is probable that most of the styrene units are joined in the "head-to-tail" fashion as follows.

$$\begin{array}{l}-CHCH_2CHCH_2CHCH_2CHCH_2-\\ \;\;|\qquad\quad\;\;|\qquad\quad\;\;|\qquad\quad\;\;|\\ C_6H_5\quad C_6H_5\quad C_6H_5\quad C_6H_5\end{array}$$

This structure is supported by the isolation of 1,3-diphenyl derivatives from the products of the pyrolytic decomposition of the polymer. The following are among the identified decomposition products.

$$\underset{\substack{| \\ C_6H_5}}{CH_2{=}C}\underset{\substack{| \\ C_6H_5}}{CH_2}CH_2 \qquad \underset{\substack{| \\ C_6H_5}}{CH_2}CH_2\underset{\substack{| \\ C_6H_5}}{CH_2} \qquad \underset{\substack{| \\ C_6H_5}}{CH_2{=}C}CH_2\underset{\substack{| \\ C_6H_5}}{CH}CH_2\underset{\substack{| \\ C_6H_5}}{CH_2}$$

$$\underset{\substack{| \\ C_6H_5}}{CH_2}CH_2\underset{\substack{| \\ C_6H_5}}{CH}CH_2\underset{\substack{| \\ C_6H_5}}{CH_2} \qquad \text{1,3,5-triphenylbenzene } (C_6H_5)_3C_6H_3$$

Not all evidence supports the simple head-to-tail structure, however. Some of the styrene units may be joined in head-to-head, tail-to-tail fashion $\left(\text{–}CH_2\underset{\substack{| \\ C_6H_5}}{CH}\text{——}\underset{\substack{| \\ C_6H_5}}{CH}CH_2CH_2\underset{\substack{| \\ C_6H_5}}{CH}\text{–}\right)$, and others may have undergone hydrogen migration, yielding units of the type $\text{–}\overset{\substack{CH_3 \\ |}}{\underset{\substack{| \\ C_6H_5}}{C}}\text{–}$.

Kinetic studies of the polymerization of styrene by the action of peroxidic catalysts have led to the postulation of a free-radical chain mechanism. The process may be considered to consist of three steps: (1) initiation, (2) propagation, (3) termination. The catalyst initiates the reaction by generating free radicals which add to styrene. The addition product is a free radical which combines with more styrene, the process continuing until the reaction chain is broken. If benzoyl peroxide is the catalyst the polymerization is initiated by benzoyl radicals or by phenyl radicals formed as follows.

$$C_6H_5\overset{\substack{O \\ \|}}{C}\text{–}OO\overset{\substack{O \\ \|}}{C}\text{–}C_6H_5 \longrightarrow 2C_6H_5\overset{\substack{O \\ \|}}{C}\text{–}O\cdot$$

$$C_6H_5\overset{\substack{O \\ \|}}{C}\text{–}O\cdot \longrightarrow CO_2 + C_6H_5\cdot$$

The benzoyl or phenyl radical combines with styrene to yield a new free radical, and the chain is propagated by similar reactions.

$$C_6H_5\cdot + CH_2{=}\underset{\substack{| \\ C_6H_5}}{CH} \longrightarrow C_6H_5CH_2\underset{\substack{| \\ C_6H_5}}{CH}\cdot$$

$$C_6H_5CH_2\underset{\substack{| \\ C_6H_5}}{CH}\cdot + CH_2{=}\underset{\substack{| \\ C_6H_5}}{CH} \longrightarrow C_6H_5CH_2\underset{\substack{| \\ C_6H_5}}{CH}CH_2\underset{\substack{| \\ C_6H_5}}{CH}\cdot$$

$$C_6H_5CH_2\underset{\substack{| \\ C_6H_5}}{CH}CH_2\underset{\substack{| \\ C_6H_5}}{CH}\cdot + xCH_2{=}\underset{\substack{| \\ C_6H_5}}{CH}$$

$$\longrightarrow C_6H_5CH_2\underset{\substack{| \\ C_6H_5}}{CH}\text{—}\left(CH_2\underset{\substack{| \\ C_6H_5}}{CH}\text{–}\right)_x\text{–}CH_2\underset{\substack{| \\ C_6H_5}}{CH}\cdot$$

Growth of the chain in this manner may be interrupted in several ways. The benzoyl or phenyl radicals that initiated the process are capable of combining with the chain radicals, or two of the latter may react, either by combination or by disproportionation. These three possible cessation reactions are indicated by the following equations.

(*a*) $$\mathrm{C_6H_5CH_2\underset{C_6H_5}{\underset{|}{CH}}\text{—}\left(CH_2\underset{C_6H_5}{\underset{|}{CH}}\text{—}\right)_x\text{—}CH_2\underset{C_6H_5}{\underset{|}{CH}}\cdot + C_6H_5\cdot}$$

$$\longrightarrow \mathrm{C_6H_5CH_2\underset{C_6H_5}{\underset{|}{CH}}\text{—}\left(CH_2\underset{C_6H_5}{\underset{|}{CH}}\text{—}\right)\text{—}CH_2\underset{C_6H_5}{\underset{|}{CH}}C_6H_5}$$

(*b*) $$\mathrm{2C_6H_5CH_2\underset{C_6H_5}{\underset{|}{CH}}\text{—}\left(CH_2\underset{C_6H_5}{\underset{|}{CH}}\text{—}\right)_x\text{—}CH_2\underset{C_6H_5}{\underset{|}{CH}}\cdot}$$

$$\longrightarrow \mathrm{C_6H_5CH_2\underset{C_6H_5}{\underset{|}{CH}}\text{—}\left(CH_2\underset{C_6H_5}{\underset{|}{CH}}\text{—}\right)_x\text{—}CH_2\underset{C_6H_5}{\underset{|}{CH}}\text{—}\underset{C_6H_5}{\underset{|}{CH}}\text{—}CH_2\left(\underset{C_6H_5}{\underset{|}{CH}}\text{—}CH_2\text{—}\right)_x\text{—}\underset{C_6H_5}{\underset{|}{CH}}CH_2C_6H_5}$$

(*c*) $$\mathrm{2C_6H_5CH_2\underset{C_6H_5}{\underset{|}{CH}}\text{—}\left(CH_2\underset{C_6H_5}{\underset{|}{CH}}\text{—}\right)_x\text{—}CH_2\underset{C_6H_5}{\underset{|}{CH}}\cdot}$$

$$\longrightarrow \mathrm{C_6H_5CH_2\underset{C_6H_5}{\underset{|}{CH}}\text{—}\left(CH_2\underset{C_6H_5}{\underset{|}{CH}}\text{—}\right)_x\text{—}CH_2\underset{C_6H_5}{\underset{|}{CH_2}} + C_6H_5CH_2\underset{C_6H_5}{\underset{|}{CH}}\text{—}\left(CH_2\underset{C_6H_5}{\underset{|}{CH}}\text{—}\right)_x\text{—}CH{=}\underset{C_6H_5}{\underset{|}{CH}}}$$

The last reaction involves the abstraction of a hydrogen atom (with one electron) by a free radical which loses its capacity for further chain propagation when it combines with the hydrogen atom. However, the carbon atom from which the hydrogen atom (with one electron) is taken becomes a free radical. This process is known as chain transfer. In the illustration the hydrogen atom was taken from the α-carbon atom of another free radical, yielding a 1,2-diradical which degenerates into an olefin. If the second free-radical grouping is introduced at a point sufficiently remote from the first that neither olefin formation nor ring formation occurs, then the diradical may continue to grow at both points. This is one way in which *branched* macromolecules may form.

It seems likely that polymerizations brought about by catalysts of other types proceed by different mechanisms. Acids and metal and metalloid halides are believed to effect polymerization by a chain reaction involving *ions*. For example, an olefin may react with an acid as follows.

$$\mathrm{H^+ + CH_2\vdots\underset{R}{\underset{|}{CH}} \longrightarrow CH_3{:}\underset{\ddot{R}}{\overset{H}{\ddot{C}^+}}}$$

A polymer chain may be propagated by further coordination, the carbonium carbon now acting as the acceptor.

$$\underset{\text{R}}{\text{CH}_3\overset{+}{\text{C}}\text{H}} + \underset{\text{R}}{\text{CH}_2\text{=CH}} \longrightarrow \text{CH}_3\underset{\text{R}}{\text{C}}\text{HCH}_2\underset{\text{R}}{\overset{+}{\text{C}}}\text{H}$$

$$\text{CH}_3\underset{\text{R}}{\text{C}}\text{HCH}_2\underset{\text{R}}{\overset{+}{\text{C}}}\text{H} + x\underset{\text{R}}{\text{CH}_2\text{=CH}} \longrightarrow \text{CH}_3\underset{\text{R}}{\text{C}}\text{H}\left(\text{CH}_2\underset{\text{R}}{\text{C}}\text{H}\right)_x\text{CH}_2\underset{\text{R}}{\overset{+}{\text{C}}}\text{H}$$

A possible cessation reaction is the elimination of a proton from the methylene group adjacent to the carbonium carbon with the formation of a terminal double bond.

$$\text{CH}_3\underset{\text{R}}{\text{C}}\text{H}\left(\text{CH}_2\underset{\text{R}}{\text{C}}\text{H}\right)_x\text{CH}_2\underset{\text{R}}{\overset{+}{\text{C}}}\text{H} \longrightarrow \text{CH}_3\text{CH}\left(\text{CH}_2\underset{\text{R}}{\text{C}}\text{H}\right)_x\text{CH=}\underset{\text{R}}{\text{C}}\text{H} + \text{H}^+$$

The course of polymerization under the influence of alkali metals may be similar to the peroxide-catalyzed process. For example, sodium may combine with an olefin to form an organometallic substance which is also a free radical.

$$\text{Na}\cdot + \underset{\text{R}}{\text{CH}_2\text{=CH}} \longrightarrow \text{NaCH}_2\underset{\text{R}}{\text{C}}\text{H}\cdot$$

However, the fact that organometallic compounds may be used in place of the alkali metal suggests that chain growth also occurs by the following path.

$$\cdot\underset{\text{R}}{\text{C}}\text{HCH}_2\text{Na} + \underset{\text{R}'}{\text{C}}\text{H=CH}_2 \longrightarrow \cdot\underset{\text{R}}{\text{C}}\text{HCH}_2\underset{\text{R}'}{\text{C}}\text{HCH}_2\text{Na}$$

The speculations concerning the intimate mechanism of thermal polymerization are not yet highly developed. It is assumed that some of the molecules become activated and initiate reaction chains similar to those mentioned above, but the exact manner of activation is not known. It seems unlikely that the initial active fragments are 1,2-diradicals formed by opening of the double bond, since these would be expected to favor the formation of cyclic trimers, which are not produced.

$$\underset{\text{R}}{\text{CH}_2\text{=CH}} \longrightarrow \cdot\text{CH}_2\underset{\text{R}}{\text{C}}\text{H}\cdot \xrightarrow{\text{CH}_2\text{=CHR}} \cdot\text{CH}_2\underset{\text{R}}{\text{C}}\text{HCH}_2\underset{\text{R}}{\text{C}}\text{H}\cdot$$

$$\xrightarrow{\text{CH}_2\text{=CHR}} \cdot\text{CH}_2\underset{\text{R}}{\text{C}}\text{HCH}_2\underset{\text{R}}{\text{C}}\text{HCH}_2\underset{\text{R}}{\text{C}}\text{H}\cdot \longrightarrow \text{cyclo-}(\text{CH}_2\text{-RCH-CH}_2\text{-CHR-CH}_2\text{-CHR})$$

(Ring: CH_2 at top bonded to RCH and CHR; RCH–CH_2 and CHR–CH_2; both CH_2 bonded to CH(R) at bottom.)

Influence of Polymerization Conditions. The factor of greatest importance in determining the physical properties of a polymeric substance is the degree of polymerization or the number of monomer units combined in the macromolecule. In the preparation of addition polymers it usually is possible to control the degree of polymerization by varying the amount of catalyst used or, in the case of thermal polymerizations, by varying the temperature. Increasing the amount of catalyst causes the formation of polymers of lower molecular weight. This observation is explicable on the basis of any of the mechanisms outlined above; the greater the amount of catalyst, the larger the number of chains initiated and hence the smaller the number of monomer molecules available to each of them.

One of the most important considerations in the preparation of polymers of high molecular weight is the purity of the monomers. Many of the common functional groups are capable of reacting with free radicals, and so any impurity present in the monomer is likely to react with the growing polymer radical in such a way as to stop its growth. Similarly, any impurity capable of reaction with a carbonium ion may stop a polymerization proceeding by an ionic mechanism of the type illustrated above.

Polystyrenes prepared by various methods have been examined by Staudinger. Table XXXIII illustrates the wide range of properties of the products.

TABLE XXXIII

Polymerization of Styrene under Various Conditions

Method of Polymerization	Molecular Weight of Polymer	Appearance	M.P., °C	Solubility in Ether
Under N_2, room temperature	600,000	White fibers	180	Insoluble
Under air, room temperature	200,000	White fibers	180	Insoluble
Under N_2, 100°	120,000	White fibers	160–180	Insoluble
Under N_2, 150°	23,000	White powder	120–130	Partly soluble
Heating with $SnCl_4$	3,000	White powder	105–110	Soluble

Emulsions of styrene polymerize readily. It has been observed that the polymers formed in emulsion (20 to 50 per cent of styrene emulsified in 5 per cent sodium oleate solution) have higher molecular weight than those obtained from pure styrene under comparable conditions. This difference is shown in Table XXXIV.

TABLE XXXIV

POLYMERIZATION OF STYRENE

Temperature, °C	Molecular Weight of Polymer from Emulsion	Pure Styrene
30	750,000	600,000
60	400,000	350,000
100	175,000	120,000

The shape of a polymeric molecule also is of importance in determining the properties of the substance. Ordinary polystyrene is believed to consist of rod-shaped molecules. Although there is evidence that the polystyrene in the latex obtained by emulsion polymerization consists of spherical molecules, after the polymer is precipitated from the latex, dried, and dissolved in benzene, the solution displays the high viscosity characteristic of rod-shaped molecules. A correlation of molecular weight and viscosity based on the assumption of the rodlike molecular shape has been developed.

Polystyrene prepared by polymerization at relatively low temperatures (ca. 150°) is a tough, transparent material soluble in organic solvents. Polymerization at higher temperatures produces lower polymers which are brittle and more soluble.

Estimation of the molecular weight from the viscosity of solutions of polymers prepared at high temperatures often leads to fictitious values. It is believed that the abnormal properties of the high-temperature product are due to the presence of branched molecules. One manner in which branching may occur has been noted (p. 375). There are other possibilities. For example, an inactive polymer molecule containing a terminal double bond may be incorporated into a growing chain by attack at the double bond. An inactive saturated macromolecule may be activated at an internal position by loss of a hydrogen atom to an active free radical. Either of these possibilities would account for the fact that molecules of polystyrene, when dissolved in a solution in which styrene is being polymerized, continue to grow. It has been suggested also that branching may result from activation of the *ortho* and *para* positions in the benzene ring.

It has been observed that the presence of divinylbenzene in styrene leads to polymers which are harder and less soluble than those obtained from pure styrene under similar conditions. Since divinylbenzene has two double bonds it may be involved in two polystyrene chains, thus giving rise to *cross links*. In consequence the molecules produced are *three-dimensional* rather than threadlike. The *cross linking* can be illustrated as shown. Cross-linked polymers are generally characterized

$-CHCH_2—CHCH_2—CHCH_2—CHCH_2—CHCH_2-$

$-CHCH_2—CHCH_2CHCH_2—CHCH_2—CHCH_2-$

$-CHCH_2—CHCH_2CHCH_2-$

by hardness and insolubility. Even extremely small amounts of cross linking profoundly affect the characteristics of polystyrene. The polymer obtained from styrene containing only 0.0025 per cent of divinylbenzene gives solutions of abnormally high viscosity. Increase of the divinylbenzene content to 0.1 per cent produces a polymer which swells when in contact with solvents but is almost insoluble. The polymer containing 1 per cent or more of divinylbenzene is a hard, glassy resin, completely unaffected by solvents.

From the figures mentioned it is apparent that a single molecule of divinylbenzene per 40,000 molecules of styrene may have an observable effect upon the properties of the polymer. When polymers of very low divinylbenzene content are left in contact with solvents they are slowly attacked. The solution so obtained appears to contain normal polystyrene molecules. It is believed that the ordinary threadlike molecules are entrapped by or interwined with the three-dimensional molecules. The effect is spoken of as *netting*, and divinylbenzene is regarded as a *netting agent*. Other netting agents that can serve are divinylacetylene, divinyl sulfide, divinylsulfone, and hexatriene. Divinyl ether, divinyl sulfoxide, diallyl, and isoprene are relatively ineffective.

Properties and Uses of Polystyrene. Polystyrene produced by polymerization in the absence of air at temperatures between 100° and 150° is a colorless solid. It softens on heating (thermoplastic) and can be molded easily. Colored resins are obtained by incorporating suitable dyes or pigments, usually before polymerization. Polystyrene is one of the best known electrical insulators, being approximately equivalent to fused quartz in this regard.

Quick-drying lacquers can be made from polystyrene and hydrocarbon solvents. Plasticizers are necessary to improve the gloss and prevent checking. Dibutyl phthalate, triphenyl and tricresyl phosphates, glyceryl ethers, esters of fatty acids, and other organic substances have been used as plasticizers.

Polystyrene undergoes depolymerization at temperatures near 300°. The resin can be identified by depolymerization and characterization of the styrene so formed.

When the copolymer of styrene and divinylbenzene is sulfonated it is converted to a sulfonic acid derivative which can serve in ion exchange. Under suitable conditions its sodium salt, for example, may exchange sodium ions for other metal ions. An important use of such ion-exchange resins is in water softening, effected by replacing the heavy-metal ions in the water by sodium ions from the polymer. The process consists in passing the hard water through the ion-exchange resin in its sodium form. From time to time the resin is "regenerated" by treatment with brine.

Theoretically any polymer containing acidic groups ($-SO_3H-$, CO_2H, etc.) can serve as a cation exchanger. If basic groups, such as amino, are present, the resin can serve to exchange anions.

Diene Polymers. Investigation of the structure of natural rubber indicates that it consists of isoprene units combined at the 1,4 positions in uniform head-to-tail fashion. There is no evidence, however, that rubber is formed in the plant by polymerization of isoprene. It appears more probable that it is built up from oxygen-containing molecules by condensation and dehydration reactions.

Polymerization of dienes by the usual methods may lead to products formed by 1,4 addition, as illustrated by the following combination of butadiene units.

$$-CH_2CH{=}CHCH_2CH_2CH{=}CHCH_2-$$

However, polymers formed by 1,2 addition might be expected also.

$$\begin{array}{ll} -CH_2\underset{|}{C}H\text{———} & CH_2\underset{|}{C}H- \\ \quad\;\; CH{=}CH_2 & \quad\; CH{=}CH_2 \end{array}$$

A third possibility is that both types of combination may be present in the polymer.

$$\begin{array}{l} -CH_2CH{=}CHCH_2\underset{|}{C}H- \\ \qquad\qquad\qquad\quad CH{=}CH_2 \end{array}$$

Structural units of either of the last two varieties contain vinyl side chains which may become incorporated in other growing chains, leading to branched chains.

$$\begin{array}{l} =CH_2CH{=}CHCH_2CH{-}CH_2CH{=}CHCH_2- \\ \qquad\qquad -CH{-}CH_2CH{-}CH_2CH_2CH{=}CHCH_2- \\ \qquad\qquad\;\; CH{=}CH_2 \end{array}$$

Ozonization of a butadiene polymer produced in aqueous emulsion yields succinic acid, β-carboxyadipic acid, and resinous acids. The first can be derived only from a unit formed by 1,4 combination of butadiene molecules.

$$-CH_2CH{=}{=}CHCH_2CH_2CH{=}{=}CHCH_2- \longrightarrow HO_2CCH_2CH_2CO_2H$$

The second product can originate only by a mixed 1,2-1,4 combination of butadiene units.

$$-CH_2CH{=}{=}CHCH_2CH_2\underset{\displaystyle CH{=}{=}CH_2-}{\underset{|}{C}}HCH_2CH{=}{=}CHCH_2-$$

$$\xrightarrow{O_3} HO_2CCH_2CH_2\underset{\displaystyle CO_2H}{\underset{|}{C}}HCH_2CO_2H$$

Resinous acids might be expected from molecules containing a number of butadiene units combined by 1,2 addition. It is indicated, therefore, that the polymerization proceeds by all the paths indicated. A similar conclusion has been reached from a study of polymers obtained by the action of alkali metals on the diene.

This difference between the structural arrangement of natural rubber and diene polymers accounts, in part, for the fact that no true synthetic rubber has been prepared as yet. However, a number of synthetic polymers are suitable for the manufacture of various articles which have been made of rubber; certain of them are superior to rubber for special applications.

The first rubber substitute prepared on a commerical scale was the dimethylbutadiene polymer manufactured in Germany during World War I. Production, at one time about 150 tons per month, has been discontinued. Neoprene, the polymer of chloroprene (2-chlorobutadiene), was the first synthetic rubberlike material to be manufactured in the United States. Among its most valuable characteristics is its resistance to petroleum solvents.

World War II required the creation of a vast American industry for the production of synthetic rubber from butadiene. The most important advances have been the development of copolymers, the employment of emulsion polymerization, and the development of low-temperature emulsion polymerization ("cold rubber").

Butadiene has been attractive because it can be prepared more readily than isoprene or dimethylbutadiene. The principal methods of production are catalytic dehydrogenation of butane or butene, and dehydration of 1,3-dihydroxybutane obtained by reduction of aldol.

Copolymers of butadiene with styrene and with acrylonitrile are the most valuable synthetic rubbers. The content of the second monomer varies between 20 and 40 per cent, depending on the exact characteristics desired. The German names for styrene copolymers are Buna S and Buna SS, the latter having the higher styrene content; for the acrylonitrile copolymers, Buna N, Perbunan, and Perbunan Extra, the last having the highest acrylonitrile content. Pre-war American manufacturers used the names Hycar and Chemigum for acrylonitrile copolymers. The products of the government-owned plants were designated by letters (GR-S, GR-N).

Emulsion polymerization leads to a latex which can be precipitated to yield a workable form of the polymer. In ordinary practice the emulsion contains 60–80 per cent of water (which must be free of salts of iron and calcium and of organic impurities). In addition to the monomer or monomers and catalyst the following must be present in the emulsion: (*a*) an emulsifying agent (a soap or a detergent); (*b*) an initiator (a substance capable of generating free radicals) such as a peroxide or an azo compound; and (*c*) a regulator or modifier (most commonly an aliphatic mercaptan containing twelve or more carbon atoms).

One function of the modifier is that of a *chain-transfer agent.* The modifier reacts with a polymer radical to convert it to an inactive molecule, thus stopping its growth, but at the same time generating a new free radical which can initiate another polymerization sequence. The process can be represented by the series of equations given below, in which, for convenience, only the 1,4 polymerization of butadiene is considered.

$$ZCH_2CH{=}CHCH_2(CH_2CH{=}CHCH_2)_xCH_2CH{=}CHCH_2\cdot + RSH$$
$$\longrightarrow ZCH_2CH{=}CHCH_2(CH_2CH{=}CHCH_2)_xCH_2CH{=}CHCH_3 + RS\cdot$$

$$RS\cdot + CH_2{=}CHCH{=}CH_2 \longrightarrow RSCH_2CH{=}CHCH_2\cdot \longrightarrow \longrightarrow \longrightarrow$$
$$RSCH_2CH{=}CHCH_2(CH_2CH{=}CHCH_2)_xCH_2CH{=}CHCH_2\cdot$$

$$RSCH_2CH{=}CHCH_2(CH_2CH{=}CHCH_2)_xCH_2CH{=}CHCH_2\cdot + RSH$$
$$\longrightarrow RSCH_2CH{=}CHCH_2(CH_2CH{=}CHCH_2)_xCH_2CH{=}CHCH_3 + RS\cdot$$

The result is that the average molecular weight of the polymer decreases with increasing concentration of the modifier, which thus can be used to control the average chain length of the polymer.

The free radicals which initiate the polymerization of unsaturated compounds can be generated in the mixture by the interaction of oxidizing and reducing agents (redox initiation). In fact, when a peroxidic catalyst is employed with a mercaptan modifier, the initiation of polymerization may occur only by way of the mercaptide radicals. These may form by interaction of the modifier with the catalyst as well as in the chain-transfer process.

$$\frac{1}{2}H_2O_2 + RSH \longrightarrow H_2O + RS\cdot$$

A great many redox combinations have been studied, and many pairs are available as initiators. The reaction between the oxidizing agent and the reducing agent may itself be subject to catalysis, with the result that a very small amount of an *activator* may be required. The development of activated recipes has made possible the production of "cold rubber" by permitting the polymerization to be carried out at satisfactory rates even at temperatures well below 0°.

The elasticity of rubber and rubberlike products depends in part on the alignment of the long-chain molecules. The molecules of a newly formed polymer apparently are in random arrangement. In the manufacture of rubber substitutes the crude product is subjected to mechanical kneading and milling to bring about the desired orientation.

The butadiene copolymers are vulcanized in much the same way as natural rubber. Vulcanization is believed to involve the formation of cross links by the action of sulfur. Neoprene is vulcanized by heating alone. No other rubber substitute can be vulcanized without some added material.

Polymers of Simple Olefins. Treatment of simple olefins (such as ethylene and propylene) with acids causes the formation of dimers, trimers, tetramers, etc. The process is used in the preparation of gasoline from cracking still gases.

High polymers are produced by heating ethylene to temperatures of 100–400° under very high pressures (about 1000 atmospheres) in the presence of carefully controlled amounts of oxygen. The polymer, first used as an electrical insulator, has since found a host of other applications.

High polymers of isobutylene are produced by the action of metal halides at low temperatures. Products of molecular weight up to 27,000 are thick liquids. Higher polymers are rubberlike. It is extremely interesting that this saturated polymeric hydrocarbon has many of the properties of the unsaturated diene polymers. The absence of reactive double bonds makes it an extraordinarily stable substance, and in resistance to oxidation it is far superior to rubber. However, for the same reason, it is unaffected by sulfur and hence cannot be vulcanized. This difficulty can be overcome by copolymerization with a small amount of a diene; the resulting polymer (Butyl rubber) has one double bond for each diene molecule employed and can be vulcanized. By balancing the amount of unsaturation introduced with the degree of vulcanization desired, a saturated vulcanized material can be produced.

The Acrylic Polymers. The fact that acrylic acid and certain of its derivatives undergo polymerization has been known for many years. At the present time the polymers of methyl acrylate ($CH_2{=}CHCO_2CH_3$) and methyl methacrylate ($CH_2{=}C(CH_3)CO_2CH_3$) are the most important industrial substances of this class. The commercial products have molecular weights of about 45,000, although it is possible to produce much higher polymers. They are insoluble in water, alcohol, and aliphatic hydrocarbons, but soluble in aromatic hydrocarbons, chloroform, *sym*-tetrachloroethane, ketones, and esters. Lower polymers, of course, are more soluble than those of higher molecular weight.

The chain structures of these polymers appears to be that derived by head-to-tail combination of the monomeric units.

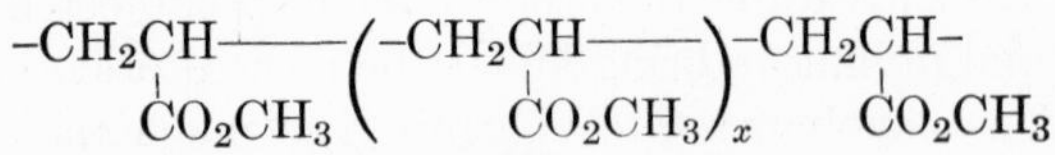

$$-CH_2\underset{\displaystyle CO_2CH_3}{\underset{|}{CH}}-\left(-CH_2\underset{\displaystyle CO_2CH_3}{\underset{|}{CH}}-\right)_x-CH_2\underset{\displaystyle CO_2CH_3}{\underset{|}{CH}}-$$

Polymethyl acrylate

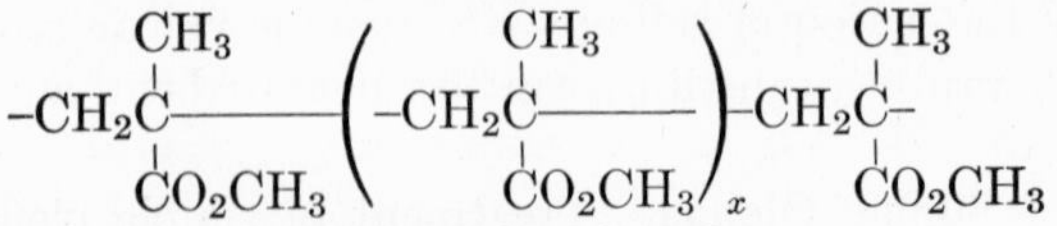

$$-CH_2\overset{\displaystyle CH_3}{\overset{|}{\underset{\displaystyle CO_2CH_3}{\underset{|}{C}}}}-\left(-CH_2\overset{\displaystyle CH_3}{\overset{|}{\underset{\displaystyle CO_2CH_3}{\underset{|}{C}}}}-\right)_x-CH_2\overset{\displaystyle CH_3}{\overset{|}{\underset{\displaystyle CO_2CH_3}{\underset{|}{C}}}}-$$

Polymethyl methacrylate

The term acrylate polymer is used more or less indiscrimately for polymers of acrylic esters, methacrylic esters, and copolymers containing either or both.

Polymethyl acrylate undergoes the usual reactions of esters. Thus it yields polyacrylic acid on hydrolysis (saponification), polyalcohols on treatment with methylmagnesium halides, and polyamides and polyimides on treatment with ammonia. In polymethyl methacrylate the ester group is attached to a tertiary carbon atom and is, therefore, extremely stable.

Methyl methacrylate polymers with a wide range of physical properties can be prepared. The higher polymers (molecular weight about 40,000) are highly transparent, tough, and elastic. They are used in molding compositions, with or without fillers and coloring agents. Lenses for cameras, spectacles, etc., are made by molding the powdered material. The plastic used for such purposes may be made harder than the normal variety by mixing substances such as methacrylic anhydride or ethylene methacrylate with the methyl methacrylate before polymerization. These undoubtedly function by introducing cross links (compare the effect of divinylbenzene on polystyrene).

Large objects of polymethyl methacrylate are cast rather than molded. The mold is filled with the monomer, containing a little benzoyl peroxide, and polymerization is effected in the mold. The cockpit enclosures of modern military airplanes are of cast acrylate resin.

Acrylates are much used to impregnate paper, cloth, wood, wallboard, etc. Polymerization is effected after the material is impregnated. As much as 60 per cent of the resin can be incorporated into wood in this way.

Like the esters of acrylic acid, the nitrile also polymerizes readily. The polymer is insoluble in the common organic solvents, a fact that delayed its commercial utilization. The development of special solvents, such as dimethylformamide, made it possible to prepare polyacrylonitrile filaments and thus to use the polymer for textile fibers. Orlon and Acrilan are such materials. Dynel is a copolymer of acrylonitrile and vinyl chloride.

The Vinyl Polymers. A number of important polymers and copolymers are derived from vinyl chloride and vinyl acetate. Commercial polyvinyl chloride is a high-melting substance of low solubility. It can be softened by the addition of tricresyl phosphate, and the plasticized polymer (Koroseal) is used as a substitute for rubber.

Polyvinyl chloride apparently contains vinyl chloride units joined in head-to-tail fashion. The earlier investigators proposed the head-to-head, tail-to-tail structure for polyvinyl halides on the basis of the fact that halogen can be removed by treatment with metallic zinc. This was taken as an indication of the presence of a 1,2-dihalogen unit. However, repetition of the experiments revealed that the dehalogenated polymer is saturated, whereas an unsaturated product would be expected by dehalogenation of the head-to-head, tail-to-tail polymer. The reaction must involve the formation of cyclopropane rings from 1,3-dihalogen units. It is interesting that not all the halogen can be removed by the action of zinc. On the basis of the head-to-tail structure it would be

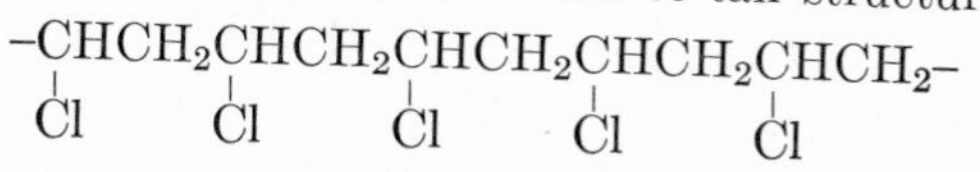

$$-\underset{\displaystyle Cl}{\underset{|}{CH}}CH_2\underset{\displaystyle Cl}{\underset{|}{CH}}CH_2\underset{\displaystyle Cl}{\underset{|}{CH}}CH_2\underset{\displaystyle Cl}{\underset{|}{CH}}CH_2\underset{\displaystyle Cl}{\underset{|}{CH}}CH_2-$$

expected that an occasional halogen atom would be isolated as follows.

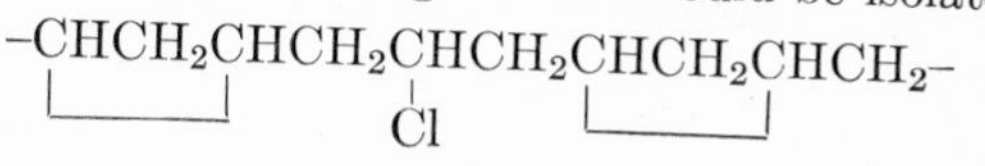

$$-\underbrace{CHCH_2CH}CH_2\underset{\displaystyle Cl}{\underset{|}{CH}}CH_2\underbrace{CHCH_2CH}CH_2-$$

One of the early disadvantages of polyvinyl chloride was its tendency to darken on exposure to sunlight. The development of color appears to be related to the loss of hydrogen chloride. It will be noted that, when one molecule of hydrogen chloride is lost, a neighboring chlorine atom becomes allylic.

```
–CH₂CHCH₂CHCH₂CHCH=CHCH₂CH–
     |     |     |         |
     Cl    Cl    Cl        Cl
```

Because of the reactivity of the allylic chlorine atom the product should lose hydrogen chloride more readily than the original polymer. In this way polyene chains would be developed and the substance would become colored.

```
–CH₂CHCH=CHCH=CHCH=CHCH=CH–
     |
     Cl
```

Fortunately, it has been possible to find stabilizers that inhibit these reactions.

Polyvinyl acetate is a clear, colorless solid. The commercial product has a molecular weight of about 20,000 and a softening point of 30–40°; higher polymers have softening points as high as 200°. It is very soluble in organic solvents, and it finds uses in coating compositions.

Polyvinyl alcohol is made by saponification of polyvinyl acetate. It can be produced as a rubberlike material, but because it is soluble in water its use as a rubber substitute is limited. It is highly resistant to organic solvents.

The fact that polyvinyl alcohol is unaffected by periodic acid, a reagent specific for 1,2-glycols, supports the 1,3-glycol structure.

```
–CH₂CHCH₂CHCH₂CHCH₂CH–
     |     |     |    |
     OH    OH    OH   OH
```

This fact, in turn, shows that vinyl acetate polymerizes in the head-to-tail fashion.

An important use of polyvinyl alcohol is in the preparation of the Alvars, polyacetals obtained by treating the alcohol with aldehydes. Butvar is the butyraldehyde derivative. It is not possible to cause all

```
          CH₂                           CH₂
         /   \                         /   \
–CH₂CH        CHCH₂CHCH₂CH        CH–
     |          |      |          |          |
     O          O      OH         O          O
      \        /                   \        /
         CH                           CH
         |                            |
         C₃H₇                         C₃H₇
```

Butvar

the hydroxyl groups to take part in the acetalization; some of them become isolated as indicated in the formula, and so survive the treatment with the aldehyde. Butvar is used as the inner sheet in safety glass. It is much superior to cellulose acetate, which becomes brittle at temperatures near 0° Fahrenheit; hence safety glass made with cellulose acetate shatters badly when broken in very cold weather. Other desirable characteristics of Butvar are its high elasticity, resistance to light, and resistance to weathering. The last property is desirable, since it makes unnecessary any special sealing at the edge of the glass.

Copolymers. Copolymers of almost any desired gradation of properties between those of polyvinyl chloride and polyvinyl acetate are produced by polymerizing mixtures. It is an interesting fact that, although vinyl acetate alone polymerizes more readily than the chloride, the first copolymer formed from a mixture is richer in vinyl chloride than the mixture undergoing polymerization. Since this causes a change in the composition of the unpolymerized monomer mixture, it can be seen that polymer chains laid down successively will have different compositions. Accordingly, more uniform copolymers are obtained by gradually adding one component to a polymerizing mixture.

The study of the structural arrangements in copolymers is complicated by the variable composition of different macromolecules just mentioned as well as by the possibility that the distribution of the different units is not uniform throughout a single polymer chain. However, a copolymer of stilbene and maleic anhydride has been found to contain equivalent amounts of the two monomers, regardless of the composition of the mixture from which it was prepared. This suggests that it has the structural unit

$$\left(\begin{array}{cccc} -CH- & CH- & CH- & CH- \\ | & | & | & | \\ C_6H_5 & C_6H_5 & CO & CO \\ & & \diagdown O \diagup & \end{array}\right)_x$$

Similarly the copolymer most readily obtained from styrene and maleic anhydride contains the monomers in a 1 to 1 ratio and presumably has a systematic chain structure. Polymeric products containing more than one molecule of styrene per molecule of the anhydride can be prepared, but it is not certain that they are not mixtures of the 1 to 1 polymer with polystyrene. The copolymer obtained from an equimolecular mixture of methyl methacrylate and butadiene, in emulsion, has been subjected to ozonization. β-Methyl-β-carbomethoxyadipic acid was obtained in a yield of about 50 per cent, indicating that the two monomer units are arranged alternately throughout a large portion of the macromolecule.

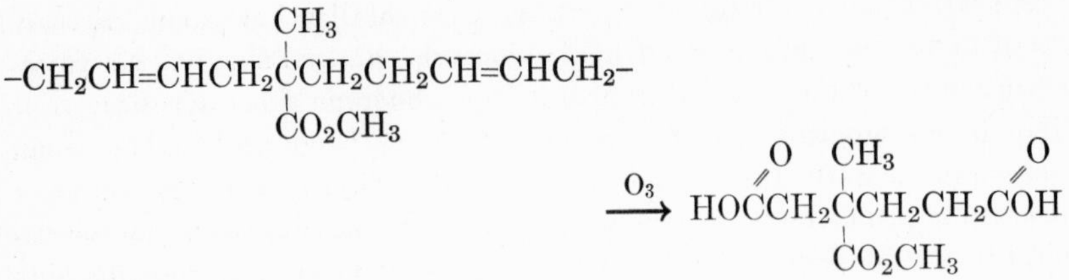

$$\begin{array}{lcl} & CH_3 & \\ & | & \\ -CH_2CH{=}CHCH_2 & C & CH_2CH_2CH{=}CHCH_2- \\ & | & \\ & CO_2CH_3 & \end{array}$$

$$\xrightarrow{O_3} \begin{array}{lclcl} & O & CH_3 & & O \\ & /\!/ & | & & /\!/ \\ HO & C & CH_2\overset{}{C}CH_2CH_2 & C & OH \\ & & | & & \\ & & CO_2CH_3 & & \end{array}$$

However, a dimethyldicarbomethoxysuberic acid, of unknown structure, also was formed, indicating the occasional direct union of two methyl methacrylate units.

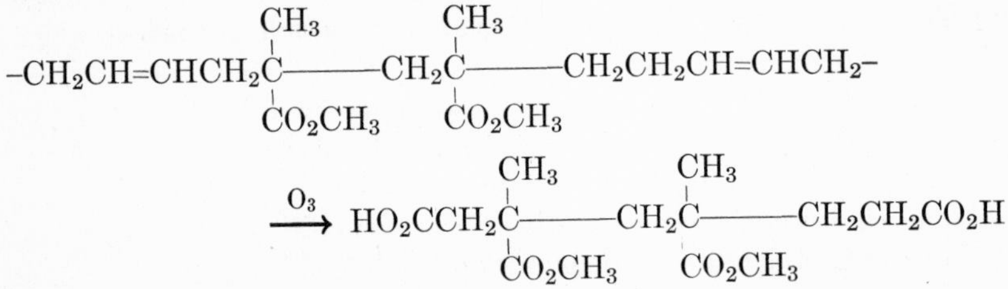

$$\begin{array}{lclcl} & CH_3 & & CH_3 & \\ & | & & | & \\ -CH_2CH{=}CHCH_2 & C & \text{———}CH_2 & C & \text{———}CH_2CH_2CH{=}CHCH_2- \\ & | & & | & \\ & CO_2CH_3 & & CO_2CH_3 & \end{array}$$

$$\xrightarrow{O_3} \begin{array}{lclcl} & CH_3 & & CH_3 & \\ & | & & | & \\ HO_2CCH_2 & C & \text{———}CH_2 & C & \text{———}CH_2CH_2CO_2H \\ & | & & & \\ & CO_2CH_3 & & CO_2CH_3 & \end{array}$$

or

$$\begin{array}{lclcl} & CH_3 & & CH_3 & \\ & | & & | & \\ -CH_2CH{=}CHCH_2 & C & \text{———}CH_2CH_2 & C & \text{———}CH_2CH{=}CHCH_2- \\ & | & & | & \\ & CO_2CH_3 & & CO_2CH_3 & \end{array}$$

$$\xrightarrow{O_3} \begin{array}{lclcl} & CH_3 & & CH_3 & \\ & | & & | & \\ HO_2CCH_2 & C & \text{———}CH_2CH_2 & C & \text{———}CH_2CO_2H \\ & | & & | & \\ & CO_2CH_3 & & CO_2CH_3 & \end{array}$$

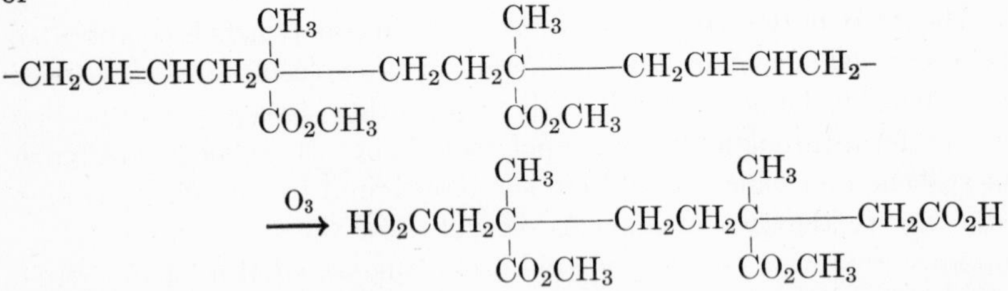

Copolymers of vinyl chloride and vinyl acetate are produced in large volume and are used in the manufacture of a myriad of articles, ranging from shoe soles to lacquers especially suitable for food containers. The copolymer from vinyl chloride and vinylidine chloride ($CH_2{=}CCl_2$), known as Saran, is an important synthetic fiber.

Although tetrachloroethylene shows little or no tendency toward polymerization, tetrafluoroethylene can be polymerized readily. The product (Teflon) is remarkable for its inertness; it is entirely unaffected by such reagents as nitric acid and alkali under conditions that bring about rapid destruction of many other materials. The polymer of chlorotrifluoroethylene (Kel-F) is a similarly stable material.

Condensation Polymers

Any reaction that brings about the combination of two organic residues and which is free of side reactions may be adapted to the preparation of condensation polymers, provided that the reaction may occur at two or more points in the molecule. In general, if the two reacting parts of the molecule are at such a distance from each other that five- or six-membered rings can form, cyclic compounds rather than polymers may be expected. Special conditions may alter the course of the reaction, however; for example, Ruggli synthesized compounds with large rings by reaction of appropriate bifunctional molecules at such high dilution that two reacting functional groups within the same molecule are nearer each other than two in different molecules (p. 366).

Polyesters from Hydroxy Acids. Hydroxy acids (other than β-hydroxy acids) undergo self-esterification when heated. α-Hydroxy acids yield lactides. Thus, lactic acid, heated to 150°, changes to lactide.

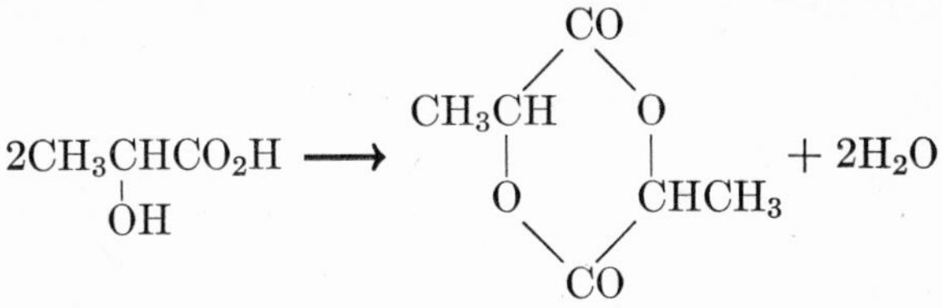

$$2CH_3\underset{\displaystyle OH}{\underset{|}{C}}HCO_2H \longrightarrow \begin{array}{ccc} & CO & \\ & \diagup \quad \diagdown & \\ CH_3CH & & O \\ | & & | \\ O & & CHCH_3 \\ & \diagdown \quad \diagup & \\ & CO & \end{array} + 2H_2O$$

If lactide is heated at about 275°, it changes to a linear polyester of molecular weight approximately 3000. In the presence of potassium carbonate the polyester forms at about 150°.

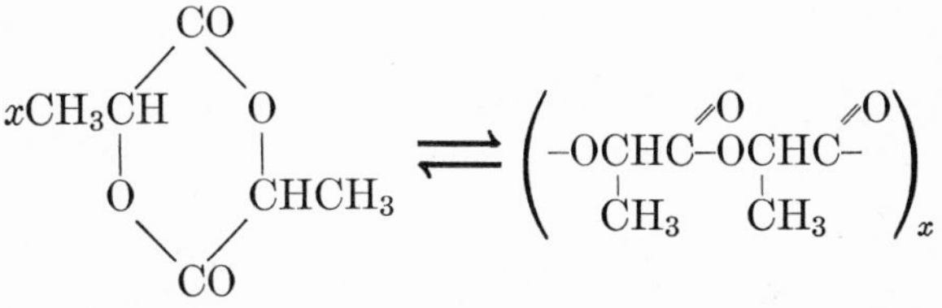

$$x\begin{array}{ccc} & CO & \\ & \diagup \quad \diagdown & \\ CH_3CH & & O \\ | & & | \\ O & & CHCH_3 \\ & \diagdown \quad \diagup & \\ & CO & \end{array} \rightleftharpoons \left(-O\underset{\displaystyle CH_3}{\underset{|}{C}}H\overset{O}{\overset{\|}{C}}-O\underset{\displaystyle CH_3}{\underset{|}{C}}H\overset{O}{\overset{\|}{C}}- \right)_x$$

β-Hydroxy acids which have hydrogen on the α-carbon atom suffer intramolecular loss of water on heating. If this reaction is not possible, then linear polyesters may form. For example, hydroxypivalic acid yields a polyester of molecular weight about 600.

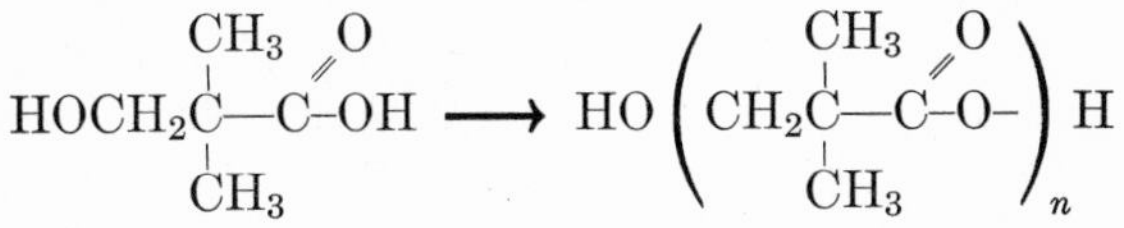

$$HOCH_2\underset{\displaystyle CH_3}{\overset{\displaystyle CH_3}{C}}-\overset{O}{\overset{\|}{C}}-OH \longrightarrow HO\left(CH_2\underset{\displaystyle CH_3}{\overset{\displaystyle CH_3}{C}}-\overset{O}{\overset{\|}{C}}-O- \right)_n H$$

γ-Hydroxy acids yield γ-lactones which are very stable and show little tendency to change to linear polyesters. δ-Hydroxy acids also give lactones, but many of the δ-lactones change spontaneously to polyesters. For example, δ-valerolactone on standing changes to a solid containing from 10 to 20 monomer units.

When the hydroxyl group is further removed from the carboxyl group the formation of polymeric products is the predominant reaction. The molecular weight varies with the conditions employed. For example, heating 10-hydroxydecanoic acid alone gives a polymer of molecular weight about 9000, but heating in benzene solution with a little *p*-toluenesulfonic acid gives a polymer of molecular weight only about 2500. The products have a hydroxyl group and a carboxyl group at the end positions.

The molecular weight of polymers such as those from the hydroxy-esters is much lower than that of ordinary addition polymers. It is probable that the chief factors that limit the size of the macromolecules are the increasingly low concentration of reacting groups as the polymerization proceeds, and the slow diffusion through the polymer of the water formed. Reaction with impurities may interrupt the chain growth, also, and it is necessary to use materials of extremely high purity if high polymers are sought.

By conducting the self-esterification in a molecular still, to assist in the removal of water, Carothers obtained polyesters of molecular weight as high as 25,000. These have been called superpolyesters.

It is remarkable that some of the polymeric esters can be depolymerized to cyclic compounds. Depolymerization may be conducted by heating under low pressure so that the cyclic products distil. Trans-esterification catalysts, acids or bases, promote the reaction. If the cyclic ester has a six-membered ring the depolymerization is very smooth, and the lactone can be reconverted to the polymer. If the lactone has a ring of eight to twelve members, it is obtained with extreme difficulty and a dilactone may be formed preferentially. For example, the polymer from ω-hydroxydecanoic acid yields the lactone and the dilactone (of the formulas shown) in a ratio of 0.17 to 1.0. On the other hand, the

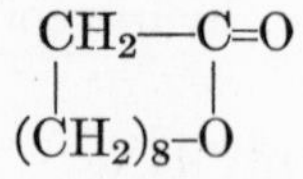

$$\begin{array}{lc}
CH_2\text{—}C{=}O \\
\;| \qquad\;\; | \\
(CH_2)_8\text{–}O
\end{array}
\qquad\qquad
\begin{array}{ccc}
 & CH_2(CH_2)_8 & \\
/ & & \backslash \\
O & & C{=}O \\
| & & | \\
O{=}C & & O \\
\backslash & & / \\
 & (CH_2)_8\text{–}CH_2 &
\end{array}$$

Lactone 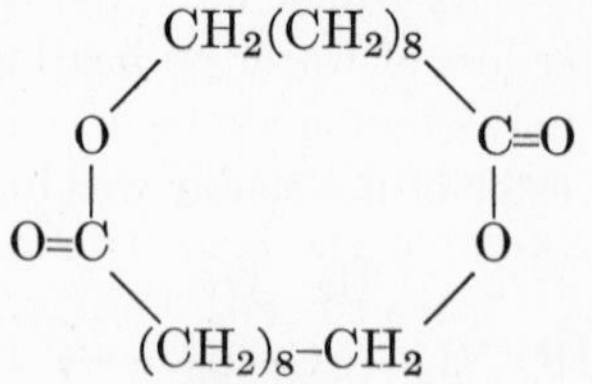 Dilactone

polyester from ω-hydroxytetradecanoic acid yields the corresponding lactone and dilactone in the ratio of 15 to 1.

Polyesters from Polyfunctional Acids and Polyfunctional Alcohols. Polyesters of this general type are commonly known as alkyd resins. If both acid and alcohol are bifunctional the product is a linear polyester.

If either has higher functionality, then three-dimensional polymers are formed.

Linear Polyesters. Polyesters of carbonic acid have been prepared by transesterification between ethyl or *n*-butyl carbonate and various glycols. The ester from ethylene glycol is the five-membered cyclic compound. That from trimethylene glycol exists both as the six-membered cyclic ester and as the linear polymer ($x = 38$ to 45), and the two forms are readily interconvertible. Esters of higher glycols are

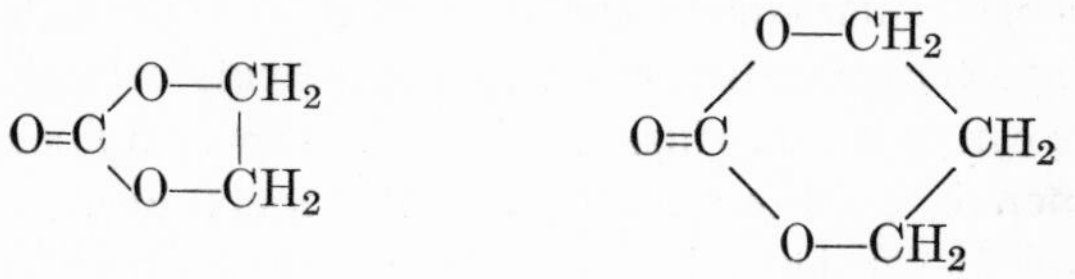

$$O{=}C\begin{matrix}\diagup O{-}CH_2\\ \quad | \\ \diagdown O{-}CH_2\end{matrix} \qquad\qquad O{=}C\begin{matrix}\diagup O{-}CH_2 \diagdown \\ \qquad\qquad CH_2 \\ \diagdown O{-}CH_2 \diagup\end{matrix}$$

$$HO(CH_2)_3{-}\left[{-}O{-}\overset{\displaystyle /\!\!/ O}{C}{-}O(CH_2)_3{-}\right]_x{-}OH$$

polymeric, and those that should give cyclic derivatives of eight to twelve members are particularly resistant to depolymerization.

The oxalate of ethylene glycol resembles trimethylene succinate in that it can form either as a six-membered cyclic or as a polymeric ester. Oxalates of higher glycols, and glycol esters of higher dibasic acids, exist as polymers. Among the many which have been prepared are ethylene malonate, succinate, adipate, sebacate, maleate, fumarate, and phthalate; trimethylene succinate, adipate, and sebacate; hexamethylene succinate, adipate, sebacate, and phthalate; decamethylene succinate, adipate, and phthalate. They can be represented by the formula

$${-}\left({-}O{-}(CH_2)_xO\overset{\displaystyle /\!\!/ O}{C}{-}(CH_2)_y{-}\overset{\displaystyle /\!\!/ O}{C}{-}\!{-}\right)_n{-}$$

The molecular weights of products most readily obtained vary from 2300 to 5000.

Ethylene succinate has been examined most carefully. When it is prepared by heating the acid with an excess of the glycol, and finally removing the excess glycol by distillation under reduced pressure, it is obtained as a linear polymer of molecular weight approximately 3000. The end groups are glycol residues, and the terminal hydroxyls can be acylated by heating with succinic or *p*-bromobenzoic anhydride. That transesterification is important in the formation of such polymers is shown by the fact that the same polymer is obtained by heating di-(β-hydroxyethyl)succinate.

If succinic acid, rather than the glycol, is used in excess the polymer has succinic acid residues in the terminal positions, and polymers containing six to twenty-three ethylene succinate residues are obtained.

The polymeric molecules of either of the above types, having two identical end groups, are unable to undergo further interaction except by transesterification. This observation indicates that in order to prepare the highest polymers the glycol and acid should be used in *exactly* equivalent amounts. By careful balance of the glycol and acid and operation under stringent conditions it is possible to prepare superpolyesters of molecular weights near 25,000.

Linear polyesters prepared from hydroxy acids or from glycols and dibasic acids can be spun as fibers. The newly formed fibers are opaque, brittle filaments. Those made from polymers of sufficiently high molecular weight can be changed to tough, transparent fibers by "cold drawing." Stretching of the fiber brings about orientation of the long molecules with an increase in crystallinity, and the fiber becomes elastic and acquires high tensile strength. For the manufacture of useful fibers the molecular weight of the polymer must be 12,000 or higher, the individual molecule having a length of 1000 Å or more.

The fiber known as Dacron is a polyester derived from terephthalic (*p*-phthalic) acid and ethylene glycol. Because of its very high melting point and low solubility, terephthalic acid is not easily converted to polyesters. The properties of the dimethyl ester are more suitable, and the polymer is made from it by transesterification in the presence of a catalyst. An outstanding property of the polyester is its resistance to hydrolysis.

$$(x + 2)HOCH_2CH_2OH + (x + 1)CH_3O_2C\text{-}C_6H_4\text{-}CO_2CH_3$$

$$\xrightarrow[\text{catalyst}]{\text{heat}} HOCH_2CH_2O_2C\text{-}C_6H_4\text{-}CO\left(OCH_2CH_2O_2C\text{-}C_6H_4\text{-}CO\right)_x OCH_2CH_2OH$$

$$+ (2x + 2)CH_3OH$$

Three-Dimensional Polyesters. The reaction of phthalic anhydride with glycerol is strongly exothermic at the start. When the anhydride groups have been converted to ester and carboxyl groups the spontaneous reaction stops, but heating causes further esterification involving these carboxyl groups and unesterified hydroxyl groups of the glycerol residues. In most reactions, the α-hydroxyl groups are more reactive than the secondary hydroxyl group. Hence, in the early stages of the reaction linear polymers are formed. However, as the reaction proceeds, the

$$\text{-}CH_2CH(OH)CH_2O\text{-}CO\text{-}C_6H_4\text{-}COOCH_2CH(OH)CH_2OCO\text{-}C_6H_4\text{-}COOCH_2CH(OH)CH_2O\text{-}CO\text{-}C_6H_4\text{-}CO\text{-}O$$

β-hydroxyl groups are attacked and cross linking occurs. It is observed that gelation occurs when esterification is about 75–79 per cent complete, evidently the point at which extensive cross linking begins.

Cross linking generally confers the properties of insolubility and infusibility. If an excess of phthalic anhydride is taken, the reaction can be made to produce a highly cross-linked product which has these properties in an extreme degree. If the polymerization is interrupted, by cooling the mixture, before extensive cross linking occurs, a heat-convertible (thermosetting) resin is obtained. These names indicate that heating causes further polymerization and cross linking to yield hard, infusible products.

The commercial glycerol-phthalic anhydride resins are modified by incorporation of a monobasic acid in quantity sufficient to permit esterification of one of the hydroxyl groups of the glycerol. The product is then an essentially linear polymer of the following type.

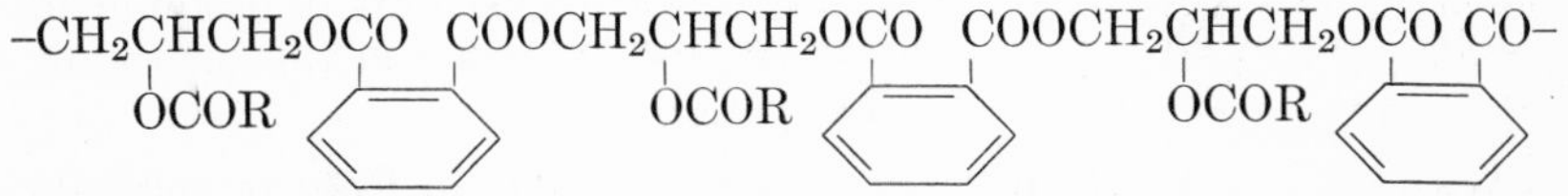

$$-CH_2CHCH_2OCO\ \ COOCH_2CHCH_2OCO\ \ COOCH_2CHCH_2OCO\ \ CO-$$
$$\quad OCOR \qquad C_6H_4 \qquad OCOR \qquad C_6H_4 \qquad OCOR \qquad C_6H_4$$

In some of the products the monobasic acid employed is obtained from a drying oil. The soluble linear polymer then undergoes drying in the air, in the same way as drying oils.

It should be noted that the polymers formed by the hardening of drying oils are very similar to the glycerol-phthalic anhydride resins. These drying oils are glycerol esters of unsaturated acids. The process of drying consists in the combination of the unsaturated hydrocarbon residues. It can be seen that combination of two acid residues will generate a dibasic acid derivative. For example, the following hypothetical dimerization of an olefinic ester produces a diester.

$$2RCH{=}CH(CH_2)_xCO_2R' \longrightarrow \begin{array}{l} RCHCH_2(CH_2)_xCO_2R' \\ \ \ | \\ RC{=}CH(CH_2)_xCO_2R' \end{array}$$

If the ester were a glyceride, and if all three of the acyl groups took part in the reaction indicated, the product would be a cross-linked alkyd-type resin.

This rough picture of the drying of unsaturated oils is in accord with the fact that ethylene glycol esters of drying oil acids do not change to hard films. Since only two unsaturated residues are present in such an ester, only linear polymers can form. On the other hand, esters of alcohols containing more than three hydroxyl groups, such as pentaerythritol and the sugar alcohols, do give hard films upon drying.

The exact mechanism of the combination of acid units in the drying reaction is not yet known. It is probable that several types of reaction occur. Drying oils containing conjugated double bonds may undergo the diene reaction. Considerable amounts of oxygen are absorbed during the drying, so that reaction of oxygen-containing functional groups as well as peroxide-catalyzed polymerization of the vinyl type may be involved.

Polyamides. Polyamides may be prepared from amino acids or from diamines and dicarboxylic acids. Whether or not a given amino acid yields a polyamide depends largely upon the relative positions of the two functional groups.

The α-amino acids provide the structural units involved in the natural polyamides, the proteins. The structures of the proteins are much more complicated than those of the polymers discussed above. They are derived from mixtures of amino acids, with the various monomeric units apparently arranged in orderly patterns throughout the polymeric chains. Although polypeptides have been prepared in the laboratory, no protein has been synthesized as yet.

Esters of α-amino acids readily change to diketopiperazines, the nitrogen analogs of the lactides. Once these cyclic compounds have been formed, they show little or no tendency to change to linear polymers. However, under certain conditions linear polymers may be formed instead of diketopiperazines.

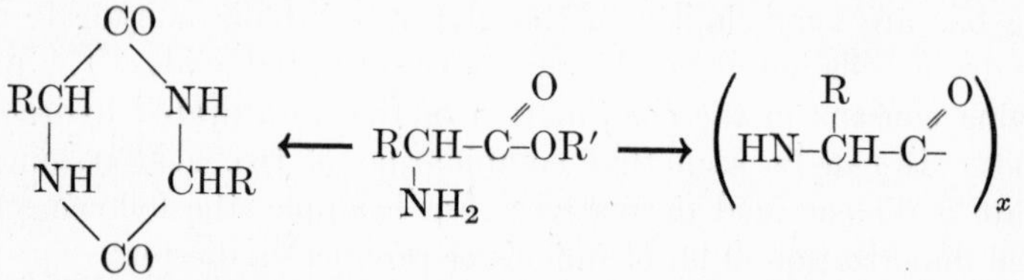

```
       CO
      /  \
  RCH     NH                  O                R    O
   |       |                 //                |   //
   NH     CHR   <--  RCH-C-OR'   -->    ( HN-CH-C-  )
      \  /            |                               x
       CO            NH2
```

Polymers of glycine have been prepared by heating the ester of the hexapeptide. The products appear to contain twelve, twenty-four, forty-eight, and ninety-six glycine units, respectively.

$$H(NHCH_2CO)_6OCH_3 \longrightarrow [H(NHCH_2CO)_6]_nOCH_3 \qquad n = 2, 4, 8, 16$$

Heating converts β-amino acids and their derivatives into unsaturated substances. Cyclic lactams are formed from γ- and δ-amino acids; neither the five- nor the six-membered lactams can be converted to polymers.

Heat converts ϵ-aminocaproic acid to a mixture of lactam and linear polymer containing about ten amino acid units. If the polymer is heated under very low pressure some lactam distils and the residual polymer becomes harder and tougher; no data on the change of molecular weight during this process have appeared. Similarly, heat converts the lactam to a linear polymer. This product has been manufactured on a large scale and finds uses similar to those of the nylons made from dibasic acids and diamines.

Polyamides from Diamines and Dibasic Acids. Polyamides of this type are prepared conveniently by heating the salt of a diamine and a dibasic acid under conditions which favor the elimination of water and under which oxidation is prevented. The polymers formed appear to have molecular weights in the same range as those of the polyesters obtained from glycols and dibasic acids. The molecular weight attained in a given preparation can be controlled by using a slight excess of amine or acid. This modification brings about the formation of polymers with identical end groups, so that further condensation cannot occur. At this point, the viscosity of solutions of the polymer becomes constant; hence the added component has been called a viscosity stabilizer, and the products are known as viscosity-stable polymers.

Among the polyamides that have been prepared are those from adipic acid and tetramethylenediamine, pentamethylenediamine, and hexamethylenediamine; from sebacic acid and ethylenediamine, hexamethylenediamine, octamethylenediamine, and piperazine. These products are known as nylons. Those of molecular weight above about 7000 yield fibers which, after being subjected to cold drawing, are very elastic and tough. The amount of stretching in the cold-drawing process may be 100 per cent or even as high as 250 per cent. Fibers may be formed by extrusion of the molten polymer, by extrusion of solutions (in formic acid) into a heated chamber, or by extrusion of a solution (in phenol) into a bath of non-solvent (aqueous alkali).

Urea-Formaldehyde Polymers. Formaldehyde and urea react reversibly to form methylolurea and dimethylolurea.

$$H_2NCONH_2 + H_2CO \rightleftharpoons H_2NCONHCH_2OH$$

$$H_2NCONHCH_2OH + H_2CO \rightleftharpoons HOCH_2NHCONHCH_2OH$$

Heat converts either of these products to an infusible polymer which is evidently highly cross-linked.

A number of possible mechanisms of the transformation have been proposed. According to one, methylolurea undergoes intermolecular dehydration, thereby building up chains. Participation of dimethylolurea leads to cross linking.

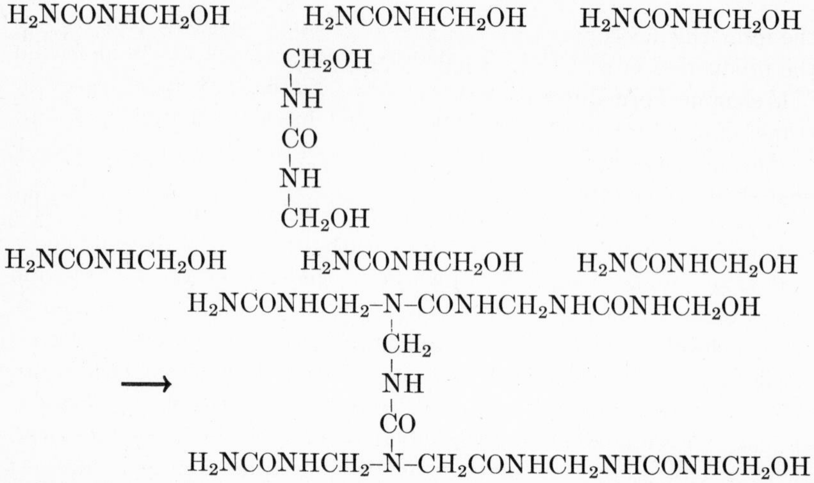

$$
\begin{array}{ccc}
H_2NCONHCH_2OH & H_2NCONHCH_2OH & H_2NCONHCH_2OH \\
 & CH_2OH & \\
 & | & \\
 & NH & \\
 & | & \\
 & CO & \\
 & | & \\
 & NH & \\
 & | & \\
 & CH_2OH & \\
H_2NCONHCH_2OH & H_2NCONHCH_2OH & H_2NCONHCH_2OH
\end{array}
$$

$$
\longrightarrow
\begin{array}{l}
H_2NCONHCH_2\text{–}N\text{–}CONHCH_2NHCONHCH_2OH \\
\qquad\qquad\qquad\;\; | \\
\qquad\qquad\qquad CH_2 \\
\qquad\qquad\qquad\;\; | \\
\qquad\qquad\qquad NH \\
\qquad\qquad\qquad\;\; | \\
\qquad\qquad\qquad CO \\
\qquad\qquad\qquad\;\; | \\
H_2NCONHCH_2\text{–}N\text{–}CH_2CONHCH_2NHCONHCH_2OH
\end{array}
$$

If pure methylolurea is the starting material the dimethylolurea is produced from the formaldehyde liberated by the decomposition of part of the methylolurea.

In another postulated mechanism, the dehydration is assumed to be intramolecular, leading to methyleneurea and dimethyleneurea.

$$H_2NCON{=}CH_2 \qquad CH_2{=}NCON{=}CH_2$$

The same type of product could arise from these methylene derivatives by addition polymerization, the dimethyleneurea being responsible for the cross linking.

An interesting suggestion is that methyleneurea trimerizes to give the cyclic derivative.

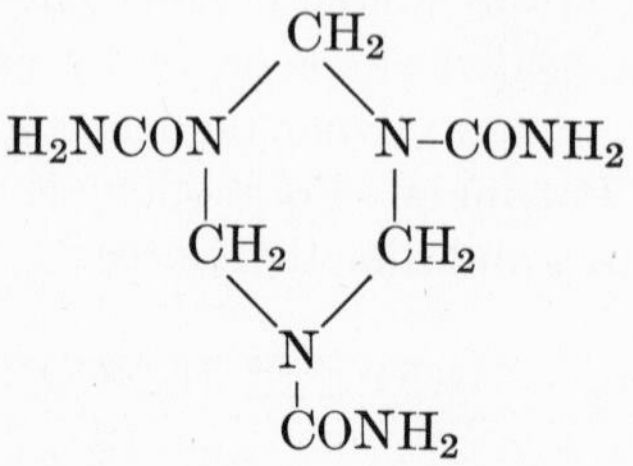

$$
\begin{array}{ccccc}
 & & CH_2 & & \\
 & / & & \backslash & \\
H_2NCON & & & & N\text{–}CONH_2 \\
| & & & & | \\
CH_2 & & & & CH_2 \\
 & \backslash & & / & \\
 & & N & & \\
 & & | & & \\
 & & CONH_2 & &
\end{array}
$$

Such a cyclic triamide might react with formaldehyde in various ways to yield three-dimensional polymers. If further reaction resulted only in the linking of unsubstituted amide groups by methylene residues a very highly cross-linked structure would be built up because of the trifunctionality of the cyclic amide.

The urea-formaldehyde resins are used extensively in moldings. The partially polymerized material is heated under pressure in a mold to bring about further polymerization and cross linking. The molded products have excellent mechanical strength. Because of the light color of the resin, the incorporation of suitable dyes and pigments makes possible the production of materials of any desired shade.

Melamine-Formaldehyde Resins. Melamine may be regarded as the trimer of cyanamide. Cyanamide is quite unstable and changes rapidly to dicyandiamide when liberated from its salts. When dicyandiamide is heated under suitable conditions it changes to melamine. Melamine

$$H_2NC{\equiv}N \qquad H_2N\overset{\overset{NH}{\|}}{C}NHC{\equiv}N \qquad \text{(ring: } C(NH_2),\ N,\ C(NH_2),\ N,\ C(NH_2),\ N\text{)}$$

Cyanamide — Dicyandiamide — Melamine

reacts with formaldehyde to form methylol derivatives which yield thermosetting resins on heating. The reactions involved are probably similar to those discussed in connection with the urea-formaldehyde resins. The products are used in moldings and are particularly valuable because of their stability to heat and light.

Tar Acid Resins. The first synthetic resins to be used commercially were the Bakelites (about 1910). These resins are prepared from phenol and formaldehyde, either acids or bases being used as catalysts in the condensation. Three stages may be distinguished in the reaction. The initial condensation product is a liquid or semi-solid, called the A stage resin. Continued heating causes it to change to a solid, insoluble in most solvents; this is the B stage resin. It softens upon heating, but if heated under pressure it hardens, becoming completely insoluble and infusible (C stage).

The reactions involved in the formation of the resin consist in the introduction of methylol groups in the positions *ortho* and *para* to the hydroxyl group and intermolecular dehydration between the alcoholic hydroxyl groups and the hydrogen atoms of the *ortho* and *para* positions of other phenol molecules. The phenolic hydroxyl group must be un-

$$\text{—}CH_2\text{—}C_6H_3(OH)\text{—}CH_2\text{—}C_6H_3(OH)\text{—}CH_2\text{—}C_6H_2(OH)(CH_2\text{—})\text{—}CH_2\text{—}C_6H_2(OH)(CH_2\text{—})\text{—}CH_2\text{—} \ \ldots$$

affected when alkaline catalysts are used, for A stage resins so formed are alkali-soluble. Since the phenol may be regarded as trifunctional, and the formaldehyde as bifunctional, the possibilities of cross linking are about the same as with the glycerol-phthalic anhydride resins, which also result from a 3:2 combination. The low-molecular-weight resins obtained by acid catalysis are alkali-insoluble. This observation indicates that the phenolic hydroxyl is involved, in the formation of either ether or acetal links, and that a 4:2 combination obtains.

The A, B, and C stage resins, produced by either acid or base catalysis, differ in the degree of condensation and cross linking. The B stage resins are used in moldings; they soften sufficiently to flow in the mold, and the heating causes further polymerization and cross linking. The pressure employed in molding varies between 1000 and 8000 lb. per square inch, and the temperature is in the range of 120–180°. The time required for molding varies from a few seconds for small objects to as much as 10 minutes for large objects.

The resin is supplied to molders either as a powder or in the form of pellets, containing appropriate fillers, plasticizers, lubricants, and pigments. The fillers include wood flour, paper pulp, and various inorganic materials. The function of the plasticizer is to increase the flow of the material in the mold. The lubricants, usually metallic soaps, assist in the ejection of the finished article from the mold. A typical molding powder contains 40–50 per cent of filler, 5 per cent of plasticizer, and 1 per cent each of lubricant or pigment.

The properties of the resin can be modified by adding phenols which have one or more of the *ortho* and *para* positions blocked. In alkali-catalyzed condensations, for example, *o*- or *p*-cresol gives essentially linear polymers. The cresols and xylenols, and mixtures of these with other coal tar phenols, are much used along with phenol in molding compositions.

Colorless and light-colored phenolic resins can be produced. These products are cast, rather than molded, and the resin from which they are made must be prepared with extreme care. Pure phenol and paraformaldehyde are heated in the presence of a little sodium hydroxide. The water formed during the reaction is removed from time to time; the clarity of the resin improves with increasing completeness of dehydration. While the resin is still fluid it is poured into lead molds. These are placed in a heated chamber and allowed to cure for several days, after which the lead molds are removed and melted. Slow polymerization of the cast objects continues for some time, with the result that they undergo slight shrinkage.

A substantial proportion of phenolic resins is used in laminated products. Sheets of paper, cloth, or wood are impregnated with the resin, then pressed and heated in molds. The timing gears of automobiles are made of laminated canvas, as are the gears used in phonographs. Such gears are silent and wear much longer than metal gears. Plywood made of sheets bonded with phenolic resins is becoming increasingly popular.

Products made from aniline and formaldehyde are known as Ciba resins. They are superior to phenolic resins in certain mechanical and electrical properties and are used for special products. Furfural resins are made from phenol and furfural. They undergo the last stage of polymerization with great rapidity, and the molded products have unusual strength and toughness.

Thiokol. Thiokol is prepared from ethylene chloride and sodium tetrasulfide.

$$ClCH_2CH_2Cl + Na_2S_4 \longrightarrow \text{–}(CH_2CH_2S_4)\text{–}_x$$

The structure of the polymer has been proved by degradation and by synthesis.

$$\text{–}CH_2CH_2S_4\text{–}CH_2CH_2S_4\text{–}CH_2CH_2S_4\text{–}$$

$$-S \downarrow \uparrow +S$$

$$\text{–}CH_2CH_2SSCH_2CH_2SSCH_2CH_2SS\text{=}$$

$$[H] \downarrow \uparrow NaOBr$$

$$HSCH_2CH_2SH$$

The nature of the polymer varies with the method of preparation. If ethylene chloride is used in excess a viscous liquid of low molecular weight is obtained. The product formed in the presence of excess sodium tetrasulfide is a tough, rubbery material of very high molecular weight. It is probable that in the presence of the excess tetrasulfide the end groups $\underset{\displaystyle S}{\overset{}{\text{–S}}}\underset{\displaystyle S}{\text{–S}}\text{–Na}$ degenerate to –SH groups. The thiol groups are oxidized by sodium tetrasulfide to –S–S– groups. Thus two reactions lead to chain growth when the tetrasulfide is used in excess.

Thiokol serves as a substitute for rubber. It is highly resistant to solvents and has been cheaper than other rubber substitutes which might be suitable for lining hose, etc., used in the oil industry.

Thiokol rubber is vulcanized with zinc oxide. The action may be due to further coupling of chains having SH groups at the terminal positions.

Silicones (Siloxanes). Among the most interesting new materials are the so-called silicone polymers. The term silicone arose from the consideration that dialkylsilicon dichlorides (R_2SiCl_2) were expected to undergo hydrolysis to dialkylsilicon oxides ($R_2Si{=}O$) having a formal structural similarity to ketones. However, hydrolysis of diethylsilicon dichloride was found to yield a viscous oily material to which a polymeric structure, formulated as shown below, was eventually assigned.

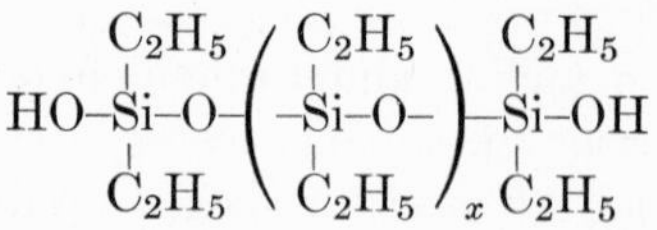

$$HO-\underset{C_2H_5}{\overset{C_2H_5}{\underset{|}{\overset{|}{Si}}}}-O-\left(-\underset{C_2H_5}{\overset{C_2H_5}{\underset{|}{\overset{|}{Si}}}}-O-\right)_x-\underset{C_2H_5}{\overset{C_2H_5}{\underset{|}{\overset{|}{Si}}}}-OH$$

The commercial silicone polymers are based largely on the methylsilicon chlorides. In one process for the preparation of the chlorides, methyl chloride is caused to react with elemental silicon in the presence of copper at temperatures near 300°. The principal product is dimethylsilicon dichloride (dimethyldichlorosilane), formed as indicated by the equation.

$$2CH_3Cl + Si \xrightarrow[\Delta]{Cu} (CH_3)_2SiCl_2$$

Side reactions leading to methyltrichlorosilane (CH_3SiCl_3), trimethylchlorosilane [$(CH_3)_3SiCl$], and silicon tetrachloride also occur. The products are separated by careful fractionation.

Methylsilicone rubber is prepared from dimethyldichlorosilane of high purity by hydrolysis. Spontaneous condensation of the primary hydrolysis product [$(CH_3)_2Si(OH)_2$], which is too unstable to permit isolation, occurs with the formation of siloxane chains and cycles.

$$(CH_3)_2SiCl_2 \xrightarrow{2H_2O} 2HCl + [(CH_3)_2Si(OH)_2]$$

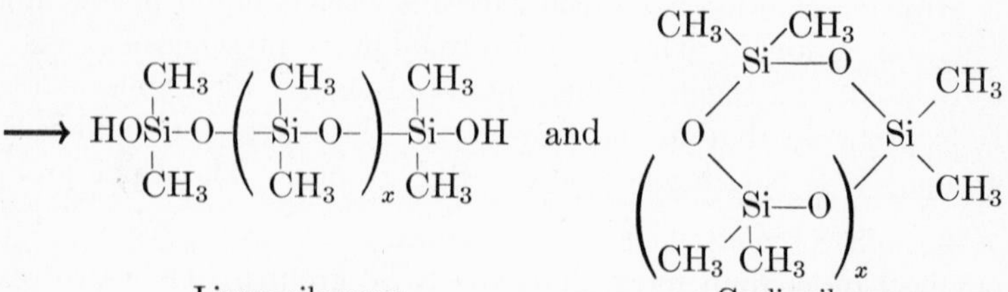

$$\longrightarrow HO\underset{CH_3}{\overset{CH_3}{\underset{|}{\overset{|}{Si}}}}-O-\left(-\underset{CH_3}{\overset{CH_3}{\underset{|}{\overset{|}{Si}}}}-O-\right)_x-\underset{CH_3}{\overset{CH_3}{\underset{|}{\overset{|}{Si}}}}-OH \quad \text{and} \quad \text{cyclic } \left[-O-Si(CH_3)_2-O-\left(Si(CH_3)_2-O\right)_x-Si(CH_3)_2-\right]$$

Linear siloxanes Cyclic siloxanes

Cyclic siloxanes (silicones) corresponding to the structure shown with x ranging from 1 to 7 are known. Treatment of the hydrolysis mixture with reagents that promote the cleavage and reforming of silicon-oxygen links brings about equilibration and chain growth, and a rubberlike linear polymer, in which the value of x ranges in the thousands, is formed. This material can be milled with silica and then cured in molds. Such products retain their elasticity over remarkable temperature ranges (-50 to $+150°$) and are extremely resistant to chemical action.

The hydrolysis product of trimethylchlorosilane is hexamethyldisiloxane, $(CH_3)_3SiOSi(CH_3)_3$; since the intermediate hydroxy compound is monofunctional, only two can combine in the condensation. Such groups can be used to terminate siloxane chains, and, by equilibration of the hydrolysis products of dimethyldichlorosilane with hexamethyldisiloxane, polymers of almost any desired molecular weight range can be obtained. These products can be represented as follows.

$$(CH_3)_3SiO\left(\begin{array}{c} CH_3 \\ | \\ Si—O \\ | \\ CH_3 \end{array}\right)_x Si(CH_3)_3$$

The larger the ratio of trimethylsilicon residues to dimethylsiloxane units, the lower the molecular weight will be. The silicone oils are made by the process indicated. They are especially remarkable not only for their stability but also for their nearly constant viscosities over wide temperature ranges.

As might be expected, methyltrichlorosilane can be used as a cross-linking agent for polymers of this group. The primary hydrolysis product $[CH_3Si(OH)_3]$ is trifunctional and hence introduces a point of branching when incorporated into a dimethylsiloxane polymer chain. The silicone resins are made by such cross linking.

The usefulness of silicone polymers in waterproofing is based on the rapid hydrolysis and condensation occurring when the various methylchlorosilanes come in contact with water. An object in equilibrium with atmosphere of ordinary relative humidity is covered with a very thin film of water; the water film on the surface of glass may be as thick as 100 molecules, under certain conditions of relative humidity. When such an object is exposed to air saturated with the methylchlorosilanes, which need not be separated for this purpose, the water layer is rapidly replaced by a siloxane film. The surface of the siloxane film, being composed essentially of methyl groups, is strongly hydrophobic. The principal application of the treatment has been in the waterproofing of electrical equipment.

Siloxane polymers containing various alkyl groups and aryl groups have been prepared. Copolymers containing both methyl and phenyl groups are in commercial use.

Miscellaneous Polymers. *Aldehyde Polymers.* Evaporation of water solutions of formaldehyde produces paraformaldehyde, a polymer containing about fifty of the monomer units. The polymer formed in the presence of sulfuric acid is of a higher degree. Various mechanisms have been proposed to account for the reaction. In one it is assumed that free formaldehyde combines with formaldehyde hydrate.

$$\mathrm{HOCH_2OH} \xrightarrow{\mathrm{H_2CO}} \mathrm{HOCH_2OCH_2OH} \xrightarrow{n\mathrm{H_2CO}} \mathrm{HO(CH_2O)}_n\mathrm{CH_2OH}$$

Another possibility is intermolecular dehydration of formaldehyde hydrate.

$$\mathrm{HOCH_2OH + HOCH_2OH + HOCH_2OH \longrightarrow HOCH_2OCH_2OCH_2OH}$$

In the third mechanism it is assumed that polymerization occurs by a chain reaction initiated by activation of the carbonyl group.

$$\mathrm{H_2C{=}O + H_2C{=}O + H_2C{=}O \longrightarrow {-}CH_2OCH_2OCH_2O{-}}$$

The last explanation is particularly attractive for the low-temperature, liquid-phase polymerization. The products are glassy solids of very high molecular weight.

The lower paraformaldehydes can be modified by changing the end groups. Paraformaldehyde prepared in water appears to have hydroxyl groups at the ends of the molecule. It is thus a hemiacetal and can be hydrolyzed by either acid or base. If methyl alcohol is present the end groups are methoxyl; the polymer is an acetal and resists hydrolysis by bases.

The higher aliphatic aldehydes undergo polymerization under extremely high pressure (12,000 atmospheres) to form hard, transparent solids. Oxygen or peroxides act as catalysts. The nature of the end groups is unknown, but the products are depolymerized by either acids or bases and hence are probably hemiacetals.

$$\mathrm{HO{-}\underset{\displaystyle R}{CH}{-}\left(O\underset{\displaystyle R}{CH}\right)_x{-}O\underset{\displaystyle R}{CH}{-}OH}$$

Polyacetals. Polyacetals have been prepared from glycols and acetylene. Lower glycols yield cyclic acetals.

$$\mathrm{HC{\equiv}CH + HO(CH_2)_nOH \longrightarrow CH_3CH\langle{}^{O}_{O}\rangle(CH_2)_n} \qquad n = 2, 3, 4$$

Octamethylene glycol and decamethylene glycol yield linear polymers.

$$\mathrm{{-}\underset{\displaystyle CH_3}{CH}{-}O(CH_2)_n{-}O\underset{\displaystyle CH_3}{CH}{-}O(CH_2)_n{-}O{-}}$$

Polyformals have been prepared by the interaction of glycols and dibutyl formal in the presence of acids.

$$HO(CH_2)_nOH + (C_4H_9O)_2CH_2 \longrightarrow -CH_2O(CH_2)_n-OCH_2O(CH_2)_n-O-$$

The products from higher glycols have a molecular weight of about 2000. When heated under low pressure they change to cyclic monomeric or dimeric acetals and to higher polymers. The high polymers so produced can be cold-drawn.

Polyanhydrides. The action of acetic anhydride or acetyl chloride on dibasic acids of the type $HO_2C(CH_2)_nCO_2H$ (n = 4, 5, 6, 7, 8, 9, 10, 11, 12, and 16) leads to linear polymers which have acetyl groups in the end positions. Polysuberic, polysebacic, and polydodecanedioic anhydrides, on heating at low pressures, decompose to cyclic dimers having 18, 22, and 26 members in the rings. All others examined gave cyclic monomers which were extremely unstable, reverting to linear polymers except when kept at liquid air temperatures.

Polyethers. Polyethers have been prepared from various combinations of dihalides and polyfunctional alcohols and phenols. Polyethylene ether is obtained from ethylene oxide. The polymer forms very readily in the presence of catalysts such as metals, metal salts, and organic and inorganic bases. Under certain conditions the change of the cyclic ether to the polymer proceeds with explosive rapidity. The reaction appears to involve participation of hydroxyl compounds; ethylene glycol may be an intermediate.

$$HOCH_2CH_2OH + \underset{\diagdown O \diagup}{CH_2-CH_2} \longrightarrow HOCH_2CH_2OCH_2CH_2OH \xrightarrow{\underset{\diagdown O \diagup}{CH_2-CH_2}} HO(CH_2CH_2O)_xH$$

The molecular weight of the polymer varies over a wide range, values as high as 120,000 having been recorded. The commercial products, known as Carbowaxes, are prepared with the aid of alkaline catalysts. They are water-soluble, waxlike substances.

SUGGESTED READINGS

C. S. Marvel and E. C. Horning, "Synthetic Polymers," Gilman's *Organic Chemistry*, Second Ed., John Wiley & Sons, New York, 1943, p. 701.

E. G. E. Hawkins, "Some Organic Peroxides and Their Reactions," *Quart. Revs.*, *4*, 251 (1950).

J. F. Duncan and A. L. Morrison, "Ion Exchange," *Quart. Revs.*, *2*, 307 (1948).

F. R. Mayo and C. Walling, "Copolymerization," *Chem. Revs.*, *46*, 191 (1950).

CHAPTER 27

Nitro Compounds

THE STRUCTURE OF THE NITRO GROUP

Three formulas have been advanced for the nitro group.

```
      O            O            O
     /            //           //
R–N  |        R–N          R–N
     \            \            \
      O            O            O
  (a)          (b)          (c)
```

Formula *a* has been abandoned because it does not explain the great stability of nitro compounds and in particular gives no suggestion as to the similarity between the groupings RCH_2CO– and RCH_2NO_2. Formula *b* gives the nitrogen atom a covalence of 5. Since no compound is known in which nitrogen exhibits this valence, this structure is less satisfactory than that represented by formula *c*. It is also clear that formula *c* is unsatisfactory in that it is unsymmetrical, whereas the two nitrogen-oxygen links in a nitro compound appear to be identical. The symmetry is due to resonance.

```
     O              O
    //             ↗
R–N      ⟷     R–N
    ↘              \\
     O              O
```

NITRATION

Aromatic nitro compounds are made by direct nitration with nitric acid, usually in the presence of sulfuric acid. As indicated above (p. 39), the first step in aromatic nitration is believed to be attack by the nitronium ion, NO_2^+. Undoubtedly the chief function of sulfuric acid in nitrating mixtures is to promote the formation of this ion.

$$HONO_2 + 2H_2SO_4 \longrightarrow 2HSO_4^- + H_3O^+ + NO_2^+$$

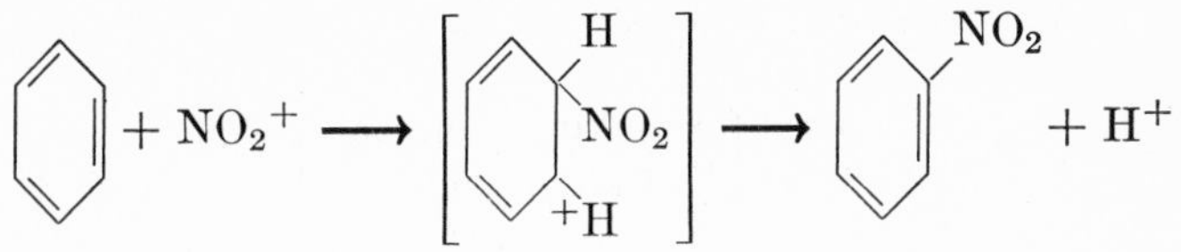

$$+ NO_2^+ \longrightarrow \left[\begin{matrix} H \\ NO_2 \\ {}^+H \end{matrix} \right] \longrightarrow \ NO_2 \quad + H^+$$

Because of the great electron-withdrawing power of the nitro group, an aromatic mononitro compound ordinarily is resistant to further nitration under conditions that suffice for its preparation. This fact makes it possible to convert benzene to nitrobenzene with very little loss owing to the formation of *m*-dinitrobenzene. Ordinary concentrated nitric and concentrated sulfuric acids are used with benzene at temperatures below 60°. For the nitration of nitrobenzene, fuming nitric acid is employed along with sulfuric acid, and the reaction is carried out at 95°. The nitration of *m*-dinitrobenzene is so difficult as to be impractical. In toluene the electron-donating effect of the methyl group partially offsets the effects of the nitro groups, and it is not difficult to carry out the triple nitration.

A few electron-rich aromatic nuclei are so readily attacked that it is difficult or impossible to convert them to mononitro derivatives by the usual nitrating mixtures or even by concentrated nitric acid alone. For example, mesitylene yields dinitromesitylene when treated with nitric acid alone.

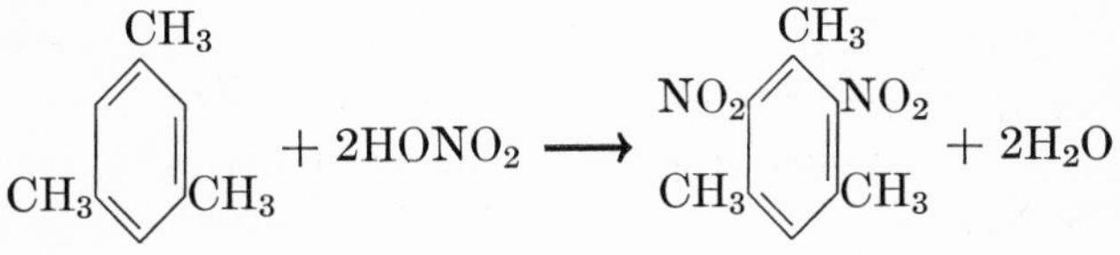

$$\begin{matrix} CH_3 \\ CH_3 \quad CH_3 \end{matrix} + 2HONO_2 \longrightarrow \begin{matrix} CH_3 \\ NO_2 \quad NO_2 \\ CH_3 \quad CH_3 \end{matrix} + 2H_2O$$

In such situations a solution of concentrated nitric acid in acetic acid and acetic anhydride can be used to advantage. Nitromesitylene can be made with the aid of this reagent. It is also used in the preparation of α-nitrothiophene.

The process of direct nitration is governed by the usual rules of orientation and as a consequence does not always permit the introduction of the nitro group into the desired position. In such cases other methods must be used. For example, nitration of nitrobenzene gives almost exclusively *m*-dinitrobenzene. To obtain *o*- or *p*-dinitrobenzene an indirect method is required. These compounds may be obtained from the corresponding nitroanilines by diazotization and replacement of the diazonium group (p. 128).

$$NO_2C_6H_4NH_2 + HNO_2 + HBF_4 \longrightarrow NO_2C_6H_4N_2BF_4 + 2H_2O$$

$$NO_2C_6H_4N_2BF_4 + NaNO_2 \xrightarrow{Cu} C_6H_4(NO_2)_2 + N_2 + NaBF_4$$

A similar method is used for making β-nitronaphthalene.

When the slightly soluble 4-nitro-1-naphthalenediazonium sulfate is isolated and added to an aqueous solution of sodium nitrite in which mixed (cuprous and cupric) copper sulfites are suspended the dinitro compound is formed in a 50–60 per cent yield.

m-Nitrotoluene is formed in small amounts in the manufacture of the *ortho* and *para* isomers by nitration of toluene. In the purification process the *meta* isomer is separated and thus is available in considerable amounts.

Aliphatic nitro compounds were first made by the action of silver nitrite on alkyl halides. This reaction produces a mixture of the corresponding alkyl nitrites and nitroparaffins.

$$RX + AgONO \begin{cases} \nearrow RONO + AgX \\ \searrow RNO_2 + AgX \end{cases}$$

If $R = CH_3$, nitromethane is the sole product; but for larger radicals the nitrite predominates. The two types are differentiated by the fact that the nitrite is easily hydrolyzed to an alcohol and the nitro compound is readily reduced to an amine.

$$RONO + H_2O \longrightarrow ROH + HNO_2$$

$$RNO_2 + 6H \longrightarrow RNH_2 + 2H_2O$$

The course of the reaction between an alkyl halide and silver nitrite is understood somewhat better by reference to the structure of the nitrite ion.

$$\overset{-}{:\ddot{\underset{..}{O}}}:\underset{..}{N}::\ddot{\underset{..}{O}} \longleftrightarrow \ddot{\underset{..}{O}}::\underset{..}{N}:\overset{-}{\ddot{\underset{..}{O}}:}$$

Only a process involving the free electron pair on the nitrogen atom leads to a nitro compound; a combination in which an electron pair from an oxygen atom participates leads to a nitrite.

REACTIONS OF NITRO COMPOUNDS

Enolization. A primary or secondary nitro compound may exist in an isonitro or *aci* form which is in equilibrium with the ordinary form.

$$\begin{array}{c}RCH_2N{=}O \\ \downarrow \\ O\end{array} \rightleftharpoons \begin{array}{c}RCH{=}N{-}OH \\ \downarrow \\ O\end{array}$$

The isonitro form is acidic, whereas the nitro form is neutral. This suggests the keto-enol tautomerism observed with acetoacetic ester and similar compounds. The *aci* forms of primary and secondary nitro compounds are very easily brominated.

$$\begin{array}{c}RCH{=}NOH \\ \downarrow \\ O\end{array} + Br_2 \longrightarrow RCHBrNO_2 + HBr$$

Condensation. Primary and secondary nitro compounds undergo condensations characteristic of active methylene compounds. For example, nitromethane reacts with benzaldehyde to give β-nitrostyrene.

$$C_6H_5CHO + CH_3NO_2 \longrightarrow C_6H_5CH{=}CHNO_2 + H_2O$$

When primary and secondary nitro compounds are treated with formaldehyde in the presence of alkalies the active hydrogen atoms are replaced by methylol groups. Nitroethane and 2-nitropropane, for example, yield 2-nitro-2-methyl-1,3-propanediol and 2-nitro-2-methyl-1-propanol, respectively.

$$CH_3CH_2NO_2 + 2CH_2O \longrightarrow \begin{array}{c}CH_2OH \\ | \\ CH_3CNO_2 \\ | \\ CH_2OH\end{array}$$

2-Nitro-2-methyl-1,3-propanediol

$$\begin{array}{c}CH_3CHCH_3 \\ | \\ NO_2\end{array} + CH_2O \longrightarrow \begin{array}{c}CH_2OH \\ | \\ CH_3CCH_3 \\ | \\ NO_2\end{array}$$

2-Nitro-2-methyl-1-propanol

Reactions analogous to the Michael condensation are known also. Benzalacetophenone condenses with the sodium derivative of nitromethane in the following way.

$$C_6H_5CH{=}CHCOC_6H_5 + \begin{array}{c}CH_2{=}NONa \\ \downarrow \\ O\end{array} \longrightarrow \begin{array}{c}C_6H_5CHCH_2COC_6H_5 \\ | \\ CH{=}NO_2Na\end{array}$$

$$\longrightarrow \begin{array}{c}C_6H_5CHCH_2COC_6H_5 \\ | \\ CH_2NO_2\end{array}$$

Bromination followed by treatment with potassium acetate gives a cyclopropane derivative.

$$C_6H_5\underset{\underset{NO_2}{|}}{\underset{CHBr}{\underset{|}{C}}}HCH_2COC_6H_5 \longrightarrow C_6H_5CH{-}CHCOC_6H_5 \;(\text{ring closed through } CHNO_2)$$

The comparison between nitromethane and its vinylogs, *o*- and *p*-nitrotoluene, is interesting, for these, in contrast to the *meta* isomer, possess active methyl groups. Commercial *m*-nitrotoluene is freed from traces of the *ortho* and *para* isomers by treatment with ethyl oxalate followed by steam distillation. The *m*-nitrotoluene is distilled, whereas the substituted pyruvic esters are nonvolatile.

$$p\text{-}CH_3C_6H_4NO_2 + \underset{CO_2C_2H_5}{\overset{CO_2C_2H_5}{|}} \xrightarrow{NaOC_2H_5} p\text{-}(CH_2COCO_2C_2H_5)C_6H_4NO_2 + C_2H_5OH$$

$$o\text{-}CH_3C_6H_4NO_2 + \underset{CO_2C_2H_5}{\overset{CO_2C_2H_5}{|}} \xrightarrow{NaOC_2H_5} o\text{-}(CH_2COCO_2C_2H_5)C_6H_4NO_2 + C_2H_5OH$$

Reaction with Nitrous Acid. Nitro compounds show conspicuous differences in their behavior toward nitrous acid depending on the number of α-hydrogen atoms in the molecule. Primary nitro compounds have two active hydrogen atoms and react to give nitrolic acids.

$$RCH_2NO_2 + HONO \longrightarrow \underset{\underset{NOH}{\|}}{RCNO_2} + H_2O$$

Nitrolic acid

Secondary nitro compounds, which have only one active hydrogen atom, form pseudonitroles.

$$R_2CHNO_2 + HONO \longrightarrow \underset{\underset{NO}{|}}{R_2CNO_2} + H_2O$$

Pseudonitrole

Tertiary nitro compounds, of course, do not react. Salts of nitrolic acids are deep red. The pseudonitroles are really nitroso compounds and are colorless in the solid form but are blue in solution or in the fused state.

This difference in color is characteristic of nitroso compounds, the colorless solid form being a dimer of the simple molecule which is blue. These colors form the basis of the "red, white, and blue" test for nitro compounds.

Decarboxylation of Nitro Acids. Many of the reactions discussed above resemble the corresponding reactions of ketones. Similarly to β-keto acids, acids having a carboxyl group and a nitro group attached to the same carbon atom lose carbon dioxide under very mild conditions. For example, nitroacetic acid is easily converted to nitromethane and carbon dioxide. In fact, even the sodium salt undergoes decarboxylation in hot water solution; the products are sodium bicarbonate and nitromethane. Before the development of the commercial nitration of propane (p. 14) this was the preparative method for nitromethane, the sodium nitroacetate being made from sodium chloroacetate and sodium nitrite.

$$ClCH_2CO_2Na + NaNO_2 \longrightarrow NO_2CH_2CO_2Na + NaCl$$

$$NO_2CH_2CO_2Na + H_2O \longrightarrow CH_3NO_2 + NaHCO_3$$

The decarboxylation of aromatic acids is facilitated by nitro groups in the *ortho* and *para* positions. 2,4,6-Trinitrobenzoic acid is unstable in hot aqueous solutions, undergoing decarboxylation to trinitrobenzene (TNB). This process provides a route to TNB, which is not accessible by the nitration of benzene (p. 405). The trinitrobenzoic acid is made by the oxidation of TNT.

$$\text{2,4,6-}(NO_2)_3C_6H_2CH_3 \xrightarrow{(O)} \text{2,4,6-}(NO_2)_3C_6H_2CO_2H \xrightarrow{-CO_2} \text{1,3,5-}(NO_2)_3C_6H_3$$

Hydrolysis. When the sodium salts of primary and secondary nitro compounds, in water solution, are acidified with mineral acids the nitro compounds usually are not regenerated. Instead, hydrolysis occurs and carbonyl compounds are formed. Primary nitro compounds give aldehydes and secondary ones ketones. The reaction is hydrolysis of the *aci*-form of the nitro compound; it is reminiscent of the hydrolysis of oximes.

$$RCH{=}NO_2H \xrightarrow[H_2O]{H^+} RCH{=}O + \tfrac{1}{2}N_2O + \tfrac{1}{2}H_2O$$

$$R_2C{=}NO_2H \xrightarrow[H_2O]{H^+} R_2C{=}O + \tfrac{1}{2}N_2O + \tfrac{1}{2}H_2O$$

The hydrolysis often can be avoided by the use of a weak acid, such as carbonic or acetic, or by operation at low temperature. When a solution of the sodium salt of phenylnitromethane is carefully acidified at 0° the free *aci*-nitro compound separates as a solid. On standing it slowly changes to the liquid nitro compound.

Primary nitro compounds can be hydrolyzed to different products by boiling with strong aqueous acids; the products of complete hydrolysis are a carboxylic acid and hydroxylamine. Hydroxylamine sulfate is produced commercially by the hydrolysis of 1-nitropropane.

$$CH_3CH_2CH_2NO_2 + H_2O + H_2SO_4 \longrightarrow CH_3CH_2CO_2H + NH_2OH \cdot H_2SO_4$$

It can be shown that hydroxamic acids are intermediates in hydrolyses of this type. These compounds (RCONHOH) are isomeric with the nitro compounds. Perhaps they are formed from the *aci*-nitro compounds by addition and loss of water.

$$RCH{=}NO_2H \xrightarrow{+H_2O} \begin{bmatrix} RCHNO_2H_2 \\ | \\ OH \end{bmatrix} \xrightarrow{-H_2O} \underset{\displaystyle OH}{\underset{|}{RCHN{=}O}}$$

$$\rightleftharpoons \underset{\displaystyle OH}{\underset{|}{RC{=}NOH}} \rightleftharpoons RC\overset{\displaystyle O}{\overset{/\!\!/}{}}NHOH$$

Tertiary nitro compounds in general do not undergo hydrolysis. There are some exceptions, however. Tetranitromethane, for example, is cleaved by concentrated potassium hydroxide to the potassium salts of nitroform and nitric acid.

$$C(NO_2)_4 + 2KOH \longrightarrow (NO_2)_2C{=}NO_2K + KNO_3 + H_2O$$

In this connection it is interesting that *ortho* and *para* dinitro derivatives of aromatic hydrocarbons also are easily hydrolyzed. The products are the salts of nitrous acid and the corresponding nitrophenol.

$$C_6H_4(NO_2)_2 \;(ortho) + 2KOH \longrightarrow C_6H_4(NO_2)(OK) + KNO_2 + H_2O$$

If three nitro groups are present on the benzene ring, one of them can be removed in this way even when they are in *meta* positions with respect to each other. For example, 1,3,5-trinitrobenzene reacts with sodium methoxide to give 3,5-dinitroanisole.

$$\text{1,3,5-}C_6H_3(NO_2)_3 + CH_3ONa \longrightarrow \text{3,5-}(NO_2)_2C_6H_3OCH_3 + NaNO_2$$

Reduction. Nitro compounds of all types are readily reduced to the corresponding primary amines. The reaction has been studied extensively in the aromatic field, where it is most useful, and it has been found that a variety of products may be obtained by suitably altering the conditions.

In acid solution the amine is formed but in neutral media the process can be arrested at an intermediate stage, giving the β-arylhydroxylamine. Presumably the nitroso derivative is formed first. Further reduction gives the amine.

$$C_6H_5NO_2 \xrightarrow{H^+} C_6H_5NH_2$$

$$C_6H_5NO_2 \longrightarrow [C_6H_5NO] \longrightarrow C_6H_5NHOH \longrightarrow C_6H_5NH_2$$

$$C_6H_5NHOH \xrightarrow{H^+} p\text{-}HOC_6H_4NH_2$$

Alkaline reagents give bimolecular reduction products.

$$C_6H_5NO_2 \xrightarrow[NaOC_2H_5]{\text{alcoholic}} \underset{\text{Azoxybenzene}}{C_6H_5N(\rightarrow O){=}NC_6H_5}$$

$$C_6H_5NO_2 \xrightarrow[NaOH]{SnCl_2} \underset{\text{Azobenzene}}{C_6H_5N{=}NC_6H_5} \longrightarrow C_6H_5NH_2$$

$$C_6H_5NO_2 \xrightarrow[C_2H_5OH]{Zn+NaOH} \underset{\text{Hydrazobenzene}}{C_6H_5NHNHC_6H_5}$$

$$\text{Azoxybenzene} \xrightarrow{Fe} \text{Azobenzene} \xleftarrow{\text{air}} \text{Hydrazobenzene}$$

$$\text{Azoxybenzene} \longrightarrow C_6H_5NH_2; \quad \text{Hydrazobenzene} \longrightarrow C_6H_5NH_2$$

β-Phenylhydroxylamine is made by reducing nitrobenzene with zinc dust and water in the presence of ammonium or calcium chloride. Chromic acid oxidizes the hydroxylamine to nitrosobenzene. β-Phenylhydroxylamine also reduces Fehling's solution. This is the basis of a test for the nitro group. The compound is reduced with zinc dust, and the reduction product is tested with Fehling's solution.

Nitrosobenzene is green in its solutions where it is monomeric but like all nitroso compounds tends to associate to a colorless dimer. It condenses with aniline and β-phenylhydroxylamine to give, respectively, azobenzene and azoxybenzene. This accounts for the formation of the bimolecular products by the reduction of nitrobenzene.

The nitroso group has a higher activating power than the nitro group, as is seen in the great lability of the bromine atom in *p*-bromonitrosobenzene and in the ease with which *p*-nitrosoanilines undergo hydrolytic cleavage.

Hydrazobenzene and β-phenylhydroxylamine rearrange in the presence of acids to give benzidine and *p*-aminophenol, respectively.

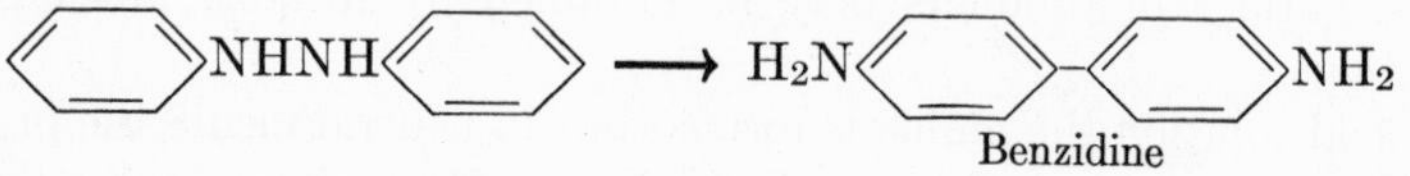

$$C_6H_5NHNHC_6H_5 \longrightarrow H_2NC_6H_4{-}C_6H_4NH_2$$

Benzidine

These rearrangements are typical of N-substituted anilines. The former is known as the benzidine rearrangement.

p-Aminobenzoic acid, now recognized as a member of the vitamin B complex, is made by the reduction of *p*-nitrobenzoic acid.

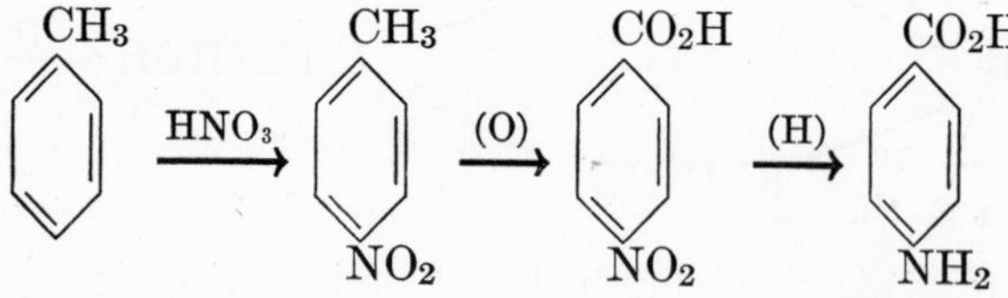

$$C_6H_5CH_3 \xrightarrow{HNO_3} CH_3C_6H_4NO_2 \xrightarrow{(O)} HO_2CC_6H_4NO_2 \xrightarrow{(H)} HO_2CC_6H_4NH_2$$

It is interesting that the powerful local anesthetic procaine or novocaine is also derived from this acid. It is made by condensing *p*-nitrobenzoyl chloride with β-diethylaminoethyl alcohol and reducing the resulting ester. In both these syntheses the starting material is toluene.

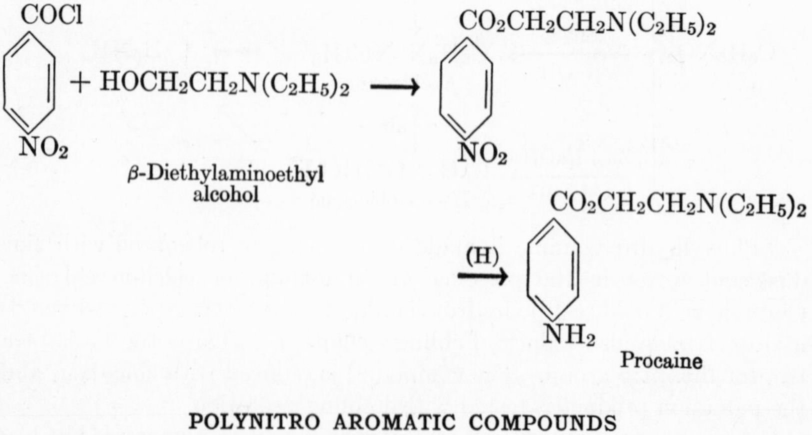

$$ClOCC_6H_4NO_2 + HOCH_2CH_2N(C_2H_5)_2 \longrightarrow C_2H_5)_2NCH_2CH_2O_2CC_6H_4NO_2$$

β-Diethylaminoethyl alcohol

$$\xrightarrow{(H)} (C_2H_5)_2NCH_2CH_2O_2CC_6H_4NH_2$$

Procaine

POLYNITRO AROMATIC COMPOUNDS

Polynitro aromatic compounds are of especial interest because they are explosive. Examples are trinitrotoluene (TNT) (p. 45), picric acid, and tetryl.

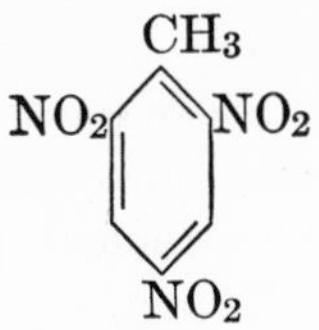

$$\text{TNT: } C_6H_2(CH_3)(NO_2)_3 \qquad \text{Picric acid: } C_6H_2(OH)(NO_2)_3 \qquad \text{Tetryl: } C_6H_2(N(CH_3)NO_2)(NO_2)_3$$

TNT 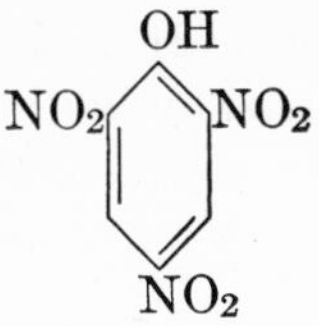   Picric acid 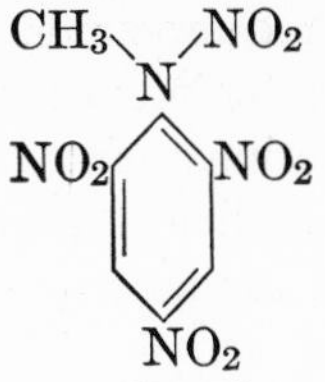   Tetryl

The chemistry of substances of this class is of great theoretical value also. The introduction of a number of nitro groups into an aromatic ring invariably brings about profound changes in the reactivity of the nucleus and of the substituents which it holds. As will be seen, these effects make possible many important synthetic methods. It will be convenient, therefore, to consider them at this point.

Reactions of Derivatives of Polynitrobenzenes

The most significant characteristic of the influence of a nitro group on the chemical properties of aromatic nitro compounds is that it is exerted chiefly on the atoms or groups that are in positions *ortho* or *para* with respect to the nitro group. By reference to the vinylogy principle (p. 345) it is easy to see why this is so. Atoms or groups that are in positions *ortho* or *para* to each other are joined by one and two vinylene groups, respectively. Accordingly, they will behave, qualitatively at least, as though they were united directly. This means that the *ortho* and *para* nitrophenyl radicals are like acyl groups.

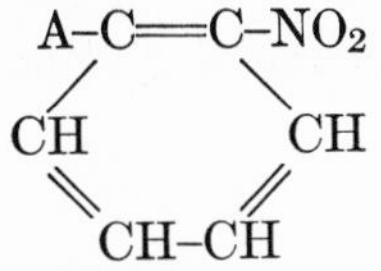

$$\text{A–C=C–NO}_2 \text{ (ring: CH, CH=CH–CH, CH)} \qquad \text{A–C=CH–CH=C–NO}_2 \text{ (ring: CH=CH)}$$

Ortho substituted nitrobenzene 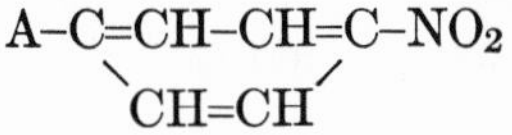   *Para* substituted nitrobenzene

No such relationship is possible in *meta* compounds.

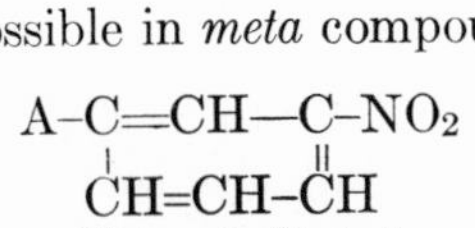

$$\text{A–C=CH–C–NO}_2 \text{ (ring: CH=CH–CH)}$$

Meta substituted nitrobenzene

This comparison of *ortho* and *para* compounds with the corresponding *meta* isomer not only explains the differences observed between *ortho* and *para* compounds on the one hand and *meta* compounds on the other but also affords a basis for predicting the nature of the activation effect. If A is chlorine, for example, the compound will have the properties of an acid chloride. That this is so is abundantly attested by the behavior of such compounds as *o*-nitrochlorobenzene, 2,4-dinitrochlorobenzene, and 2,4,6-trinitrochlorobenzene. In each, treatment with alkali causes the chlorine atom to be removed by hydrolysis and yields the salt of the corresponding phenol. Moreover, as the number of nitro groups increases, the ease with which this replacement occurs is enhanced. The trinitro compound, in fact, is readily hydrolyzed by water. Because of this property it is known as picryl chloride—the chloride of picric acid.

The reactions of picryl chloride are very similar to those of acid chlorides. Ammonia converts it into the corresponding amino compound which, because of its resemblance to amides, is known as picramide. Methanol replaces the chlorine atom with the methoxyl group, yielding trinitroanisole. The methoxyl group is readily attacked by hydrolytic agents—a fact that strengthens the analogy between this compound and esters.

Cl; NO_2, NO_2; NO_2 — Picryl chloride

NH_2; NO_2, NO_2; NO_2 — Picramide

OCH_3; NO_2, NO_2; NO_2 — Trinitroanisole

The reactivity of the chlorine atom in picryl chloride and similar substances is apparent also in the ease with which they undergo the Ullmann coupling reaction (p. 263).

TNT is a vinylog of nitromethane and, accordingly, should have an active methyl group. This agrees with the facts. When TNT is heated with benzaldehyde in the presence of an alkaline catalyst, trinitrostilbene is formed.

$$(NO_2)_3C_6H_2CH_3 + C_6H_5CHO \longrightarrow (NO_2)_3C_6H_2CH{=}CHC_6H_5 + H_2O$$

Trinitrostilbene

The reactivity of the methyl group in TNT is shown also by the fact that it is easily oxidized to trinitrobenzoic acid.

$$(NO_2)_3C_6H_2CH_3 \xrightarrow{(O)} (NO_2)_3C_6H_2CO_2H$$

Trinitrobenzoic acid

2,4,6-Trinitrobenzoic acid might be expected to behave as an α-keto acid. This analogy is borne out; this acid loses carbon dioxide at temperatures below 100° and yields 1,3,5-trinitrobenzene (TNB, p. 409).

If the 2,4,6-trinitrophenyl radical is thought of as an acyl group, then TNB should behave as an aldehyde. It does, in fact, yield picric acid when oxidized with ferricyanides.

TNT. The most important high explosive is TNT. It is made by nitrating toluene. The nitration is carried out commercially in three stages. In the first stage monitration occurs, yielding *o*- and *p*-nitrotoluenes. These are then converted to 2,4-dinitrotoluene. A small amount of the 2,6-isomer is also formed. Both the 2,4- and 2,6-isomers yield TNT in the last stage of the nitration.

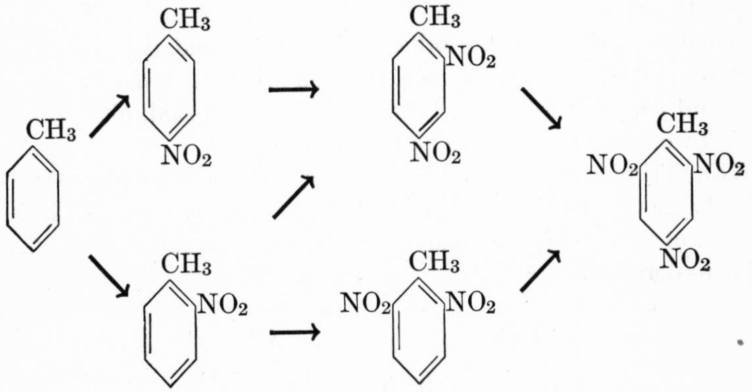

Crude TNT contains small amounts of certain isomers which are produced by the nitration of *m*-nitrotoluene, a little of which is formed in the nitration of toluene (p. 408). Chief among these isomers is 2,3,4-trinitrotoluene or β-TNT (ordinary TNT is known as α-TNT).

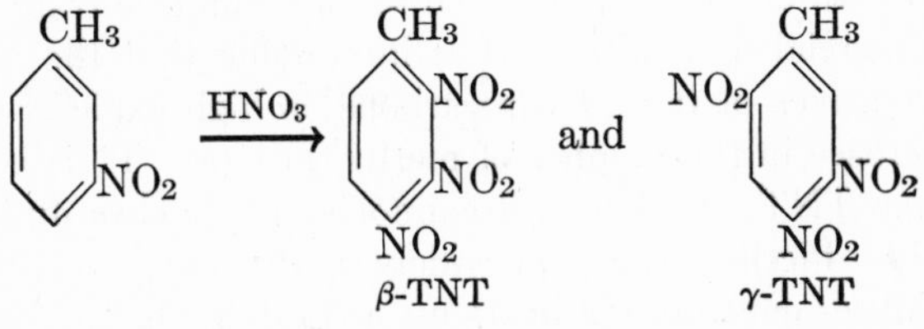

$\xrightarrow{HNO_3}$ β-TNT and γ-TNT

γ-TNT, the 2,4,5-isomer, is formed in small amounts. These impurities can be removed from α-TNT by washing with sodium sulfite solution, which rapidly converts them into water-soluble sulfonates.

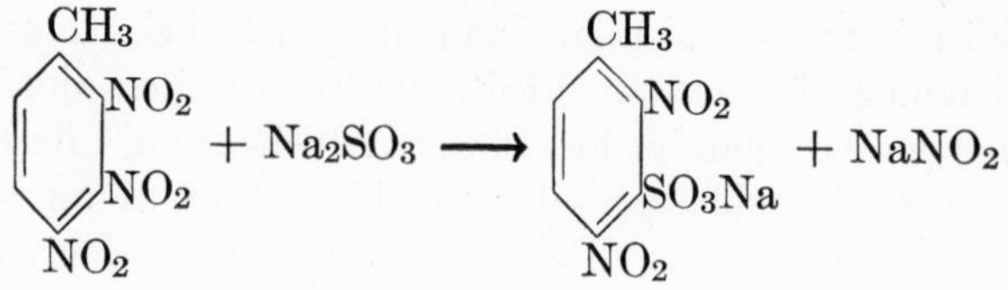

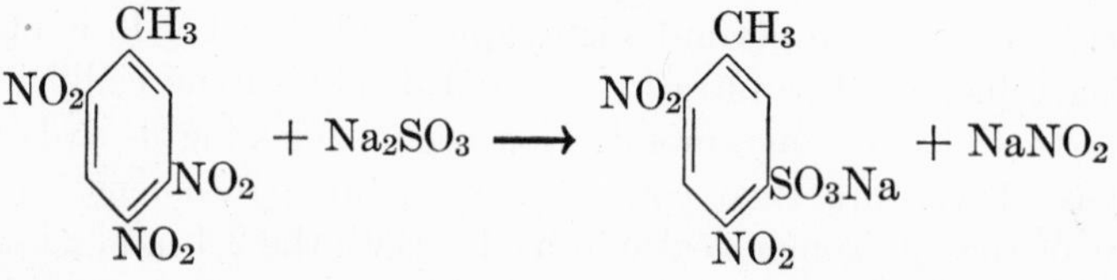

$$CH_3,\ NO_2,\ NO_2,\ NO_2 \text{ (ring)} + Na_2SO_3 \longrightarrow CH_3,\ NO_2,\ SO_3Na,\ NO_2 \text{ (ring)} + NaNO_2$$

$$CH_3,\ NO_2,\ NO_2,\ NO_2 \text{ (ring)} + Na_2SO_3 \longrightarrow CH_3,\ NO_2,\ SO_3Na,\ NO_2 \text{ (ring)} + NaNO_2$$

This method is of interest because it involves a replacement of a nitro group. It will be seen that the nitro group that is attacked in β-TNT is flanked on either side by other nitro groups and that the reactive group of γ-TNT is situated in a position which is *ortho* to one nitro group and *para* to the other. From what has been said, nitro groups so situated would be expected to be held loosely.

TNX. Trinitro-*m*-xylene (TNX) is prepared in much the same way as TNT. *m*-Xylene is more easily nitrated than is toluene. It is the only one of the xylenes that can be made to give a satisfactory yield of a trinitro derivative.

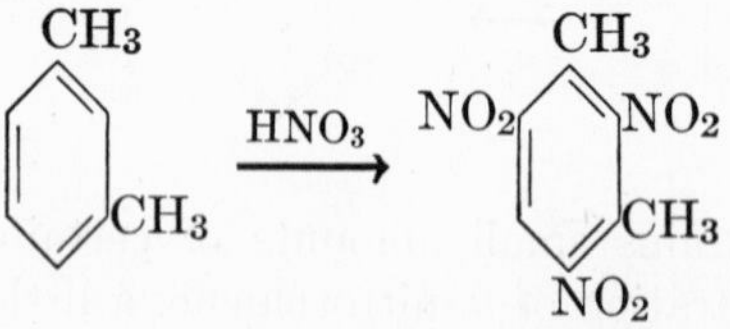

$$CH_3,\ CH_3 \text{ (ring)} \xrightarrow{HNO_3} NO_2,\ CH_3,\ NO_2,\ CH_3,\ NO_2 \text{ (ring)}$$

TNX

As a high explosive TNX is less powerful than TNT and is useful only when mixed with other materials such as ammonium nitrate. It is used also in commercial dynamites. It is interesting that the value of the trinitro derivatives of these hydrocarbons as high explosives decreases with the increase in the number of methyl groups. TNB is even more powerful than TNT. However, it cannot be made cheaply.

Picric Acid. Picric acid is very widely used as a high explosive. One of the difficulties encountered in its use is that its melting point (122°) makes it hard to introduce into containers. For this reason, it is generally mixed with other, similar nitro compounds such as 2,4-dinitrophenol and trinitro-*m*-cresol. The composition of the mixtures is such that they can be melted with steam.

Ammonium picrate and guanidine picrate are less sensitive to shock than picric acid and are used with *boosters*.

There are several methods for preparing picric acid. Direct nitration of phenol is attended with losses due to oxidation and is not a satisfactory method. In practice the phenol is first sulfonated and then nitrated. The sulfonic acid group makes the phenol less sensitive and is itself replaced by a nitro group at a certain point in the process.

OH $\xrightarrow{H_2SO_4}$ OH, SO_3H $\xrightarrow{HNO_3}$ OH, NO_2, SO_3H, NO_2 $\xrightarrow{HNO_3}$ OH, NO_2, NO_2, NO_2

The sulfonation leads to mixtures of *ortho* and *para* derivatives and may yield di- and even trisulfonic acids. This does not cause loss, however, since all these substances yield picric acid when nitrated.

It might be expected that picric acid could be made from chlorobenzene by nitration to produce picryl chloride which could then be hydrolyzed to the acid. Chlorobenzene is much more difficult to nitrate than toluene, and only the dinitro derivative can be made economically. Because of the influence of the nitro groups, however, the chlorine atom in this compound can be replaced by a hydroxyl group by hydrolysis. The resulting dinitrophenol can then be nitrated to yield picric acid.

Cl $\xrightarrow{HNO_3}$ Cl, NO_2, NO_2 $\xrightarrow{H_2O}$ OH, NO_2, NO_2 $\xrightarrow{HNO_3}$ OH, NO_2, NO_2, NO_2

It is to be noted that picryl chloride can be made by treating picric acid with phosphorus pentachloride (p. 168). This is yet another reaction that is to be ascribed to the influence of the nitro groups. It is a reaction characteristic of carboxylic acids rather than phenols.

In the presence of mercuric nitrate, benzene can be nitrated and oxidized at the same time to yield picric acid in one step. The mechanism of this process is complex. The mercuric salt serves to mercurate benzene, and the resulting phenylmercuric nitrate is converted to nitrosobenzene by the action of nitrous acid (or nitrogen oxides) with the regeneration of the mercuric salt. In one path for further reaction of nitrosobenzene it is converted to the benzenediazonium cation by reaction with more nitrous acid or its equivalent; hydrolysis and nitration of the resulting phenol follow. Reduction of some of the nitric acid by the organic materials present is responsible for the formation of the nitrous acid needed for the process.

Picric acid unites with aromatic hydrocarbons and aryl ethers to give molecular addition compounds known as picrates. These are much used for purposes of identification.

Tetryl. Tetryl is a tetranitro derivative of methylaniline. It is manufactured from dimethylaniline by treatment with nitric acid in the presence of concentrated sulfuric acid. During the reaction, three nitro groups are introduced into the ring, and one of the methyl groups is replaced by a nitro group. The various processes take place in the following order.

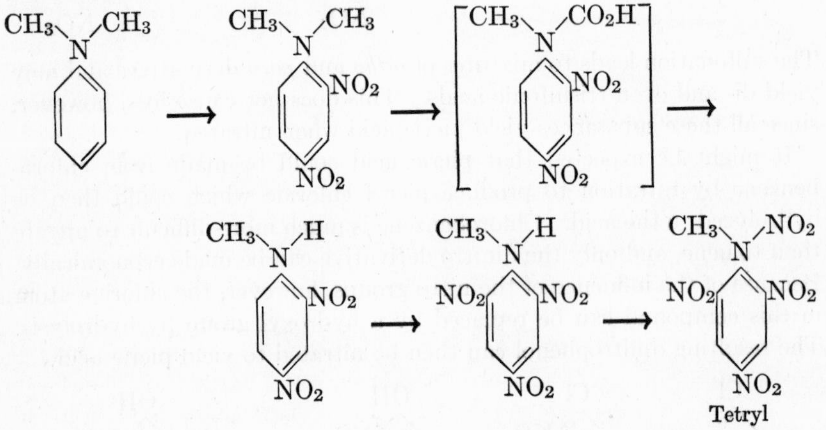

CH_3 CH_3 N → CH_3 CH_3 N NO_2 NO_2 → [CH_3 CO_2H N NO_2 NO_2] →

CH_3 H N NO_2 NO_2 → CH_3 H N NO_2 NO_2 NO_2 → CH_3 NO_2 N NO_2 NO_2 NO_2

Tetryl

2,4-Dinitromethylaniline can be made by the condensation of 2,4-dinitrochlorobenzene with methylamine.

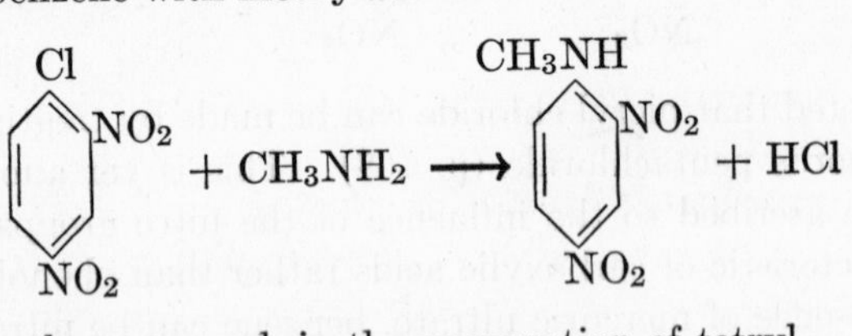

Cl NO_2 NO_2 + CH_3NH_2 → CH_3NH NO_2 NO_2 + HCl

This offers another approach in the preparation of tetryl.

Tetryl is a more powerful explosive than either picric acid or TNT. It is likewise more sensitive to shock and finds use in boosters and detonators.

CHAPTER 28

Reactions of Amines

Salt Formation. Most amines tend to form salts with acids. This tendency can be increased or diminished by the presence in the molecule of other groups. In commenting on the basicity of amines, it is convenient to include other nitrogen compounds such as nitriles, amides, oximes, imides, sulfonamides, and hydrazines, all of which can be considered derivatives of ammonia.

When the hydrogen atoms of ammonia are replaced by aliphatic radicals such as methyl and ethyl, which are electron-donating as compared to hydrogen, there is an increase in the basic properties of the nitrogen atom. The apparent basic dissociation constants of methylamine and ammonia in water are 5×10^{-4} and 2×10^{-5}, respectively. A separation of ammonia and methylamine is based on this difference. When a mixture of the two is treated with an insufficient amount of hydrogen chloride the amine is neutralized preferentially and the ammonia is left free.

On the other hand, replacement of a hydrogen atom of ammonia with an aryl radical decreases the basicity of the nitrogen. Aniline is a very weak base. Its apparent basic dissociation constant is 3×10^{-10}. Its hydrochloride can be dissolved in water and titrated with standard alkali in the presence of phenolphthalein as an indicator. Electron-withdrawing groups in the ring diminish even further the basicity of aniline; nitro groups and halogens are the most common substituents acting in this way. If two of the hydrogen atoms of ammonia are replaced by aryl groups, the compound formed is essentially neutral. Diphenylamine forms salts with concentrated sulfuric acid or with dry hydrogen chloride in benzene solution. In water these salts are hydrolyzed to the free amine. Three phenyl (or aryl) groups attached to a nitrogen atom remove basic properties.

When a methyl group is attached to the nitrogen atom in aniline, the basicity is increased. Methylaniline and dimethylaniline are stronger bases than aniline. Ring nitrogen compounds such as quinoline and pyridine are very much like aryl amines such as dimethylaniline.

If one replaces a hydrogen atom of ammonia with such a strongly electron-withdrawing group as an acyl residue, a neutral compound results. Thus one acyl group has about the same effect as two aryl groups. Urea, which has two ammonia residues attached to one acyl group, resembles a monobasic amine; nitric acid converts it to urea nitrate (p. 133).

$$H_2NCONH_2 + HNO_3 \longrightarrow \underset{\text{Urea nitrate}}{H_2NCONH_3NO_3}$$

If two acyl groups are introduced in place of two hydrogen atoms of ammonia, the resulting imide is acidic rather than basic. Imides form salts with aqueous alkalies. One sulfonyl group seems to be approximately equal in effect to two acyl groups because the sulfonyl derivatives of primary amines are alkali-soluble.

In pyrrole and carbazole the basicity of the nitrogen atom is very low and the tendency to act as an acid appears. These compounds resemble acid imides in their ability to form salts with potassium hydroxide.

CH—CH
CH CH
N
H
Pyrrole

N
H
Carbazole

The basicity of aniline is greatly diminished by the introduction of nitro or other *m*-directing groups in the *ortho* or *para* position. This is another manifestation of the influence of such groups.

Cl, NO_2, NO_2 — Halogen active

OH, NO_2, NO_2 — Strongly acid

NH_2, NO_2, NO_2 — Neutral

Certain amides such as N-ethylacetanilide exhibit pronounced basic properties.

Alkylation. The reaction of ammonia with alkyl halides (p. 247) is a result of the basicity of the nitrogen atom. The halogen is displaced as the halide ion, and the salt of an amine is formed. The reaction, known as the Hofmann synthesis, is of great value in the preparation of primary amines.

As might be expected, amines react with alkyl halides in the same way. The reaction sometimes complicates the synthesis of a primary amine from a halide and ammonia by converting the desired primary amine salt to the secondary and tertiary amines and to the quaternary salt. The various reactions that may occur are shown below.

$$RX + NH_3 \longrightarrow [RNH_3]^+X^- \xrightarrow{NH_3} \underset{\text{Primary amine}}{RNH_2} + NH_4^+X^-$$

$$RX + RNH_2 \longrightarrow [R_2NH_2]^+X^- \xrightarrow{NH_3} \underset{\text{Secondary amine}}{R_2NH} + NH_4^+X^-$$

$$RX + R_2NH_2 \longrightarrow [R_3NH]^+X^- \xrightarrow{NH_3} \underset{\text{Tertiary amine}}{R_3N} + NH_4^+X^-$$

$$RX + R_3N \longrightarrow \underset{\text{Quaternary ammonium salt}}{[R_4N]^+X^-}$$

Despite the apparent complexity of the Hofmann process it can often be used for the preparation of a simple primary amine in excellent yield by employing a large excess of ammonia. In the commercial application involving ethyl chloride and ammonia the reaction is run under conditions which produce all the expected amines—ethylamine, diethylamine, and triethylamine. These products are separated by fractional distillation, and all of them are of value.

Secondary and tertiary amines can be made from primary and secondary amines, respectively, by alkylation. Alkyl sulfates, alkyl sulfonates, and olefin oxides may serve as alkylating agents instead of alkyl halides. Methyl sulfate is commonly used as a methylating agent; an illustration is the conversion of *o*-bromoaniline to its dimethyl derivative in 70 per cent yield by treatment with methyl sulfate and aqueous potassium hydroxide.

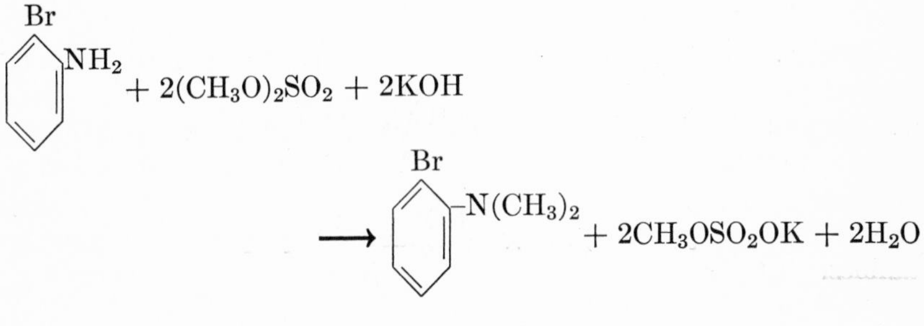

$$o\text{-}BrC_6H_4NH_2 + 2(CH_3O)_2SO_2 + 2KOH$$

$$\longrightarrow o\text{-}BrC_6H_4N(CH_3)_2 + 2CH_3OSO_2OK + 2H_2O$$

Since the nitrogen atom of an amide is nearly neutral it does not readily attack alkyl halides. Imides, being weak acids, are readily converted to alkali metal salts, the anions of which are strong bases. It follows, then, that imides should be easily alkylated by alkyl halides if they are first converted to the sodium or potassium salts. In Gabriel's synthesis of primary amines potassium phthalimide is alkylated and the resulting N-alkylphthalimide is hydrolyzed to the primary amine, which cannot be contaminated by the secondary or tertiary amine. An interesting example involves the use of γ-chlorobutyronitrile as the alkylating agent. In the hydrolysis step the nitrile group is attacked as well as the imide group, and γ-aminobutyric acid is formed.

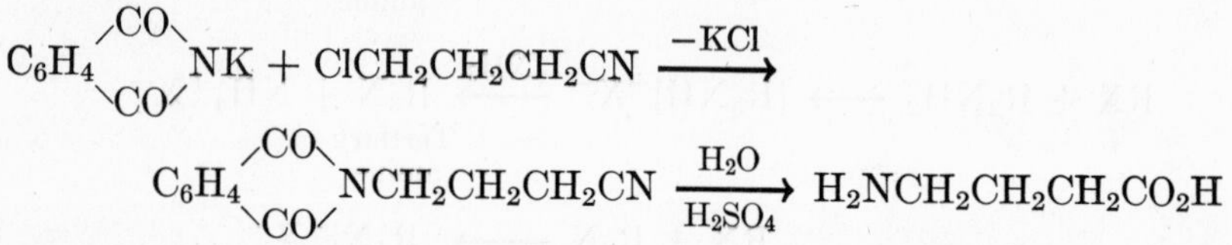

$$C_6H_4\begin{matrix}\diagup CO \diagdown \\ \diagdown CO \diagup\end{matrix}NK + ClCH_2CH_2CH_2CN \xrightarrow{-KCl}$$

$$C_6H_4\begin{matrix}\diagup CO \diagdown \\ \diagdown CO \diagup\end{matrix}NCH_2CH_2CH_2CN \xrightarrow[H_2SO_4]{H_2O} H_2NCH_2CH_2CH_2CO_2H$$

A convenient modification of the last step of the Gabriel synthesis consists in the cleavage of the imide with hydrazine. Reaction occurs as shown in the following equation.

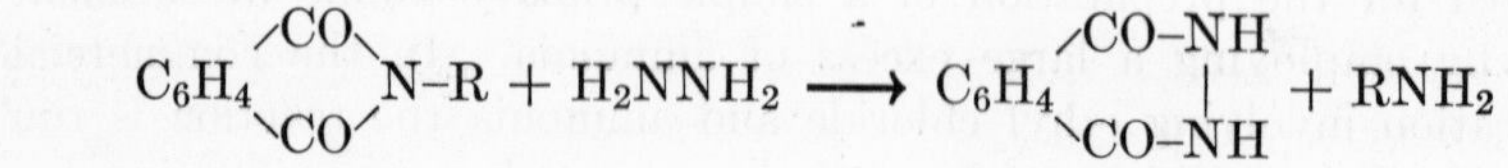

$$C_6H_4\begin{matrix}\diagup CO \diagdown \\ \diagdown CO \diagup\end{matrix}N\text{–}R + H_2NNH_2 \longrightarrow C_6H_4\begin{matrix}\diagup CO\text{–}NH \\ \qquad | \\ \diagdown CO\text{–}NH\end{matrix} + RNH_2$$

Phthalhydrazide

The use of hydrazine permits the removal of the phthalyl group under conditions that do not affect a simple amide linkage.

An elegant synthesis of peptide derivatives, based on this fact, is illustrated by the following preparation of L-phenylalanylglycine anilide from L-phenylalanine and glycine anilide.

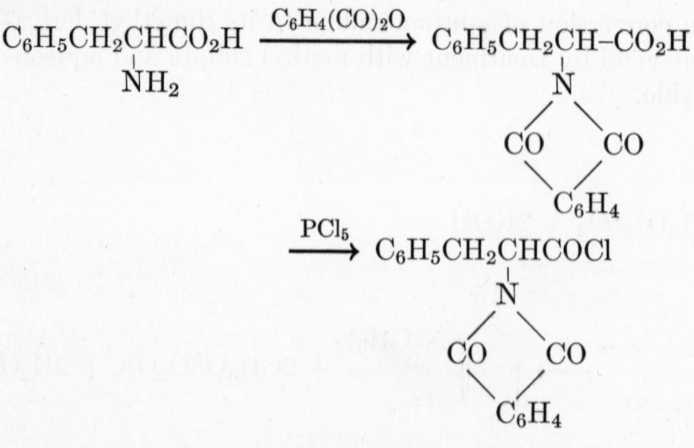

$$\underset{\displaystyle NH_2}{C_6H_5CH_2CHCO_2H} \xrightarrow{C_6H_4(CO)_2O} C_6H_5CH_2CH\text{–}CO_2H \text{ (N attached, with } N\begin{matrix}\diagup CO \diagdown \\ \diagdown CO \diagup\end{matrix}C_6H_4)$$

$$\xrightarrow{PCl_5} C_6H_5CH_2CHCOCl \text{ (N attached, with } N\begin{matrix}\diagup CO \diagdown \\ \diagdown CO \diagup\end{matrix}C_6H_4)$$

$$\xrightarrow{H_2NCH_2CONHC_6H_5} C_6H_5CH_2\underset{\underset{\underset{C_6H_4}{CO\quad CO}}{|}}{\underset{N}{|}}{C}HCONHCH_2CONHC_6H_5$$

$$\xrightarrow{H_2NNH_2} C_6H_5CH_2\underset{NH_2}{\underset{|}{C}}HCONHCH_2CONHC_6H_5$$

Oxidation of Amines. A few oxidizing agents, including hydrogen peroxide, organic peracids, and Caro's acid (H_2SO_5), attack amines by giving up oxygen to them. Most oxidizing agents act by removing hydrogen from amines. Tertiary amines are converted to amine oxides by the action of reagents of the first type.

$$(CH_3)_3N + H_2O_2 \longrightarrow (CH_3)_3N{\rightarrow}O + H_2O$$

$$C_6H_5N(CH_3)_2 + C_6H_5CO_3H \longrightarrow C_6H_5\overset{CH_3}{\underset{CH_3}{N}}{\rightarrow}O + C_6H_5CO_2H$$

The amine oxides are basic. Their aqueous solutions are alkaline, and they form salts with acids. Evidently these properties are due to the coordination of the oxygen atom with a proton.

$$R_3N{\rightarrow}O + HOH \longrightarrow [R_3NOH]^+OH^-$$

$$R_3N{\rightarrow}O + HCl \longrightarrow [R_3NOH]^+Cl^-$$

The positive ion of these compounds is related to the hydroxylammonium ion. That the free base contains one coordinately bound hydroxyl group and one hydroxyl ion has been proved by the synthesis of two isomers in which first one and then the other of the two hydroxyl groups is replaced by methoxyl.

$$(CH_3)_3N{\rightarrow}O + CH_3I \searrow$$

or $\qquad [(CH_3)_3NOCH_3]^+I^- \searrow$

$$(CH_3)_2NOCH_3 + CH_3I \nearrow$$

$$[(CH_3)_3NOCH_3]^+OH^-$$

$$(CH_3)_3N{\rightarrow}O + HI \longrightarrow [(CH_3)_3NOH]^+I^- \longrightarrow [(CH_3)_3NOH]^+OCH_3^-$$

The two products were indeed isomeric.

Secondary amines yield hydroxylamines by oxidation of this type. Unstable amine oxides may be intermediates.

$$R_2NH \longrightarrow \left[\begin{matrix} R_2N\!\rightarrow\!O \\ | \\ H \end{matrix}\right] \longrightarrow R_2NOH$$

The method is of preparative value for dialkylhydroxylamines. Primary amines are capable of further oxidation, since monoalkylhydroxylamines are very easily oxidized to nitroso compounds. In the aromatic series the nitroso group may be oxidized to a nitro group; azoxy and azo compounds may be formed also by condensations of the intermediates. The preparation of nitro compounds by oxidation of amines is of value in certain instances. For example, 2,5-dinitrobenzoic acid is made from 2-amino-5-nitrotoluene by oxidation.

$$\text{2-amino-5-nitrotoluene } (CH_3, NH_2, NO_2) + 2[O] \xrightarrow[(H_2SO_5)]{} \text{2-nitroso-5-nitrotoluene } (CH_3, NO, NO_2) \xrightarrow[CrO_3]{[O]} \text{2,5-dinitrobenzoic acid } (CO_2H, NO_2, NO_2)$$

The nitroaminotoluene is made from *o*-toluidine, which, in turn, is made from *o*-nitrotoluene. Thus the entire process amounts to reducing the nitro group to permit utilization of the directive influence of the amino group and then regenerating the nitro group by oxidation of the amine.

Aniline and substituted anilines are oxidized directly to nitro compounds in excellent yields by a solution of hydrogen peroxide in trifluoroacetic acid. The actual oxidizing agent presumably is pertrifluoroacetic acid (CF_3COOOH).

The oxidation of aliphatic primary amines is a process of little value. With oxidizing agents of the first type, the intermediate nitroso compound may isomerize to an oxime and this may undergo hydrolysis to an aldehyde or ketone. Oxidizing agents that act by removal of hydrogen also convert primary aliphatic amines to carbonyl compounds.

$$RCH_2NH_2 \xrightarrow{-2H} RCH{=}NH \xrightarrow{H_2O} RCHO \xrightarrow{[O]} RCO_2H$$

Secondary amines are converted to tetrasubstituted hydrazines by the action of oxidizing agents which abstract hydrogen. Presumably a free radical is an intermediate.

$$R_2NH \xrightarrow{-H} R_2N\cdot \longrightarrow R_2NNR_2$$

When aniline is oxidized by reagents of the second type deeply colored substances are first formed, but these are broken down by further oxidation and hydrolysis to *p*-benzoquinone. This is the ordinary method for preparing the quinone. The colored substances appear to be polymeric compounds formed by coupling of free radicals. The existence of free radicals is indicated by the isolation of triphenylmethylaniline from an oxidation of aniline in the presence of hexaphenylethane.

$$C_6H_5NH_2 \xrightarrow{PbO_2} C_6H_5NH\cdot + (C_6H_5)_3C\cdot \longrightarrow C_6H_5NHC(C_6H_5)_3$$

$$(C_6H_5)_3C\cdot \rightleftharpoons (C_6H_5)_3CC(C_6H_5)_3$$

Ordinarily the aniline radicals couple to give products capable of further oxidation.

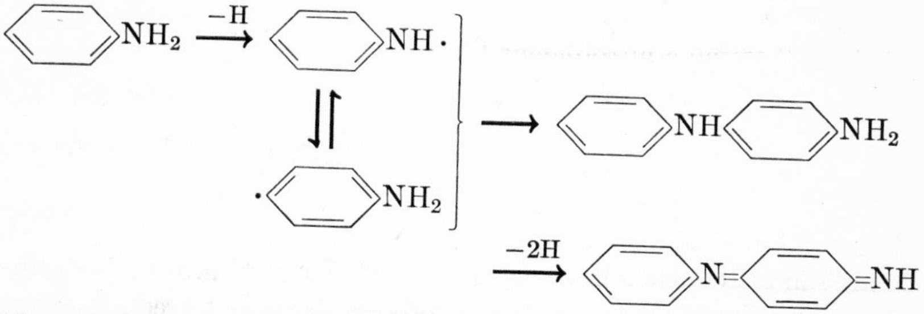

$$C_6H_5NH_2 \xrightarrow{-H} C_6H_5NH\cdot \rightleftharpoons \cdot C_6H_4NH_2 \longrightarrow C_6H_5NHC_6H_4NH_2 \xrightarrow{-2H} C_6H_5N{=}C_6H_4{=}NH$$

Through further condensation and oxidation very long molecules result. The most highly oxidized such polymer, known as perinigraniline, apparently has alternate benzenoid and quinoid rings joined by nitrogen atoms. Nigraniline and emeraldine differ from perinigraniline

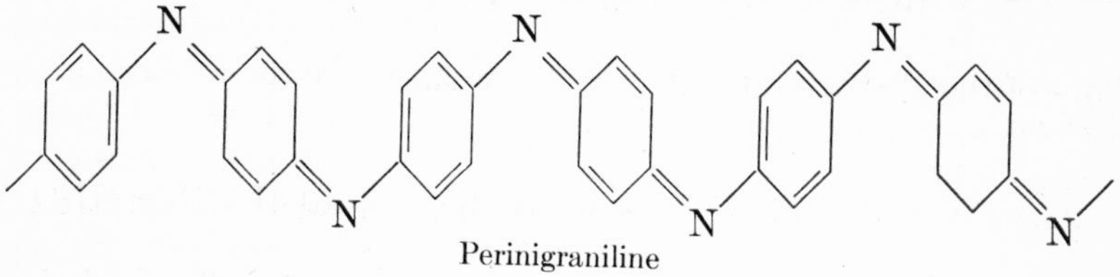

Perinigraniline

in being less highly oxidized.

Aniline black is deposited in fabrics by steaming the cloth after impregnation with a paste of aniline, an oxidizing agent, and a small amount of a copper salt or a ferricyanide. It appears to be a polyphenazine formed by condensation of aniline with perigraniline.

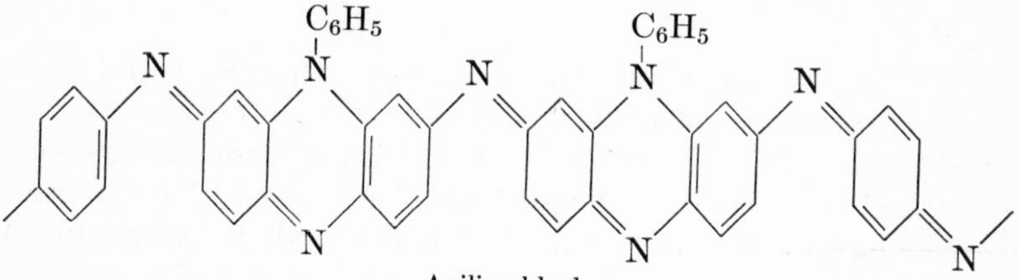

Aniline black

Quaternary Salts and Bases. Most tertiary amines react readily with methyl iodide to give methiodides. Many other alkyl halides give quaternary salts, as do also sulfates and sulfonates. The quaternary bases are prepared from halides by treatment with either silver oxide and water or alkali hydroxide in ethyl alcohol.

$$C_6H_5CH_2\overset{+}{N}(CH_3)_3Cl^- \xrightarrow[H_2O]{Ag_2O} C_6H_5CH_2\overset{+}{N}(CH_3)_3OH^- + AgCl$$

$$C_6H_5CH_2\overset{+}{N}(CH_3)_3Cl^- \xrightarrow[C_2H_5OH]{KOH} C_6H_5CH_2\overset{+}{N}(CH_3)_3OH^- + KCl$$

The second method is successful because of the insolubility of the alkali chloride in ethyl alcohol. Benzyltrimethylammonium hydroxide solutions are available commercially.

Quaternary hydroxides decompose on moderate heating. Tetramethylammonium hydroxide yields the alcohol and the tertiary amine.

$$[(CH_3)_4N]^+OH^- \xrightarrow{\text{heat}} (CH_3)_3N + CH_3OH$$

If one of the alkyl groups is larger the products are the tertiary amine, an olefin, and water.

$$[(CH_3)_3NCH_2CH_2R]^+OH^- \longrightarrow (CH_3)_3N + RCH{=}CH_2 + H_2O$$

Some quaternary hydroxides decompose very readily. Those derived from β-p-nitrophenylethylamine decompose at room temperature.

$$NO_2C_6H_4CH_2CH_2\overset{+}{N}R_3OH^- \longrightarrow NO_2C_6H_4CH{=}CH_2 + R_3N + H_2O$$

The decomposition of quaternary salts is extremely useful in the study of the structures of alkaloids and other cyclic nitrogen compounds. The amine is exhaustively methylated, that is until a quaternary salt is formed, and the quaternary hydroxide is decomposed. The process is repeated until a nitrogen-free product is obtained. Its application to piperidine is illustrative. The process, known as the Hofmann ex-

$$\text{piperidine } (CH_2)_5NH \xrightarrow[CH_3I]{\text{excess}} (CH_2)_5\overset{+}{N}(CH_3)_2\ I^- \xrightarrow[H_2O]{Ag_2O} (CH_2)_5\overset{+}{N}(CH_3)_2\ OH^-$$

$$\xrightarrow{\Delta} H_2O + CH_2{=}CHCH_2CH_2CH_2N(CH_3)_2 \longrightarrow CH_2{=}CHCH_2CH_2CH_2\overset{+}{N}(CH_3)_3\ OH^-$$

$$\xrightarrow{\Delta} (CH_3)_3N + H_2O + [CH_2{=}CHCH_2CH{=}CH_2]$$

$$\longrightarrow CH_3CH{=}CHCH{=}CH_2$$

haustive methylation, has been used for the synthesis of olefins as well as in structure studies.

The Hofmann method does not give nitrogen-free products when applied to benzylamines, since the benzyltrimethylammonium hydroxides cannot decompose to olefins. The nitrogen atom can be removed from such quaternary salts by catalytic reduction or by sodium amalgam reduction. This is the method of Emde. Application of the process to tetrahydroisoquinoline is an example.

$$C_6H_4(CH_2CH_2)(CH_2)\overset{+}{N}(CH_3)_2\ X^- \xrightarrow{\text{Hofmann}} C_6H_4(CH{=}CH_2)(CH_2N(CH_3)_2)$$

$$\longrightarrow C_6H_4(CH{=}CH_2)(CH_2\overset{+}{N}(CH_3)_3X^-) \xrightarrow[\text{not Hofmann}]{\text{Emde but}} C_6H_4(CH{=}CH_2)(CH_3)$$

If the nitrogen atom is part of an aromatic heterocyclic ring, such as the pyridine nucleus, the Hofmann method fails because of rearrangement of the quaternary hydroxides.

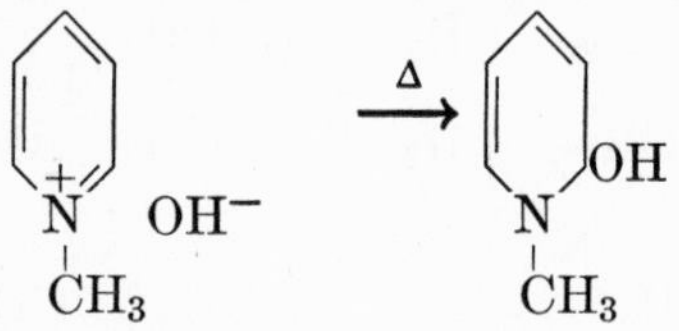

$$\overset{+}{N}\ OH^- \quad CH_3 \xrightarrow{\Delta} N \quad OH \quad CH_3$$

Hexamethylenetetramine reacts with active alkyl halides to give quaternary ammonium, salts which have found novel uses in synthesis. Delepine found that such salts are cleaved by ethanolic hydrochloric acid to yield primary amines. The method is satisfactory only for

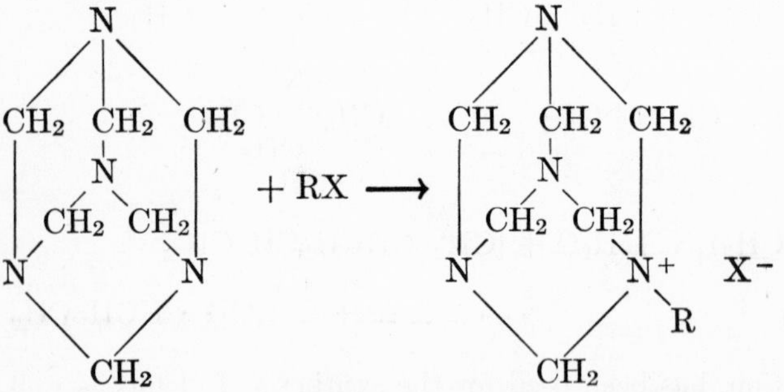

$$N \quad CH_2\ CH_2\ CH_2 \quad N \quad CH_2\ CH_2 \quad N \quad N \quad CH_2 \quad + RX \longrightarrow N \quad CH_2\ CH_2\ CH_2 \quad N \quad CH_2\ CH_2 \quad N \quad N^+ \quad X^- \quad R \quad CH_2$$

$$\xrightarrow[C_2H_5OH]{HCl} 6CH_2(OC_2H_5)_2 + 3NH_4Cl + RNH_2 \cdot HCl$$

amines that boil high enough to be separated easily from ammonia. The advantage of the process is that it permits an alkyl halide to be converted to a *pure* primary amine, uncontaminated by traces of secondary and primary amines which would be formed if the alkyl halide were used to alkylate ammonia.

Sommelet discovered that hydrolysis of the quaternary hexamine salts in less strongly acid medium produced aldehydes. It is now known that the Delepine hydrolysis occurs first, but under the conditions of the Sommelet reaction the primary amine is oxidized by hexamethylenetetramine or its partial hydrolysis products with the formation of the aldehyde.

$$RCH_2X + (CH_2)_6N_4 \longrightarrow [RCH_2N(CH_2)_6N_3]^+X^-$$

$$\xrightarrow{H_2O} NH_3 + H_2CO + RCH_2NH_2 \xrightarrow[pH\ 3\text{–}6.5]{(CH_2)_6N_4} RC\begin{smallmatrix}\nearrow O\\ \searrow H\end{smallmatrix}$$

Interconversions of Aromatic Amines. Bucherer discovered that naphthylamines react with primary and secondary amines in the presence of sodium bisulfite to give secondary and tertiary amines. For example, β-naphthylamine and *p*-aminophenol react as shown.

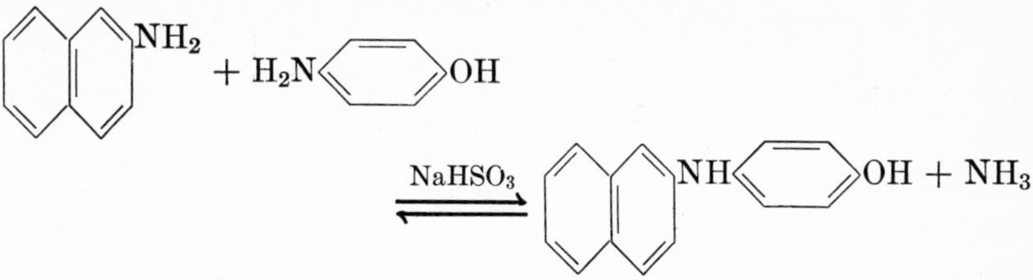

$$\beta\text{-}C_{10}H_7NH_2 + H_2N\text{-}C_6H_4\text{-}OH \xrightleftharpoons{NaHSO_3} C_{10}H_7NH\text{-}C_6H_4\text{-}OH + NH_3$$

Similarly the naphthyl amines react with water in the presence of bisulfite to yield naphthols and ammonia. This process is reversible; β-naphthylamine is formed in good yields when β-naphthol is heated in an autoclave with aqueous ammonium sulfite. This is the industrial method of synthesis of β-naphthylamine.

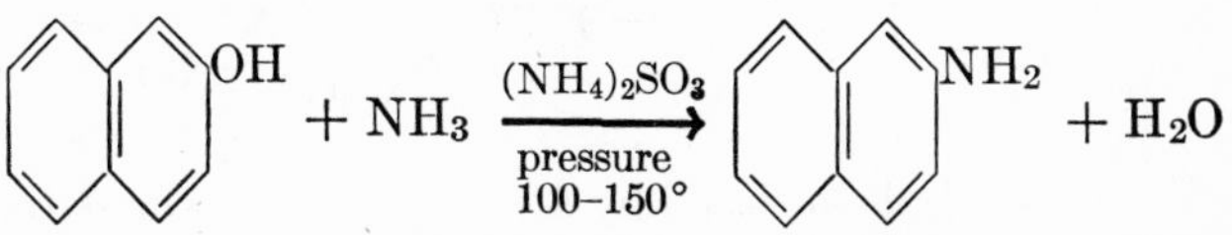

$$\beta\text{-}C_{10}H_7OH + NH_3 \xrightarrow[\text{pressure, } 100\text{–}150°]{(NH_4)_2SO_3} \beta\text{-}C_{10}H_7NH_2 + H_2O$$

Heating of a primary aromatic amine with its hydrochloride causes the formation of the diarylamine, a process formally similar to some varieties of the Bucherer reaction. This is the commercial method for diphenylamine.

$$C_6H_5NH_2 + C_6H_5NH_2 \cdot HCl \xrightarrow{200\text{–}230°} (C_6H_5)_2NH + NH_4Cl$$

Reactions of Amines with Nitrous Acid. Amines of nearly all types react with nitrous acid in the presence of water and mineral acid. Tertiary aliphatic amines react only to give salts from which the amines can be regenerated by treatment with alkali. Tertiary aromatic amines having open *ortho* or *para* positions undergo substitution. The occurrence of such reactions demonstrates the strong electron-donating property of the amine residue, rendering the aromatic system susceptible to attack by the nitrosyl cation.

$$HONO + H^+ \rightleftharpoons H_2O + NO^+$$

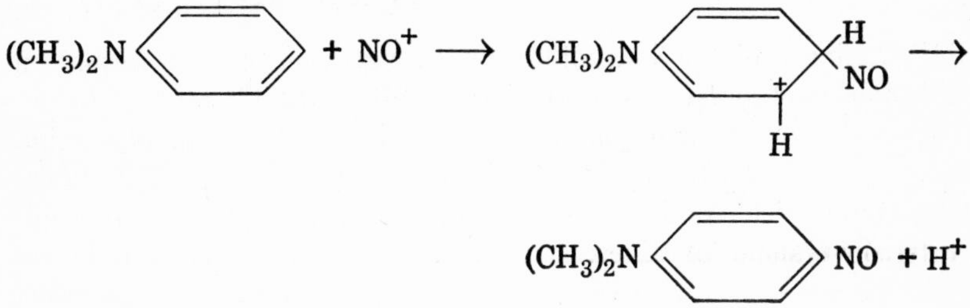

$$(CH_3)_2N\text{-}C_6H_5 + NO^+ \longrightarrow (CH_3)_2N\text{-}C_6H_5^+(H)(NO) \longrightarrow$$

$$(CH_3)_2N\text{-}C_6H_4\text{-}NO + H^+$$

The dimethylamino group in *p*-nitrosodimethylaniline is so labile that it is easily removed by hydrolysis. This fact suggests that it may have the quinoid structure shown in the equation.

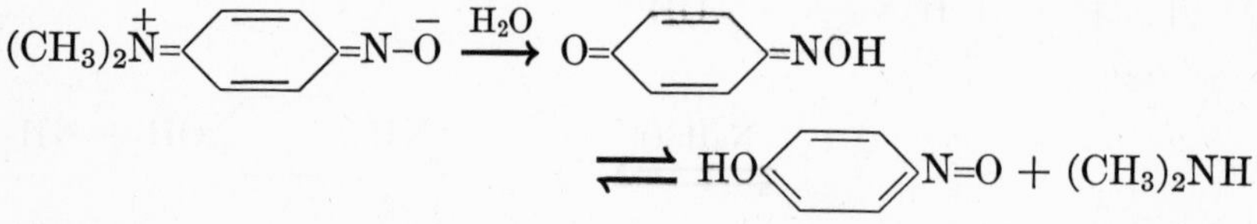

$$(CH_3)_2\overset{+}{N}{=}C_6H_4{=}N{-}\overset{-}{O} \xrightarrow{H_2O} O{=}C_6H_4{=}NOH$$

$$\rightleftharpoons HOC_6H_4N{=}O + (CH_3)_2NH$$

The nitrosation and hydrolysis of N,N-dialkylanilines afford a route to *pure* secondary aliphatic amines.

If no *o* or *p* position is open an alkyl group may be displaced from the nitrogen atom. For example, dimethyltribromoaniline reacts as shown.

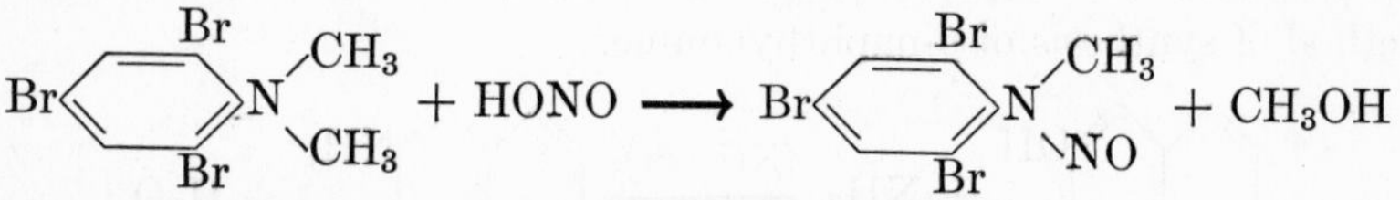

$$Br_3C_6H_2N(CH_3)_2 + HONO \longrightarrow Br_3C_6H_2N(CH_3)NO + CH_3OH$$

The reaction evidently is initiated by attack of the nitrogen atom by the nitrosyl cation. The N-nitrosoamine may be hydrolyzed to the secondary amine.

Secondary amines of either aliphatic or aromatic type react to give the nitrogen nitroso derivatives. These are neutral substances.

$$R_2NH + HONO \longrightarrow R_2NN{=}O$$

Primary aliphatic amines react with nitrous acids to give alcohols and olefins. Usually the alcohol is the major product, but it is likely to be formed by rearrangement. For example, *n*-propylamine yields the following products.

$$CH_3CH_2CH_2NH_2 + HONO \longrightarrow \begin{cases} CH_3CH_2CH_2OH & (7\%) \\ CH_3CH(OH)CH_3 & (32\%) \\ CH_3CH{=}CH_2 & (28\%) \end{cases}$$

Methylamine, which is incapable of rearrangement or olefin formation, yields methanol, but the reaction occurs only in the *p*H range 3–6.

Application of the reaction of nitrous acid to cycloalkylmethylamines constitutes the Demjanov method of ring expansion. Cyclobutylmethylamine yields both the expected cyclobutane derivatives and both the cyclopentane derivatives.

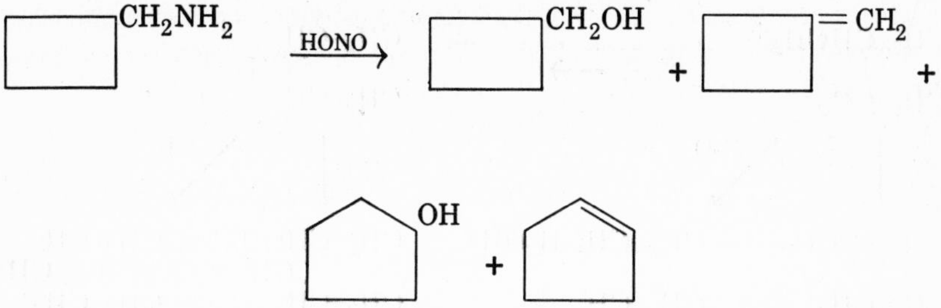

$$\text{cyclobutyl}-CH_2NH_2 \xrightarrow{HONO} \text{cyclobutyl}-CH_2OH + \text{cyclobutylidene}=CH_2 + \text{cyclopentanol (OH)} + \text{cyclopentene}$$

In some instances one or two of the possible products predominate. Thus cyclohexylmethylamine yields chiefly cycloheptanol.

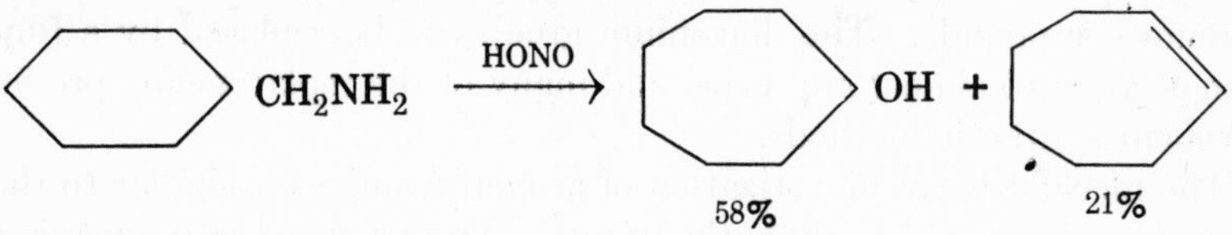

$$\text{cyclohexyl}-CH_2NH_2 \xrightarrow{HONO} \underset{58\%}{\text{cycloheptyl}-OH} + \underset{21\%}{\text{cycloheptene}}$$

The reaction of a primary aliphatic amine with nitrous acid proceeds through an unstable diazonium ion intermediate. This ion loses nitrogen to form a carbonium ion. Rearrangement of the carbonium ion before neutralization by ejection of a proton or reaction with water accounts for changes in the carbon skeleton. The various steps are shown for the reaction of cyclobutylmethylamine.

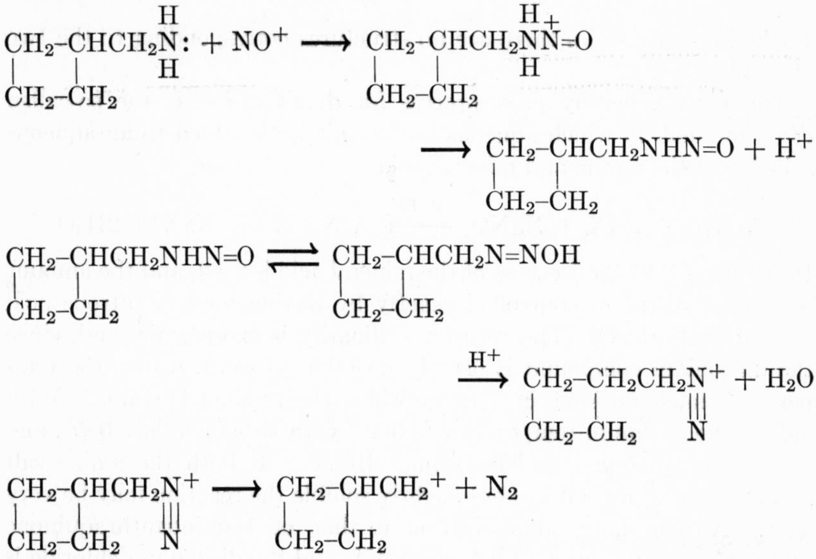

$$\begin{array}{l} CH_2{-}CHCH_2\overset{H}{\underset{H}{N}}{:} \\ | \quad\;\; | \\ CH_2{-}CH_2 \end{array} + NO^+ \longrightarrow \begin{array}{l} CH_2{-}CHCH_2\overset{H}{\underset{H}{N}}\overset{+}{N}{=}O \\ | \quad\;\; | \\ CH_2{-}CH_2 \end{array}$$

$$\longrightarrow \begin{array}{l} CH_2{-}CHCH_2NHN{=}O \\ | \quad\;\; | \\ CH_2{-}CH_2 \end{array} + H^+$$

$$\begin{array}{l} CH_2{-}CHCH_2NHN{=}O \\ | \quad\;\; | \\ CH_2{-}CH_2 \end{array} \rightleftharpoons \begin{array}{l} CH_2{-}CHCH_2N{=}NOH \\ | \quad\;\; | \\ CH_2{-}CH_2 \end{array}$$

$$\xrightarrow{H^+} \begin{array}{l} CH_2{-}CH_2CH_2N^+ \\ | \quad\;\; | \qquad\quad \vert\vert\vert \\ CH_2{-}CH_2 \qquad N \end{array} + H_2O$$

$$\begin{array}{l} CH_2{-}CHCH_2N^+ \\ | \quad\;\; | \qquad\quad \vert\vert\vert \\ CH_2{-}CH_2 \qquad N \end{array} \longrightarrow \begin{array}{l} CH_2{-}CHCH_2{}^+ \\ | \quad\;\; | \\ CH_2{-}CH_2 \end{array} + N_2$$

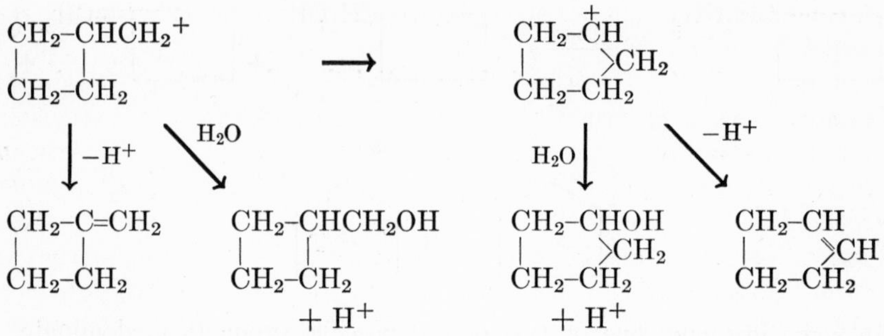

$$\begin{array}{c}CH_2\text{–}CHCH_2^+\\ |\quad\ |\\ CH_2\text{–}CH_2\end{array} \longrightarrow \begin{array}{c}CH_2\text{–}\overset{+}{C}H\\ |\qquad \rangle CH_2\\ CH_2\text{–}CH_2\end{array}$$

Left cation: $\downarrow -H^+$ and $\searrow H_2O$. Right cation: $H_2O \downarrow$ and $\searrow -H^+$.

$$\begin{array}{c}CH_2\text{–}C{=}CH_2\\ |\quad\ |\\ CH_2\text{–}CH_2\end{array} \quad \begin{array}{c}CH_2\text{–}CHCH_2OH\\ |\quad\ |\\ CH_2\text{–}CH_2\\ +H^+\end{array} \quad \begin{array}{c}CH_2\text{–}CHOH\\ |\qquad \rangle CH_2\\ CH_2\text{–}CH_2\\ +H^+\end{array} \quad \begin{array}{c}CH_2\text{–}CH\\ |\qquad \rangle CH\\ CH_2\text{–}CH_2\end{array}$$

Diazotization of Primary Aromatic Amines. Aromatic primary amines are most useful in synthesis as intermediates for the preparation of diazonium compounds. The diazonium group can be replaced by a functional group of almost any type, and many of the replacements provide excellent synthetic methods.

The mechanism of diazotization of aromatic amines is similar to that just given for primary aliphatic amines. The principal difference is in the greater stability of the aromatic diazonium ion. The increase in stability is ascribed to the increased resonance.

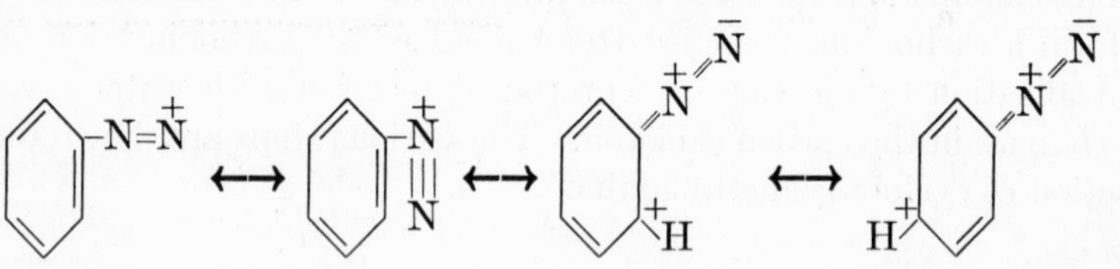

$$C_6H_5\text{–}N{=}\overset{+}{N} \longleftrightarrow C_6H_5\text{–}\overset{+}{N}{\equiv}N \longleftrightarrow \text{(quinoid, } {=}\overset{+}{N}{=}\bar{N}\text{, } \overset{+}{\text{H}}\text{ ortho)} \longleftrightarrow \text{(quinoid, } {=}\overset{+}{N}{=}\bar{N}\text{, } \overset{+}{\text{H}}\text{ para)}$$

In the aliphatic series there are no structures corresponding to the two quinoid forms.

The most generally used process for diazotization is the so-called *direct* method, in which aqueous sodium nitrite is added to an aqueous solution of the amine and mineral acid.

$$ArNH_2 + 2HX + NaNO_2 \xrightarrow{0\text{–}12^\circ} ArN_2{}^+X^- + NaX + 2H_2O$$

In practice, a 10–25% excess of the mineral acid is used, and the amount of sodium nitrite is controlled exactly by testing for free nitrous acid (starch-iodide test). The reaction ordinarily is exothermic, and, since the diazonium compound is usually unstable to warm water, the temperature must be kept in a range where the product is stable. With aniline the optimum temperature is 0–2°, with *m*-haloanilines 0–5°, and with naphthylamines and benzidines 10–12°. If both the amine salt and the diazonium salt are but slightly soluble the reaction may be very slow. A remarkable diazotization is that of 1-aminoanthraquinone hydrochloride; it is carried out at 30–40°, and the diazonium chloride is crystallized from hot water! This diazonium salt is exceptionally resistant to hydrolysis.

For diazotization to occur it is essential that the solution contain an appreciable concentration of the free aromatic amine. Since aromatic amines are weak bases, a certain amount of the free amines will exist in acid solutions required for the formation of the nitrosyl cation from nitrous acid. However, it is necessary to avoid the presence of a high concentration of free amine. Diazonium salts couple with amines to form diazoamino compounds; this reaction, illustrated below, becomes a serious side reaction in the diazotization of very weakly basic amines.

$$C_6H_5N_2^+ + H_2NC_6H_5 \longrightarrow C_6H_5N{=}N{-}NHC_6H_5 + H^+$$

This coupling occurs to an undersirable extent when *p*-nitroaniline is diazotized by the direct method; even though an excess of hydrochloric acid is present the amine salt undergoes appreciable hydrolysis because of the effect of the nitro group on the basicity and solubility of the amine. The hydrolysis might be repressed by increasing the concentration of hydrochloric acid, but this also represses the solubility of the hydrochloride. A more successful method consists in dissolving the amine in the hot aqueous acid and cooling rapidly so that most of the hydrochloride separates in small, and therefore rapidly soluble, crystals. The sodium nitrite is added in one lot, and the mixture is kept at 10°. The excess of nitrous acid over the dissolved salt prevents the formation of the diazoamino compound.

Special methods are available for the diazotization of still weaker bases; even picramide can be diazotized.

Diazonium compounds are amphoteric. When a strong base is added to a solution of a diazonium salt the diazonium cation is converted to the diazotate anion. Careful acidification may yield the diazoic acid, which is tautomeric with the nitrosoamine, but which reacts further with acid to regenerate the diazonium cation. These changes are illustrated below.

$$[C_6H_5{-}N{\equiv}N]^+Cl^- \xrightarrow{2KOH} C_6H_5{-}N{=}NOK \xrightarrow{HX}$$

Diazonium salt — Diazotate

$$C_6H_5N{=}NOH \rightleftharpoons C_6H_5{-}N(H){-}NO \xrightarrow{HX} [C_6H_5{-}N{\equiv}N]^+X^-$$

Diazoic acid — Nitrosamine (isolated)

The most valuable reactions of the diazonium compounds are those of the diazonium cation. These involve the loss of molecular nitrogen and replacement by such substituents as CN, I, Br, Cl, F, and OH (p. 128). The coupling with phenols and amines to give azo compounds also appears to involve the diazonium cation. Coupling with phenols is carried out in weakly basic solution, in which the concentration of diazonium cation is not high, but the union with the phenoxide anion, with the essentially irreversible formation of the azo compound, shifts the equilibrium. The reaction is most simply represented as involving the resonance structures of the diazonium cation and phenoxide anion shown in the equation.

$$C_6H_5{-}N{=}N^+ + {}^-\overset{}{\underset{H}{C}}{<}C_5H_4{=}O \longrightarrow C_6H_5{-}N{=}N{-}\overset{H}{C}{<}C_5H_4{=}O$$

$$\downarrow\uparrow$$

$$C_6H_5{-}N{=}N{-}C_6H_4{-}OH$$

Coupling with tertiary aromatic amines proceeds by attack at an electron-rich position, usually *para,* in the neutral amine molecule. Such couplings are carried out in weakly acidic solutions, in which, owing to the hydrolysis of the amine salt, a certain concentration of the free amine will exist.

$$C_6H_5{-}N{=}\overset{+}{N} + C_6H_5{-}N(CH_3)_2$$

$$\longrightarrow C_6H_5{-}N{=}N{-}\overset{H}{C}{<}\overset{+}{C_5H_4}{-}N(CH_3)_2$$

$$\longrightarrow C_6H_5{-}N{=}N{-}C_6H_4{-}N(CH_3)_2 + H^+$$

This coupling closely resembles the ordinary aromatic substitutions.

A coupling of an altogether different type occurs when a diazonium compound and a liquid aromatic substance are brought together in the presence of very strong alkali. For example, diazotized *p*-bromoaniline and benzene react under these conditions to give *p*-bromobiphenyl.

$$Br{-}C_6H_4{-}N_2^+Cl + C_6H_6 + KOH$$

$$\longrightarrow Br{-}C_6H_4{-}C_6H_5 + KCl + H_2O + N_2$$

Couplings of this type appear to proceed through free-radical intermediates. It is probable that in the reaction cited *p*-bromobenzenediazoic acid is extracted into the benzene layer where it decomposes to a *p*-bromophenyl radical, a hydroxyl radical, and nitrogen. The aryl radical then attacks a molecule of benzene. The various steps are shown below.

$$\text{Br}\text{C}_6\text{H}_4\text{N{=}NOH} \longrightarrow \text{Br}\text{C}_6\text{H}_4\cdot + \text{N}_2 + \text{HO}\cdot$$

$$\text{Br}\text{C}_6\text{H}_4\cdot + \text{C}_6\text{H}_6 \longrightarrow \text{Br}\text{C}_6\text{H}_4\text{-C}_6\text{H}_5 + \text{H}\cdot$$

$$\text{H}\cdot + \text{HO}\cdot \longrightarrow \text{H}_2\text{O}$$

Diazoparaffins. The simplest and most important diazoparaffin is diazomethane, CH_2N_2. It is formed when a nitrosomethylamide is hydrolyzed with strong base, apparently as a decomposition product of the diazotate anion. The preparation from nitrosomethylurethan is shown. Diazomethane and its homologs are extremely reactive com-

$$\underset{\text{NO}}{\text{CH}_3\text{N}}\text{CO}_2\text{C}_2\text{H}_5 + 3\text{KOH} \longrightarrow \text{K}_2\text{CO}_3 + \text{C}_2\text{H}_5\text{OH} + [\text{CH}_3\text{N{=}NOK}]$$

$$\longrightarrow \text{CH}_2\text{N}_2 + \text{KOH}$$

pounds. They behave as nucleophilic reagents in many of their reactions, as might be expected from consideration of their structures. Most of the reactions are easily interpreted as resulting from the contribution of the first of the two structures shown for diazomethane.

$$\text{H-}\underset{\text{H}}{\text{C}}\leftarrow\text{N}{\equiv}\text{N} \longleftrightarrow \text{H-}\underset{\text{H}}{\text{C}}{=}\text{N}\rightleftarrows\text{N}$$

Diazomethane is a highly poisonous yellow gas; it is generally used in ether solutions. It is a very effective methylating agent for acids, phenols, enols, and imides but does not ordinarily attack alcohols or amines. Its most important reactions are illustrated below.

$$\text{RCO}_2\text{H} + \text{CH}_2\text{N}_2 \longrightarrow \text{RC(=O)-OCH}_3 + \text{N}_2$$

$$\text{C}_6\text{H}_5\text{OH} + \text{CH}_2\text{N}_2 \longrightarrow \text{C}_6\text{H}_5\text{OCH}_3 + \text{N}_2$$

$$\text{RC(=O)-Cl} + \text{CH}_2\text{N}_2 \longrightarrow \text{RC(=O)-CHN}_2 + \text{HCl}$$

$$\text{RC(=O)-H} + \text{CH}_2\text{N}_2 \longrightarrow \text{R-C(=O)-CH}_3 + \text{N}_2$$

A cyclic ketone when treated with diazomethane yields the next higher cyclanone. Thus cyclopentanone and cyclohexanone yield, respectively, cyclohexanone and cycloheptanone.

$$\begin{array}{c}\text{CO}\\ \diagup\quad\diagdown\\ \text{CH}_2\quad\text{CH}_2\\ |\qquad\quad|\\ \text{CH}_2\text{—CH}_2\end{array} \xrightarrow{CH_2N_2} \begin{array}{c}\text{CO}\\ \diagup\quad\diagdown\\ \text{CH}_2\quad\text{CH}_2\\ |\qquad\quad|\\ \text{CH}_2\quad\text{CH}_2\\ \diagdown\quad\diagup\\ \text{CH}_2\end{array} \xrightarrow{CH_2N_2} \begin{array}{c}\text{CO}\\ \diagup\quad\diagdown\\ \text{CH}_2\quad\text{CH}_2\\ |\qquad\quad|\\ \text{CH}_2\quad\text{CH}_2\\ |\qquad\quad|\\ \text{CH}_2\text{—CH}_2\end{array}$$

In an attempt to use this method in the preparation of cyclopropanone by treating ketene with diazomethane it was observed that the chief product was cyclobutanone; presumably cyclopropanone was an intermediate.

$$CH_2{=}C{=}O \xrightarrow{CH_2N_2} \left[\begin{array}{c}CH_2\text{–}C{=}O\\ \diagdown\ \diagup\\ CH_2\end{array}\right] \xrightarrow{CH_2N_2} \begin{array}{c}CH_2\text{–}C{=}O\\ |\qquad|\\ CH_2\text{–}CH_2\end{array}$$

Of great interest is the reaction of diazomethane with the Grignard reagent. It does not behave like ketene or isocyanates but adds both the R and the MgX to the terminal nitrogen atom.

$$CH_2{=}N\text{–}N\langle + RMgX \longrightarrow CH_2{=}N\text{–}N\begin{array}{l}\diagup MgX\\ \diagdown R\end{array}$$

Diazoacetic Ester. Although diazomethane must be prepared indirectly, aliphatic amines can be converted to diazo compounds if the amino group is *alpha* to a carbonyl group. Diazoacetic ester, for example, is prepared from the ethyl ester of glycine.

$$C_2H_5O_2CCH_2NH_2 + HNO_2 \longrightarrow [C_2H_5O_2CCH_2N{=}NOH]$$
$$\longrightarrow C_2H_5O_2CCHN_2$$

Most of the reactions of this compound appear to be those of the $C_2H_5O_2CCH\langle$ diradical. Hydrogen ion or heat causes the loss of nitrogen, and the radical so formed dimerizes or reacts with other molecules that may be present.

$$C_2H_5O_2CHN_2 \xrightarrow{heat} C_2H_5O_2CCH\langle \longrightarrow C_2H_5O_2CCH{=}CHCO_2C_2H_5$$
$$C_2H_5O_2CCH\langle + H_2O \longrightarrow HOCH_2CO_2C_2H_5$$

It gives similar reactions with hydrogen chloride, iodine, acids, aldehydes, etc. With unsaturated compounds nitrogen is not lost; cyclic compounds are formed which do lose nitrogen on heating.

$$C_2H_5O_2CCHN_2 + \begin{matrix} CHCO_2C_2H_5 \\ \| \\ CHCO_2C_2H_5 \end{matrix} \longrightarrow \begin{matrix} & N{=}N \\ C_2H_5O_2CCH & | \\ | & | \\ C_2H_5O_2CC\text{---} & CHCO_2C_2H_5 \\ | & \\ H & \end{matrix}$$

Pyrazoline derivative

$$\xrightarrow{\text{heat}} \begin{matrix} C_2H_5O_2CCH \\ / \ \backslash \\ C_2H_5O_2CCH\text{—}CHCO_2C_2H_5 \end{matrix}$$

Diazoacetic ester reacts with benzene at 130° to form norcaradienecarboxylic ester and its rearrangement product, cycloheptatrienecarboxylic ester.

$$C_6H_6 + N_2CHCO_2C_2H_5 \longrightarrow \begin{matrix} & CH & \\ // & & \backslash \\ CH & & CH\diagdown \\ | & & | \quad CHCO_2C_2H_5 \\ CH & & CH\diagup \\ \backslash\backslash & & / \\ & CH & \end{matrix} \text{ and }$$

$$\begin{matrix} CH{=}CHCH_2\diagdown \\ | \qquad\qquad CCO_2C_2H_5 \\ CH{=}CHCH\diagup\!\diagup \end{matrix} + N_2$$

Rearrangement. The rearrangement of certain N-substituted anilines has already been mentioned. This is a rather general phenomenon and may be summarized by the following transformation where A equals halogen, alkyl, hydroxyl, amino, nitroso, nitro, etc.

$$C_6H_5\text{–}\overset{+}{N}A \xrightarrow{H^+} A\text{–}C_6H_4\text{–}\overset{+}{N}H \quad (\text{A in para position})$$

In all cases the nitrogen atom must be in the tetravalent condition.

By heating trimethylphenylammonium iodide at temperatures from 250 to 335° the ring may be methylated progressively.

$$C_6H_5N(CH_3)_3^+I^- \longrightarrow (CH_3)_2N\cdot HI\text{–}C_6H_4\text{–}CH_3 \longrightarrow CH_3\text{–}NH\cdot HI\text{–}C_6H_3(CH_3)_2 \longrightarrow NH_2\cdot HI\text{–}C_6H_2(CH_3)_3$$

This is known as the Hofmann rearrangement.

Nitrosoamines undergo a similar change known as the Fischer-Hepp rearrangement.

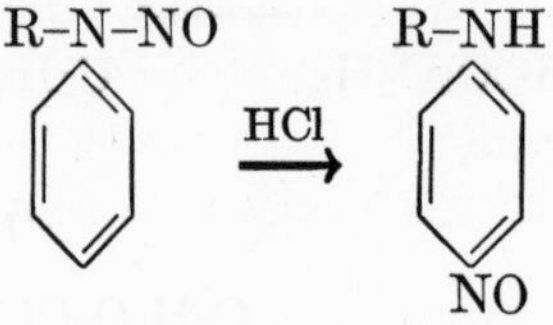

$$C_6H_5N(R)NO \xrightarrow{HCl} p\text{-}ON\text{-}C_6H_4\text{-}NHR$$

Similarly phenylnitroamines yield nitroanilines.

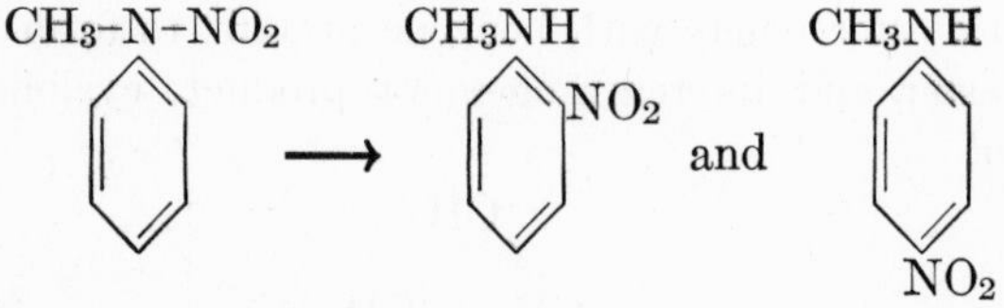

$$C_6H_5N(CH_3)NO_2 \longrightarrow o\text{-}O_2N\text{-}C_6H_4\text{-}NHCH_3 \text{ and } p\text{-}O_2N\text{-}C_6H_4\text{-}NHCH_3$$

The rearrangement of phenylhydrazine hydrochloride at 200° is another example.

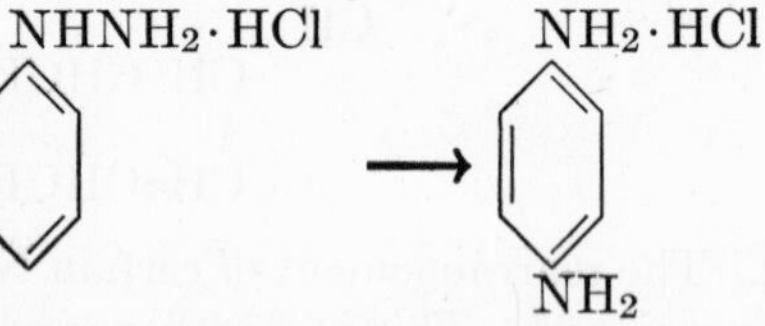

$$C_6H_5NHNH_2 \cdot HCl \longrightarrow p\text{-}H_2N\text{-}C_6H_4\text{-}NH_2 \cdot HCl$$

The benzidine rearrangement, mentioned earlier, is of this type.

In the Beckmann rearrangement of oximes, the characteristic feature is the migration of an organic residue from carbon to nitrogen (p. 307), rather than from nitrogen to carbon as in the above reactions. A reaction which closely resembles the Beckmann rearrangement is the Lossen reaction; in this process the hydroxylamine derivative of a carboxylic acid (a hydroxamic acid) is transformed into an isocyanate by the action of a dehydrating agent such as polyphosphoric acid. The conversion of benzhydroxamic acid to aniline by way of phenyl isocyanate is an illustration.

$$C_6H_5C(=O)\text{-}NHOH \longrightarrow H_2O + C_6H_5N{=}C{=}O \xrightarrow{H_2O} C_6H_5NH_2 + CO_2$$

If the hydroxamic acid is considered to react in the tautomeric form, $C_6H_5C(=NOH)\text{-}OH$, the change can be regarded as a variation of the Beckmann transformation.

The Lossen reaction provides one way of degrading an acid to the primary amine of one less carbon atom. Other methods of accomplishing the same change are the Hofmann degradation of amides, the Curtius reaction of hydrazides, and the Schmidt reaction of acids. In the Hofmann reaction the acid is converted to the amide, which is treated with an alkali hypohalite solution. Warming the aqueous alkaline solution liberates the amine. It has been shown that the intermediates are the N-haloamide and the isocyanate. The individual steps are represented in the equations.

$$R{-}\overset{\nearrow O}{C}{-}NH_2 \xrightarrow{OBr^-} R\overset{\nearrow O}{C}{-}NHBr + OH^-$$

$$R{-}\overset{\nearrow O}{C}{-}NHBr \xrightarrow{OH^-} \left[R{-}\overset{\nearrow O}{C}{-}NBr\right]^-$$

$$\left[R{-}\overset{\nearrow O}{C}{-}NBr\right]^- \longrightarrow R{-}N{=}C{=}O + Br^-$$

$$RN{=}C{=}O + H_2O \longrightarrow RNH_2 + CO_2$$

The rearrangement occurs in the third step; evidently, as the bromine moves away from the nitrogen atom, with the electron pair, the alkyl group moves to it, bringing its electron pair to neutralize the deficiency developing on the nitrogen atom.

In the Curtius reaction an acid is converted to an azide ($RCON_3$) which is decomposed thermally to yield nitrogen and an isocyanate. The azide can be made from the acid chloride and sodium azide, or it can be prepared from the acid hydrazide by reaction with nitrous acid.

$$R\overset{\nearrow O}{C}{-}Cl + NaN_3 \searrow$$

$$R\overset{\nearrow O}{C}{-}N_3$$

$$RCO_2C_2H_5 + H_2NNH_2 \longrightarrow R\overset{\nearrow O}{C}{-}NHNH_2 \overset{HONO}{\nearrow}$$

$$R\overset{\nearrow O}{C}{-}N{\leftarrow}N{\equiv}N \longrightarrow RN{=}C{=}O + N_2$$

The rearrangement here occurs in the last step shown, and it is very similar to that in the Hofmann process. The loss of the molecule of nitrogen and the migration of the alkyl group are believed to occur simultaneously, as in the corresponding step of the Hofmann reaction.

The Schmidt reaction occurs when an acid is treated with hydrazoic acid (HN_3) in sulfuric acid solution. It yields the amine directly, as shown in the equation.

$$RCO_2H + HN_3 \longrightarrow RNH_2 + CO_2 + N_2$$

It appears to be closely similar to the Curtius reaction.

Separation of Mixtures of Amines. Ever since Hofmann found that he could get a mixture of amines by treating ammonia with an alkyl halide, the problem of the separation of amines has occupied the attention of chemists.

1. *Fractional distillation* is still the best method.

2. *Hinsberg* devised a procedure using benzenesulfonyl chloride. After the amines have been steam-distilled from the basic solution of the ammonium salts, the distillate is made alkaline and benzenesulfonyl chloride is added. The products obtained are as follows:

$$RNH_2 + C_6H_5SO_2Cl \longrightarrow C_6H_5SO_2\text{–}\overset{\displaystyle H}{\overset{|}{N}}\text{–}R + HCl$$

$$R_2NH + C_6H_5SO_2Cl \longrightarrow C_6H_5SO_2\text{–}NR_2 + HCl$$

$$R_3N + C_6H_5SO_2Cl \longrightarrow \text{no reaction}$$

The three substances are separable because the primary amine derivative is alkali-soluble, the unchanged tertiary amine is acid-soluble, and the secondary amine derivative insoluble in both acid and base. This method is not very satisfactory in the laboratory, particularly since primary amines usually form some of the neutral dibenzenesulfonyl derivative.

$$RN\begin{matrix}\nearrow SO_2C_6H_5\\ \searrow SO_2C_6H_5\end{matrix}$$

The Hinsberg method is of greater value in classifying unknown amines than in separating mixtures.

3. Another method of separation employs *ethyl oxalate*. When it is heated with a mixture of amines the following reactions take place.

$$2RNH_2 + (CO_2C_2H_5)_2 \longrightarrow \begin{matrix}CONHR\\ | \\ CONHR\end{matrix} + 2C_2H_5OH$$

$$R_2NH + (CO_2C_2H_5)_2 \longrightarrow \begin{matrix}CO_2C_2H_5\\ | \\ CONR_2\end{matrix} + C_2H_5OH$$

$$R_3N + (CO_2C_2H_5)_2 \longrightarrow \text{no reaction}$$

The primary derivative is a high-melting crystalline solid, whereas the secondary is an oil. The three products can be separated by their solubility behavior. This method of separation is complicated by the fact that the higher primary amines tend to stop at the monoamide stage.

4. *Phthalic acid* has also been used to separate amines. On heating, the primary and secondary amines react to form amides while the tertiary does not. These amides are alkali-soluble. On further heating the primary amide forms an imide which is not alkali- or acid-soluble.

$$C_6H_4(CO_2H)_2 + RNH_2 \longrightarrow C_6H_4(CONHR)(CO_2H) \longrightarrow C_6H_4(CO)_2N\text{–}R$$

$$C_6H_4(CO_2H)_2 + R_2NH \longrightarrow C_6H_4(CONR_2)(CO_2H)$$

$$C_6H_4(CO_2H)_2 + R_3N \longrightarrow C_6H_4(CO_2^-)(CO_2H) + R_3NH^+$$

Halogenated Amines and Amides. Hypohalites convert primary and secondary amines and amides to the corresponding N-halo derivatives. Chloramine-T (p. 450) is made in this way. Certain chloroamines have attracted attention because treatment with sulfuric acid converts them to pyrrolidines. Di-*n*-butylchloroamine, for example, yields *n*-butylpyrrolidine.

$$(C_4H_9)_2NH \xrightarrow[NaOH]{Cl_2} (C_4H_9)_2NCl \xrightarrow{H_2SO_4} \begin{matrix} CH_2\text{–}CH_2 \\ | \\ CH_2\text{–}CH_2 \end{matrix}\!\!\!\!\!\!> N\text{–}C_4H_9$$

Compounds having halogen attached to nitrogen can serve as halogenating agents. The halogen atom is said to be "positive." N-Bromosuccinimide, employed as a brominating agent, is produced by the action of an alkali hypobromite on succinimide. Compounds are known in which halogens joined to carbon are "positive."

CHAPTER 29

Organic Sulfur Compounds

One of the early efforts to classify organic compounds containing oxygen and nitrogen was to regard them as substitution products, respectively, of water and ammonia. Thus ethers are obtained by putting alkyl or aryl groups in place of the two hydrogen atoms of water, and amines by replacing similarly one or more of the hydrogen atoms of ammonia. By analogy sulfur compounds might be regarded as derivatives of hydrogen sulfide. Those having one radical are mercaptans (p. 62) or thiophenols; those with two are thio ethers (p. 66).

RSH	ArSH	RSR
Mercaptan	Thiophenol	Thio ether

Disulfides are also known (p. 63), but they show only a formal resemblance to peroxides.

R–S–S–R	R–O–O–R
Disulfide	Peroxide

In general, the analogies between sulfur and oxygen compounds are of a structural rather than a chemical nature.

The more important sulfur compounds are those in which the sulfur atom shows a valence higher than 2, and they are very much different from any known compounds of oxygen. The sulfonic acids are the most important examples.

Mercaptans

Mercaptans differ from alcohols in being much less associated. Table XXXV, of boiling points, shows this difference. The most characteristic property of the mercaptans and thiophenols is their intensely disagreeable odor. It is said that 1/460,000,000 mg. of ethyl mercaptan can be detected by its odor. This is 1/250 of the smallest amount of sodium that can be detected spectroscopically. The unpleasant odor of crude petroleum is due primarily to mercaptans. *n*-Butyl mercaptan is a constituent of the secretion of the skunk.

TABLE XXXV

MERCAPTANS AND ALCOHOLS

	Boiling Point		Boiling Point
H_2S	−61°	H_2O	+100°
CH_3SH	6	CH_3OH	65
C_2H_5SH	37	C_2H_5OH	78
n-C_3H_7SH	68	n-C_3H_7OH	97
n-C_4H_9SH	98	n-C_4H_9OH	117

Mercaptans and thiophenols are also more acidic than the corresponding oxygen compounds. This could be predicted from the fact that they are monosubstituted derivatives of hydrogen sulfide, which is an acid. A characteristic property of mercaptans is the ease with which their salts form mercury derivatives.

$$RSH + NaOH \longrightarrow RSNa + H_2O$$

$$2RSNa + HgCl_2 \longrightarrow (RS)_2Hg + 2NaCl$$

The name mercaptan (corpus mercurium captans) comes from this fact.

Mercaptans react with acids to form esters.

$$RSH + RC{\overset{\diagup\!\!\diagup O}{-}}OH \longrightarrow RC{\overset{\diagup\!\!\diagup O}{-}}SR + H_2O$$

This reaction provided the first indication that in esterification, in general, the hydroxyl group comes from the acid rather than the alcohol.

Mercaptans form mercaptals with aldehydes and mercaptoles with ketones. Acetaldehyde and acetone may be cited as illustrations.

$$CH_3CHO + 2C_2H_5SH \longrightarrow CH_3CH\begin{matrix}\diagup SC_2H_5\\ \diagdown SC_2H_5\end{matrix} + H_2O$$

$$\begin{matrix}CH_3\diagdown\\ CH_3\diagup\end{matrix}CO + 2C_2H_5SH \longrightarrow \begin{matrix}CH_3\diagdown\\ CH_3\diagup\end{matrix}C\begin{matrix}\diagup SC_2H_5\\ \diagdown SC_2H_5\end{matrix} + H_2O$$

The latter equation represents one step in the process used to manufacture sulfonal (p. 83).

The most interesting reaction of mercaptans is the conversion to disulfides by oxidation (p. 63).

$$2RSH + [O] \longrightarrow RS\text{–}SR + H_2O$$

The formation of cystine from cysteine is an example.

$$\begin{array}{l} CH_2SH \\ 2CHNH_2 \\ CO_2H \end{array} + [O] \longrightarrow \begin{array}{ll} CH_2S-SCH_2 & \\ CHNH_2 & CHNH_2 \\ CO_2H & CO_2H \end{array} + H_2O$$

Cysteine — Cystine

The disulfides are probably formed as intermediates in the oxidation of mercaptans to sulfonic acids (p. 447).

$$2RSH + [O] \longrightarrow RS\text{–}SR + H_2O$$

$$RS\text{–}SR + 5[O] + H_2O \longrightarrow 2RSO_3H$$

It will be noted that this behavior is entirely different from that of alcohols, which undergo oxidation at the α-carbon atom.

Thio Ethers

Thio ethers (p. 66) are prepared by the interaction of mercaptides and alkyl halides.

$$RSNa + R'X \longrightarrow RSR' + NaX$$

They may also be made by treating alkyl halides with alkali sulfides.

$$2RX + Na_2S \longrightarrow RSR + 2NaX$$

sym-Trithianes, compounds closely related to thio ethers, are formed by the treatment of aldehydes or ketones with hydrogen sulfide in the presence of hydrochloric acid. Thioaldehydes and thioketones are presumably intermediates in this reaction.

$$RCHO + H_2S \xrightarrow{HCl} [RCHS] + H_2O$$

$$\downarrow$$

```
        R
        CH
       /  \
      S    S
      |    |
    RCH    CHR
       \  /
        S
```

These substances are analogous to paraldehydes. The parent compound, *sym*-trithiane, is a trimer of thioformaldehyde.

$$3H_2CS \longrightarrow \text{(trithiane ring: } -S-CH_2-S-CH_2-S-CH_2- \text{)}$$

The trithianes from higher aldehydes exist in *cis* and *trans* modifications.

cis Form

trans Form

A few *thioketones* have been prepared in the monomeric forms. Benzophenone is converted to thiobenzophenone by treatment with hydrogen sulfide and hydrogen chloride.

$$(C_6H_5)_2CO + H_2S \xrightarrow{HCl} (C_6H_5)_2CS + H_2O$$

It is a deep blue solid, melting at 52°. Thiocamphor can be made by a similar method.

Thio ethers react with alkyl halides to give sulfonium halides in which the sulfur atom is trivalent.

$$R{-}S{-}R + RX \longrightarrow R_3S^+X^-$$

These compounds have the following electronic structure.

$$\left[\begin{matrix} & R & \\ R: & \ddot{S}: & \\ & \ddot{R} & \end{matrix}\right]^+ X^-$$

Sulfoxides and Sulfones

Thio ethers may be oxidized to sulfoxides and these in turn may be oxidized to sulfones. The question of the structures of these oxidation products has been debated for many years. Early structures were predicated on the assumption that the sulfur atom, like carbon, is tetrahedral and that a double bond between sulfur and oxygen would have many of the properties of the carbonyl double bond. Neither of these assumptions is necessarily correct. Certainly sulfur can have an outer electron shell of twelve, as is shown by the existence of the hexafluoride, SF_6. Certain physical properties of the sulfur oxygen bond in sulfoxides have been interpreted as indicating a double bond, but others seem indicative of a coordinate link. Whether the second linkage in sulfones is a coordinate bond or a double bond is likewise uncertain; possibly the sulfones are hybrids of the resonance structures shown.

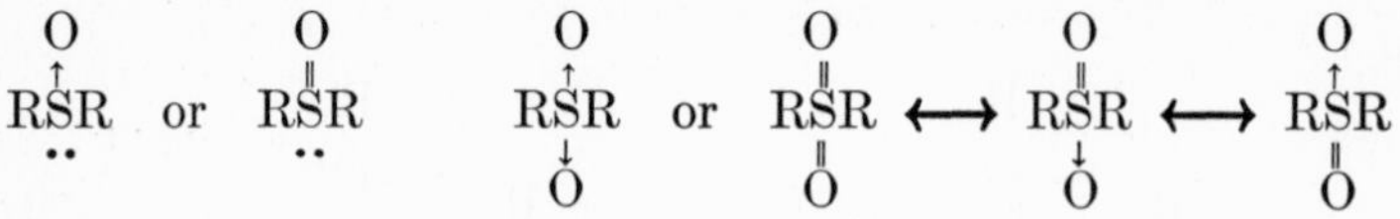

$$\underset{a}{R\overset{\overset{O}{\uparrow}}{\underset{\cdot\cdot}{S}}R} \quad \text{or} \quad \underset{b}{R\overset{\overset{O}{\|}}{\underset{\cdot\cdot}{S}}R} \qquad\qquad R\overset{\overset{O}{\uparrow}}{\underset{\underset{O}{\downarrow}}{S}}R \quad \text{or} \quad R\overset{\overset{O}{\|}}{\underset{\underset{O}{\|}}{S}}R \longleftrightarrow R\overset{\overset{O}{\|}}{\underset{\underset{O}{\downarrow}}{S}}R \longleftrightarrow R\overset{\overset{O}{\uparrow}}{\underset{\underset{O}{\|}}{S}}R$$

Sulfoxide — Sulfone

An alternative structure, $R{-}\overset{\overset{O}{\|}}{S}{-}R$, for sulfoxides can be rejected on the basis of the fact that dithiane disulfoxide exists in *cis* and *trans* modifications; in this structure the sulfur atom, having only eight electrons in the outer shell, would almost certainly be tetrahedral, and the structure would be planar. The observed isomerism requires that if the sulfur atom is tetrahedral the sulfur-oxygen link must be coordinate (structure *a*); a double link is acceptable only if the sulfur atom is pyramidal and has an expanded valence shell.

Trisulfones from certain trithianes are acidic and form sodium salts, presumably owing to enolization.

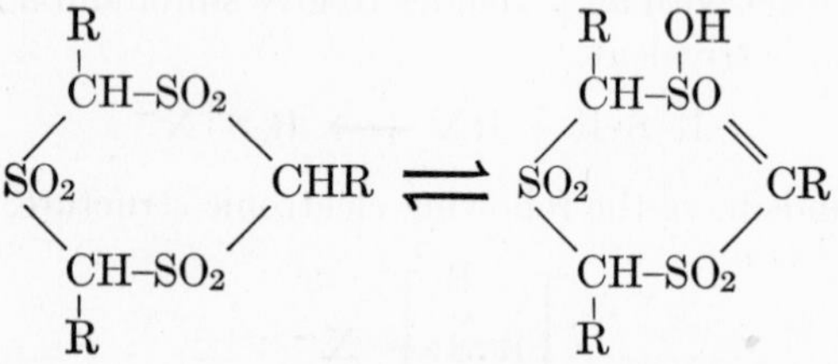

```
     R                        R  OH
     |                        |  |
     CH–SO2                   CH–SO
    /      \                 /     \\
SO2         CHR   ⇌     SO2          CR
    \      /                 \      /
     CH–SO2                   CH–SO2
     |                        |
     R                        R
```

The structures of other oxygen-containing sulfur compounds resemble those of the sulfoxides and sulfones. The fact that esters of sulfinic acids have been resolved shows that the structure $R{-}\overset{O}{S}{-}OR$ is not planar, again requiring a pyramidal sulfur atom if the sulfur oxygen link is double.

Sulfonic Acids

The sulfonic acids of the aromatic series are of great importance. Aliphatic sulfonic acids are also known, however. These can be prepared by the sulfonation of paraffins, by the oxidation of mercaptans (p. 444), or by the action of sodium sulfite on an alkyl halide.

$$RX + Na_2SO_3 \longrightarrow NaX + RSO_3Na \xrightarrow{H^+} RSO_3H$$

Aromatic sulfonic acids also can be prepared by oxidation of compounds containing less highly oxidized sulfur. The reverse processes are more useful, however, and sulfonic acids are employed as sources of thiophenols and sulfinic acids. The reductions actually are carried out on the sulfonyl chlorides, which can be made from the sulfonic acids by the action of one of the phosphorus halides. Acid reduction with zinc yields the thiophenols.

$$ArSO_2Cl + 3H_2 \xrightarrow[H_2SO_4]{Zn} ArSH + HCl + 2H_2O$$

Neutral reduction with zinc produces the zinc salts of the sulfinic acids.

$$2ArSO_2Cl + 2Zn \longrightarrow (ArSO_2)_2Zn + ZnCl_2$$

The most interesting sulfonic acid of the aliphatic group is taurine. It occurs in the bile of animals and is thought to be a degradation product of cystine.

$$\begin{array}{l} CH_2CHCO_2H \\ |\quad\;\; | \\ S\quad NH_2 \\ | \\ S\quad NH_2 \\ |\quad\;\; | \\ CH_2CHCO_2H \end{array} \longrightarrow \begin{array}{c} HO_3SCH_2CHCO_2H \\ | \\ NH_2 \end{array} \xrightarrow{-CO_2} H_2NCH_2CH_2SO_3H$$

Cystine — Taurine

It can be synthesized by the following sequence of reactions.

$$\underset{\diagdown O \diagup}{CH_2CH_2} + NH_3 \longrightarrow HOCH_2CH_2NH_2$$

$$HOCH_2CH_2NH_2 + 2HBr \longrightarrow BrCH_2CH_2NH_3Br + H_2O$$

$$BrCH_2CH_2NH_3Br + Na_2SO_3 \longrightarrow NH_2CH_2CH_2SO_3H + 2NaBr$$

Aromatic sulfonic acids frequently are used as intermediates in the synthesis of other substances; also, the sulfonic acid group may be introduced to increase the water solubility of a molecule. Aryl sulfonic acids and most of their sodium salts are water-soluble. These substances usually are made by direct sulfonation of aromatic compounds.

The sulfonation of benzene will serve as an example. Mono-, di-, and trisubstituted derivatives are obtained.

$$C_6H_6 + H_2SO_4 \longrightarrow C_6H_5SO_3H + H_2O$$

Benzenesulfonic acid

$$C_6H_5SO_3H \longrightarrow C_6H_4(SO_3H)_2 \longrightarrow C_6H_3(SO_3H)_3$$

Commercially, benzenesulfonic acid is isolated as the sodium salt. This separation depends on the fact that the calcium sulfonates are soluble in water. The process, known as *liming out*, consists in neutralizing the sulfonation mixture (after dilution with water) with lime. The insoluble calcium sulfate is separated by filtration and the calcium sulfonate remains in the filtrate. Addition of sodium carbonate converts it to the sodium salt, which is obtained by evaporating the filtered solution to dryness.

$$(C_6H_5SO_3)_2Ca + Na_2CO_3 \longrightarrow 2C_6H_5SO_3Na + CaCO_3$$

Another method of obtaining sodium sulfonates is to treat the sulfonation mixture with sodium chloride. The sodium sulfonate precipitates because it is insoluble in brine.

$$C_6H_5SO_3H + NaCl \longrightarrow C_6H_5SO_3Na + HCl$$

The free sulfonic acids are rarely prepared. They are obtained by treating the calcium, barium, or lead salts with the calculated amount of sulfuric acid, removing the insoluble sulfate, and concentrating the aqueous solution.

The sulfonic acids are solids and generally crystallize as hydrates. Some are hygroscopic. Benzenesulfonic and *p*-toluenesulfonic acids are sometimes used as catalysts where a strong nonvolatile acid is required. Sulfonic acids resemble mineral acids in strength.

Replacement of the SO_3H Group. The sulfonic acid group may be replaced by hydroxyl, cyano, or hydrogen. All these reactions furnish important synthetic methods.

$$C_6H_5SO_3Na + 2NaOH \longrightarrow C_6H_5ONa + Na_2SO_3 + H_2O \quad (1)$$

$$C_6H_5ONa + H_2SO_4 \longrightarrow C_6H_5OH + NaHSO_4$$

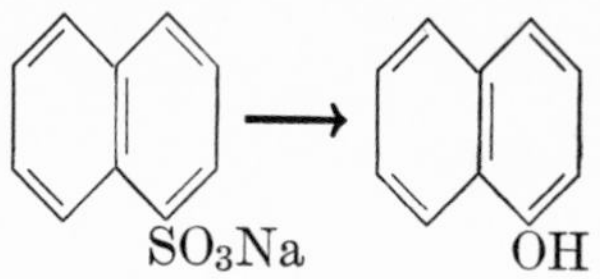

SO₃Na → OH

α-Naphthol

$$C_6H_5SO_3Na + NaCN \longrightarrow C_6H_5CN + Na_2SO_3 \quad (2)$$

$$C_6H_5SO_3H + H_2O \longrightarrow C_6H_6 + H_2SO_4 \quad (3)$$

Reaction 3 takes place when the sulfonic acid is heated with water above 100° under pressure. An example of its use is met in the synthesis of *o*-bromophenol. Phenol is sulfonated to block the *para* and one *ortho* position, and after the bromination has been effected the reaction mixture is subjected to steam distillation. The sulfonic acid groups are removed, and *o*-bromophenol passes over with the steam.

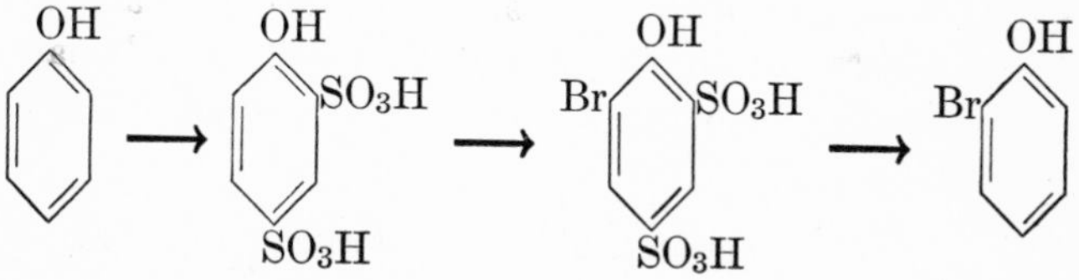

OH → OH, SO_3H, SO_3H → OH, Br, SO_3H, SO_3H → OH, Br

Derivatives of Sulfonic Acids

Sulfonic acids are converted to the corresponding chlorides by phosphorus pentachloride or oxychloride.

$$3C_6H_5SO_3Na + PCl_5 \longrightarrow 3C_6H_5SO_2Cl + 2NaCl + NaPO_3$$

$$2C_6H_5SO_3Na + POCl_3 \longrightarrow 2C_6H_5SO_2Cl + NaCl + NaPO_3$$

Aromatic sulfonyl chlorides are best prepared by treating the aromatic compound with chlorosulfonic acid.

$$C_6H_6 + 2ClSO_3H \longrightarrow C_6H_5SO_2Cl + HCl + H_2SO_4$$

Direct esterification of sulfonic acids does not take place; esters are usually made by treating the acid chloride with alcohols in pyridine.

Ammonia and primary and secondary amines react with the chlorides to give amides. Those having a hydrogen atom on the nitrogen atom are soluble in alkali. This is very interesting in view of the fact that these amides cannot enolize without violating the octet rule (see p. 446).

Sulfonamide derivatives have found a variety of uses. Chloramine-T, for example, has antiseptic properties.

$$p\text{-}CH_3C_6H_4SO_2NCl^-Na^+$$

Chloramine-T

The artificial sweetening agent saccharin is closely related to the sulfonamides. It is several hundred times as sweet as sugar and is used by diabetics as a substitute for sugar. It is made from toluene by an interesting sequence of reactions.

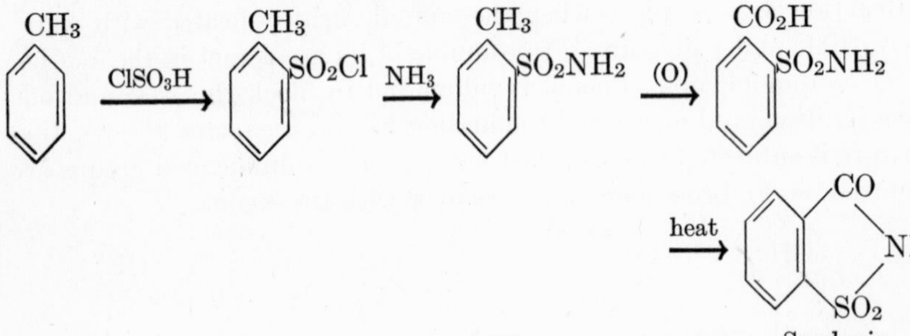

CH_3 $\xrightarrow{ClSO_3H}$ CH_3, SO_2Cl $\xrightarrow{NH_3}$ CH_3, SO_2NH_2 $\xrightarrow{(O)}$ CO_2H, SO_2NH_2

$\xrightarrow{heat}$ CO, NH, SO_2

Saccharin

Saccharin is a cyclic imide and, like phthalimide, is a weak acid. It is used in the form of its sodium salt, which is soluble in water.

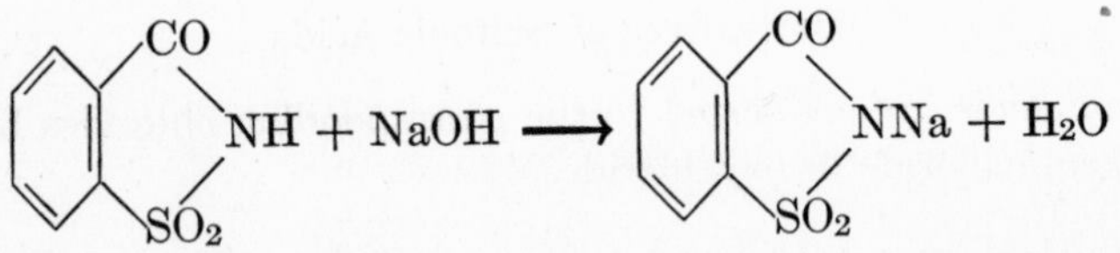

CO, NH, SO_2 $+ NaOH \longrightarrow$ CO, NNa, SO_2 $+ H_2O$

The Sulfa Drugs. Certain sulfonamides have been found to be remarkably effective in the treatment of disease. Sulfanilamide has a high bactericidal activity and is particularly valuable in the treatment of streptococcal infections. It is made from acetanilide by the following transformations.

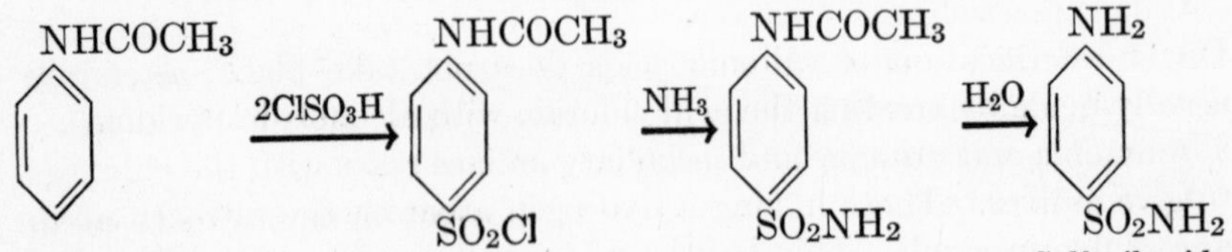

$NHCOCH_3$ $\xrightarrow{2ClSO_3H}$ $NHCOCH_3$, SO_2Cl $\xrightarrow{NH_3}$ $NHCOCH_3$, SO_2NH_2 $\xrightarrow{H_2O}$ NH_2, SO_2NH_2

Acetanilide — Sulfanilamide

Very closely related to sulfanilamide is sulfapyridine, which has proved amazingly effective in combating pneumonia. It is a derivative of α-aminopyridine (p. 497) and is made in much the same way as sulfanilamide.

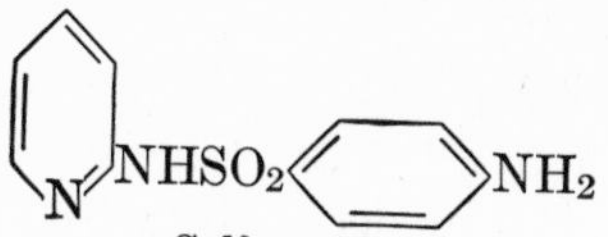

$C_5H_4N{-}NHSO_2{-}C_6H_4{-}NH_2$

Sulfapyridine

Sulfathiazole and sulfadiazine are useful drugs particularly for staphylococcal and pneumococcal infections. They differ from sulfapyridine in having thiazole and pyrimidine rings, respectively, instead of the pyridine ring. Thiazole and pyrimidine are among the many less common heterocyclic compounds containing more than one heteroatom. These rings are present in vitamin B_1 or thiamine.

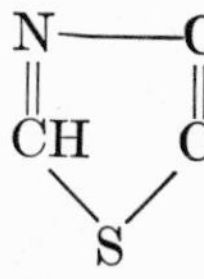

Thiazole 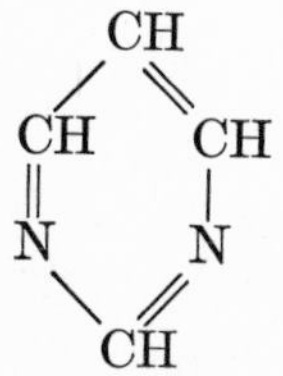   Pyrimidine 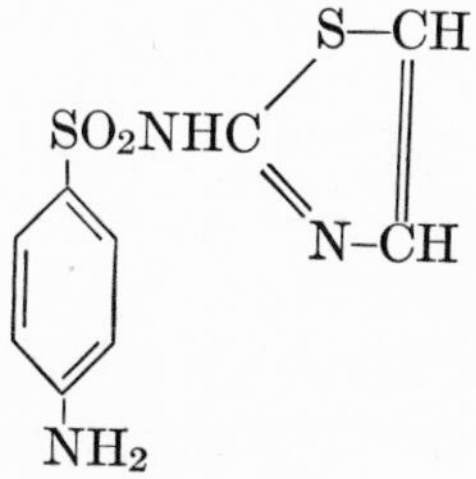   Sulfathiazole 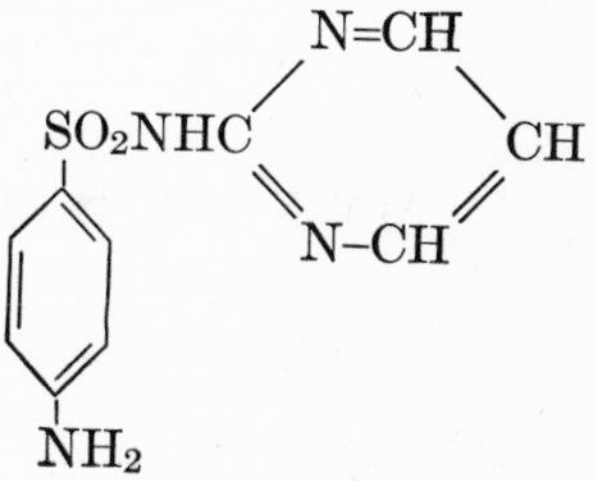   Sulfadiazine

Sulfaguanidine, because it is not absorbed from the alimentary tract, is valuable in the treatment of bacillary dysentery and in pre-operative disinfection of the intestinal tract.

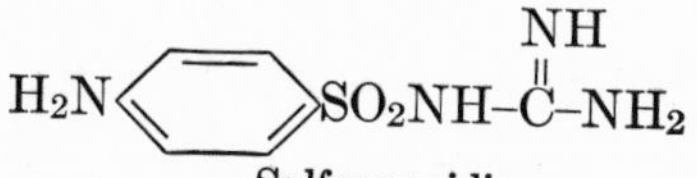

$H_2N{-}C_6H_4{-}SO_2NH{-}C({=}NH){-}NH_2$

Sulfaguanidine

Derivatives of Sulfur Analogs of Carbonic Acid

Only a few of these substances can be mentioned. *Carbon disulfide*, CS_2, is manufactured by passing sulfur vapors over red-hot coke. It is a volatile, inflammable liquid which finds use as a solvent. It is generally employed in this way in the Friedel-Crafts reaction.

Carbon oxysulfide, COS, is made by adding carbon monoxide to sulfur at low temperatures. It is a gas.

The most important derivatives of carbon disulfide are the *xanthates*. They are formed when alkali alcoholates react with carbon disulfide.

$$RONa + CS_2 \longrightarrow ROC(=S)\text{–}SNa$$

These salts are water-soluble, and this fact is used to advantage in the manufacture of rayon from cellulose. The cellulose is converted to the xanthate and later regained by decomposing the xanthate solution.

Alkylation and arylation of sodium or potassium ethyl xanthate yield dithiocarbonates which can be hydrolyzed to mercaptans or thiophenols. Alkylation can be effected with an alkyl halide. Arylation is brought about by the action of diazonium salts.

$$RX + NaSC(=S)\text{–}OC_2H_5 \longrightarrow RSC(=S)\text{–}OC_2H_5 + NaX$$

$$\downarrow H_2O$$

$$RSH + COS + C_2H_5OH$$

$$ArN_2X + KSC(=S)\text{–}OC_2H_5 \longrightarrow ArSC(=S)\text{–}OC_2H_5 + N_2 + KX$$

$$ArSC(=S)\text{–}OC_2H_5 + H_2O \longrightarrow ArSH + COS + C_2H_5OH$$

Thiocyanates are made by adding sulfur to cyanides.

$$KCN + S \longrightarrow KSCN$$

Ferric thiocyanate, $Fe(SCN)_3$, has a deep red color and is used to detect iron. Mercury thiocyanate burns to give Pharoah's serpents. Alkyl thiocyanates can be made by the action of alkyl iodides or sulfates on potassium thiocyanate.

$$RI + KSCN \longrightarrow RSCN + KI$$

Alkyl thiocyanates and certain of their derivatives are used as contact insecticides. They rearrange to alkyl isothiocyanates when heated. Generally this requires long treatment but in allyl thiocyanate takes place readily. One distillation is sufficient to effect the conversion.

$$CH_2{=}CHCH_2SCN \longrightarrow CH_2{=}CHCH_2NCS$$

Isothiocyanates or *mustard oils* take their name from allyl isothiocyanate, which occurs as a glucoside in mustard. The general methods for making them involve the use of primary amines. These are treated with carbon disulfide and lead nitrate.

$$RNH_2 + CS_2 \longrightarrow [RNHCS_2H] \xrightarrow{Pb(NO_3)_2} R{-}N{=}C{=}S$$

If aniline is heated with carbon disulfide *thiocarbanilide* is formed. It yields phenyl isothiocyanate when boiled with strong hydrochloric acid.

$$2C_6H_5NH_2 + CS_2 \longrightarrow \underset{\text{Thiocarbanilide}}{C_6H_5NHCSNHC_6H_5} + H_2S$$

$$C_6H_5NHCSNHC_6H_5 + HCl \longrightarrow \underset{\text{Phenyl isothiocyanate}}{C_6H_5NCS} + C_6H_5NH_2 \cdot HCl$$

CHAPTER 30

Aromatic Compounds

Aromaticity has always been associated with certain types of reactions more or less peculiar to benzene and its derivatives, among them being halogenation, nitration, mercuration, sulfonation, the Friedel-Crafts reaction, and coupling with diazonium salts. However, all these reactions are encountered in the aliphatic series and provide no very satisfactory basis for distinguishing between the two classes.

The most important characteristics of aromatic compounds—those that set them off from the aliphatic group—are to be found in their low degree of unsaturation, their tendency to form, and their remarkable ability to retain their peculiar nature.

Although benzene can be hydrogenated and will react additively with halogens—is therefore clearly an unsaturated hydrocarbon—it does not decolorize alkaline permanganate solutions. Moreover it tends to undergo substitution rather than addition reactions. Aromatic compounds differ chiefly from unsaturated aliphatic compounds in having only a slight tendency to form compounds of the dihydrobenzene type. In some aromatic compounds such as pyridine and nitrobenzene only substitution occurs and that with difficulty. These compounds are more aromatic than benzene. On the other hand naphthalene gives derivatives of the dihydrobenzenoid type more readily than benzene and is, accordingly, regarded as less aromatic.

The formation of aromatic nuclei from aliphatic or alicyclic compounds is a remarkable phenomenon. Sometimes it occurs in ways that do not seem peculiar but more often it involves transformations bespeaking a conspicuous tendency for this type of ring to develop. By way of illustration and contrast may be cited the formation of 2,4-diisopropyltoluene and of 2,4-dimethylphenylacetic acid.

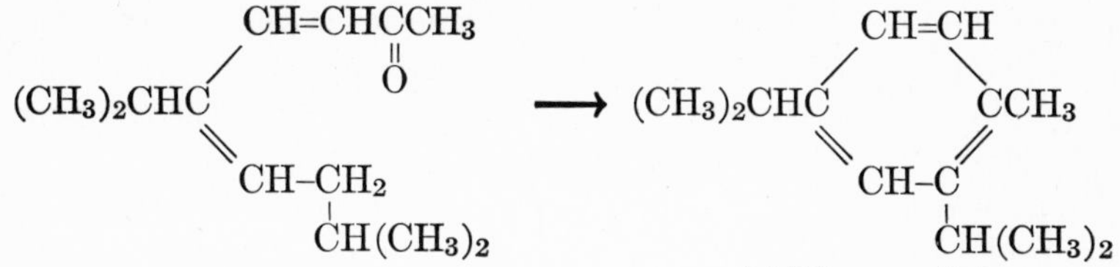

```
            CH=CHCCH3                                   CH=CH
           /      ||                                   /     \
(CH3)2CHC         O          ⟶    (CH3)2CHC          CCH3
          \\                                  \\      //
           CH-CH2                              CH-C
              |                                   |
              CH(CH3)2                            CH(CH3)2
```

2,4-Diisopropyltoluene

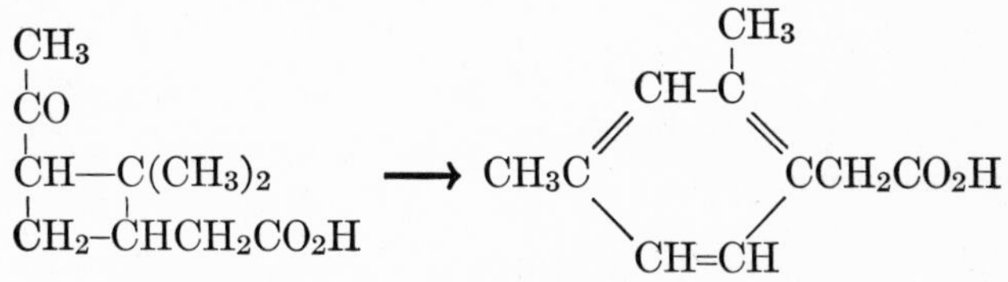

```
CH3                                     CH3
|                                       |
CO                                  CH-C
|                                  //     \\
CH—C(CH3)2          ⟶   CH3C             CCH2CO2H
|   |                        \           /
CH2-CHCH2CO2H                 CH=CH
```

Pinonic acid

2,4-Dimethylphenylacetic acid

The Structure of Benzene

It will be noted that on the basis of the vinylogy principle the first example would be expected to form methyldiisopropyl*cyclohexatriene.* In general, reactions which might be expected to give *cyclohexatriene* yield benzene or one of its derivatives. Studies in wave mechanics indicate that the peculiarly diminished unsaturation of the ring is due to resonance. Thus benzene is pictured as a symmetrical ring which is a resonance hybrid of the two structures resulting from a shift of the bonds.

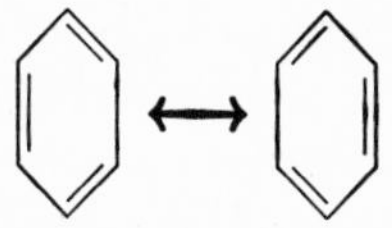

The resonance stabilization in conjugated systems of double bonds is extreme in benzene because the arrangement of the double bonds in a ring makes the system endless. Another carbocycle that exhibits the same structural characteristic is azulene. Like benzene, it can be represented by two equivalent resonance structures.

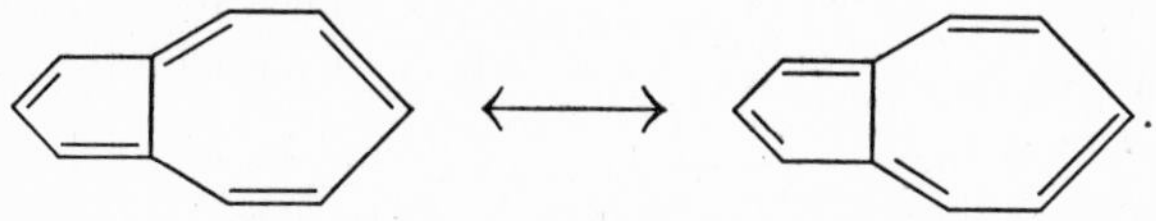

Azulene

Azulene, however, does not exhibit marked aromatic properties. Lack of complete planarity of the azulene ring system would offer an explanation of the observed low order of aromaticity, since the resonance theory requires coplanarity of the system for the maximum effect.

Another molecule that resembles benzene in having a cyclic system of conjugated double bonds is cycloöctatetraene, which appears, however, to be devoid of the typical aromatic properties. The eight-membered ring is known not to be planar (p. 365).

There is evidence that the bond structure of the benzene ring can be stabilized. Mills and Nixon calculated that the six bonds holding the hydrogen atoms in the Kekule model of benzene do not extend from the ring in an entirely symmetrical manner, but that those separated by a double bond form a somewhat larger angle with one another than those separated by a single bond; that is, the distance *a* in the figure is greater than distance *b*.

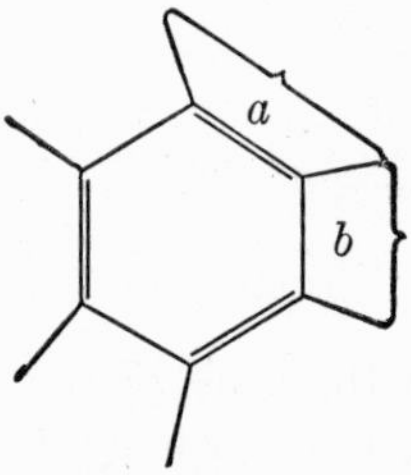

This hypothesis suggests that if a five-membered ring is fused on the benzene ring, as in hydrindene, the strain involved will be less if there is a single rather than a double bond common to the two rings.

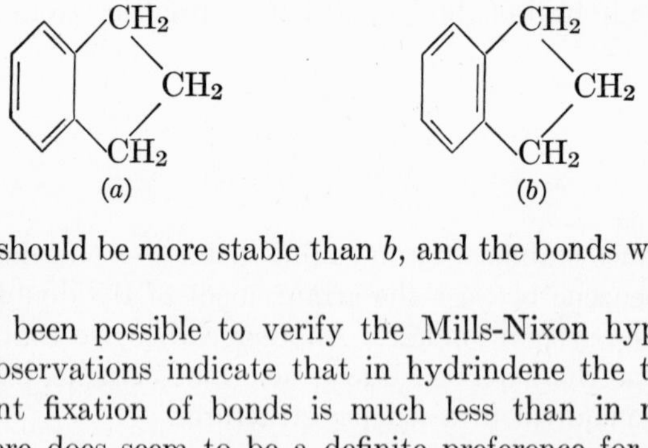

(*a*) (*b*)

Thus form *a* should be more stable than *b*, and the bonds would tend to become fixed.

It has not been possible to verify the Mills-Nixon hypothesis; experimental observations indicate that in hydrindene the tendency toward apparent fixation of bonds is much less than in naphthalene. However, there does seem to be a definite preference for structure *a*. A few related observations may be mentioned. Compound *c* couples with diazonium salts much less readily than *d* does.

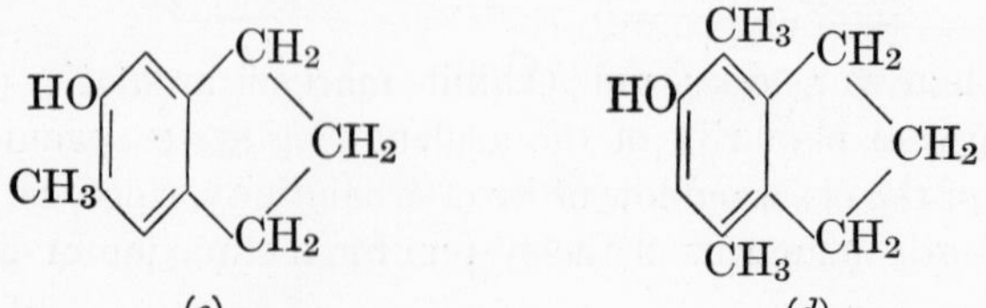

(*c*) (*d*)

The wide difference in the physical properties of 2,4- and 4,6-diacetylresorcinols has been ascribed to chelation. The former melts at 91° and is volatile with steam; the latter melts at 182° and is not volatilized by steam. It will be seen that if we use the Kekule structure only one chelate ring is possible in the 4,6-isomer whereas two can be present in the 2,4-derivative.

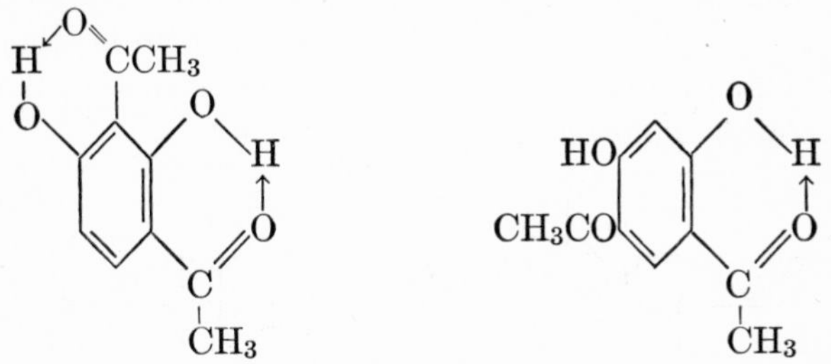

This, of course, involves the assumption that chelation takes place only when there is a double bond between the hydroxyl group and the acetyl group involved.

The introduction of the aldehyde group into resacetophenone by the Gattermann reaction gives the 3- rather than the 5-derivative. This has been explained by assuming fixation of the bonds by chelation.

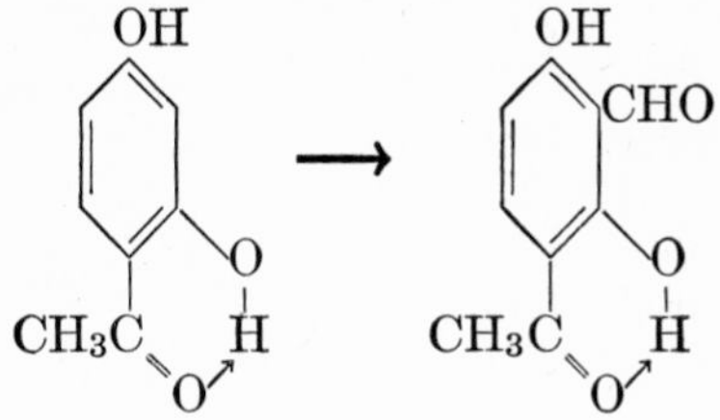

Reactions of Aromatic Compounds

The reactions involving functional groups attached to an aromatic ring are generally similar to those observed with the aliphatic analogs. However, many exceptions to this rule have been recorded. Some of them have already been discussed; others that are of considerable interest will be mentioned briefly.

Side Chains. Side chains owe their reactivity to the adjoining ring and are much more easily attacked than are paraffins. Not only can they be halogenated (p. 47), but with strong oxidizing agents they are converted to carboxyl groups (pp. 46, 409). As has been seen the reactivity is greatly enhanced by nitro groups in the *ortho* or *para* positions.

A remarkable peculiarity of *o*-dialkylbenzenes is that, in contrast to the *meta* and *para* isomers, they are completely oxidized by chromic acid. With this reagent *o*-xylene is destroyed whereas *m*-xylene gives isophthalic acid. No explanation has been advanced for this difference.

During the process of sulfonation, highly alkylated benzenes readily undergo isomerization owing to the migration of groups. This is called the Jacobsen rearrangement. In the presence of cold concentrated sulfuric acid the groups may move from one position to another or from one ring to another. For example, prehnitene is obtained from durene or isodurene by the following sequence of changes.

Durene $\xrightarrow{H_2SO_4}$ durenesulfonic acid (SO_3H; CH_3, CH_3, CH_3, CH_3) $\xrightarrow{H_2SO_4}$ prehnitenesulfonic acid (SO_3H; CH_3, CH_3, CH_3, CH_3) $\longrightarrow$ Prehnitene

Isodurene $\xrightarrow{H_2SO_4}$ isodurenesulfonic acid (SO_3H; CH_3, CH_3, CH_3, CH_3) $\xrightarrow{H_2SO_4}$ prehnitenesulfonic acid

Pentamethylbenzene, on the other hand, yields a mixture of hexamethylbenzene and prehnitene.

$$2\ C_6H(CH_3)_5 \xrightarrow{H_2SO_4} C_6(CH_3)_6 \text{ and } C_6H_2(CH_3)_4$$

Pentamethylbenzene — Hexamethylbenzene — Prehnitene

It has been shown that in these migrations the sulfonic acids and not the original hydrocarbons undergo the rearrangement.

The Reimer-Tiemann Reaction

Phenols react with chloroform and alkalies to give *o*- and *p*-hydroxy aldehydes (p. 170).

The reaction gives predominantly *ortho* derivatives, but *para* isomers are also formed. The presence of nitro, carboxyl, and other *meta*-directing groups prevents the reaction from taking place. If one *ortho* position is filled the aldehyde group tends to go to the *para* position. An example is the synthesis of vanillin from guaiacol.

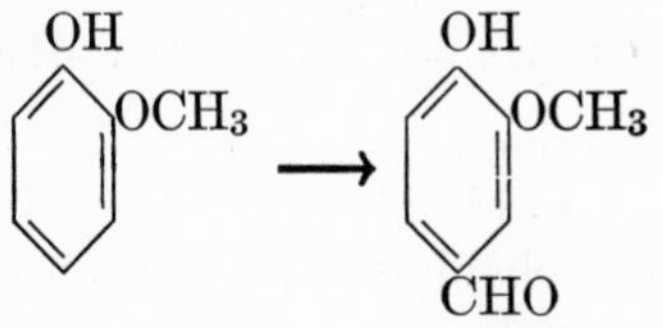

OH OCH_3 → OH OCH_3 CHO

Guaiacol Vanillin

Here the mechanism would appear to be a displacement in which the phenoxide anion behaves as if the negative charge were on the carbon atom *para* to the hydroxyl group.

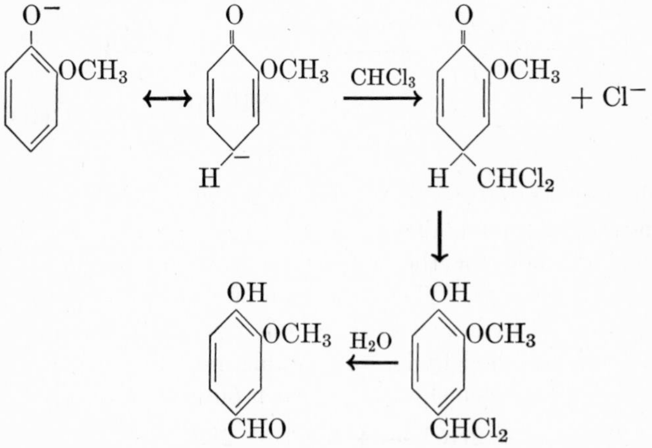

O^- OCH_3 ⟷ O OCH_3 H⁻ $\xrightarrow{CHCl_3}$ O OCH_3 H $CHCl_2$ + Cl^-

↓

OH OCH_3 CHO $\xleftarrow{H_2O}$ OH OCH_3 $CHCl_2$

When carbon tetrachloride is used in place of chloroform an exactly similar reaction occurs, the final product being an acid instead of an aldehyde (p. 246).

Gattermann's Methods

Aromatic aldehydes may be made by the use of carbon monoxide, dry hydrogen chloride, aluminum chloride, and an activator such as cuprous chloride. The use of pressure eliminates the necessity for an activator.

$$ArH + CO \xrightarrow[HCl]{AlCl_3} ArCHO$$

This is known as the Gattermann-Koch reaction. It probably involves the intermediate formation of the unstable formyl chloride, and is to be regarded as a typical example of the Friedel-Crafts reaction. By this method toluene yields 50 to 55 per cent of *p*-tolualdehyde.

$$\mathrm{HCl + CO \underset{}{\overset{CuCl}{\rightleftharpoons}} HCOCl}$$

$$\mathrm{HCOCl + CH_3C_6H_5 \xrightarrow{AlCl_3} \textit{p}\text{-}CH_3C_6H_4CHO + HCl}$$

A similar method also due to Gattermann involves the use of hydrogen cyanide and hydrogen chloride. In this reaction the unstable imino chloride of formic acid probably is formed as an intermediate. The reaction is useful when phenols are employed.

$$\mathrm{HCl + HCN \longrightarrow HC(=NH)Cl}$$

$$\mathrm{C_6H_5OH + HC(=NH)Cl \xrightarrow{AlCl_3} \textit{p}\text{-}HOC_6H_4CH{=}NH\cdot HCl \xrightarrow{H_2O} \textit{p}\text{-}HOC_6H_4CHO}$$

Zinc chloride is often used in place of aluminum chloride when sensitive compounds are involved. The procedure has been improved by substituting zinc cyanide for the anhydrous hydrogen cyanide, which is troublesome to prepare. The interaction of zinc cyanide and hydrogen chloride gives the hydrogen cyanide and zinc chloride needed for the reaction. β-Resorcylaldehyde, for example, may be made conveniently in this way. It has been shown that when pure zinc cyanide is used the

$$\mathrm{Zn(CN)_2 + 2HCl \longrightarrow ZnCl_2 + 2HCN}$$

$$\mathrm{HCl + HCN \longrightarrow HC(=NH)Cl}$$

$$\mathrm{C_6H_4(OH)_2 + HC(=NH)Cl \xrightarrow{ZnCl_2} (HO)_2C_6H_3HC{=}NH\cdot HCl \xrightarrow{H_2O} (HO)_2C_6H_3CHO}$$

β-Resorcylaldehyde

reaction fails to take place. Satisfactory results are obtained, however, if small amounts of sodium or potassium chloride are added to the zinc salt.

A method that is formally somewhat similar involves the interaction of formylmethylaniline and aromatic compounds possessing highly active nuclear hydrogen atoms. The synthesis of 2-ethoxy-1-naphthaldehyde is an example.

$$C_{10}H_7OC_2H_5 + C_6H_5N(CH_3)CHO \xrightarrow{POCl_3} C_{10}H_6(CHO)OC_2H_5 + C_6H_5NHCH_3$$

The use of dimethylformamide is illustrated by the synthesis of *p*-dimethylaminobenzaldehyde.

$$C_6H_5N(CH_3)_2 + (CH_3)_2NCHO \xrightarrow{POCl_3} p\text{-}(CH_3)_2NC_6H_4CHO + (CH_3)_2NH$$

The Houben-Hoesch Synthesis

Another method which is really a variation of the Friedel-Crafts synthesis is the Houben-Hoesch process; it consists in the condensation of nitriles with phenols in the presence of hydrogen chloride and zinc chloride. Here again an imino chloride is probably formed as an intermediate.

$$RCN + HCl \longrightarrow RC{\begin{matrix}=NH\\-Cl\end{matrix}}$$

The synthesis of resacetophenone from resorcinol will serve as an example.

$$CH_3CN + HCl \longrightarrow CH_3C{\begin{matrix}=NH\\-Cl\end{matrix}}$$

$$C_6H_4(OH)_2 + CH_3C{\begin{matrix}=NH\\-Cl\end{matrix}} \xrightarrow{ZnCl_2} C_6H_3(OH)_2C(CH_3){=}NH \cdot HCl \xrightarrow{H_2O} C_6H_3(OH)_2COCH_3$$

This is a general reaction for nitriles and phenols.

Polyatomic Phenols. Aromatic rings that carry more than one hydroxyl group exhibit many peculiarities. For example, *o*- and *p*-dihydroxy compounds are readily oxidized to the corresponding quinones.

$$\text{p-}C_6H_4(OH)_2 \underset{-H_2}{\overset{+H_2}{\rightleftharpoons}} \text{p-}C_6H_4O_2 \qquad \text{o-}C_6H_4(OH)_2 \underset{-H_2}{\overset{+H_2}{\rightleftharpoons}} \text{o-}C_6H_4O_2$$

With the quinones they form highly colored addition compounds known as quinhydrones.

$$C_6H_4(OH)_2 \cdot C_6H_4O_2$$

Quinhydrone

The attachment of the two molecules in the quinhydrone is not understood but appears not to involve primary valence forces. *Meta* dihydroxy compounds cannot give quinones.

Catechol. Catechol may be made by demethylation of guaiacol, which occurs in beechwood tar.

$$\text{o-}C_6H_4(OH)(OCH_3) \longrightarrow \text{o-}C_6H_4(OH)_2 \longleftarrow \text{o-}C_6H_4(CHO)(OH)$$

Guaiacol — Catechol — Salicylaldehyde

A more unusual synthesis is the conversion of salicylaldehyde to catechol by the action of alkaline hydrogen peroxide.

Catechol is remarkable for the ease with which it is carboxylated. It is converted to protocatechuic acid merely by heating with aqueous ammonium carbonate at 140°.

$$C_6H_4(OH)_2 \longrightarrow C_6H_3(OH)_2CO_2H$$

Protocatechuic acid

Resorcinol. Resorcinol results from the alkali fusion of *m*- or *p*-benzenedisulfonic acid or of *o*-, *m*-, or *p*-bromobenzenesulfonic acid. Possibly in the latter examples the sulfonic acid group migrates to the *meta* position before replacement occurs.

Phloroglucinol. Phloroglucinol is obtained in several ways, of which three will be listed.

1. Hydrolysis of 1,3,5-triaminobenzene or 2,4,6-triaminobenzoic acid. The starting point in this synthesis is TNT, and the steps are as follows.

$$C_6H_2(CH_3)(NO_2)_3 \longrightarrow C_6H_2(CO_2H)(NO_2)_3 \longrightarrow C_6H_2(CO_2H)(NH_2)_3 \longrightarrow C_6H_3(OH)_3$$

Phloroglucinol

2. Alkali fusion of resorcinol in the presence of air. This is a characteristic of many phenolic substances, but it is not clear why the entering hydroxyl group takes up position 5 rather than some other.

3. Condensation of malonyl chloride with acetone.

$$COCl{-}CH_2{-}COCl + CH_3{-}CO{-}CH_3 \longrightarrow CH_2\begin{matrix} \diagup CO{-}CH_2 \diagdown \\ \diagdown CO{-}CH_2 \diagup \end{matrix}CO \rightleftharpoons C_6H_3(OH)_3$$

This is especially interesting because it would seem to involve the intermediate formation of the keto form of the phenol. As a matter of fact phloroglucinol yields a trioxime and must exist to some extent in the keto form. This suggests an explanation of the facile hydrolysis of 1,3,5-triaminobenzene. By analogy with oxygen derivatives the triamine would be expected to be in tautomeric equilibrium with the triketimine, a substance which would be hydrolyzed readily.

$$C_6H_3(NH_2)_3 \rightleftharpoons (HN{=}C{<})_3(CH_2)_3 \longrightarrow (CO)_3(CH_2)_3 \rightleftharpoons C_6H_3(OH)_3$$

Phloroglucinol is thus very near the borderline which divides aromatic from alicyclic compounds, being under suitable conditions a mixture of tautomers one of which is aromatic and the other alicyclic.

The vicinal (1,2,3-) trihydroxybenzene, known as pyrogallol, is important as a developing agent and as a dye intermediate. It resembles resorcinol in the ease with which it can be carboxylated to give the corresponding acid.

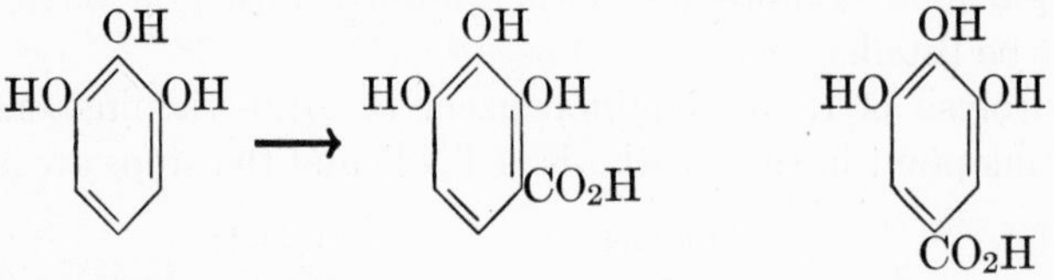

Pyrogallol → (pyrogallolcarboxylic acid, CO_2H) Gallic acid

Gallic acid is an isomer of this acid and is obtained from tannic acid, a constituent of gallnuts. The tannic acid of commerce is gallotannin. It is used as a mordant in dyeing cotton cloth (p. 506), in the manufacture of inks, as an astringent, and in the treatment of burns.

m-Digallic acid is a depside and is closely related to certain types of tannins.

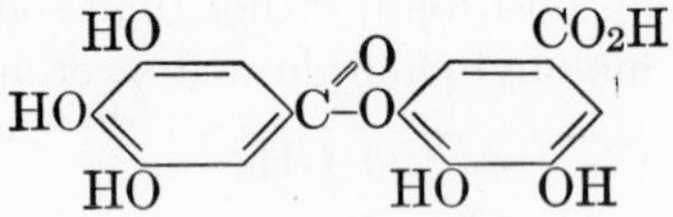

m-Digallic acid

Depsides are esters of aromatic hydroxy acids with hydroxy acids. By esterification of glucose with gallic acid and *m*-digallic acid, compounds are formed which resemble natural tannins.

Hydrolysis of natural tannins of this type yields gallic acid. Like pyrogallolcarboxylic acid, gallic acid loses carbon dioxide when heated and yields pyrogallol.

Quinones. Quinones are readily formed from certain aromatic compounds and yield dihydroxybenzenes on reduction. The oxidation of aniline with potassium dichromate is one of the common methods for making quinone. The change from quinone to hydroquinone is rapid and reversible, and is one of the few such reactions of organic compounds.

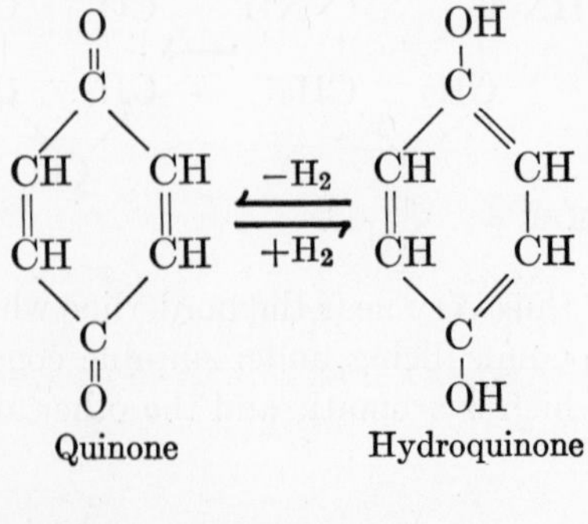

$$\text{Quinone} \underset{+H_2}{\overset{-H_2}{\rightleftharpoons}} \text{Hydroquinone}$$

Quinone Hydroquinone

A potential is developed on a platinum wire dipped into a quinone-hydroquinone mixture in the presence of an electrolyte such as dilute acid. This system can function as a half cell.

In spite of their close genetic relationship it must be recognized that whereas the hydroquinone is typically aromatic the quinone is alicyclic. It is an unsaturated diketone. It undergoes reactions characteristic of α,β-unsaturated ketones. For example, hydrogen chloride adds to it in the 1,4 manner. The product is the chlorohydroquinone formed by subsequent enolization.

```
      O                    ┌      OH        ┐         OH
      ‖                    │      |         │         |
      C                    │      C         │         C
     / \                   │     / \\       │        / \\
   CH   CH                 │   CH    CH     │      CH    CH
   ‖    ‖   + HCl ⟶        │   ‖     |      │  ⟶   ‖     |
   CH   CH                 │   CH    CHCl   │      CH    CCl
     \ /                   │     \  /       │        \  //
      C                    │      C         │         C
      ‖                    │      ‖         │         |
      O                    └      O         ┘         OH
```

In the presence of an oxidizing agent the chlorohydroquinone is changed to the corresponding quinone. This process is repeated until the tetrachloroquinone is formed. This explains the formation of chloranil by the oxidation of aniline in the presence of hydrochloric acid.

```
                    O                 O
                    ‖                 ‖
    NH2             C                 C
                   / \               / \
  (benzene)  ⟶   CH   CH    ⟶     ClC   CCl
                 ‖    ‖            ‖     ‖
                 CH   CH          ClC   CCl
                   \ /               \ /
                    C                 C
                    ‖                 ‖
                    O                 O
                                   Chloranil
```

The ketonic nature of quinones is demonstrated by the formation of dioximes and other typical derivatives of diketones. The monoxime of quinone is identical with the product obtained by the action of nitrous acid on phenol. Nitrosophenol and quinone oxime are evidently tautomers; which formula better represents the product is not yet certain.

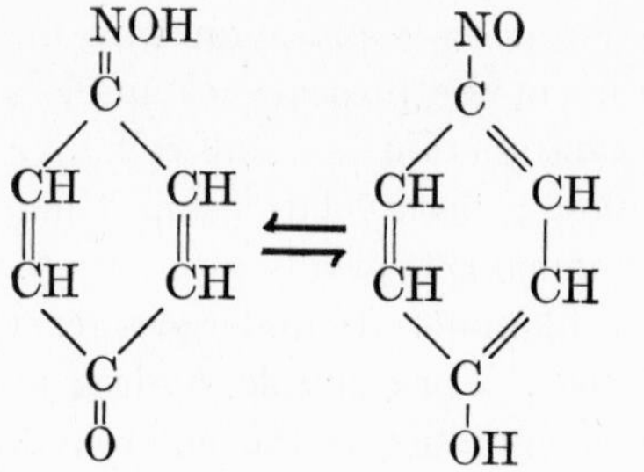

```
        NOH                  NO
        ‖                    |
        C                    C
      /   \                /  ⫽
    CH     CH            CH    CH
    ‖      ‖      ⇌      ‖     |
    CH     CH            CH    CH
      \   /                \  ⫽
        C                    C
        ‖                    |
        O                    OH
```

Although quinone is generally made by the oxidation of hydroquinone or aniline it can be obtained from benzene directly. It has been postulated as an intermediate in the catalytic oxidation of benzene to maleic anhydride.

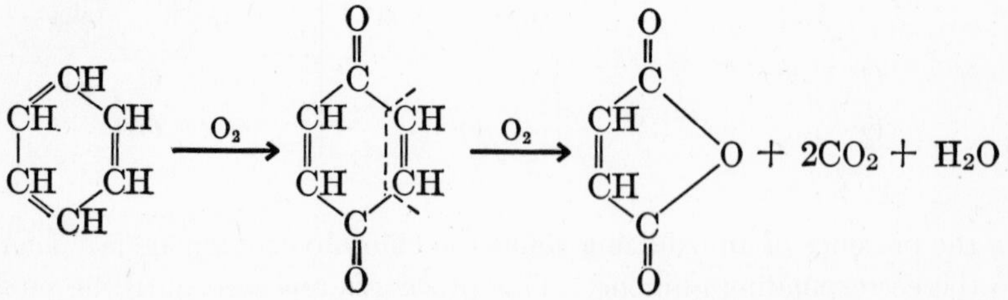

```
                          O                    O
                          ‖                    ‖
       CH                 C                    C
    CH    CH    O₂     CH   CH     O₂      CH    \
    |     ‖    ───→    ‖     ‖    ───→     ‖      O + 2CO₂ + H₂O
    CH    CH           CH   CH             CH    /
       CH                 C                    C
                          ‖                    ‖
                          O                    O
```

It can be demonstrated that, under the conditions used, quinone will yield the observed products.

Rearrangement of Allyl Phenyl Ethers. Allyl phenyl ethers rearrange under the influence of heat to give the corresponding *o*-allylphenols. The rearrangement was discovered by Claisen and generally bears his name. *o*-Allylphenol is obtained in yields of 80 per cent by heating allyl phenyl ether at 190–220° for 6 hours.

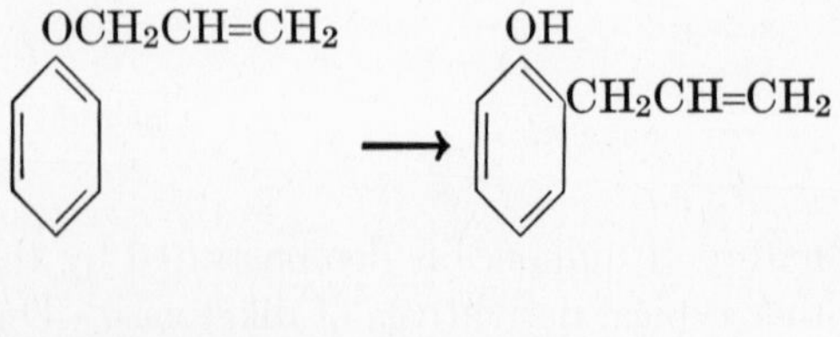

$$C_6H_5OCH_2CH{=}CH_2 \longrightarrow o\text{-}C_6H_4(OH)CH_2CH{=}CH_2$$

If the resulting phenol is allylated the rearrangement can be repeated until the *ortho* and *para* positions are filled.

$$\text{C}_6\text{H}_4(\text{OCH}_2\text{CH=CH}_2)(o\text{-CH}_2\text{CH=CH}_2) \longrightarrow \text{C}_6\text{H}_3(\text{OH})(\text{CH}_2\text{=CHCH}_2)(\text{CH}_2\text{CH=CH}_2)$$

$$\longrightarrow \text{C}_6\text{H}_2(\text{OH})(\text{CH}_2\text{=CHCH}_2)(\text{CH}_2\text{CH=CH}_2)(p\text{-CH}_2\text{CH=CH}_2)$$

In general the allyl group goes to an *ortho* position, but if both these are filled it migrates to the *para* position. It has been established also that the carbon atom attached to the oxygen atom in the ether is not the one that becomes attached to the ring; the γ-carbon atom of the allyl group is joined to the aromatic nucleus in the rearrangement product. This is illustrated by phenyl cinnamyl ether which yields not cinnamylphenol but o-α-phenylallylphenol.

$$\text{C}_6\text{H}_5\text{OCH}_2\text{CH=CHC}_6\text{H}_5 \longrightarrow o\text{-HOC}_6\text{H}_4\text{CH(C}_6\text{H}_5\text{)CH=CH}_2$$

o-α-Phenylallylphenol

The rearrangement of allyl phenyl ethers is general and is remarkable for the simplicity of the procedure and the excellence of the yields. This type of reaction has been observed with other phenyl ethers and also with vinyl allyl ethers.

An interesting example of the same sort is the rearrangement of the cinnamyl ether of ethyl acetoacetate. The product is not identical with that formed by treatment of the sodium derivative of ethyl acetoacetate with cinnamyl chloride. This shows that the enol ether cannot be intermediate in the formation of ethyl cinnamylacetoacetate.

$$\underset{\text{OCH}_2\text{CH=CHC}_6\text{H}_5}{\text{CH}_3\text{C=CHCO}_2\text{C}_2\text{H}_5} \longrightarrow \underset{\text{C}_6\text{H}_5\text{CHCH=CH}_2}{\text{CH}_3\text{COCHCO}_2\text{C}_2\text{H}_5}$$

$$[\text{CH}_3\text{COCHCO}_2\text{C}_2\text{H}_5]\text{Na} + \text{C}_6\text{H}_5\text{CH=CHCH}_2\text{Cl} \longrightarrow \underset{\text{CH}_2\text{CH=CHC}_6\text{H}_5}{\text{CH}_3\text{COCHCO}_2\text{C}_2\text{H}_5}$$

The inversion of the allyl group during rearrangement to the *ortho* (or *gamma*) position suggests that some sort of ring closure may be involved.

$$C_6H_5-O-CH_2-CH=CH_2 \ (\text{cyclic transition: } O-CH_2-CH=CH_2 \cdots \text{ring}) \longrightarrow o\text{-}HOC_6H_4CH_2CH{=}CH_2$$

A reaction that bears a remarkable resemblance to the Claisen rearrangement has been observed in the aliphatic series. It involves the isomerization of alkyl alkylene derivatives of certain active methylene compounds. The following is an illustration.

$$CH_3CH{=}\overset{CH_3}{\overset{|}{C}}-\underset{CH_2=CHCH_2}{\underset{|}{\overset{CN}{\overset{|}{C}}}}CO_2C_2H_5 \longrightarrow \underset{CH_2=CHCH_2}{CH_3\underset{|}{C}H}\overset{CH_3}{\overset{|}{C}}{=}\overset{CN}{\overset{|}{C}}CO_2C_2H_5$$

The rearrangment is peculiar in that the migrating radical goes from one carbon atom to another. However, this is in harmony with the fact that atoms attached to the α-carbon atom in malonic, acetoacetic, and cyanoacetic esters tend to be very mobile.

The Fries Rearrangement

Phenyl esters and substituted phenyl esters rearrange to the corresponding *ortho* and *para* acyl phenols when heated with aluminum or zinc chloride. This is known as the Fries rearrangement, but the process is probably not a true rearrangement. The mechanism may involve scission of the molecule into an acid chloride and phenol—compounds which react normally to give the keto phenol.

$$C_6H_5OCOR \xrightarrow[ZnCl_2]{AlCl_3 \text{ or}} o\text{-}HOC_6H_4COR$$

Phenyl propionate yields 45 to 50 per cent of p-propiophenol and 32 to 35 per cent of the *ortho* isomer.

The Ortho Effect. It is a familiar observation that the behavior of substituents on the benzene ring may be more or less profoundly influenced by the atoms or groups of atoms in the adjacent positions. These variations from the normal, taken collectively, are referred to as the *ortho effect*. It is one of many effects ascribed to steric hindrance. The only data that are in any sense quantitative are the rates of racemization of certain optically active biphenyls. These rates seem to be proportional to the space-filling properties of the *ortho* groups involved. This evidence supports the theory that nonrotation about the single bond is a purely steric effect.

Other observations are not only less exact but also more difficult to explain on the basis of space considerations. One important generalization can be made, however. Reactions of the additive type appear to be slowed down or inhibited whereas substitution reactions usually are unaffected. For example, ketones of the type

$$2,6\text{-}(CH_3)_2C_6H_3COR$$

fail to give the usual reactions of the carbonyl group. On the other hand the bromination of mesitylene or the acetylation of mesitol proceeds normally.

$$CH_3C_6H_3(CH_3)_2 + Br_2 \longrightarrow CH_3C_6H_2(CH_3)_2Br + HBr$$

$$CH_3C_6H_2(CH_3)_2OH + CH_3COCl \longrightarrow CH_3C_6H_2(CH_3)_2OCOCH_3 + HCl$$

Substitution Reactions

In addition to halogenation, nitration, sulfonation, and other substitution reactions that have already been discussed, two others should be mentioned here: arsonation and mercuration.

Arsonation. Aromatic amines and phenols react with arsenic acid to yield the corresponding amino and hydroxy arsonic acids.

$$C_6H_5NH_2 + H_3AsO_4 \longrightarrow p\text{-}H_2NC_6H_4AsO_3H_2 + H_2O$$

Arsanilic acid

$$C_6H_5OH + H_3AsO_4 \longrightarrow p\text{-}HOC_6H_4AsO_3H_2 + H_2O$$

In each instance the principal product is the *para* isomer. Small amounts of the *ortho* isomers are also produced. A more general method of making arsonic acids is furnished by the Bart reaction. This reaction takes place when a diazonium salt is decomposed in the presence of sodium arsenite or arsenic trichloride and a copper salt. Phenylarsonic acid can be made from benzenediazonium chloride and sodium arsenite in yields of 45 per cent.

$$C_6H_5N_2Cl + Na_3AsO_3 \xrightarrow{CuSO_4} C_6H_5AsO_3Na_2 + N_2 + NaCl$$

$$C_6H_5AsO_3Na_2 + 2HCl \longrightarrow C_6H_5AsO_3H_2 + 2NaCl$$

The value of arsonation in synthetic work may be illustrated by reference to arsphenamine and neoarsphenamine. The discovery of arsphenamine or salvarsan was one of the early triumphs in the history of chemotherapy. This compound is also called "606" because it was the 606th arsenical tried by its discoverer, Ehrlich. It has proved to be extremely useful in the treatment of syphilis. It is made from arsanilic acid by the following method.

$$p\text{-}H_2NC_6H_4AsO_3H_2 \longrightarrow p\text{-}CH_3CONHC_6H_4AsO_3H_2 \longrightarrow 4\text{-}CH_3CONH\text{-}3\text{-}NO_2C_6H_3AsO_3H_2$$

$$\longrightarrow 4\text{-}H_2N\text{-}3\text{-}NO_2C_6H_3AsO_3H_2 \longrightarrow 4\text{-}HO\text{-}3\text{-}NO_2C_6H_3AsO_3H_2 \longrightarrow (4\text{-}HO\text{-}3\text{-}H_2NC_6H_3As{=})_2$$

Arsphenamine

From a practical viewpoint, arsphenamine has several disadvantages. For example, it is so easily oxidized that it deteriorates in contact with the air. Many attempts have been made to find a derivative in which the undesirable properties are minimized. One such derivative is neoarsphenamine, made by treating arsphenamine with a solution of the addition compound formed by formaldehyde and sodium hydrosulfite. It appears to have the following structure.

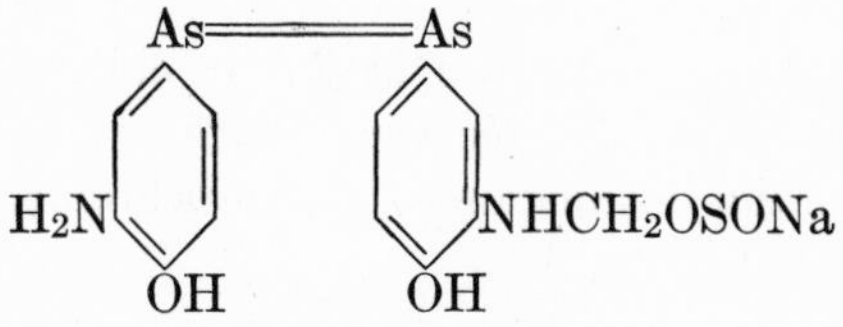

As=As
H_2N $NHCH_2OSONa$
OH OH

Neoarsphenamine

Mercuration. One of the most interesting substitution reactions of aromatic compounds is the direct introduction of a mercuri acid group such as acetoxymercuri. This can be brought about by treatment with mercuric acetate or, what amounts to the same thing, mercuric oxide in acetic acid.

$$ArH + Hg(OCOCH_3)_2 \longrightarrow ArHgOCOCH_3 + CH_3CO_2H$$

Hydrocarbons are mercurated by treatment at 90–160° for 1 hour or more. Amines and phenols react very much more readily. Nitro compounds and aryl halides undergo mercuration with difficulty.

Acids are usually mercurated by refluxing the sodium salt with aqueous mercuric acetate solution until no ionic mercury remains in solution. When *o*-phthalic acid is used, one of the carboxyl groups is replaced.

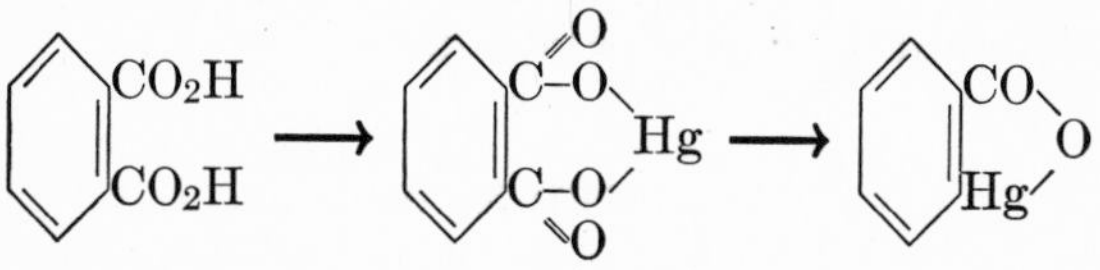

CO_2H, CO_2H → C(=O)–O, C(=O)–O, Hg → CO, O, Hg

Mercuration, like nitration and sulfonation, may give mono-, di-, or polysubstituted derivatives. Monosubstituted aromatic compounds such as phenol and aniline yield *ortho* and *para* derivatives as would be expected. Substitution is abnormal, however, with compounds that have *meta*-directing groups. For example, nitrobenzene yields 52 per cent of the *ortho*, 38 per cent of the *meta*, and 9 per cent of the *para* derivative. One explanation of these anomalous results postulates that the mercurating agent is not a positive ion but the undissociated mercuric acetate molecule. In confirmation of this theory it has been found that mercuration with mercuric perchlorate in perchloric acid (in which mercuric ion is the attacking agent) gives orientation effects typical of electrophilic substitution.

The position taken by the acetoxymercuri group can be determined by treatment with halogens, which replace the group by halogen. Bromine, iodine, and iodine monochloride are used most often for this purpose. Iodobenzene can be made in this way.

$$C_6H_5HgOCOCH_3 + I_2 \longrightarrow C_6H_5I + HgIOCOCH_3$$

The interest in mercury compounds derives chiefly from their use in medicine. Among the many compounds which have been developed may be mentioned the disinfectants, mercurochrome, mercurosal, and mercurophen.

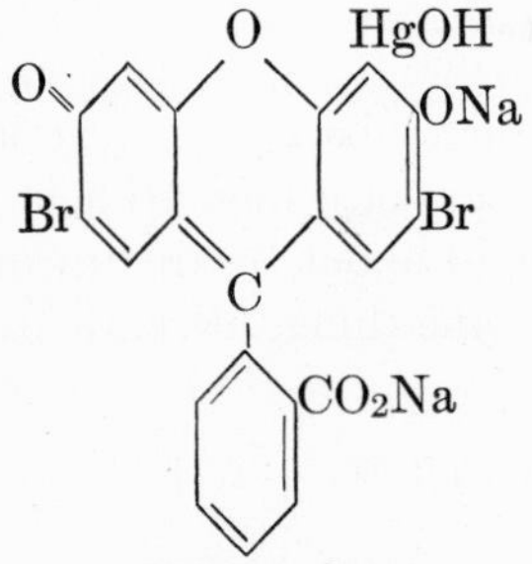

Mercurochrome 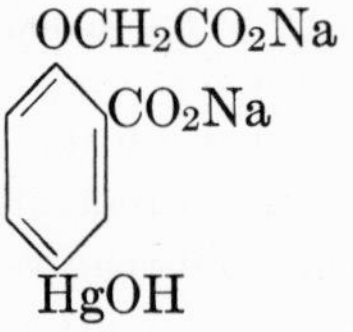 Mercurosal 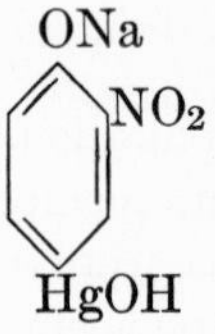 Mercurophen

PROBLEMS

1. What reasons can you give for classifying quinones as aliphatic compounds? as aromatic compounds?
2. What are *vicinal* trisubstituted benzene derivatives?
3. Indicate a method of synthesis for prehnitene.

SUGGESTED READINGS

L. F. Fieser, "Theory of the Structure and Reactions of Aromatic Compounds," Gilman's *Organic Chemistry*, Second Ed., Chapter 2, John Wiley & Sons, New York, 1943.

A. H. Blatt, "The Fries Reaction," *Org. Reactions*, *1*, 342, 1942.

L. I. Smith, "The Jacobsen Reaction," *Org. Reactions*, *1*, 370, 1942.

M. G. Evans and J. De Heer, "Relation between the Oxidation-Reduction Potentials of Quinones and Their Chemical Structure," *Quart. Revs.*, *4*, 94 (1950).

J. F. Bunnett and R. E. Zahler, "Aromatic Nucleophilic Substitution Reactions," *Chem. Revs.*, *49*, 273 (1951).

D. S. Tarbell, "The Claisen Rearrangement," *Org. Reactions*, *2*, 1, 1944.

R. C. Fuson and C. H. McKeever, "Chloromethylation of Aromatic Compounds," *Org. Reactions*, *1*, 63, 1942.

CHAPTER 31

Polynuclear Aromatic Hydrocarbons

Similarities rather than differences have been stressed in discussing properties common to aliphatic as well as aromatic compounds. Recent studies have done much to break down the line of demarcation which formerly separated these two classes of substances. It is becoming increasingly apparent that their differences are of degree rather than of type. Yet the benzenoid structure permits the formation of condensed nuclei and offers certain other peculiarities which as yet have no close parallel in the aliphatic series. These appear in sharp relief in the polynuclear aromatic hydrocarbons and their derivatives. These are among the most useful and most interesting types of organic compounds, and include naphthalene, biphenyl, triphenylmethane, anthracene, phenanthrene, and numerous similar substances.

Biphenyl. Biphenyl was made formerly by treating bromobenzene with sodium, but is now prepared on a commercial scale by bringing benzene into contact with a hot metal.

$$2C_6H_6 \xrightarrow[\text{metal}]{\text{hot}} C_6H_5C_6H_5 + H_2$$

This hydrocarbon is stable at its boiling point (254°) and is useful where a high-boiling liquid is required.

Derivatives of biphenyl are named according to either of the two systems shown in the following figure:

5′ 6′ 6 5
4′ (p′, m′, o′, m′, o′) 1′——1 (o, m, p, o, m) 4
3′ 2′ 2 3

Thus $NO_2C_6H_4$—$C_6H_4NO_2$ is called 4,4′- or *p,p′*-dinitrobiphenyl.

The most useful derivative of biphenyl is benzidine, obtained by the rearrangement of hydrazobenzene, a reduction product of nitrobenzene.

$$2C_6H_5NO_2 \xrightarrow{\text{Zn + NaOH}} C_6H_5NHNHC_6H_5$$

$$C_6H_5NHNHC_6H_5 \xrightarrow{\text{acid}} H_2NC_6H_4\text{—}C_6H_4NH_2$$

Benzidine

Benzidine is used in the preparation of certain dyes which are direct for cotton. These will be mentioned later.

Many biphenyl derivatives are most conveniently made by means of Ullmann's method, which involves the treatment of halobenzenes with copper powder (p. 263).

$$2NO_2C_6H_4I + 2Cu \longrightarrow NO_2C_6H_4{-}C_6H_4NO_2 + 2CuI$$

The halogen atom must be active, and for this reason iodo compounds are commonly employed.

Derivatives of biphenyl in which both rings are unsymmetrically substituted and which contain groups in the *ortho* positions that prevent free rotation about the central linkage have been shown to possess optical activity. An example is 6,6′-dinitro-2,2′-dicarboxybiphenyl.

NO_2 NO_2

CO_2H CO_2H

p-Bromobiphenyl is made by treating benzene with *p*-bromobenzenediazonium chloride in the presence of sodium hydroxide.

Terphenyl. The best method of synthesis for terphenyl and its derivatives depends on a condensation reaction between an aromatic hydrocarbon or ether with an N-nitrosoacetylarylamine. Benzene and the nitroso derivative of 4-acetaminobiphenyl give terphenyl.

$$C_6H_5{-}C_6H_4N(NO)COCH_3 + C_6H_6 \longrightarrow C_6H_5{-}C_6H_4{-}C_6H_5 + N_2 + CH_3CO_2H$$

p-Terphenyl

Triphenylmethane. This hydrocarbon is made by condensing benzene with chloroform.

$$3C_6H_6 + CHCl_3 \xrightarrow{AlCl_3} (C_6H_5)_3CH + 3HCl$$

A derivative of great interest is the free radical, triphenylmethyl. When triphenylmethyl chloride in benzene solution is treated with zinc, hexaphenylethane is formed; this extraordinary hydrocarbon dissociates to some extent into triphenylmethyl.

$$2(C_6H_5)_3CCl + Zn \longrightarrow (C_6H_5)_3CC(C_6H_5)_3 + ZnCl_2$$

$$(C_6H_5)_3CC(C_6H_5)_3 \rightleftharpoons 2(C_6H_5)_3C\cdot$$

This dissociation is evidenced by color formation which increases with temperature. The free radical is not only colored but also extremely reactive. Two of its reactions are listed below.

$$2(C_6H_5)_3C + O_2 \longrightarrow (C_6H_5)_3COOC(C_6H_5)_3$$

$$2(C_6H_5)_3C + I_2 \longrightarrow 2(C_6H_5)_3CI$$

Actually the amount of dissociation of hexaphenylethane is very small. Hexabiphenylethane, however, is almost completely dissociated in the solid form.

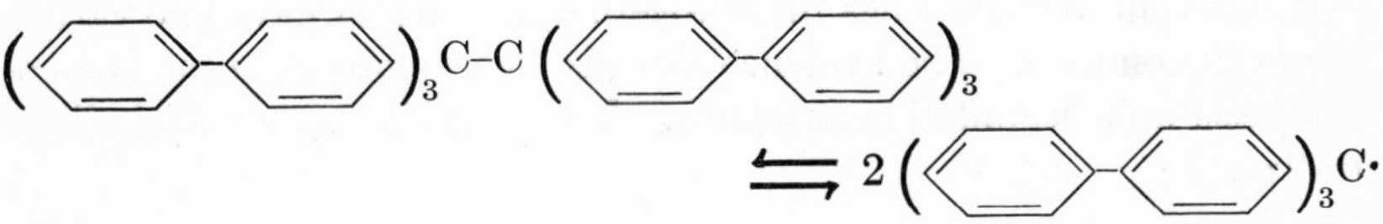

$$(C_6H_5C_6H_4)_3C{-}C(C_6H_4C_6H_5)_3 \rightleftharpoons 2(C_6H_5C_6H_4)_3C\cdot$$

As has been stated previously the free radicals are odd molecules and owe their color and great reactivity to the lone electron.

$$R{:}\overset{\textstyle R}{\underset{\textstyle R}{\overset{\cdot\cdot}{\underset{\cdot\cdot}{C}}}}\cdot$$

It has been demonstrated that six aryl groups are not necessary to produce dissociation. Four aryl and two alkyl groups may give the same effect. Substitution of alkyl groups for the two hydrogen atoms in bixanthyl brings about dissociation. Cyclohexyl groups are particularly effective.

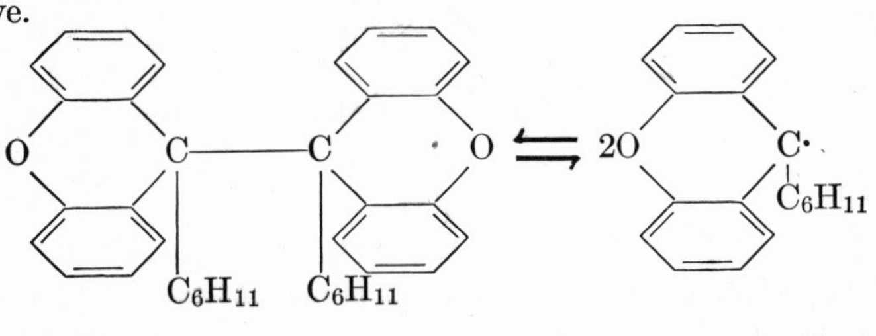

O C——C O ⇄ 2O C·

C₆H₁₁ C₆H₁₁ C₆H₁₁

Alkylethynyl groups appear to exert a similar influence. The central linkage in *sym*-tetraphenyldi-(*t*-butylethynyl)-ethane, for example, is very weak, being cleaved by alkali metals.

$$\begin{array}{l}(C_6H_5)_2C{-}C{\equiv}CC(CH_3)_3\\ \quad\quad\quad\ \ |\\ (C_6H_5)_2C{-}C{\equiv}CC(CH_3)_3\end{array}$$

This observation calls to mind Kuhn's remarkable synthesis of cumulenes. The acetylenic glycol derived from diacetylene and benzophenone is treated with hydrogen chloride and chromous chloride. Presumably a biradical forms and rearranges to the cumulene.

$$(C_6H_5)_2\underset{\displaystyle OH}{\underset{|}{C}}-C{\equiv}C-C{\equiv}C-\underset{\displaystyle OH}{\underset{|}{C}}(C_6H_5)_2 \longrightarrow [(C_6H_5)_2\underset{\bullet}{C}-C{\equiv}C-C{\equiv}C-\underset{\bullet}{C}(C_6H_5)_2]$$

$$\longrightarrow (C_6H_5)_2C{=}C{=}C{=}C{=}C{=}C(C_6H_5)_2$$

The cumulenes are more highly colored than conjugated polyenes $[C_6H_5(CH{=}CH)_n{-}C_6H_5]$.

Naphthalene. The most abundant constituent of coal tar is naphthalene. It contains two rings fused together, i.e., which have two carbon atoms in common. The evidence for this comes both from methods of synthesis and degradation products. The following synthesis is illustrative.

C_6H_5CHO + CH_2CO, CH_2CO (O) $\longrightarrow$ C_6H_5–CH–$CHCO_2H$, O, CH_2, CO

$\xrightarrow{-CO_2}$ C_6H_5–CH=CH–CH_2–CO_2H $\xrightarrow{-H_2O}$ CH, CH, CH_2, CO

$\longrightarrow$ CH, CH, CH, C–OH $\xrightarrow[\text{dust}]{\text{Zn}}$ CH CH, HC, C, CH, HC, C, CH, CH CH

That naphthalene contains two rings is demonstrated by the following degradations.

CO_2H, CO_2H, NO_2 $\longleftarrow$ NO_2 $\longrightarrow$ NH_2 $\longrightarrow$ CO_2H, CO_2H

This shows also that both rings are or may become true benzene rings, and leaves the question of the internal structure of naphthalene in much the same state as that of benzene. The following formulas of β-naphthol illustrate the structures commonly used.

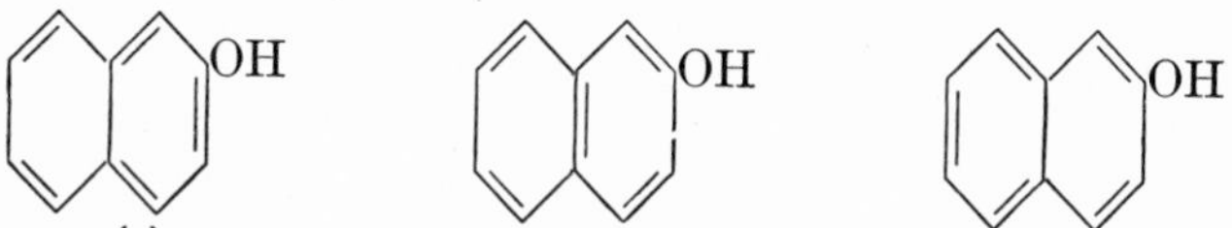

OH OH OH

(*a*) (*b*) (*c*)

Evidence indicates that the Erlenmeyer structure *b* is the principal structure and that *a* and *c* probably do not make an appreciable contribution. For example, the following types of compounds fail entirely to undergo coupling with diazonium salts—a fact which is interpreted to mean that there are only single bonds between carbon atoms 2 and 3 or 6 and 7 (see p. 479 for the method of numbering).

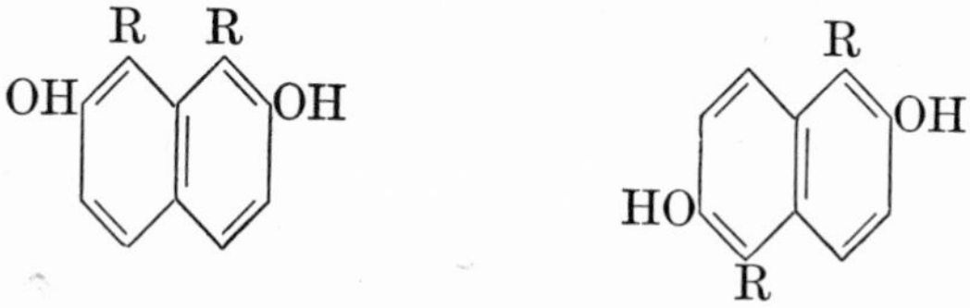

R R OH OH R OH HO R

The rearrangement of allyl β-naphthyl ether points to the same conclusion. The allyl group migrates to the α-position exclusively. Moreover, allyl β-(α-allyl) naphthyl ether does not undergo rearrangement.

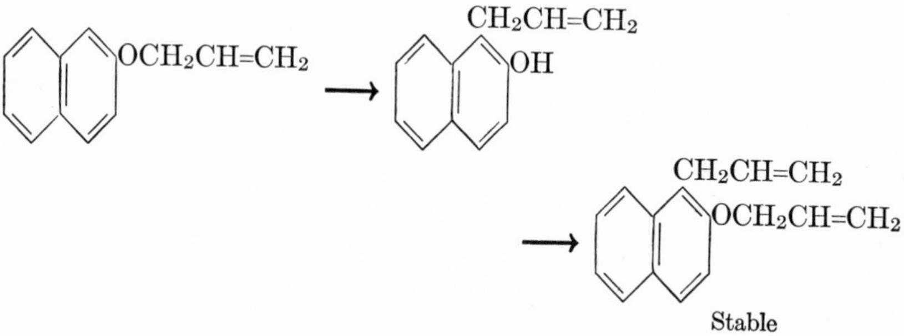

$OCH_2CH{=}CH_2$ ⟶ $CH_2CH{=}CH_2$ OH

⟶ $CH_2CH{=}CH_2$ $OCH_2CH{=}CH_2$

Stable

Evidence in favor of the Erlenmeyer formula for naphthalene has been obtained by a study of bromonaphthylamines. In certain of these the bromine atoms are "positive" and can be removed by treatment with stannous chloride and hydrochloric acid. This property appears to be possessed by those compounds containing the grouping

$$\underset{NH_2}{-\overset{|}{C}}{=}\underset{Br}{\overset{|}{C}}- \quad \text{or} \quad \underset{NH_2}{-\overset{|}{C}}{=}CH{-}CH{=}\underset{Br}{\overset{|}{C}}-$$

In conformity with this it is found that 1-bromo-2-naphthylamine and 1-bromo-4-naphthylamine are debrominated, whereas 3-bromo-2-naphthylamine is recovered unchanged. 1,3-Dibromo-2-naphthylamine loses only the bromine atom in the 1 position (see p. 479 for the method of numbering).

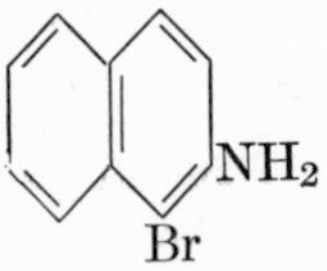

NH_2, Br

1-Bromo-2-naphthylamine

NH_2, Br

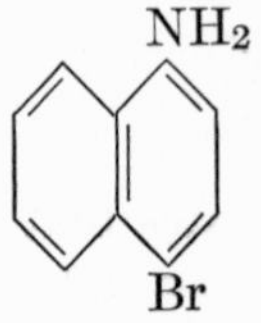

4-Bromo-1-naphthylamine

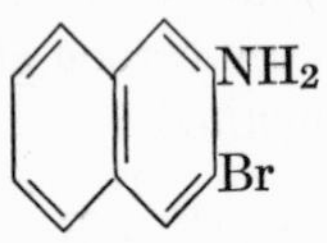

NH_2, Br

3-Bromo-2-naphthylamine

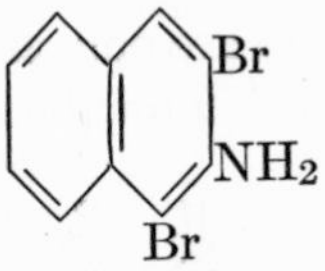

Br, NH_2, Br

1,3-Dibromo-2-naphthylamine

These results are in accord with predictions based on the principle of vinylogy.

A neat proof of the equivalence of positions 1 and 5 is furnished by the demonstration that naphthalene-1,5-disulfinylacetic acid can exist in *meso* and *racemic* forms.

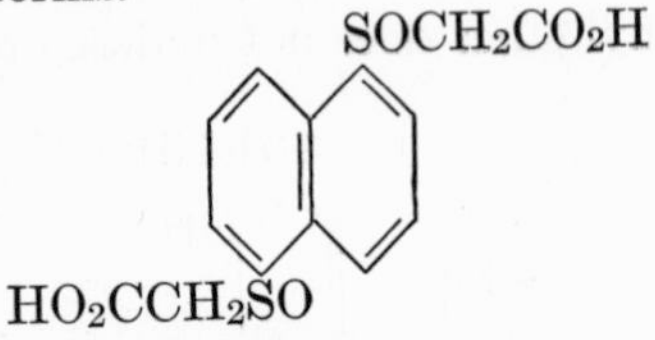

$SOCH_2CO_2H$

HO_2CCH_2SO

This could be possible only if the nucleus is symmetrical, for the optical activity resides in the sulfur atoms.

Naphthalene yields only two monosubstitution products—a fact which proves that the eight hydrogen atoms must be symmetrically located. These are known as the α and β forms; α- and β-naphthol are examples.

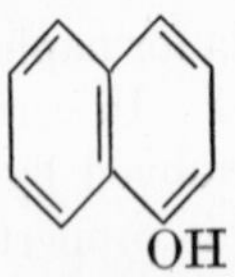

OH

α-Naphthol

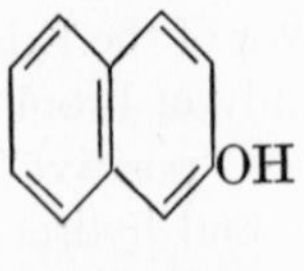

OH

β-Naphthol

The orientation of naphthalene derivatives is indicated by one of the systems which follow.

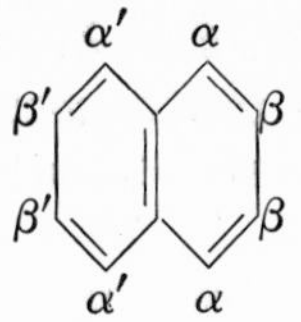

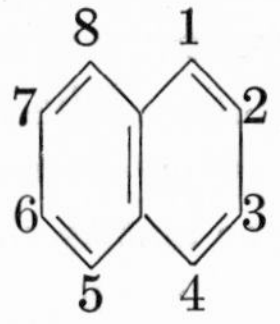

The 4,5 (and 1,8) are often called the *peri* positions.

These positions are joined with a two-carbon bridge in acenaphthene, a constituent of coal tar.

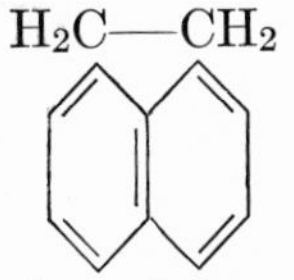

Acenaphthene

Substituents in the *peri* positions may react with each other much as do *ortho* substituents. Naphthalic acid, for example, forms a monomeric anhydride.

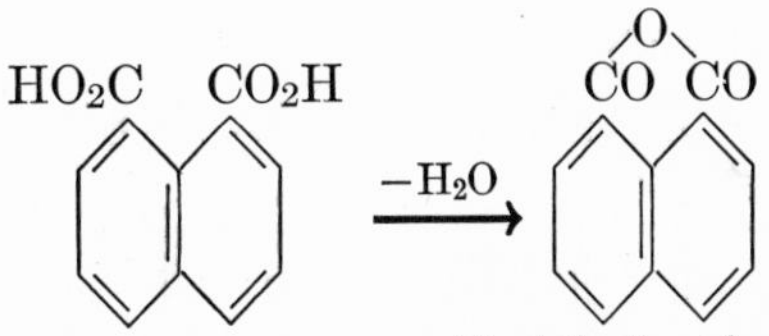

Naphthalic anhydride

Ten disubstitution products are possible if the substituents are alike —fourteen if they are unlike.

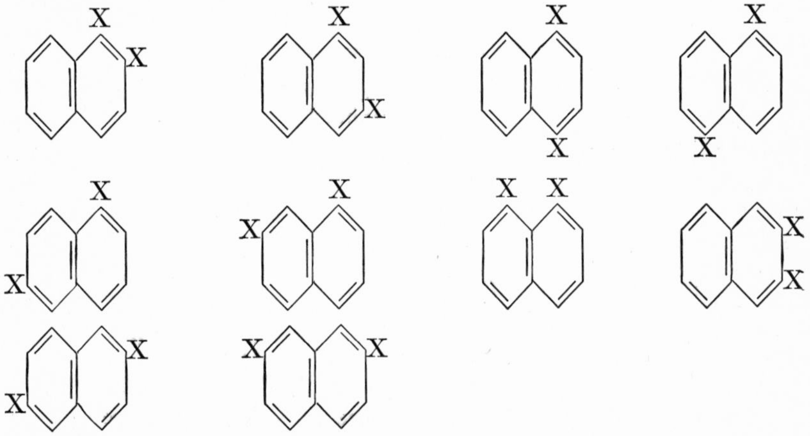

Naphthalene can be halogenated, nitrated, and sulfonated and undergoes the Friedel-Crafts reaction. In all cases α-substitution products result. The latter two reactions give β-substitution products also.

The sulfonation of naphthalene is reversible and gives rise to the α-isomer at low temperatures (about 80°) and the β- at higher temperatures (about 160°) (p. 48). The α-compound is transformed into the β- by heating in the presence of sulfuric acid. This is because it is hydrolyzed about fifty times as fast as the β-acid.

Hydrogenation of naphthalene gives the tetra- and decahydro derivatives—generally called, respectively, tetralin and decalin.

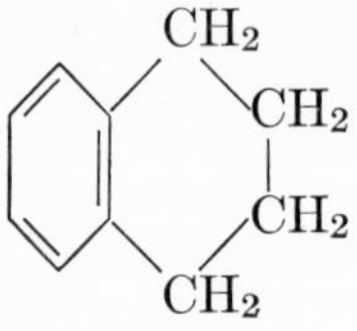

Tetralin 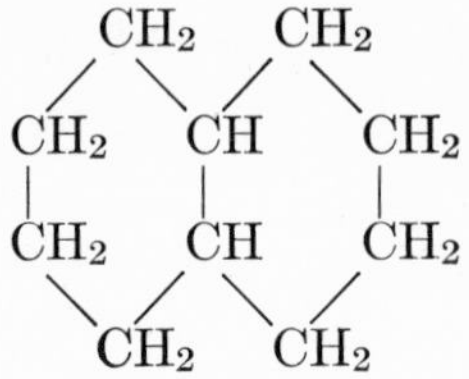 Decalin

These compounds are used as solvents in paints, varnishes, and lacquers Decalin exists in *cis* and *trans* modifications.

Naphthalene reacts with sodium to give a disodium derivative. Carbonation yields a dicarboxylic acid.

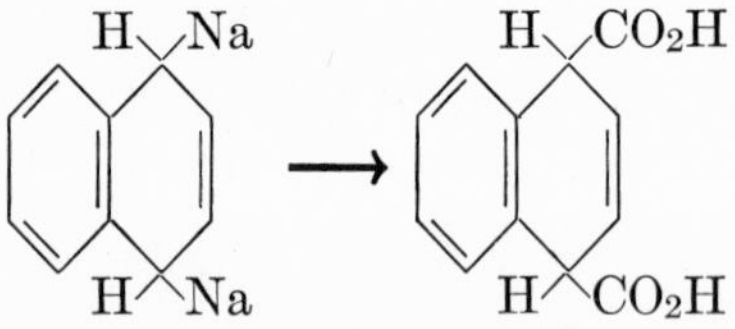

Oxidation of α-naphthol with ferric chloride gives binaphthol.

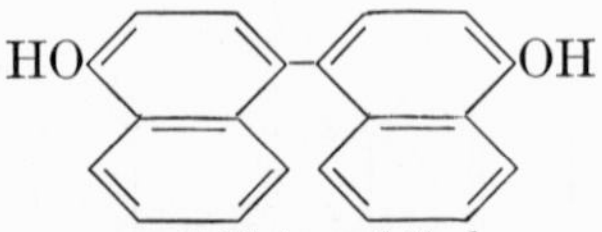

4,4′-Bi-1-naphthol

Chromic acid oxidizes naphthols to quinones. Three different naphthoquinones are known.

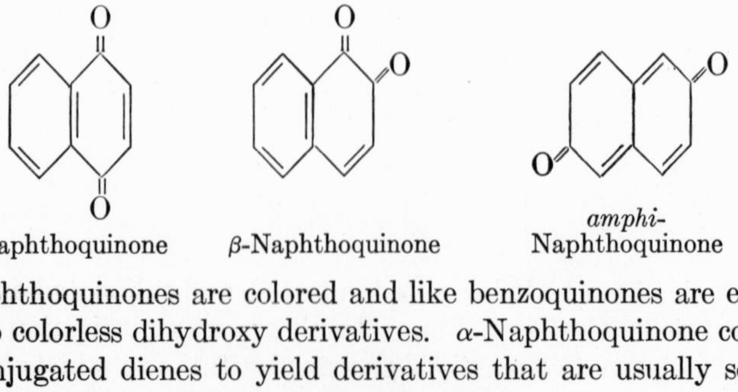

α-Naphthoquinone β-Naphthoquinone *amphi*-Naphthoquinone

The naphthoquinones are colored and like benzoquinones are easily reduced to colorless dihydroxy derivatives. α-Naphthoquinone condenses with conjugated dienes to yield derivatives that are usually solid and therefore useful for purposes of identification.

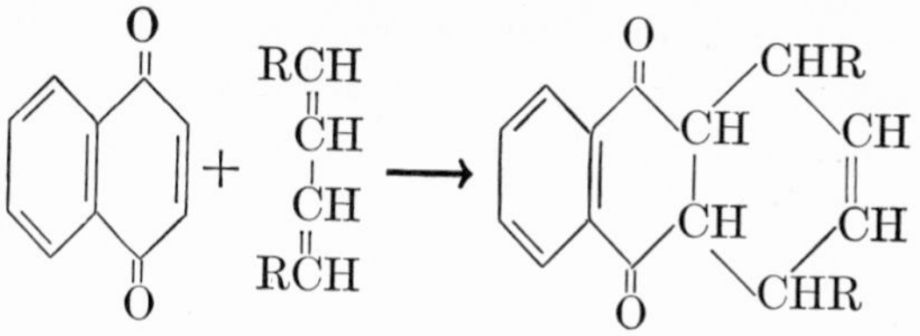

The α-naphthoquinone nucleus occurs in vitamin K_1, the antihemorrhagic factor, which has been shown to be 2-methyl-3-phytyl-1,4-naphthoquinone.

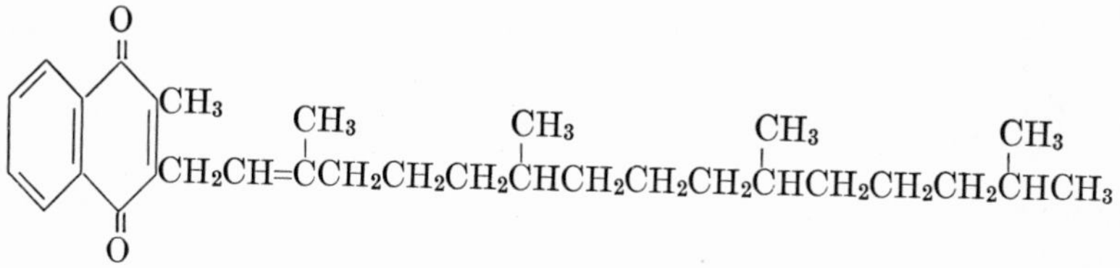

Vitamin K_1

In vitamin K therapy 2-methyl-1,4-naphthoquinone and certain of its simple derivatives have proved to be as effective as the vitamin itself. It may be that the phytyl group is supplied in the organism.

The most important naphthalene derivatives are those used as dye intermediates. Some of these are listed below.

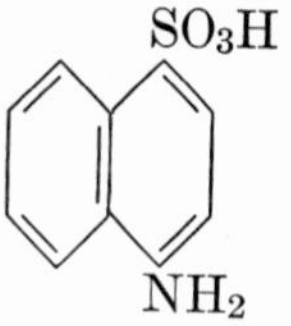

1,4-Naphthylaminesulfonic acid or naphthionic acid

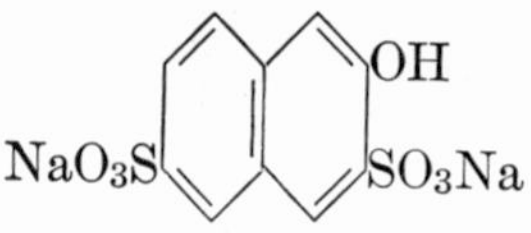

Sodium 2-naphthol-3,6-disulfonate or R salt

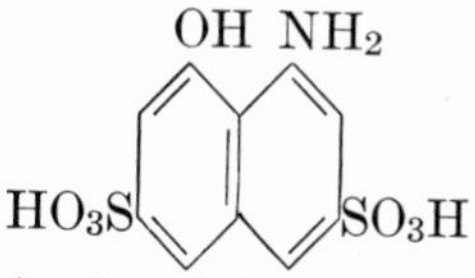

1-Amino-8-naphthol-3,6-disulfonic acid or H acid

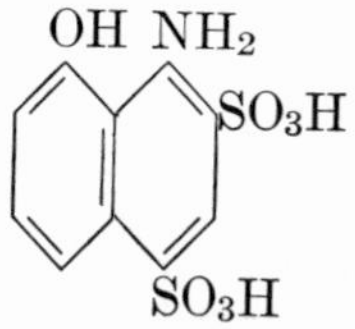

1-Amino-8-naphthol-2,4-disulfonic acid or Chicago acid

Anthracene. Anthracene occurs to the extent of 0.2 to 0.4 per cent in coal tar. When isolated from this source it is always contaminated with carbazole and phenanthrene.

Anthracene Carbazole Phenanthrene

The fact that these impurities are very hard to remove has to some extent diminished the importance of coal tar anthracene as a source of anthracene derivatives. It has been found that dimethylacetamide is a good solvent for separating carbazole and anthracene. It dissolves the carbazole, presumably by hydrogen bonding.

Anthracene contains three condensed rings as is shown by the following synthesis.

SO_3H $\xrightarrow[160°]{H_2SO_4}$ $\xrightarrow[\text{fuse}]{NaCN}$ CN $\xrightarrow{H_2O}$

CO_2H $\xrightarrow{\text{Na-Hg}}$ CH_2, $C\text{-}CO_2H$, CH, CH_2 $\xrightarrow[H_2SO_4]{C_2H_5OH}$

CH_2, $CCO_2C_2H_5$, CH, CH_2 $\xrightarrow[CH_3COCH_2CO_2C_2H_5]{NaOC_2H_5}$ CH_2, CO, CH, OC_2H_5, CH, CH_2, $CHCOCH_3$, $CO_2C_2H_5$

$\longrightarrow$ CH_2, CO, CH, CH_2, CH, CO, CH_2, $CHCO_2C_2H_5$ $\xrightarrow[\text{cleavage}]{\text{ketone}}$ CH_2, CO, CH, CH_2, CH, CO, CH_2, CH_2

$\xrightarrow[\text{heat}]{\text{zinc dust}}$

This synthesis does not disclose the arrangement of the bonds. The structures usually written are given here.

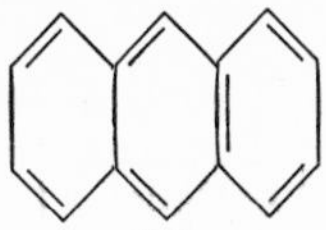

(*a*) 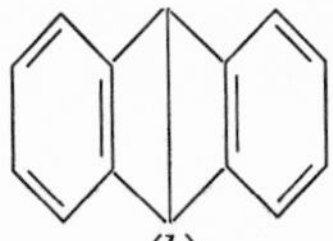 (*b*)

Formula *b* is made to appear plausible by the following synthesis.

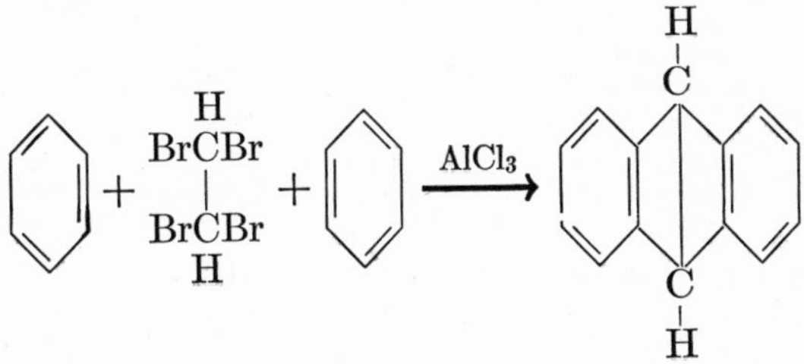

H
BrCBr
|
BrCBr
H
AlCl₃

It should be noted, however, that aluminum chloride is very effective in breaking carbon-to-carbon linkages. The evidence shows *a* to be the correct structure. It is one of four possible resonance forms. The others are the following.

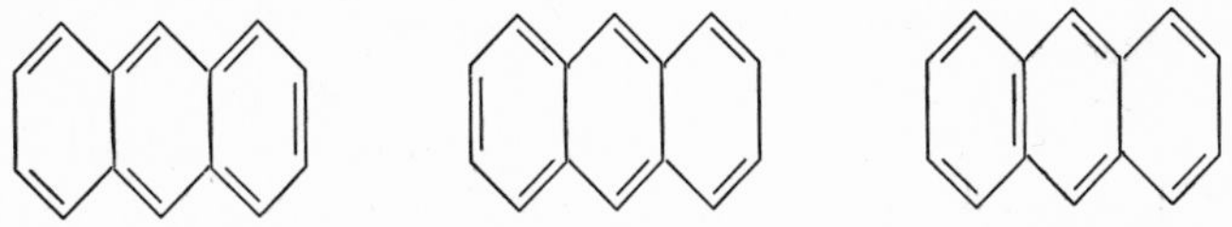

Anthracene undergoes the Diels-Alder reaction and, therefore, must have a system of conjugated double bonds in the middle ring.

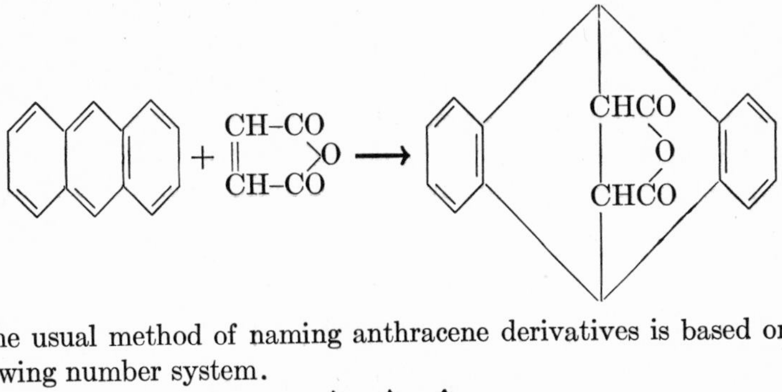

CH–CO
O
CH–CO
CHCO
O
CHCO

The usual method of naming anthracene derivatives is based on the following number system.

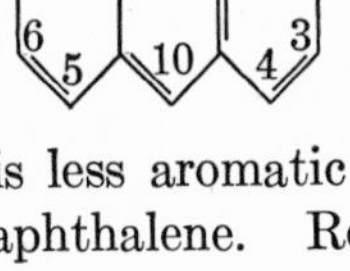

In general, naphthalene is less aromatic than benzene, and anthracene still less so than naphthalene. Reduction and oxidation of anthracene to the dihydro derivative and the quinone, respectively, take place very readily.

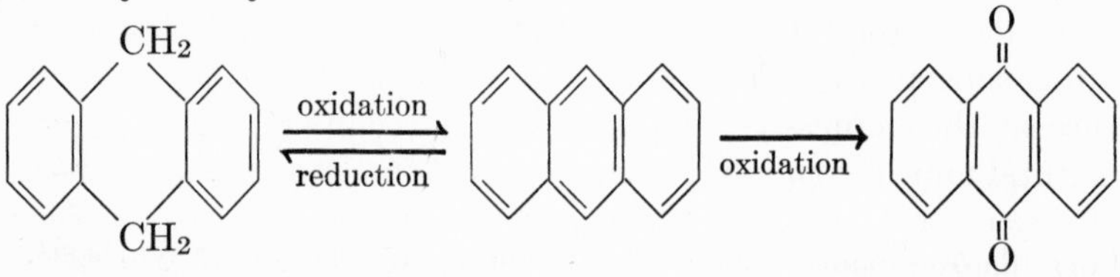

CH_2 … CH_2 ⇌ (oxidation / reduction) anthracene → (oxidation) anthraquinone (O, O)

Bromine attacks the molecule at the 9 and 10 positions, forming an addition compound which is fairly stable but which loses hydrogen bromide when heated.

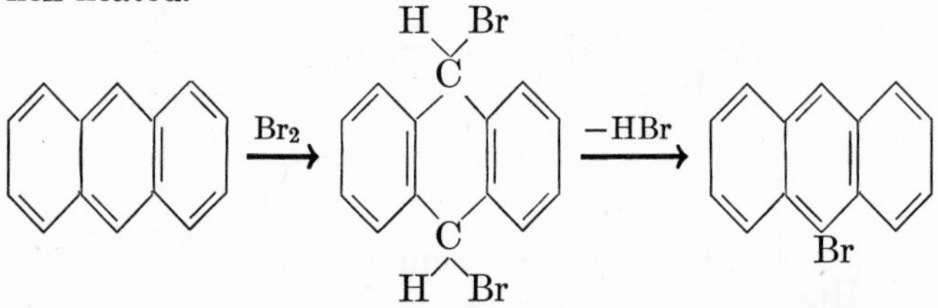

anthracene $\xrightarrow{Br_2}$ (H, Br, C; C, H, Br) $\xrightarrow{-HBr}$ (Br)

Sulfuric acid sulfonates anthracene, usually yielding a disulfonic acid. At low temperatures this is the 1,8- and at higher temperatures the 2,7-acid.

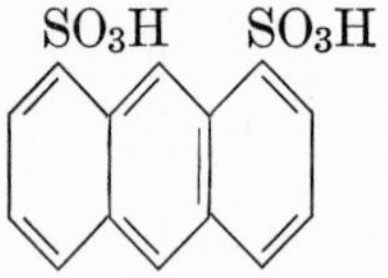

SO_3H SO_3H

1,8-Anthracenedisulfonic acid

HO_3S SO_3H

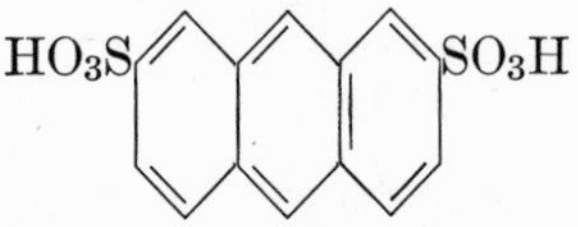

2,7-Anthracenedisulfonic acid

Nitric acid acts not as a nitrating but as an oxidizing agent, giving anthraquinone. This compound is truly aromatic and is the mother substance of the more important anthracene derivatives.

Anthraquinone and many of its derivatives are made by the following type of synthesis which involves not anthracene but benzene and naphthalene.

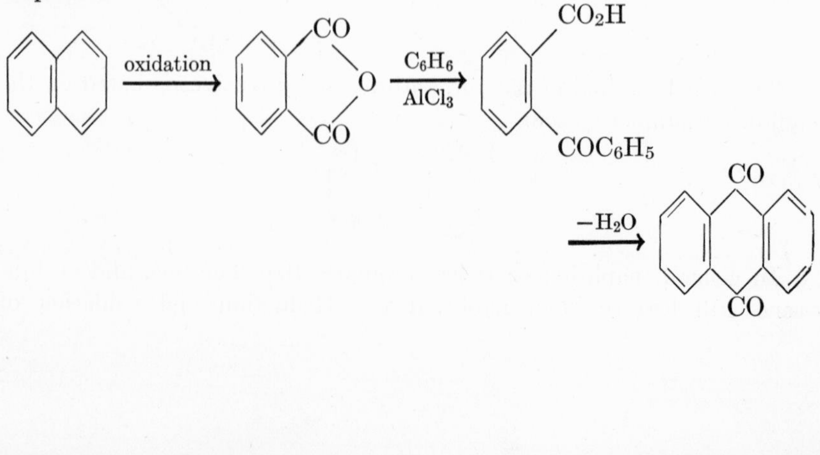

naphthalene $\xrightarrow{\text{oxidation}}$ (CO, O, CO) $\xrightarrow[AlCl_3]{C_6H_6}$ (CO_2H, COC_6H_5) $\xrightarrow{-H_2O}$ (CO, CO)

Phenanthrene. Phenanthrene is an isomer of anthracene and occurs with it in coal tar. It has attracted considerable attention because of the discovery that its skeletal structure occurs in a wide variety of natural substances. The significance of this is made apparent by a glance at the impressive array of types of compounds that have this structural unit in common. Examples are found among morphine alkaloids, resin acids,* carcinogenic hydrocarbons, sterols, bile acids, sex hormones, heart poisons, and saponins. The following compounds are illustrative.

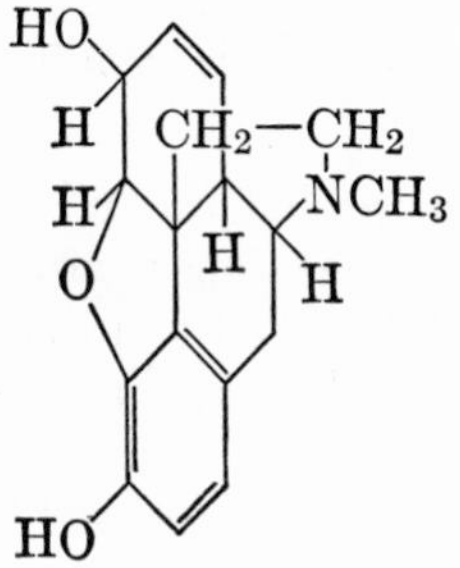

Morphine

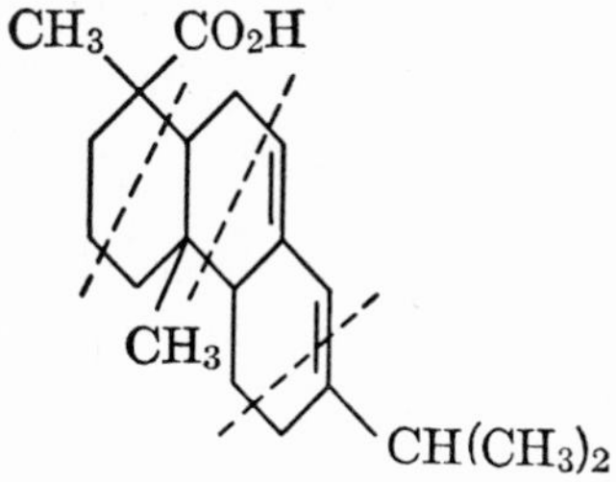

Abietic acid

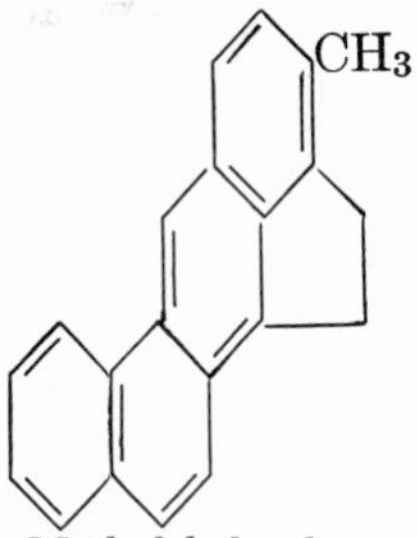

Methylcholanthrene

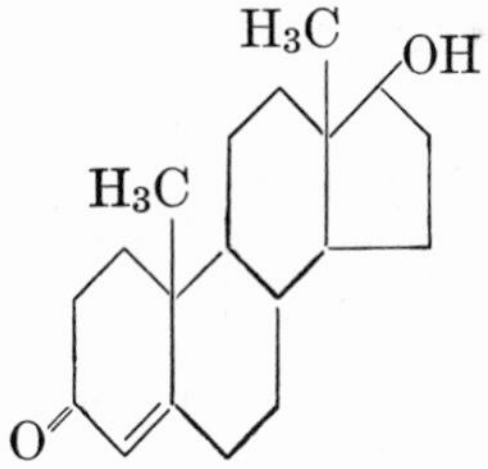

Testosterone

The fact that phenanthrene has three six-membered rings arranged as shown in the formula was proved by the following degradation to biphenyl.

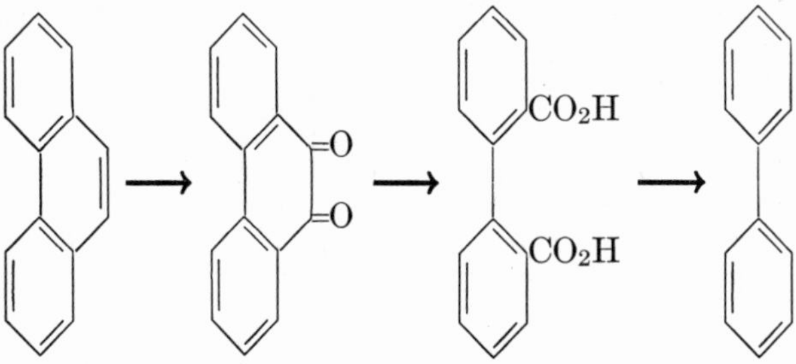

* It is interesting to observe in passing that the formula of abietic acid obeys the isoprene rule.

The nomenclature of phenanthrene derivatives is based on the following system.

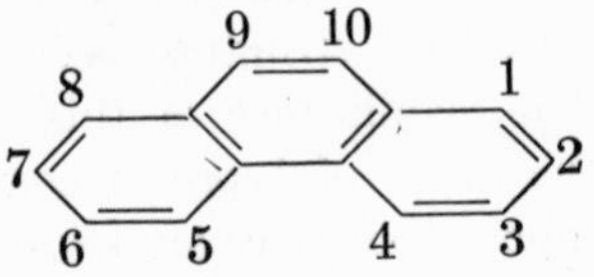

9 10
8 1
7 2
6 5 4 3

The foregoing arrangement of the bonds is in accord with the Fries rule, which states that each ring of a polynuclear aromatic compound strives to assume the bond structure which most nearly approaches the condition of an isolated benzene ring. This formula is, in fact, considered to be the most probable one.

Phenanthrene is more reactive than naphthalene and less reactive than anthracene. It undergoes all the usual reactions of aromatic hydrocarbons such as sulfonation, nitration, and the Friedel-Crafts reaction.

Other Condensed Polynuclear Aromatic Hydrocarbons. Many other hydrocarbons of this group are known, and there seems to be no limit to the number of benzenoid rings which may be condensed into a molecule. Striking illustrations are given below.

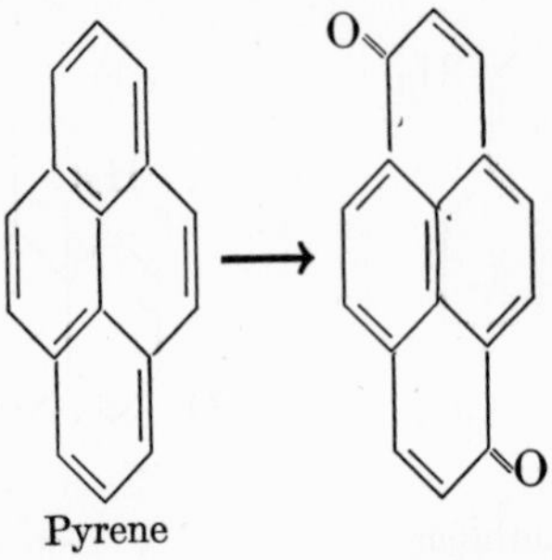

O

O

Pyrene

Pyrene occurs in coal tar. Oxidation converts it to the quinone shown above.

One of the most interesting of the more complex aromatic hydrocarbons is hexabenzobenzene or coronene; it has been synthesized by the following transformations.

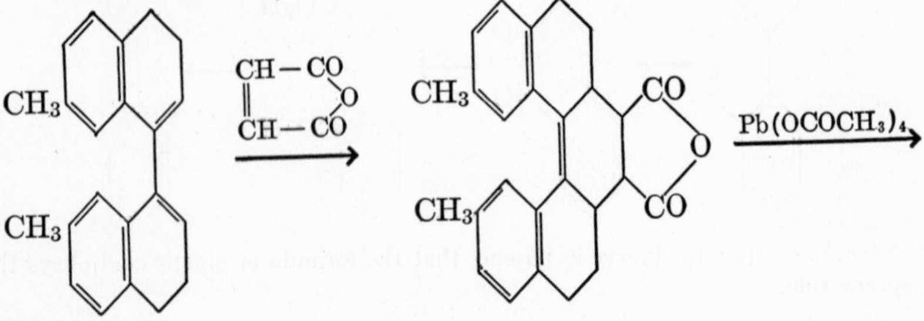

CH_3

CH_3

CH—CO
‖ O
CH—CO

CH_3 CO

O

CH_3 CO

$Pb(OCOCH_3)_4$

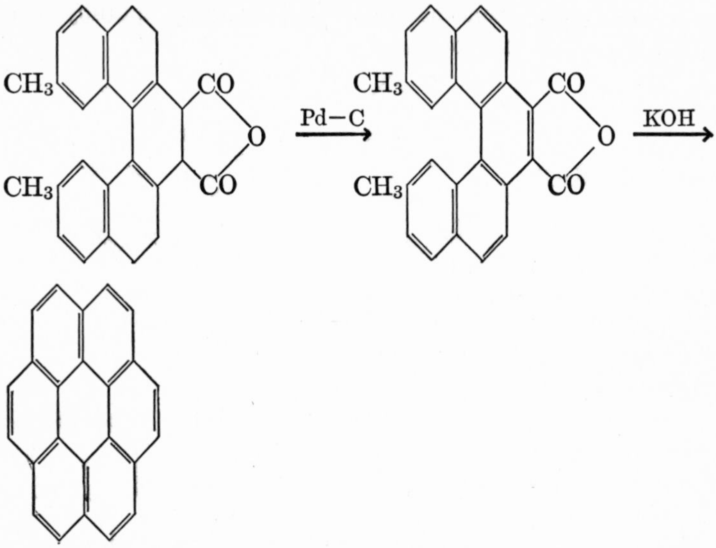

CH_3 CO O CO CH_3 $\xrightarrow{Pd-C}$ CH_3 CO O CO CH_3 $\xrightarrow{KOH}$

The positions of the double bonds in highly condensed aromatic compounds such as the foregoing are not known with certainty. The most probable arrangement of the bonds is thought to be that which affords the maximum number of truly benzenoid rings.

The Scholl reaction. Certain aromatic ketones may undergo intramolecular dehydrogenation under the influence of aluminum chloride. This is the Scholl reaction; it has proved of great value in the synthesis of polynuclear compounds. An example is the conversion of α-benzoylnaphthalene to benzanthrone.

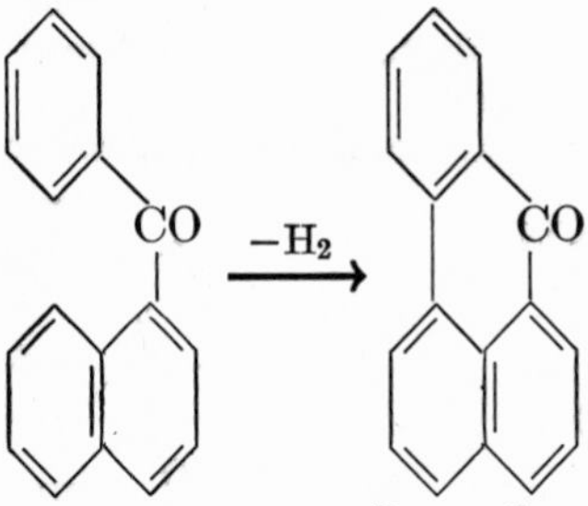

CO $\xrightarrow{-H_2}$ CO

Benzanthrone

2,3,6,7-Dibenzanthracene is blue and exceedingly reactive.

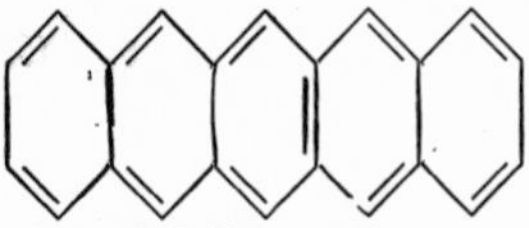

2,3,6,7-Dibenzanthracene

1,2,5,6-Dibenzanthracene has been made from β-naphthoyl chloride by the following sequence of changes.

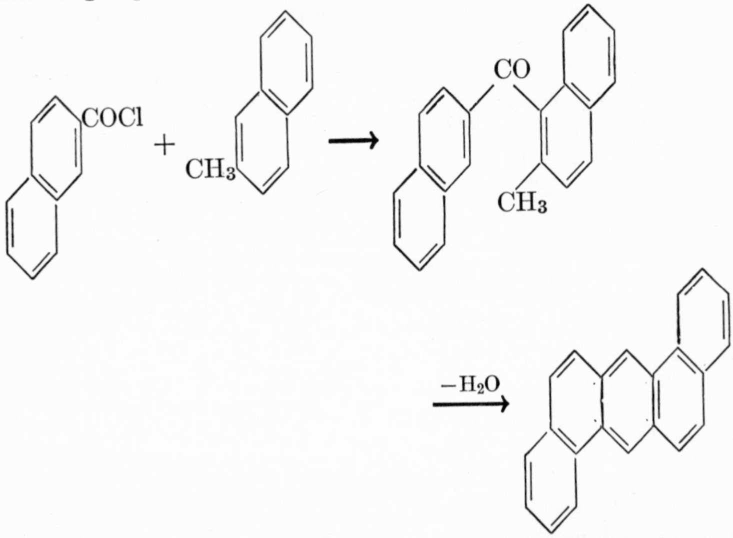

COCl + CH_3 ⟶ CO CH_3

$\xrightarrow{-H_2O}$

1,2,5,6-Dibenzanthracene

This type of ring closure, known as the Elbs reaction, is general for *o*-alkylbenzophenones and has been used widely in the synthesis of anthracene derivatives. The reaction is induced by heating; it gives low yields.

PROBLEMS

1. Arrange the following hydrocarbons in the order of decreasing reactivity: toluene, naphthalene, phenanthrene, benzene, anthracene.
2. Suggest an explanation of the fact that the course of the sulfonation of anthracene depends on the temperature.
3. Outline methods of synthesis for the following compounds.

a. 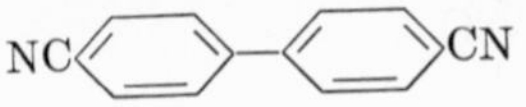 NC–C_6H_4–C_6H_4–CN

b.  CH_3–C_6H_4–$CH(C_6H_5)_2$

c. HO_2C COC_6H_5 (naphthalene)

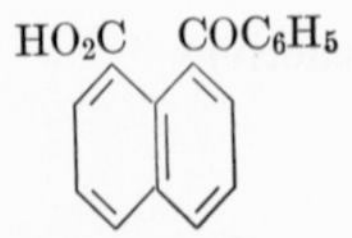

d. 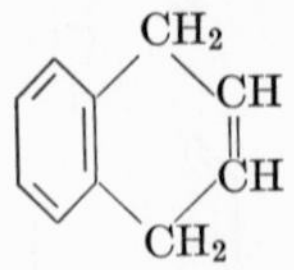 CH_2 CH ‖ CH CH_2

e. 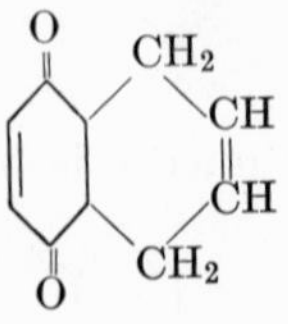 O CH_2 CH ‖ CH CH_2 O

SUGGESTED READINGS

R. Adams and H. C. Yuan, "The Stereochemistry of Diphenyls and Analogous Compounds," *Chem. Revs.*, *12*, 262 (1933).

L. F. Fieser and M. Fieser, "Natural Products Related to Phenanthrene," Third Ed., Reinhold Publishing Corporation, New York, 1949.

L. F. Fieser, "The Elbs Reaction," *Org. Reactions*, *1*, 129, 1942.

CHAPTER 32

Aromatic Heterocyclic Compounds

Cyclic compounds in which not all the atoms forming the ring are alike are known as heterocyclic compounds. Many of these rings are easily opened and for this reason are classified as aliphatic. Others are very stable and possess many of the properties of the aromatic hydrocarbons. This chapter will deal with this group.

The most important types of heterocyclic compounds are listed below.

```
CH——CH          CH——CH          CH——CH
||    ||        ||    ||        ||    ||
CH    CH        CH    CH        CH    CH
  \  /            \  /            \  /
   O                S               N
                                    |
                                    H
 Furan          Thiophene        Pyrrole
```

```
       O
       ||
       C                     CH
     /   \                 /    \\
   CH     CH             CH      CH
   ||     ||             ||      |
   CH     CH             CH      CH
     \   /                 \    //
       O                      N
   γ-Pyrone               Pyridine
```

All these substances, except γ-pyrone, undergo reactions typical of aromatic hydrocarbons. They differ in the degree of reactivity which they possess. Some, for example, couple with diazonium salts whereas others fail to do so.

It is easy to understand why pyridine and its derivatives are aromatic since they possess a hexatriene ring system similar to that in benzene. The aromaticity of furan, thiophene, and pyrrole is ascribed to resonance.

Furan. Furan is relatively rare, but several of its derivatives are widely used. Furfural is the most important of them. It is manufactured on a large scale from oat hulls (p. 254) and is used extensively as an extraction liquid in petroleum refining. It is very much like benzaldehyde in its reactions. For example, it undergoes the benzoin condensation to give furoin.

```
  CH——CH          KCN   CH——CH              CH——CH
2 ||   ||        ————→  ||   ||             ||   ||
  CH   CCHO             CH   C–CHCO–C       CH
    \ /                    \ /    |    \   /
     O                      O     OH    O
  Furfural                       Furoin
```

Similarly, the Cannizzaro reaction converts it into 2-furfuryl alcohol and 2-furoic acid (the usual method of naming heterocyclic compounds is by reference to number systems in which the hetero atom is numbered 1).

```
  CH——CH                   CH——CH               CH——CH
2 ||   ||      + H2O ——→   ||   ||         +    ||   ||
  CH   CCHO                CH   CCH2OH          CH   CCO2H
    \ /                      \ /                  \ /
     O                        O                    O
                        2-Furfuryl alcohol     2-Furoic acid
```

Furan and its derivatives undergo nuclear substitution.

An interesting and useful transformation of furfural is its conversion to fumaric acid by oxidation with sodium chlorate.

```
CH——CH          NaClO3     HO2CCH
||   ||        ————→           ||
CH   C–CHO                   HCCO2H
  \ /
   O
                          Fumaric acid
```

The presence of a diene system in the furan molecule is indicated by the fact that it undergoes a typical diene condensation with maleic anhydride.

```
     CH                                    CH
    //  \                                 / | \
  CH     \           CH–CO              CH  |  CH–CO
  |       O    +     ||    >O   ——→     ||  O  |     >O
  CH     /           CH–CO              CH  |  CH–CO
    \\  /                                 \ | /
     CH                                    CH
```

Coumarone or benzofuran is found in coal tar along with indene, which it resembles in some respects. Although fairly stable to alkalies and ammonia, coumarone is resinified by sulfuric acid. Valuable commercial resins are obtained by polymerizing the crude mixture of coumarone and indene.

Coumarone Indene

Thiophene. If close similarity to benzene is taken as a criterion of aromaticity, thiophene is very aromatic indeed. For although benzene from coal tar contains about 0.5 per cent of thiophene this contaminant passed unnoticed for nearly sixty years after benzene became known. Indeed up to the year 1883 the indophenin test was used to detect benzene—a test which is not given by benzene at all but by thiophene. Victor Meyer, in a popular lecture on benzene, prepared the hydrocarbon by decarboxylation of benzoic acid. To prove the identity of the product he used the test—isatin and sulfuric acid—but to his surprise the expected blue color was not observed. Subsequent work disclosed the presence of thiophene in coal tar benzene and showed that it was responsible for the color test so long incorrectly ascribed to benzene.

Thiophene is prepared from *n*-butane and sulfur at high temperatures.

$$CH_3CH_2CH_2CH_3 + 4S \longrightarrow \begin{matrix} CH{=}CH \\ | \qquad \rangle S \\ CH{=}CH \end{matrix} + 3H_2S$$

It readily undergoes nitration and sulfonation. In fact, sulfonation takes place more rapidly than with benzene—a fact which is used in freeing benzene from thiophene. This process consists in shaking the impure benzene with sulfuric acid.

A good yield of 2-acetothienone is obtained by treating thiophene with acetyl chloride in the presence of stannic chloride.

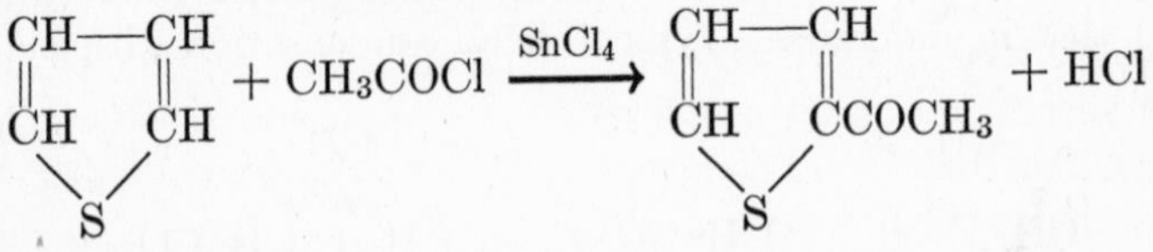

$$\begin{matrix} CH{-}{-}CH \\ \| \qquad \| \\ CH \quad CH \\ \diagdown \; \diagup \\ S \end{matrix} + CH_3COCl \xrightarrow{SnCl_4} \begin{matrix} CH{-}{-}CH \\ \| \qquad \| \\ CH \quad CCOCH_3 \\ \diagdown \; \diagup \\ S \end{matrix} + HCl$$

Methylthiophenes can be oxidized to the corresponding carboxylic acids and can be brominated in the side chain with N-bromosuccinimide.

Pyrrole. Pyrrole occurs in coal tar and bone oil and can be made by distilling succinimide with zinc dust.

$$\begin{matrix} CH_2{-}CO \\ | \qquad \rangle NH \\ CH_2{-}CO \end{matrix} \longrightarrow \begin{matrix} CH{=}CH \\ | \qquad \rangle NH \\ CH{=}CH \end{matrix}$$

Pyrrole boils at 129°, is sparingly soluble in water, and has very weakly basic properties. The last characteristic is interesting when contrasted with the strongly basic nature of pyrrolidine, the reduction product of pyrrole.

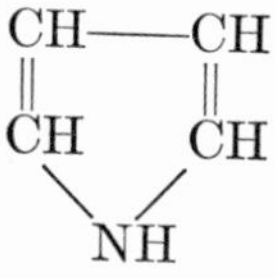

```
CH——CH              CH2——CH2
||    ||            |      |
CH    CH            CH2    CH2
  \  /                \   /
   NH                  NH
 Pyrrole            Pyrrolidine
```

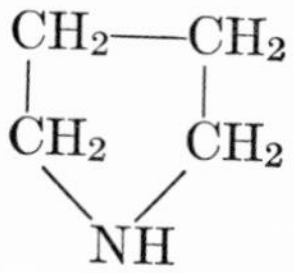

Interesting also is the fact that pyrrolidine is water-soluble whereas pyrrole is not. Pyrrole imparts a red color to pine wood shavings in the presence of hydrochloric acid. This serves as a test for its presence.

Pyrrole is the principal building block in the construction of certain pigments such as hemoglobin of the blood and chlorophyll of plants.

Among the many pyrrolidine derivatives found in nature is proline or 2-pyrrolidinecarboxylic acid.

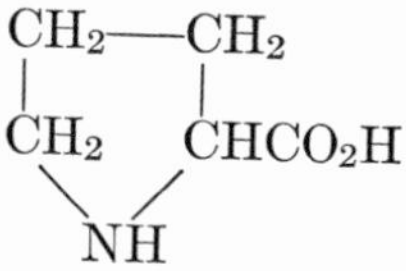

```
CH2——CH2
|      |
CH2    CHCO2H
  \   /
   NH
```

It is a product of hydrolysis of most proteins.

Dimethylpyrrole is formed from acetonylacetone and ammonia.

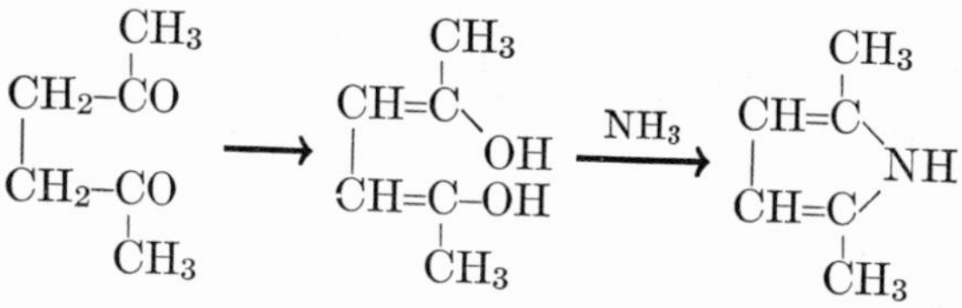

```
    CH3          CH3                 CH3
    |            |                   |
CH2–CO        CH=C\        NH3    CH=C\
|        →    |     OH    ——→     |     NH
CH2–CO        CH=C–OH             CH=C/
    |            |                   |
    CH3          CH3                 CH3
```

This synthesis, due to Knorr, is general for γ-diketones. A more useful method likewise due to Knorr involves the condensation of an amino ketone with a ketone or 1,3-diketone. The amino ketone is made by reducing the corresponding oxime and is used without being isolated. An example is the following.

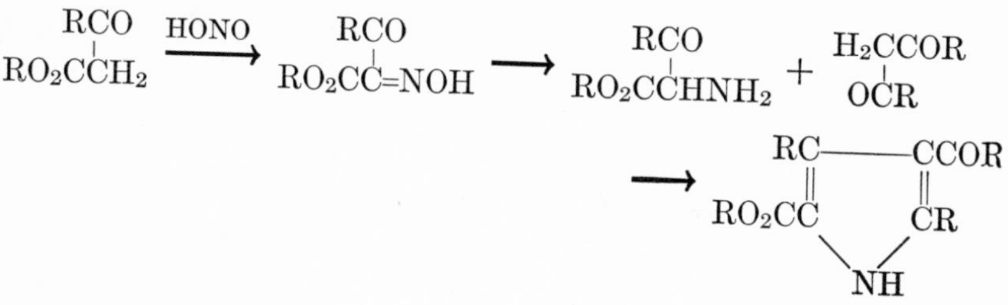

```
  RCO    HONO       RCO                 RCO             H2CCOR
  |      ——→        |          →        |          +    |
RO2CCH2          RO2CC=NOH          RO2CCHNH2           OCR

                                         RC———CCOR
                                    →    ||     ||
                                    RO2CC       CR
                                          \    /
                                            NH
```

Pyrrole appears to contain a typical butadiene system, but unlike furan it does not undergo the diene reaction with maleic anhydride. The reaction is one of simple addition.

```
CH——CH     CH–CO           CH——CH
‖    ‖  +  ‖    >O  ⟶     ‖    ‖
CH   CH    CH–CO           CH   C–CH–CO
  \  /                       \  /   |   >O
   N                          N    CH2CO
   |                          |
   H                          H
```

In acid solution pyrrole seems to lose its aromatic character and undergoes polymerization in much the same manner as does cyclopentadiene.

Pyrrole couples with diazonium salts to give azo compounds.

```
CH——CH                         CH——CH
‖    ‖  + C6H5N2Cl  ⟶         ‖    ‖              + HCl
CH   CH                        CH   CN=NC6H5
  \  /                           \  /
   NH                             NH
```

Indole is benzopyrrole and is the parent substance of indigo. Indigo occurs in the plant as the glucoside of indoxyl. Air oxidation of indoxyl gives indigo.

```
                        —CO               CO        NH
[benzene]‖‖        [benzene] |     [benzene]   \      /   [benzene]
                         CH2                 C=C
      N                 N                   /     \
      |                 |                 NH        CO
      H                 H
    Indole            Indoxyl                Indigo
```

3-Indoleacetic acid has been shown to possess the properties of auxins and is known as heteroauxin. Auxins regulate the growth of plants and determine their behavior with respect to growing away from the ground and toward the light.

```
[benzene]——CCH2CO2H
           ‖
           CH
     N  /
     |
     H
```

3-Indoleacetic acid

γ-Pyrones. γ-Pyrone can be made from acetone and ethyl oxalate.

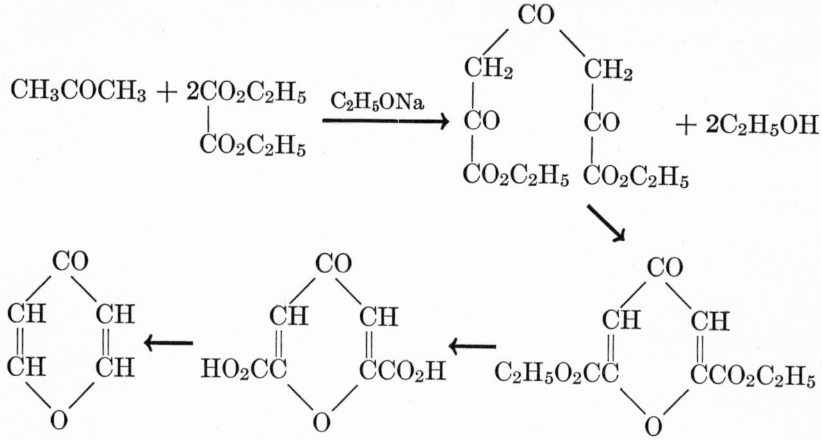

$$CH_3COCH_3 + 2\,\underset{\displaystyle CO_2C_2H_5}{\underset{|}{CO_2C_2H_5}} \xrightarrow{C_2H_5ONa} \begin{matrix} & CO & \\ CH_2 & & CH_2 \\ | & & | \\ CO & & CO \\ | & & | \\ CO_2C_2H_5 & & CO_2C_2H_5 \end{matrix} + 2C_2H_5OH$$

$$\searrow$$

$$\begin{matrix} & CO & \\ CH & & CH \\ \| & & \| \\ CH & & CH \\ & O & \end{matrix} \longleftarrow \begin{matrix} & CO & \\ CH & & CH \\ \| & & \| \\ HO_2CC & & CCO_2H \\ & O & \end{matrix} \longleftarrow \begin{matrix} & CO & \\ CH & & CH \\ \| & & \| \\ C_2H_5O_2CC & & CCO_2C_2H_5 \\ & O & \end{matrix}$$

γ-Pyrone Chelidonic acid

If ethyl acetoacetate and phosgene are used, 2,6-dimethyl-γ-pyrone results.

The most remarkable property of the γ-pyrones is the ability to form oxonium salts with acids.* The exact structure of these salts has not been established.

Pyrylium Salts. These salts occur in nature and are responsible for the colors of certain flowers. The colored materials are known as anthocyanidins and in the plant are combined with one or more molecules of sugar. An example is **cyanin** which is responsible for the red color of roses and the blue color of the corn flower.

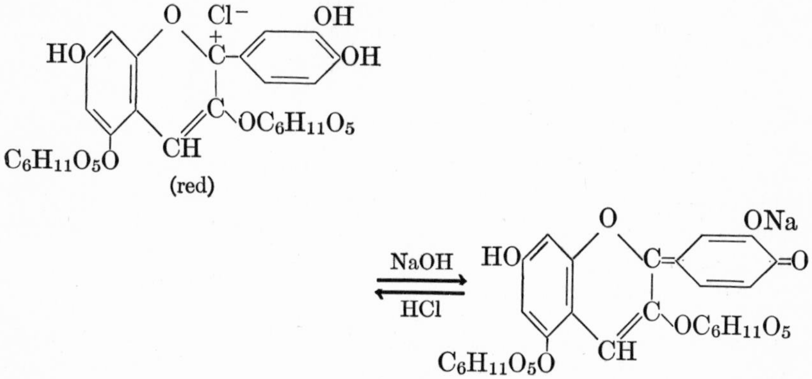

[Structure: cyanin chloride — benzopyrylium ring with HO and $C_6H_{11}O_5O$ on the benzene ring; O (with Cl^-), $\overset{+}{C}$ bearing a 3,4-dihydroxyphenyl group (OH, OH), C bearing $OC_6H_{11}O_5$, CH]

(red)

$$\underset{HCl}{\overset{NaOH}{\rightleftharpoons}}$$

[Structure: HO and $C_6H_{11}O_5O$ on the benzene ring; O, C= quinonoid ring bearing ONa and =O; C bearing $OC_6H_{11}O_5$; CH]

Cyanin (blue)

* It must not be thought that the formation of oxonium compounds is rare in organic chemistry. However, only in isolated cases have they proved to be stable

The color is a function of pH; this explains why the same pigment gives a blue color to one flower and a red color to another.

A simple pyrylium salt may be prepared from dimethylpyrone by the following reactions.

```
        O                                 CH3\  /OMgI
        ‖                                     C
        C                                   /   \
      /   \                               CH     CH       HCl
    CH     CH                             ‖      ‖       ⟶
    ‖      ‖      + CH3MgI ⟶         CH3C      CCH3
 CH3C      CCH3                            \   /
     \    /                                  O
       O

                                     ┌  CH3 OH   ┐
                                     │     \ /    │
                                     │      C     │
                                     │    /   \   │
                                     │  CH     CH │  HCl   Pyrylium
                                     │  ‖      ‖  │  ⟶       salt
                                     │CH3C      CCH3│
                                     │    \   /   │
                                     └      O     ┘
```

Pyridine. Pyridine is an unpleasant-smelling liquid, boiling point 116°, found in coal tar. It is a weak base and is soluble in water. Its outstanding property is its inertness. Strong oxidizing agents such as chromic oxide do not attack it and it is brominated, nitrated, or sulfonated only with great difficulty. The relative ease with which rings are alkylated and acylated by the Friedel-Crafts method places them in the following order of decreasing reactivity: pyrrole, furan, thiophene, anthracene, naphthalene, benzene, cyclohexene, cyclohexane, and pyridine.

Pyridine has been compared with nitrobenzene because it undergoes substitution with about the same order of difficulty. For example, neither will undergo the Friedel-Crafts condensation. The comparison can be carried further for in α- and γ-chloropyridines as in *o*- or *p*-chloronitrobenzene the halogen atom is reactive. For example, it can be replaced by a phenylamino group by treatment of the chloropyridine with aniline. Similarly α- and γ-picolines, like *o*- and *p*-nitrotoluenes, have active methyl groups.

under ordinary conditions. It is highly probable that oxonium salt formation is involved in the conversion of alcohols to carbonium ions by the action of acids (p. **57**).

$$ROH + H^+ \longrightarrow [ROH_2]^+ \longrightarrow R^+ + H_2O$$

These oxonium salts frequently have been isolated; those from highly branched alcohols such as diisopropylcarbinol seem to be most stable.

Hydrogenation transforms pyridine to piperidine.

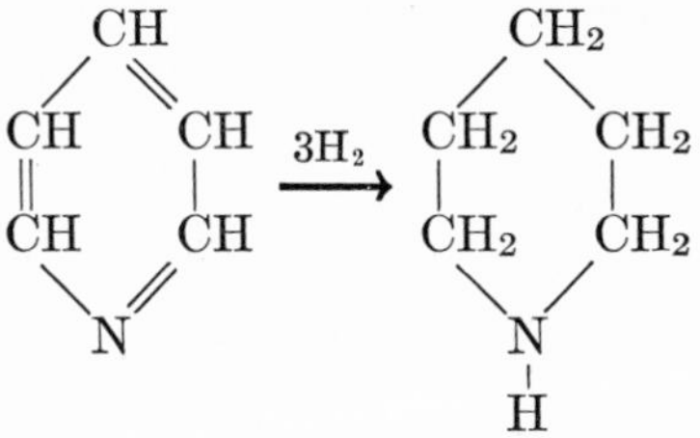

$$C_5H_5N \xrightarrow{3H_2} C_5H_{10}NH$$

CH, CH, CH, CH, CH, N $\xrightarrow{3H_2}$ CH_2, CH_2, CH_2, CH_2, CH_2, N—H

Vitamin B_6 or pyridoxine is the factor of vitamin B which prevents or cures a type of dermatitis produced in young rats by a diet in which the only vitamin B components present are purified thiamin and riboflavin. It has been shown to be a derivative of pyridine having the following formula.

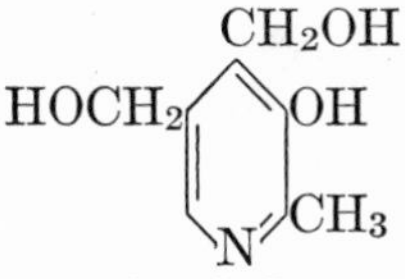

CH_2OH, $HOCH_2$, OH, CH_3, N

Vitamin B_6

Nitration of pyridine can be effected only at high temperatures; 3-nitropyridine is formed. Amino pyridines are prepared by the action of ammonia on α- and γ-chloropyridines. All three aminopyridines have been made by the Hofmann hypobromite degradation of the corresponding amides. α-Aminopyridine is conveniently prepared by the action of sodium amide on pyridine.

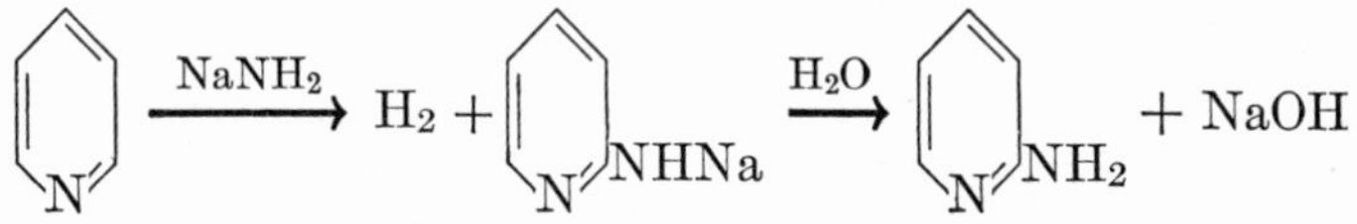

$$C_5H_5N \xrightarrow{NaNH_2} H_2 + C_5H_4N\text{—}NHNa \xrightarrow{H_2O} C_5H_4N\text{—}NH_2 + NaOH$$

The α- and γ-aminopyridines differ from the β-isomer in that they can be diazotized only with difficulty. The diazonium salts cannot be isolated. In water they decompose to give the corresponding hydroxypyridines.

Picolines are methylpyridines. Oxidation converts them to the corresponding carboxylic acids—picolinic, nicotinic, and isonicotinic acids.

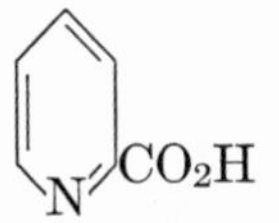

$C_5H_4N\text{—}CO_2H$ (α)

Picolinic acid

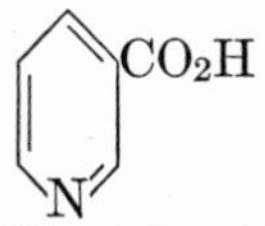

$C_5H_4N\text{—}CO_2H$ (β)

Nicotinic acid

$C_5H_4N\text{—}CO_2H$ (γ)

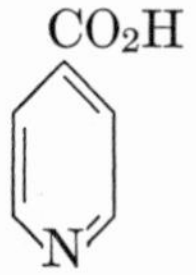

Isonicotinic acid

Nicotinic acid is one of the vitamins of the B group. It is the pellagra-preventive factor and is found in liver, muscle meats, fish, milk, green vegetables, and yeast.

Lutidines are dimethylpyridines and *collidines* are trimethylpyridines. Although pyridine is water-soluble and very hygroscopic, its homologs become increasingly less soluble with increase in molecular weight. Many of them are more soluble in cold than in hot water—a typical property of tertiary amines. The most striking example is nicotine. Below 60° and above 210° it is soluble in water in all proportions, but between these temperatures it is only partly miscible.

CH_3 CH_3 N — α,γ-Lutidine

CH_3 CH_3 CH_3 N — Collidine

CH_2—CH_2 CH CH_2 N CH_3 N — Nicotine

Quinoline is benzopyridine. It occurs in coal tar and bone oil. It is most conveniently made by the Skraup synthesis, which involves the condensation of aniline with glycerol in the presence of sulfuric acid and nitrobenzene. In all probability the mechanism is the following.

$$CH_2OH-CHOH-CH_2OH \xrightarrow{H_2SO_4} CH_2{=}CH{-}CHO$$

$$C_6H_5NH_2 + CH_2{=}CH{-}C(H){=}O \longrightarrow \text{(HO–CH–CH=CH... adduct, N–H)} \xrightarrow{(O)} \text{quinoline (CH, CH, CH, N)}$$

The great stability of the pyridine ring to oxidizing agents is shown by the fact that oxidation of quinoline destroys the benzene ring preferentially, yielding quinolinic acid.

Quinoline (N) $\longrightarrow$ pyridine with CO_2H, CO_2H (N)

Quinolinic acid

Quinaldine is made by heating aniline with acetaldehyde in the form of paraldehyde. The mechanism is probably similar to that proposed for the Skraup synthesis.

$$CH_3CHO + CH_3CHO \longrightarrow CH_3CH{=}CHCHO$$

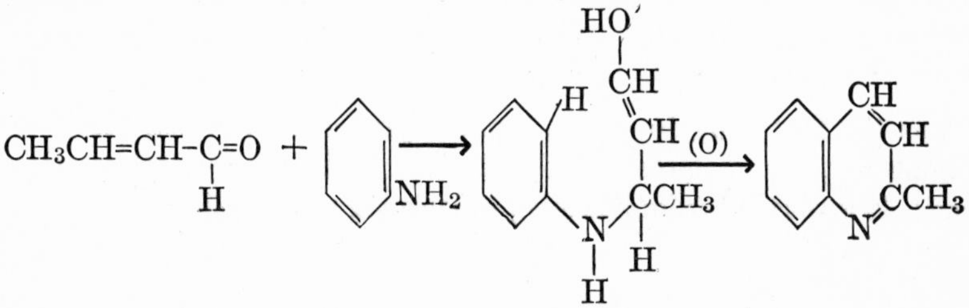

8-Hydroxyquinoline, known as "oxine," is used in the separation of certain metals with which it forms insoluble chelate derivatives. Chief of these are aluminum, magnesium, and zinc. The zinc compound, for example, has the following structure.

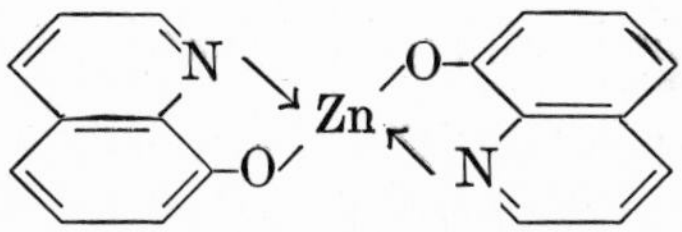

Many quinoline derivatives possess marked physiological activity and certain of them are important drugs. The alkaloid, quinine, belongs to this group. It is used in the treatment of malaria.

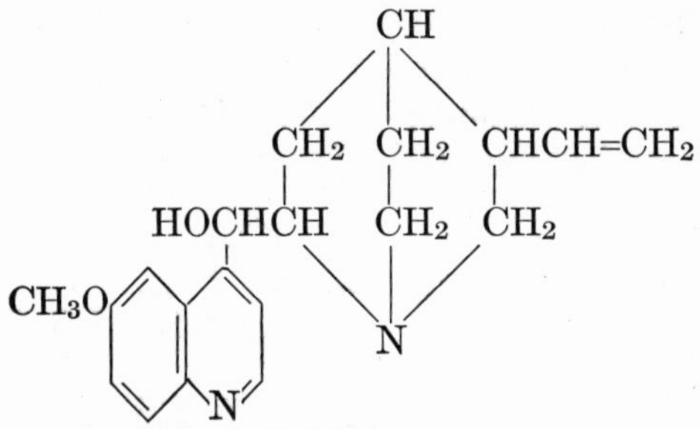

Quinine

There are two functional phases of the malarial parasite, the schizonts (which cause the fever) and the sexual forms or gametocytes (which spread the disease). Quinine is effective only against the former.

Intensive research has developed many synthetic anti-malarials of which plasmochin and atebrin were the first to be useful. Plasmochin is a quinoline derivative with a complex side chain.

CH_3O (quinoline ring) N

$NHCHCH_2CH_2CH_2N(C_2H_5)_2$

CH_3

Plasmochin

It was the first drug to attack gametocytes and was used along with quinine to prevent spread of the disease. Atebrin is a schizonticidal drug. It is derived from acridine, a benzolog of quinoline.

CH_3

$NHCHCH_2CH_2CH_2N(C_2H_5)_2$

CH_3O N Cl

Acridine

Atebrin

Isoquinoline is isomeric with quinoline and occurs in coal tar.

N

Isoquinoline

Side-Chain Activation in the Pyridine Series and in Related Compounds. It was observed long ago that certain methylpyridines were capable of undergoing the reactions of compounds containing active methyl groups. For example, α- and γ-picolines react with benzaldehyde to give benzal derivatives. The β-isomer will not do this.

N CH_3 + $C_6H_5CHO \longrightarrow$ N $CH{=}CHC_6H_5 + H_2O$

CH_3 N + $C_6H_5CHO \longrightarrow$ $CH{=}CHC_6H_5$ N + H_2O

CH_3 N + $C_6H_5CHO \longrightarrow$ no reaction

Evidently the $>C{=}N-$ grouping activates the methyl group attached to it as in α-picoline, i.e., the group $CH_3\underset{|}{C}{=}N-$ has essentially the properties of the corresponding methyl ketone, $CH_3\underset{|}{C}{=}O$. By reference to the principle of vinylogy it is clear that the γ- but not the β-isomer would share this property.

Similar reasoning shows why 1-methylisoquinoline has an active methyl group whereas the 3-isomer has not. Also 2-methyl-4-phenylthiazole has an active methyl group whereas its isomer, 2-phenyl-4-methylthiazole, does not.

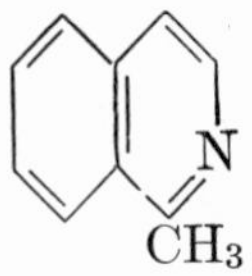

N, CH_3

1-Methylisoquinoline

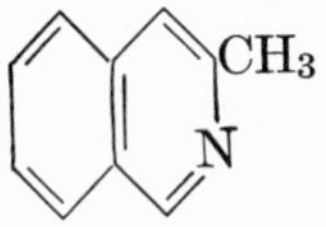

CH_3, N

3-Methylisoquinoline

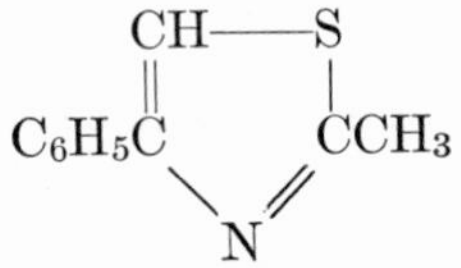

CH——S, C_6H_5C, CCH_3, N

2-Methyl-4-phenylthiazole

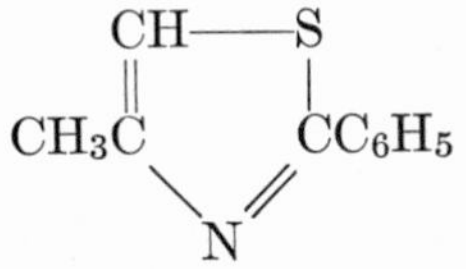

CH——S, CH_3C, CC_6H_5, N

2-Phenyl-4-methylthiazole

Alkaloids. Alkaloids are naturally occurring basic organic nitrogen compounds. The term is generally limited to include only those of plant origin. Alkaloids are usually optically active and have marked physiological activity. With few exceptions they contain at least one nitrogen atom linked in a cyclic structure. These substances are found almost exclusively in seed-bearing plants, chiefly in dicotyledons. The view is commonly held that they are by-products of plant metabolism.

It is an interesting fact that in alkaloids which have an alkyl group attached to a nitrogen or oxygen atom this group is nearly always methyl. This has been interpreted as support for the theory that formaldehyde is involved in plant synthesis. Pyridine, pyrrole, quinoline, and isoquinoline rings are of frequent occurrence, generally in reduced form.

For the determination of structure of alkaloids several general procedures are available. Methoxyl groups are determined by Zeisel's method. Methyl groups on nitrogen are split off by heating the alkaloid hydroiodide at 200–300°. It is a general rule that thermal decomposition of quaternary ammonium halides gives a methyl halide if a methyl group is attached to the nitrogen atom.

The Degradation of Nitrogen Bases. Hofmann's celebrated method has already been mentioned. However, no discussion of alkaloids is complete without reference to this powerful tool. Primary amines react with methyl halides to give secondary amines which in turn yield tertiary amines, and these by addition give quaternary ammonium halides. This is properly known as "exhaustive methylation." The bases corresponding to the quaternary ammonium salts generally decompose when heated and give a tertiary amine and an olefin. The ethyl radical is the one which is most easily split off (p. 427).

An interesting application of Hofmann's method is found in the transformation of piperidine into N,α-dimethylpyrrolidine.

```
        CH2                         ┌      CH2           ┐
       /   \                        │     /   \          │
    CH2     CH2     CH3I            │  CH2     CH2       │
     |       |    ──────→           │   |       |        │ OH
    CH2     NH      Ag2O            │  CH2     N(CH3)2   │
       \   /                        │     \   /          │
        CH2                         └      CH2           ┘
                                            │ distil
                                            ↓
                                         CH2CH2
                                        /      \
    CH2—CH2                HCl        CH        CH2
     |   |               ←──────       ‖         |
 CH3CHCl CH2                          CH2       N(CH3)2
         |
    │    N(CH3)2
    ↓
┌   CH2—CH2  ┐                       CH2—CH2
│    |   |   │ Cl  ──────→            |    |     + CH3Cl
│ CH3CH  CH2 │                    CH3CH    CH2
│     \ /    │                         \  /
│      N     │                          N
└   (CH3)2   ┘                          CH3
```

Here again use is made of the fact that the methyl group can be eliminated preferentially by thermal decomposition of the quaternary ammonium halide containing it.

Pyrrolidine itself yields butadiene when subjected to exhaustive methylation.

$$\begin{array}{c} CH_2\text{—}CH_2 \\ | \quad\quad | \\ CH_2 \quad CH_2 \\ \diagdown \ \diagup \\ NH \end{array} \xrightarrow[Ag_2O]{CH_3I} \left[\begin{array}{c} CH_2\text{—}CH_2 \\ | \quad\quad | \\ CH_2 \quad CH_2 \\ \diagdown \ \diagup \\ N \\ \diagup \ \diagdown \\ CH_3 \quad CH_3 \end{array}\right] OH$$

$$\downarrow \text{distil}$$

$$\left[\begin{array}{l} CH_2\text{–}CH{=}CH_2 \\ | \\ CH_2 \\ | \\ N(CH_3)_3 \end{array}\right] OH \xleftarrow[Ag_2O]{CH_3I} \begin{array}{l} CH_2\text{–}CH{=}CH_2 \\ | \\ CH_2 \\ | \\ N(CH_3)_2 \end{array}$$

$$\downarrow \text{distil}$$

$$CH_2{=}CH\text{–}CH{=}CH_2 + (CH_3)_3N + H_2O$$

The Hofmann degradation fails with unhydrogenated pyridine, quinoline, and isoquinoline rings and with hydrogenated quinolines. Useful modifications by Emde (p. 428) involve reduction of the quaternary ammonium halide with sodium amalgam or hydrogen and a catalyst. An example follows.

$$\left[C_6H_4 \begin{array}{l} CH_2\text{—}CH_2 \\ \quad\quad\quad | \diagup CH_3 \\ \quad\quad\quad N \\ CH_2 \diagup \quad \diagdown CH_3 \end{array} \right] Cl \xrightarrow{\text{Hofmann}} C_6H_4 \begin{array}{l} CH{=}CH_2 \\ \\ CH_2\text{—}N(CH_3)_2 \end{array}$$

$$\longrightarrow C_6H_4 \begin{array}{l} CH{=}CH_2 \\ CH_2N(CH_3)_3Cl \end{array} \xrightarrow[\text{Hofmann}]{\text{Emde but not}} C_6H_4 \begin{array}{l} CH{=}CH_2 \\ CH_3 \end{array}$$

The failure of exhaustive methylation when applied to heterocyclic bases such as pyridine is due to the rearrangement of the quaternary hydroxides (p. 428).

Oxidation is a useful tool also. The following transformations of tropine (from atropine) illustrate its value. Gentle oxidation gives tropinone. The latter yields a dibenzal derivative and must have two CH_2 groups adjacent to the ketone group. Vigorous oxidation converts tropinone to tropinic acid, which can be converted to pimelic acid.

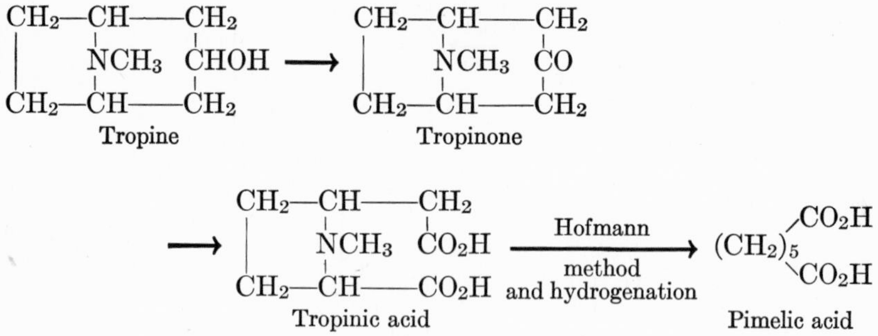

```
CH2—CH——CH2              CH2—CH——CH2
|    |     |             |    |     |
|   NCH3  CHOH  ⟶        |   NCH3  CO
|    |     |             |    |     |
CH2—CH——CH2              CH2—CH——CH2
  Tropine                  Tropinone

      CH2—CH——CH2                                      CO2H
      |    |     |           Hofmann                  /
  ⟶   |   NCH3  CO2H    ——————————————————⟶   (CH2)5
      |    |                  method                  \
      CH2—CH——CO2H      and hydrogenation              CO2H
       Tropinic acid                              Pimelic acid
```

PROBLEMS

1. Indicate a method of converting furfural to furil. What would happen if furil were heated with a strong alkali?

2. Compare the chemical properties of pyridine with those of nitrobenzene.

3. Apply the Hofmann degradation method to the following bases.

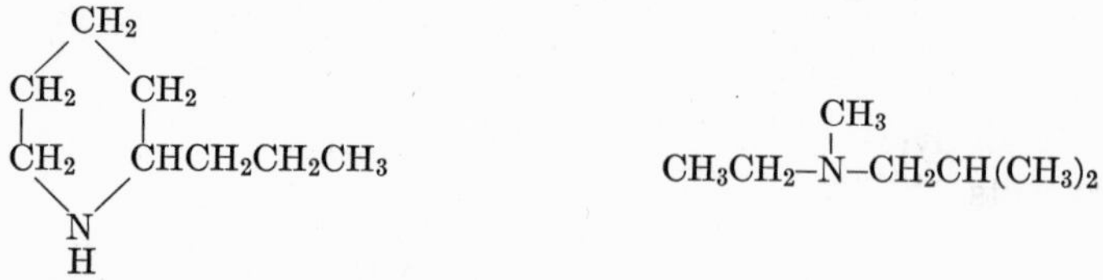

```
      CH2
     /   \
  CH2     CH2                                CH3
  |       |                                   |
  CH2     CHCH2CH2CH3            CH3CH2–N–CH2CH(CH3)2
     \   /
      N
      H
```

SUGGESTED READINGS

N. V. Sidgwick, *Organic Chemistry of Nitrogen*, Chapters 17 and 18, Oxford University Press, 1937.

L. F. Small, "Alkaloids," Gilman's *Organic Chemistry*, Second Ed., Chapter 12, John Wiley & Sons, New York, 1943.

R. H. Manske, "The Chemistry of Quinolines," *Chem. Revs.*, *30*, 113 (1942).

R. C. Elderfield and J. N. Dodd, Jr., "Furan," Vol. I, p. 119, Elderfield's *Heterocyclic Compounds*, John Wiley & Sons, New York, 1950.

F. F. Blicke, "The Chemistry of Thiophene," Vol. I, p. 208, Elderfield's *Heterocyclic Compounds*, John Wiley & Sons, New York, 1950.

H. S. Mosher, "The Chemistry of the Pyridines," Vol. I, p. 397, Elderfield's *Heterocyclic Compounds*, John Wiley & Sons, New York, 1950.

CHAPTER 33

Synthetic Dyes

History. A dye is a colored substance which can be made to adhere to fabrics such as cotton, silk, or linen. The use of dyestuffs to impart color to fabrics was practiced by the ancients and was known to the most primitive peoples. Nearly all the early dyes were of vegetable origin, indigo and alizarin being the best-known examples.

Alizarin was obtained from the madder plant and used to produce Turkey red. Indigo likewise came from a plant, and up to the latter part of the nineteenth century large areas of land were devoted to the production of these plants.

Nearly all dyes now in use are derivatives of benzene and other coal tar products—hence coal tar dyes—and it is not surprising that very little was known about them up to 1865, the date of Kekule's announcement of the structure of benzene. As a matter of fact the first synthetic dye was made nine years before by Perkin who was trying to convert aniline—then of unknown constitution—to quinine by oxidation. He obtained a substance whose beautiful violet solution dyed silk and wool. It was named *mauve* and proved later to be a triphenylmethane derivative.

This dye and similar ones were put on the market almost immediately, and from that time forward synthetic dyes rapidly crowded the natural dyestuffs from the market. Graebe and Liebermann worked out the structure of alizarin in 1868, and within a few years the synthetic dye displaced that obtained from the madder. Similarly in 1882 Baeyer elucidated the structure of indigo and in the course of time synthetic indigo replaced the natural form.

The famous Tyrian purple prized by the Romans 2000 years ago was obtained from certain shell fish in the Mediterranean Sea. It has been shown to be a dibromo derivative of indigo and is not now manufactured because similar shades can be produced by other dyes which are manufactured more cheaply.

Color and Chemical Constitution. All organic compounds absorb light but the absorbed light usually lies beyond the visible portion of the spectrum. Hence we say the compounds are colorless. Experience has shown that unsaturated compounds are more likely to be colored than saturated compounds. Certain unsaturated groups are definitely associated with color and are known as *chromophoric groups* or *chromophores.* The following are the most important of these.

–N=N–
Azo group

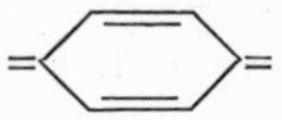

p-Quinoid linkage

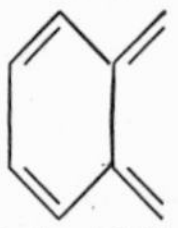

o-Quinoid linkage

–C=O
 |
–C=O
α-Diketone

C=C–C=O
α,β-Unsaturated ketone group

$-NO_2$
Nitro group

–N=O
Nitroso group

The presence of one or more aryl groups attached to the chromophore is usually necessary.

A substance containing a chromophore is a *chromogen.* However, in order to be a dye a chromogen must contain a second group—known as an *auxochrome group*—which renders the color more intense and gives the chromogen an acidic or basic character so that it will adhere to the fabric. The most effective auxochrome groups are –OH, $-NH_2$, –NHR, $-NR_2$, and $-CO_2H$. The sulfonic acid group is of value not only as an auxochrome group but also is often used to render the dye water-soluble.

The Classification of Dyes According to Use. Dyes are classified not only according to their structures but also after the manner in which they are used. On the latter basis they are classed as direct dyes, mordant dyes, ingrain or developed dyes, vat dyes, and sulfur dyes.

A *direct dye* is dissolved in water as its sodium salt if *acidic* and as its hydrochloride if *basic.* The fabric is then dyed by immersion in the hot aqueous solution. Cotton fabrics are more difficult to dye in this manner than are textiles derived from animal fibers. Most direct dyes are used only with animal fibers.

Since proteins are amphoteric it is presumed that they tend to hold acidic and basic dyes through salt formation. However, this theory leaves much to be desired and cannot be applied to cotton dyeing.

Direct dyes for cotton—called substantive dyes—nearly always have two azo groups. An example is Congo red, to be described later.

Mordant dyes require the use of mordants such as the hydroxides or basic salts of aluminum, iron, or chromium. The fabric is first impregnated with the mordant and then dipped in a solution of the dye. The mordant is generally put on the fabric in the form of the water-soluble acetate or formate and then subjected to treatment with steam. This hydrolyzes the salt to the metal hydroxide. When certain dyes are precipitated by such mordants an insoluble, colored substance results to which the name *lake* has been given. The use of a mordant dye involves the formation of such a lake in the fibers of the cloth. The function of the mordant will be discussed more fully in the sequel.

Ingrain or developed dyes. These dyes are insoluble and are produced in the cloth by the interaction of suitable substances. Thus if a cloth is dipped successively in a solution of a naphthol and a diazonium solution an azo dye is formed.

Vat dyes such as indigo are insoluble but can be reduced to a soluble form by the action of sodium hydrosulfite ($Na_2S_2O_4$). The soluble form is placed on the cloth and subsequently reoxidized to the insoluble dye.

Sulfur dyes are produced by heating phenols or anilines with sulfur or a metal polysulfide. They are reduced by sodium sulfite. The fabric, after being immersed in the resulting solution, is exposed to air which slowly reoxidizes the dye to the colored form. This process is essentially that used with vat dyes.

The Classification of Dyes According to Structure. A clearer idea of the great variety of dyes may be obtained by considering typical examples from the standpoint of structure. A few of these are listed here according to structural types.

1. *Nitroso.* The nitroso group imparts a green color to the molecule even in the aliphatic series. An example of a nitroso dye is *gambine.*

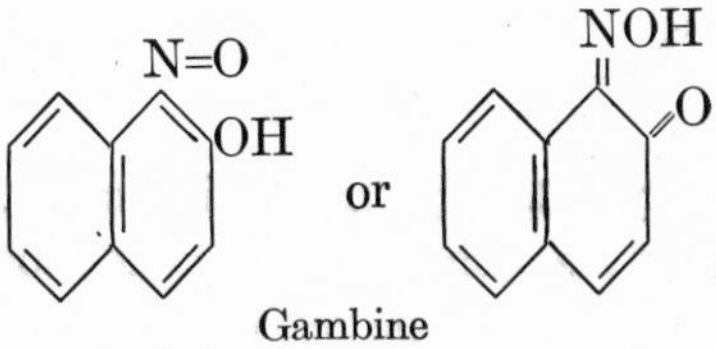

N=O OH or NOH O

Gambine

Mordanted with ferric chloride it dyes cotton a fast green. The function of the mordant is probably to form an insoluble chelate derivative.

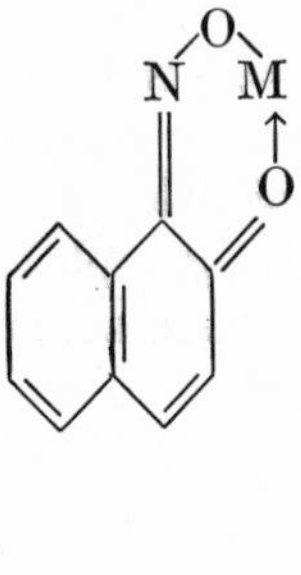

O N M O

2. *Nitro.* *Picric acid* illustrates this type. It dyes silk and wool yellow but the color is fugitive.

Picric acid

Naphthol yellow

Naphthol yellow S

Naphthol yellow and naphthol yellow S are similar in type.

3. *Azo dyes.* These dyes are made by coupling a diazonium salt with an amine or phenol. An example is Congo red, which is derived from benzidine and naphthionic acid.

Congo red

This dye is direct to cotton. However, it turns blue when treated with a strong acid and for this reason is not a satisfactory dye.

Orange II is obtained from sulfanilic acid and β-naphthol.

Orange II

Methyl orange is really not a dye but an indicator. Its color change is interesting since it involves a change of chromophore. The yellow form owes its color to the azo group, the red to the paraquinoid group.

$(CH_3)_2N$–C_6H_4–N=N–C_6H_4–SO_3Na yellow

OH^- ⇅ H^+

$(CH_3)_2\overset{+}{N}$=C_6H_4=N–NH–C_6H_4–SO_3H red

Para red is a good example of a developed dye. The cloth is passed successively through solutions of β-naphthol, diazotized *p*-nitroaniline, and sodium acetate. The sodium acetate lowers the *p*H so that coupling will take place.

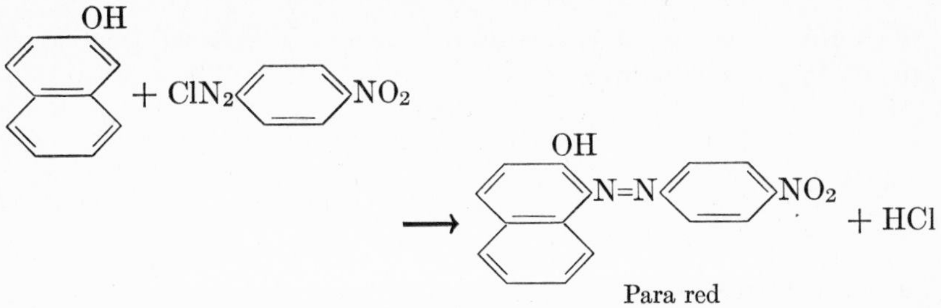

OH

$+ ClN_2$ NO_2

OH

N=N NO_2

$\longrightarrow$ $+ HCl$

Para red

Nearly all the azo dyes of known constitution which can be mordanted with salts of polyvalent metals contain a replaceable hydrogen atom and a donor atom so situated as to permit chelation. It is well known that of this group those which are mordant dyes either (*a*) have a hydroxy group in a position *ortho* to the chromophore group or (*b*) are derivatives of salicylic acid.

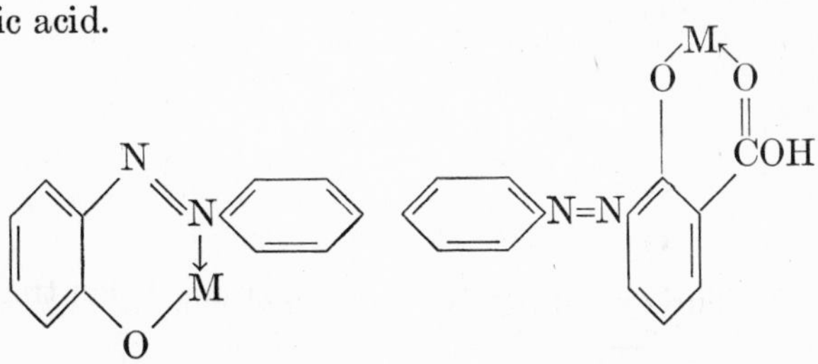

(*a*) (*b*)

In the light of extensive studies it has been concluded that the power of dyeing fabrics conferred upon a dye by metal salts is evidence that the dye is capable of forming a chelate ring involving the metal atom.

4. *Anthraquinone dyes. Alizarin* belongs to this group. It is manufactured by fusing sodium anthraquinone-β-sulfonate with sodium hydroxide to which chlorate has been added. This gives the sodium salt from which alizarin is obtained by treatment with acids.

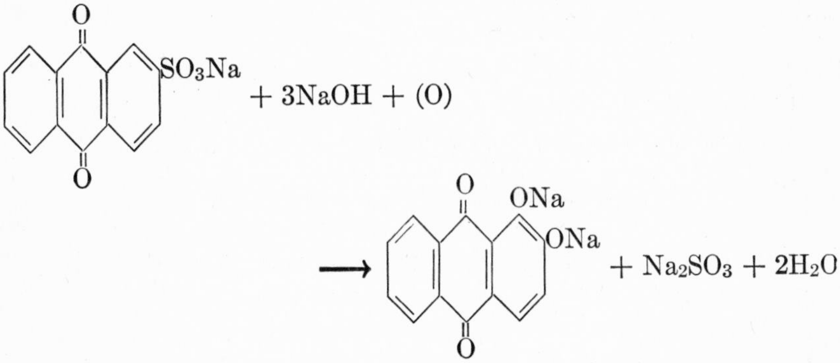

SO_3Na $+ 3NaOH + (O)$

ONa
ONa

$\longrightarrow$ $+ Na_2SO_3 + 2H_2O$

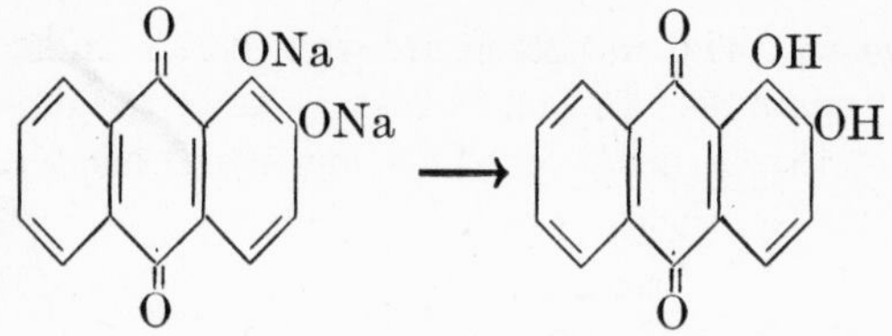

Alizarin

Alizarin is used with a mordant; usually salts of iron, chromium, tin, or aluminum are employed. The last gives Turkey red, much used for dyeing cotton. In this connection it is significant that all anthraquinone dyes which can be mordanted have a hydroxyl group in position 1. This is taken to mean that the mordant functions by chelate ring formation.

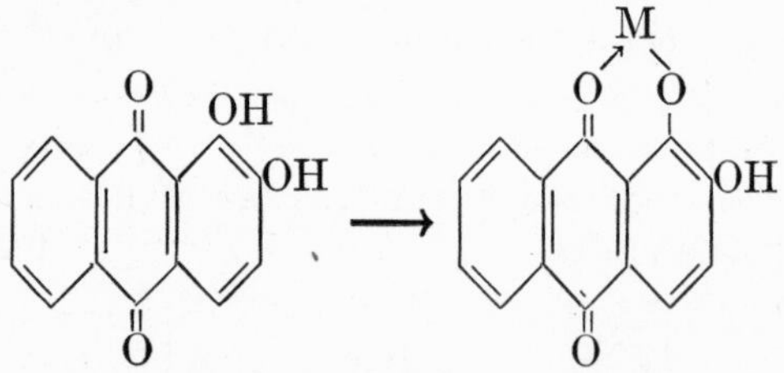

The formula for Turkey red involves three molecules of alizarin.

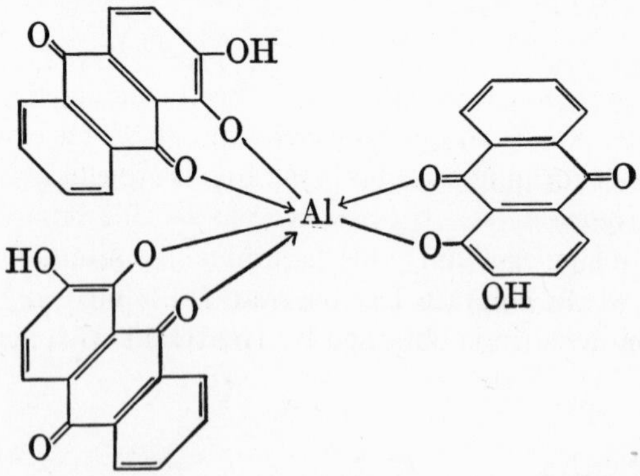

However, the more important anthraquinone dyes are vat dyes This type is illustrated by *algol yellow W.G.*

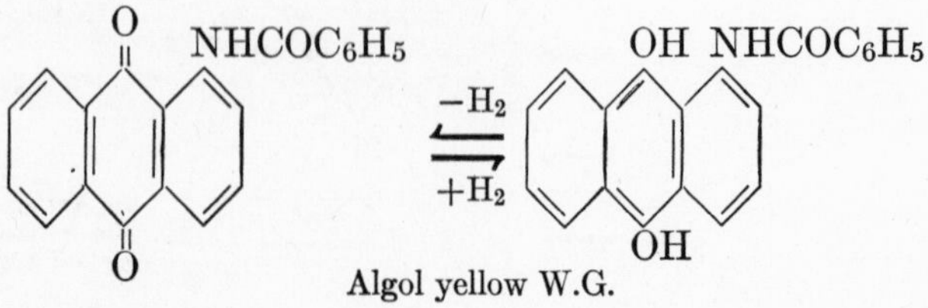

Algol yellow W.G.

5. *The indigoids.* The indigoids are vat dyes. Indigo itself is the most important example. In fact it is still one of the most widely used dyes. It is a derivative of *indole.* This compound has been synthesized in many ways; the synthesis of Stephen follows.

$$C_6H_4(CH_2CN)(NO_2) \xrightarrow[\text{HCl (dry ether)}]{SnCl_2} C_6H_4(CH_2CH{=}NH)(NH_2) \longrightarrow C_6H_4(CH_2CHO)(NH_2)$$

$$\longrightarrow C_6H_4(CH{=}CH{-}OH)(NH_2) \longrightarrow \text{indole } (C_6H_4{<}^{CH=CH}_{NH})$$

Indole occurs in coal tar, jasmine, orange blossoms, and feces. Its homolog, β-methylindole or skatole, is largely responsible for the fecal odor. Curiously enough α-methylindole has a pleasant fruity odor. The origin of indole and skatole in feces is apparently due to decomposition of tryptophan.

$$\text{(indol-3-yl)}CH_2CH(NH_2)CO_2H$$

Tryptophan

As noted earlier 3-indole acetic acid is heteroauxin and is a growth hormone of plants.

In nature indigo occurs as indican, the glucoside of indoxyl or β-hydroxyindole. Indoxyl has the remarkable property of being oxidized to indigo by the air. The older commercial synthesis of indigo follows.

$$C_{10}H_8 \longrightarrow C_6H_4{<}^{CO}_{CO}{>}O \longrightarrow C_6H_4{<}^{CO}_{CO}{>}NH$$

$$\longrightarrow C_6H_4(NH_2)(CO_2H) \xrightarrow[HCN]{CH_2O} C_6H_4(NHCH_2CO_2H)(CO_2H)$$

$$\longrightarrow C_6H_4{<}^{NH}_{CO}{>}CHCO_2H \xrightarrow[\text{air } -CO_2]{\text{oxidation}} \text{Indigo}$$

A simpler and now more important synthesis is the following.

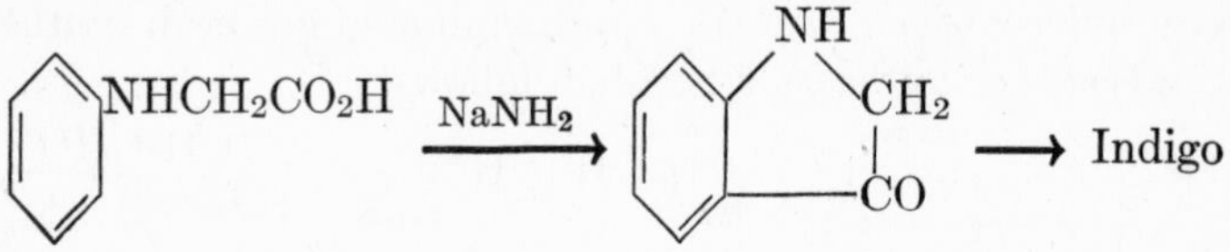

$$C_6H_5NHCH_2CO_2H \xrightarrow{NaNH_2} C_6H_4\langle NH\rangle CH_2 \ (-CO-) \longrightarrow \text{Indigo}$$

The chromophore of indigo is O=C–C=C–C=O. Reduction with sodium hydrosulfite converts the dye to a colorless alkali-soluble form known as indigo white. Oxidation by the air converts indigo white to indigo.

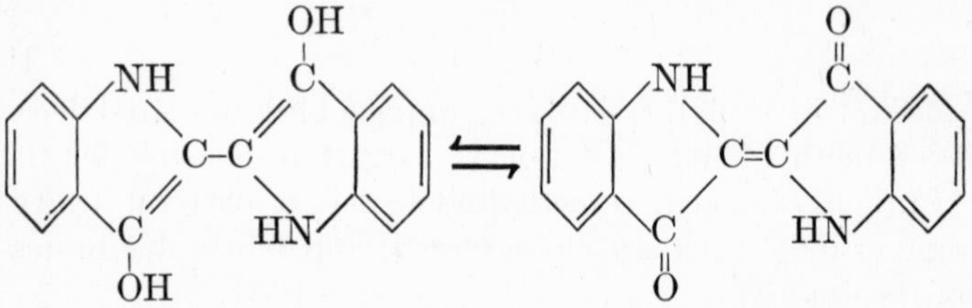

Indigo white ⇌ Indigo

X-ray studies show that indigo has a center of symmetry and hence must be the *trans* form. The *cis* modification is not known. The stability of the *trans* form is probably due to hydrogen bonding.

The structure of indigo which Baeyer established in 1882 is strongly supported by the behavior of analogously constituted substances; an example is indanthrene blue R. In both this dye and indigo the chromophore group, O=C–C=C–C=O, is joined to a benzene ring which holds an imino group.

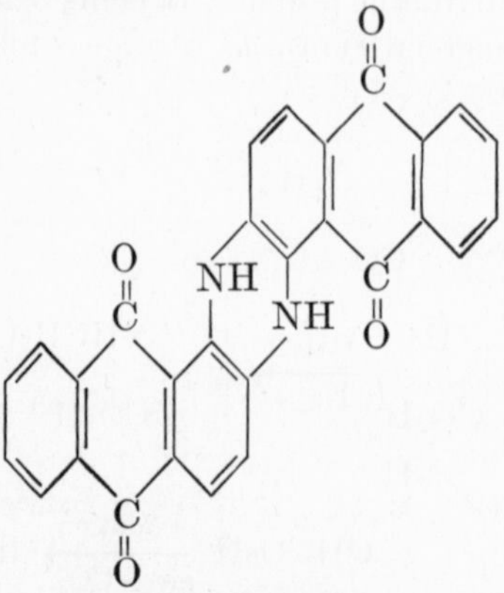

Indanthrene blue R

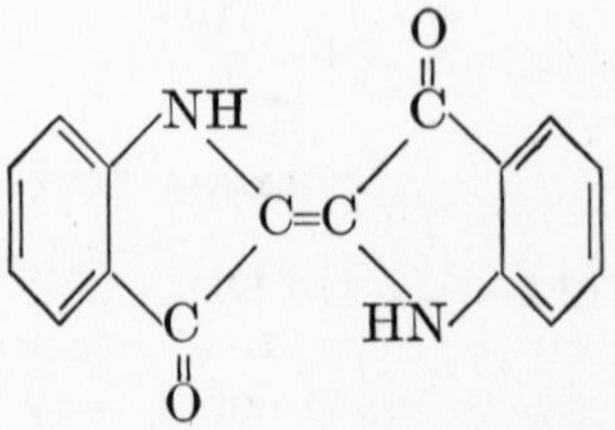

Indigo

6. *Triphenylmethane dyes.* These dyes have the type of structure illustrated by the following; the chromophore group is the quinoid nucleus.

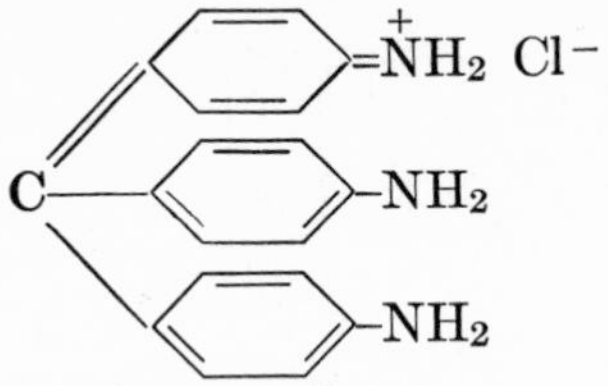

$$C(=C_6H_4=\overset{+}{N}H_2\ Cl^-)(C_6H_4-NH_2)(C_6H_4-NH_2)$$

Pararosaniline

$$C(=C_6H_4=O)(C_6H_4-OH)(C_6H_4-OH)$$

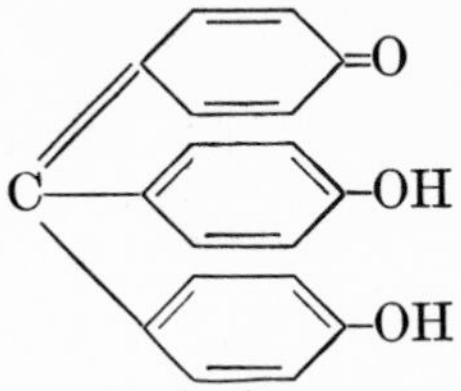

Aurine

From Michler's ketone and dimethylaniline is obtained hexamethylpararosaniline or *crystal violet.* The substitution of methyl groups for the six amino hydrogen atoms in pararosaniline changes the shade from red to violet. Resonance would permit each ring in turn to be represented by the quinoid structure and is supposed to enhance the color.

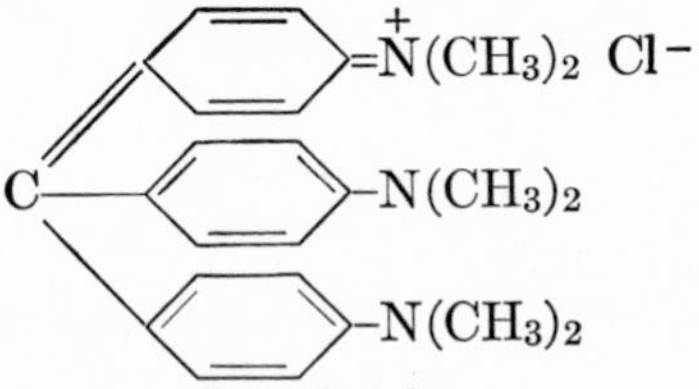

$$C(=C_6H_4=\overset{+}{N}(CH_3)_2\ Cl^-)(C_6H_4-N(CH_3)_2)(C_6H_4-N(CH_3)_2)$$

Crystal violet

7. *Pyronine dyes.* From phthalic anhydride are obtained fluorescein, eosin, and similarly constituted dyes. These are known as pyronine dyes.

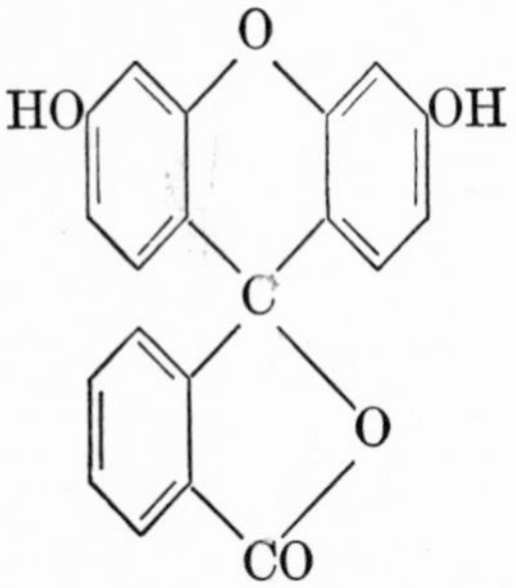

Fluorescein

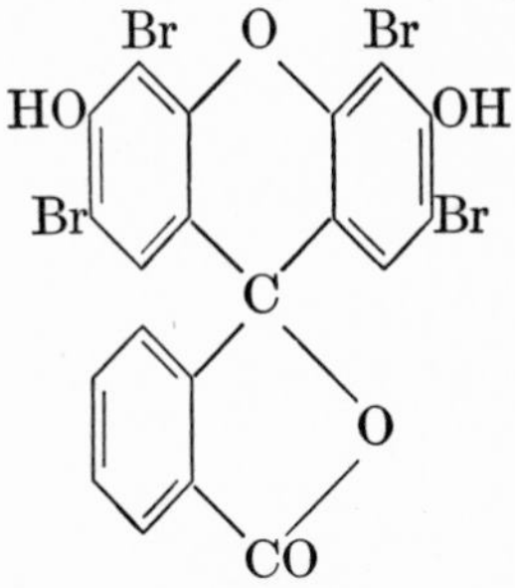

Eosin

Eosin is used in red inks. The colored form of a pyronine dye is illustrated by the formula of mercurochrome (p. 472), which is a disinfectant belonging to this group.

Although not a true pyronine dye, phenolphthalein is very closely related to this group. The color changes of phenolphthalein are explained as indicated below.

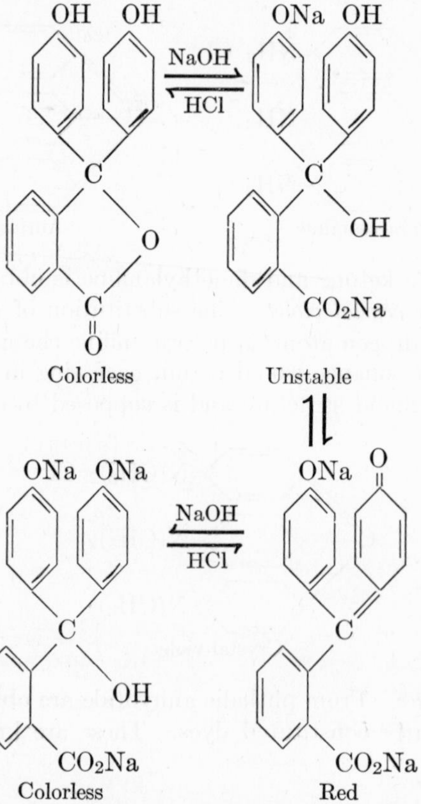

OH OH ONa OH

NaOH / HCl

C C

O OH

C CO_2Na

O

Colorless Unstable

ONa ONa ONa O

NaOH / HCl

C C

OH

CO_2Na CO_2Na

Colorless Red

8. *Cyanine dyes.* Particular attention has been given to the cyanine dyes because they are capable of functioning as photographic sensitizers. Ordinary silver halide photographic plates are sensitive only to the violet and blue regions of the spectrum, but by adding suitable cyanine dyes to the liquid emulsion the plates may be rendered remarkably sensitive to green, yellow, orange, and red.

The essential structural feature of these dyes is formed by two nitrogen atoms—one trivalent and the other tetravalent—joined together by a conjugated system of single and double bonds. An example is quinoline blue.

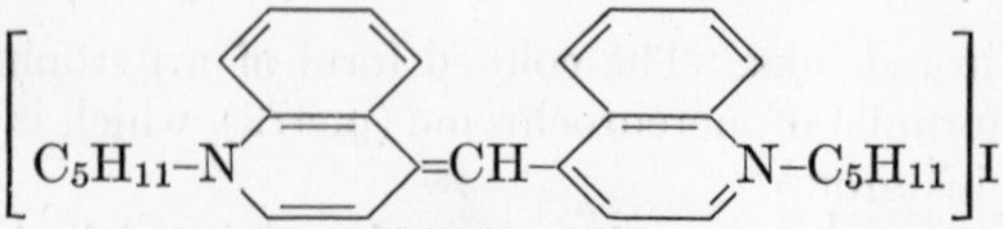

$$\left[C_5H_{11}\text{–N} \quad =\text{CH–} \quad \text{N–}C_5H_{11}\right]\text{I}$$

Quinoline blue

A similar dye, pinacyanole, is made by condensing quinaldine ethiodide and ethyl orthoformate.

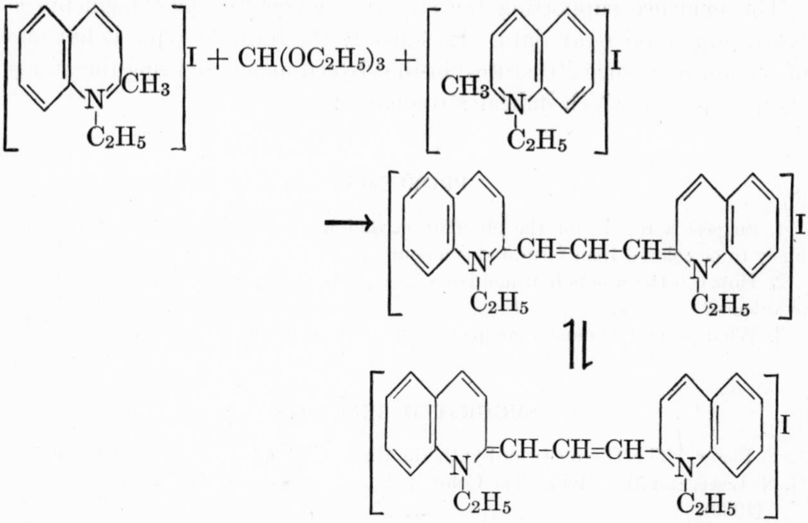

$$\left[C_9H_6N(CH_3)(C_2H_5)\right]I + CH(OC_2H_5)_3 + \left[C_9H_6N(CH_3)(C_2H_5)\right]I \longrightarrow \left[C_9H_6N(C_2H_5){=}CH{-}CH{=}CH{-}C_9H_6N^{+}(C_2H_5)\right]I \rightleftharpoons \left[C_9H_6N^{+}(C_2H_5){-}CH{=}CH{-}CH{=}C_9H_6N(C_2H_5)\right]I$$

The possibility of resonance between the two forms is necessary if the compound is to be a dye.

9. *Phthalocyanine dyes.* One of the most interesting and valuable types of chromophores is that in phthalocyanine and its metal derivatives. Copper phthalocyanine may be taken as an example of the latter. It is formed by treating *o*-phthalonitrile with copper and has a complex structure similar to those of chlorophyll and hemin.

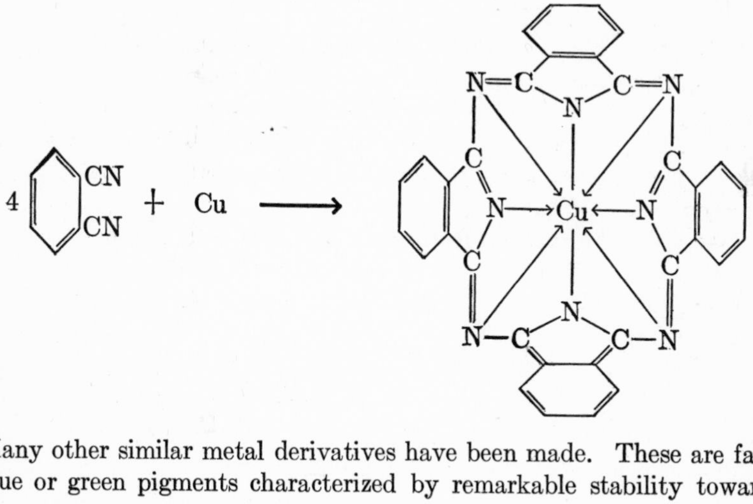

$$4\,C_6H_4(CN)_2 + Cu \longrightarrow \text{Copper phthalocyanine}$$

Many other similar metal derivatives have been made. These are fast blue or green pigments characterized by remarkable stability toward acids, bases, and heat. They are employed in practically every field in which colored pigments are of use.

The evidence supporting the structure given for these pigments is based largely on x-ray data. Presumably the formula given is but one of several resonance structures; in the sixteen-membered ring the atoms show a spacing which indicates resonance.

PROBLEMS

1. Suggest a reason for the observation that unsaturated compounds are more likely to be colored than saturated compounds.
2. How can the function of mordants be explained by use of the electronic theory of valence?
3. What properties must a compound possess to be useful as an indicator?

SUGGESTED READINGS

L. F. Fieser, "The Discovery of Synthetic Alizarin," *J. Chem. Educ.*, *7*, 2609 (1930).

G. N. Lewis and M. Calvin, "The Color of Organic Substances," *Chem. Revs.*, *25*, 273 (1939).

H. W. Grimmel, "Organic Dyes," Gilman's *Organic Chemistry*, Vol. III, p. 243, John Wiley & Sons, New York, 1953.

A. Maccoll, "Color and Constitution," *Quart. Revs.*, *1*, 1 (1947).

APPENDIX

PROBLEMS AND QUESTIONS FOR REVIEW

I. Show how the following concepts are used to explain the properties of organic molecules.

1. Resonance.
2. Chelation.
3. Polar-equatorial bonds.
4. Coordinate covalent bond.
5. Hydrogen bond.
6. Tautomerism.
7. Restriction of rotation.
8. Vinylogy.
9. Strain.
10. Steric hindrance.

II. Show how the following concepts or entities are helpful in representing the mechanisms of organic reactions.

1. Carbonium ion.
2. Free radical.
3. Rearward approach.
4. Carbanion.
5. Chain reaction.
6. Hyperconjugation.
7. Bromonium ion.
8. Hydride transfer.
9. Oxonium salt.
10. Push-pull process.
11. Pseudo cyclic process.
12. Neutralization.
13. Electron withdrawal.
14. Electron donation.
15. Participation of neighboring groups.
16. Nucleophilic displacement.
17. Electrophilic substitution.
18. *trans*-Elimination.
19. Inversion.
20. Solvolysis.

III. Illustrate the following types of reactions.

1. Reformatsky reaction.
2. Gabriel's synthesis.
3. Rosenmund reduction.
4. Malonic ester synthesis.
5. Hydrogenation.
6. Thorpe's reaction.
7. Transesterification.
8. Gattermann-Koch reaction.
9. Hoesch reaction.
10. Perkin's condensation.
11. Strecker's reaction.
12. Wurtz reaction.
13. Diazotization.
14. Skraup reaction.
15. Acetal formation.
16. Saponification.
17. Aldol condensation.
18. Sandmeyer reaction.
19. Schotten-Baumann reaction.
20. Hofmann's exhaustive methylation.
21. Von Braun's cyanogen bromide reaction.
22. Gattermann reaction.
23. Haloform reaction.
24. Nitration.
25. Hydrolysis.
26. Cyclodehydration.
27. Hofmann's hypobromite reaction.
28. Claisen condensation.
29. Dehydrohalogenation.
30. Hydrogenolysis.
31. Kolbe's synthesis of hydroxybenzoic acids.
32. Reductive amination.

33. Ozonolysis.
33. Bouveault synthesis of aldehydes.
34. Wurtz-Fittig synthesis.
36. Reimer-Tiemann reaction.
57. Clemmensen reduction.
38. Ullmann reaction.
39. Claisen-Schmidt reaction.
40. Benzoin condensation.
41. Knoevenagel condensation.
42. Kolbe's electrolysis.
43. Grignard methods.
44. Williamson's synthesis.
45. Autoxidation.
46. Sulfonation.
47. Halogenation.
48. Dehydration.
49. Dehydrogenation.
50. The modified Strecker reaction.
51. Hell-Volhard-Zelinsky reaction.
52. Cannizzaro reaction.
53. Hinsberg reaction.
54. Diels-Alder reaction.
55. Tishchenko reaction.
56. Coupling reaction.
57. Michael condensation.
58. Wolff-Kishner reduction.
59. Dieckmann condensation.
60. Acetoacetic ester synthesis.
61. Selenium dioxide oxidation.
62. Friedel-Crafts reaction.

IV. Discuss the use of the following reagents in organic chemistry.

1. Acetic anhydride.
2. Acetyl chloride.
3. Acetylene.
4. Aluminum amalgam.
5. Aluminum chloride.
6. Aluminum isopropoxide.
7. Ammonium chloride.
8. Ammonium sulfide.
9. Barium hydroxide.
10. Benzenesulfonyl chloride.
11. Benzoyl peroxide.
12. Boron trifluoride.
13. Bromine.
14. N-Bromosuccinimide.
15. Calcium hydroxide.
16. Chlorine.
17. Chlorosulfonic acid.
18. Chromic anhydride.
19. Copper.
20. Copper-bronze.
21. Copper sulfate.
22. Cuprous chloride.
23. Cuprous cyanide.
24. Diazomethane.
25. Ethylene oxide.
26. Ferric chloride.
27. Hydrazoic acid.
28. Hydrogen.
29. Hydrogen chloride.
30. Hydrogen cyanide.
31. Hydrogen iodide.
32. Hydrogen peroxide.
33. Hydroxylamine.
34. Iodine.
35. Ion-exchange resins.
36. Iron.
37. Lithium aluminum hydride.
38. Magnesium amalgam.
39. Maleic anhydride.
40. Mercuric acetate.
41. Methyl sulfate.
42. Nickel.
43. Nitric acid.
44. Nitrous acid.
45. Oxygen.
46. Ozone.
47. Palladium.
48. Perbenzoic acid.
49. Pertrifluoroacetic acid.
50. Phenylhydrazine.
51. Phenyl isocyanate.
52. Phosphorus oxychloride.
53. Phosphorus pentabromide.
54. Phosphorus pentachloride.
55. Phosphorus pentoxide.
56. Phosphorus trichloride.
57. Picric acid.
58. Piperidine.
59. Platinum.
60. Potassium cyanide.
61. Potassium hydroxide (alcoholic).
62. Potassium permanganate.
63. Selenium.
64. Selenium dioxide.
65. Semicarbazide.
66. Silver.

67. Silver nitrate.
68. Silver oxide.
69. Sodium.
70. Sodium acetate.
71. Sodium amalgam.
72. Sodium amide.
73. Sodium bisulfite.
74. Sodium dichromate.
75. Sodium ethoxide.
76. Sodium hydroxide.
77. Sodium hypochlorite.
78. Sodium iodide.
79. Sodium nitrite.
80. Sodium sulfite.
81. Stannic chloride.
82. Stannous chloride.
83. Sulfur.
84. Sulfur dioxide.
85. Sulfuric acid.
86. Thionyl chloride.
87. Tin.
88. Zinc.
89. Zinc chloride.
90. Zinc cyanide.

V. Define and illustrate the following terms.

1. Quinhydrone.
2. Sulfone.
3. *cis-trans* Isomerism.
4. Chromophore group.
5. Terpene.
6. Mercaptol.
7. Lactol.
8. Acetal.
9. Walden inversion.
10. Mordant dye.
11. Diazotization.
12. Glycoside.
13. Fulvene.
14. Free radical.
15. Lactam.
16. Ketene.
17. Aromaticity.
18. Alkaloid.
19. Azulene.
20. Ketopentose.

VI. Illustrate the following types of molecular rearrangements.

1. Fries.
2. Enolization.
3. Jacobsen.
4. Claisen.
5. Lossen.
6. Hofmann (2).
7. Benzidine.
8. Allylic.
9. Pinacol-pinacolone.
10. Curtius.
11. Beckmann.
12. Demjanow.
13. Fischer-Hepp.
14. Benzilic acid.

VII. Outline satisfactory methods for making the following compounds from readily available raw materials. Indicate the catalysts used, and classify the condensation reactions which are involved.

1. m-$NO_2C_6H_4CH{=}CHCO_2H$
2. $O{=}C_6H_4{=}O$ (ring)
3. $C_6H_5CH{=}CHNO_2$
4. $C_6H_5CH(OH)CO_2H$
5. $CH_3COCH_2COCO_2C_2H_5$
6. $CHCO_2H{=}CHCO_2H$
7. $CO(CH_2CO_2H)_2$
8. $C_6H_5COCH_2CO_2C_2H_5$
9. $CH_3CH_2CH(OH)CH_3$
10. $CH_3COCH(C_6H_5)CO_2C_2H_5$
11. $CH_3COCH_2C_6H_5$
12. (naphthalene ring)$NHNH_2$
13. $CH_2{-}CO{-}CHCO_2C_2H_5$, $CH_2{-}CH_2$ (ring: CH_2 joined to CH_2, CH joined to CH_2)

14. $CH{=}CH$ ring: CH_3C, CCH_3, O

15. $CH(CO_2C_2H_5)_3$

16. $CH_3CHCO_2C_2H_5$ with $COCO_2C_2H_5$ on the CH

17. $C_6H_5CH(CO_2C_2H_5)_2$

18. $(CH_3)_2C{=}CHCO_2H$

19. $(CH_3)_2C(OH)CO_2C_2H_5$

20. NH_2, Br (benzene ring)

21. $CH_3COCHCO_2C_2H_5$ with $CH_2CO_2C_2H_5$ on the CH

22. $C_6H_5CH{=}CHCOCH{=}CHC_6H_5$

23. HO, OH, OH (benzene ring)

24. p-$CH_3C_6H_4CHO$

25. $(C_2H_5O_2C)_2C{=}C(CO_2C_2H_5)_2$

26. OH, HO, $(CH_2)_3CH_3$ (benzene ring)

27. $HO_2C(CH_2)_5CO_2H$

28. $C_6H_5CH(CN)CH_2COC_6H_5$

29. NO_2, NO_2 (benzene ring)

30. $CH_3COCH{-}CHCOCH_3$ with CH_3 on each CH

31. CH_3 and C_2H_5 on $C_6H_5CH_2{-}CCO_2H$

32. $CH_3COCH_2CH_2CO_2H$

33. CH_3NO_2

34. C_6H_5SH

35. C_6H_5CO, CH_3 (benzene ring)

36. SO_3H, NH_2 (benzene ring)

37. $CH_2{=}CH{-}C{=}CH_2$ with Cl on the C

38. CH_3, N (quinoline ring)

39. Br, $COCH_2Br$ (benzene ring)

40. $CH_2{-}CHCO_2H$ and $CH_2{-}CH_2$, joined in a ring

41. S, $(CH_3)_2C$, $C(CH_3)_2$, S, S, $C(CH_3)_2$ (ring)

42. $C_6H_5N{=}NC_6H_5$

43. $CH_2{=}CHOCOCH_3$

44. $CH_3NHC_2H_5$

45. $CH_2{=}CCO_2CH_3$ with CH_3 on the C

46. CO_2H, I, OH, I (benzene ring)

47. $CH_2{=}CHCl$

48. $CH_3CH_2SO_3H$

49. $CH_3CHBrCO_2H$

50. $CH_3CHBrCH_2CO_2H$

51. C_6H_5COCHO

52. C_6H_5F

53. Br, Br (benzene ring)

54. $CHCl_2COCl$

55. $C_6H_5CH{=}CHBr$

56. I, NO_2 (benzene ring)

VIII. Discuss the significance of the following in connection with the properties of polymers.

1. Functionality of reactants in condensation polymerization.
2. Degree of polymerization.
3. Cold-drawing.
4. Chain transfer agents.
5. Vulcanization.
6. End groups in condensation polymers.
7. Purity of monomers in addition polymerization.
8. Purity of reactants in condensation polymerization.
9. Temperature of addition polymerization.
10. Amount of catalyst in addition polymerization.

IX. Indicate the characteristic type of structure in each of the following polymers.

1. Natural rubber.
2. Synthetic rubber (GR-S).
3. Neoprene.
4. Silicone rubber.
5. Nylon.
6. Polyvinyl alcohol.
7. Polyacrylonitrile.
8. Cellulose acetate.
9. Glyptal resins.
10. Butyl rubber.
11. Polyethylene.
12. Dried linseed oil.
13. Phenol-formaldehyde resins.
14. Dacron.
15. Nitrocellulose.
16. Teflon.
17. Alvar resins.
18. Vinylites.
19. Urea-formaldehyde resins.
20. Starches.

X. Write electronic formulas for the following compounds.

1. Carbon monoxide.
2. Diazomethane.
3. An amine oxide.
4. Methyl.
5. Diphenyl sulfone.
6. Sulfur dioxide.
7. An oxonium compound.
8. Triphenylmethyl.
9. Methyl ether.
10. A chelate ring.
11. Nitromethane.
12. A sulfinic acid.
13. Hydrogen peroxide.
14. Methyl isocyanide.
15. Ketene.

XI. Show what occurs when the following compounds react with an excess of ethylmagnesium bromide. In each case write the formula of the principal product obtained when the condensation product is treated with dilute sulfuric acid.

1. $(CH_3)_3CCOC(CH_3)_3$
2. $CH_3CH_2CH_2C{\equiv}CH$
3. $C_6H_5CH{=}CHCOC_6H_5$
4. Benzene ring with OH and adjacent CH_2OCH_3 (o-methoxymethylphenol)
5. SO_2
6. $C_6H_5NHCH_3$
7. C_6H_5CN
8. CH_2—CH_2 bridged by O (ethylene oxide)
9. CO_2
10. $HCON(CH_3)_2$
11. $CH_3COCO_2C_2H_5$
12. $(CH_3)_2SO_4$
13. CH_3CH—CH_2 bridged by O (propylene oxide)
14. $(CH_3O)_2CO$

15. $C_6H_5COCHC_6H_5$ (with OH on the CH)

16. 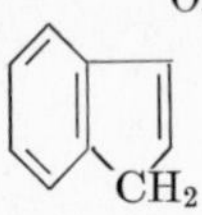

17. $CH_2{=}CBrCH_2Br$

18. $HCO_2C_2H_5$

19. $CH(OC_2H_5)_3$

20. O_2

XII. Indicate the number and type of stereoisomers possible for the following structures.

1. $CH_3CH{=}CHCH_3$
2. $CH_3CH\langle^{CH_2}_{CH_2}\rangle C{=}CHCH_3$
3. $C_6H_5CH{=}NNHC_6H_5$
4. $CH_2{-}CHCO_2H$ / $CH_2{-}CHCO_2H$ (the two CH_2 and the two CH joined)
5. 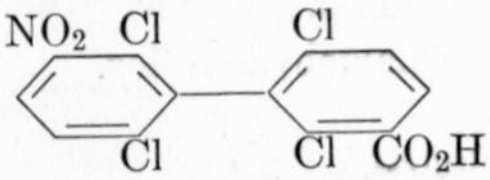
6. 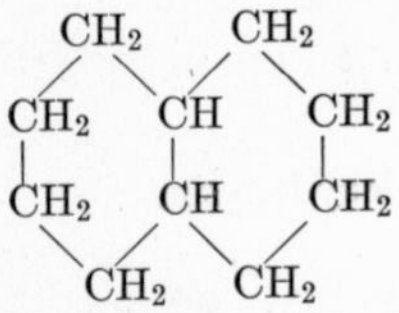
7. $C_6H_5SOC_2H_5$ (with O on the S)
8. $SO\langle^{CH_2CH_2}_{CH_2CH_2}\rangle SO$
9. 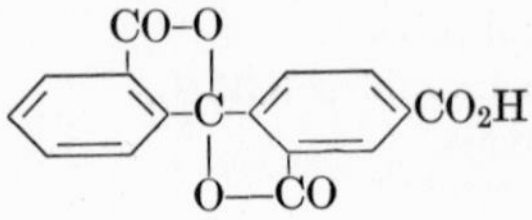
10. 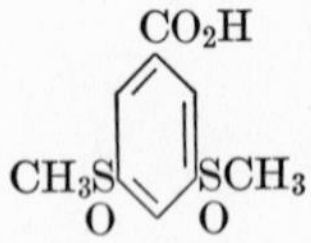

XIII. Compare the basic strengths of the following nitrogen compounds.

1. $(CH_3)_2NH$
2. $(CH_3)_2C{=}NOH$
3. $C_6H_5NHNH_2$
4. 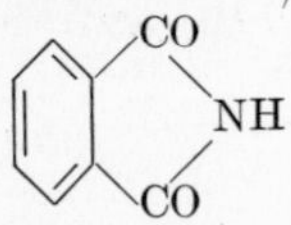
5. 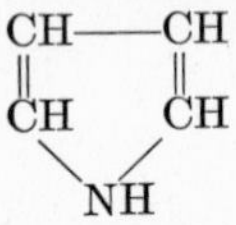
6. 

XIV. Arrange the following compounds in a decreasing order of reactivity toward methylmagnesium iodide.

(*a*) CH_3CH_2CN

(*b*) $CH_2{-}CH_2$ / $CH_2{-}CH_2$ $\rangle CO$ (the two CH_2 on the left joined)

(*c*) $(CH_3)_3CCOC(CH_3)_3$

(*d*) CH_3CH_2CHO

(*e*) $(CH_3CH_2)_2CHOH$

XV. Show by equations what happens when phenylmagnesium bromide is treated with a limited amount of

(*a*) $CH_2{=}C{=}O$

(*b*) $HCON(CH_3)_2$

(*c*) $C_6H_5COCH{=}CH_2$

(*d*) 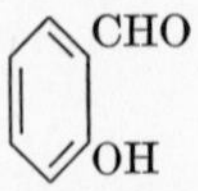

(*e*) $CH_2{-}CH_2$ with O bridging ($\backslash O /$)

XVI. For each of the following pairs of compounds indicate a useful reaction that may be caused to take place, and mention any catalysts that may be involved.

1. $CH_2(CO_2C_2H_5)_2$ and $(CH_3)_2C{=}CHCO_2CH_3$
2. CH_3COCH_3 and $CH_2(CO_2H)_2$
3. $C_6H_5COCH_2CO_2C_2H_5$ and $C_6H_5NHNH_2$
4. $CH_3CH_2CO_2C_2H_5$ and $(CO_2C_2H_5)_2$
5. $CH_3COCH_2CH_3$ and C_6H_5CHO
6. $CH_3CH{=}CHCO_2C_2H_5$ and $(CO_2C_2H_5)_2$
7. $CH_3COCH_2CO_2C_2H_5$ and $BrCH_2CO_2C_2H_5$
8. CH–CO / ‖ >O / CH–CO and CH——CH / ‖ ‖ / CH CH / \ / / O

XVII. Arrange the following halogen compounds in a decreasing order of reactivity toward silver nitrate. Which of these compounds will yield Grignard reagents?

1. C_6H_5F
2. Br⟨ ⟩Br
3. $CHCl_2COCl$
4. $CH_3CH_2CH_2CH_2Br$
5. 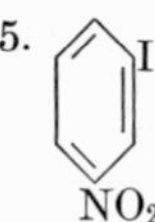

XVIII. (*a*) Discuss the reduction of nitro compounds.

(*b*) What types of compounds are colored?

(*c*) What is a dye? Give several types.

(*d*) Why is a more alkaline medium employed for the coupling of a diazonium salt with a phenol than for the coupling with an amine?

(*e*) Compare the chemical reactions of primary amines (RNH_2) and simple amides ($RCONH_2$).

(*f*) In what types of nitro compounds is the nitro group replaceable?

Index